THE COMPLETE VEGETABLE GARDENER'S SOURCEBOOK

THE COMPLETE VEGETABLE GARDENER'S SOURCEBOOK

DUANE NEWCOMB

AVON
PUBLISHERS OF BARD, CAMELOT AND DISCUS BOOKS

THE COMPLETE VEGETABLE GARDENER'S SOURCEBOOK is an original
publication of Avon Books. This work has never before appeared in book form.

A division of
The Hearst Corporation
959 Eighth Avenue
New York, New York 10019

Copyright © 1980 by Duane Newcomb
Published by arrangement with the author.
Library of Congress Catalog Card Number: 79-55568
ISBN: 0-380-75318-9

Cover illustration by Jackie Geyer
Cover and interior design by Hermann Strohbach

First Avon Printing, February, 1980

AVON TRADEMARK REG. U.S. PAT. OFF. AND IN
OTHER COUNTRIES, MARCA REGISTRADA, HECHO EN
U.S.A.

Printed in the U.S.A.

LIST OF CHARTS

ACKNOWLEDGEMENT

I am indebted to hundreds of people who have provided pictures and information for inclusion in this book. I am especially grateful to Karen Newcomb for her time and effort in compiling the vegetable charts. Without her organizational ability this portion of the book would have been almost impossible to complete.

Thanks also to Susan Moldow, Senior Editor of Avon Books, and sourcebook editor John Berseth, whose great effort and encouragement with the mass of sourcebook material was greatly appreciated. John Deere Company kindly provided some of the material used in Chapter 1. And thanks to many others: Jack Combs, AG-Drip Sales Inc.; and Warren Vollman, Allis-Chalmers; Jo L. Sanders, AMF; A. Moore, Aquatrols Corporation of America; Lulu Warkentin, Geo J. Ball Inc.; R. G. Kruger, Beeco Products Inc.; Bonnie Bevis, Burgess Vibrocrafters Inc.; Jeannette Lowe, W. Atlee Burpee Co.; D.V. Burrell Jr., D.V. Burrell Seed Growers Co.; Sharla A. Horton, J.I. Case; Richard Jackson, Chapin Watermatics Inc.; Stephen O. Corsale, Coating Products Inc.; W.F. Bennett, Continental Nutriculture Company; A. F. Coletta, Dayton Electric Mfg. Co.; Barbara J. Bounds, Dexol Industries; Corinne Stake, Environmental Dynamics; Frank K. Chestnut and W.L. Marlow, FMC Corporation; Shirley Carbonero, Ford Tractor Operations; Walter A. Houston, Green Garde; David Shorr, Homeland Industries Inc.; A. H. Hummert III, A. H. Hummert Seed Co.; A. Herbruck, Lambert Corporation; W. Lawson Cording, La Motte Chemical Products Co.; J. R. Strom, Leffingwell Chemical Co.; John Lindig, Lindig Manufacturing; Manson Pitcher, Michigan Peat Company; Ana G. Lopo, Minnesota Mining and Manufacturing Co.; Reginald K. Nearing, J.A. Nearing Co. Inc.; Alan R. McClure, Olin; Scott West, OMC-Lincoln; Marshall T. Gleason, Organic Nutrients Inc.; C. H. Aydelotte, Chevron Chemical Co.; James P. Brown, Roper Sales; Jon A. Berg, North Central Plastics Inc; Robert J. Houlehen, Simplicity Manufacturing Co.; Thomas J. Curtin, Sudbury Laboratory Inc.; Kenneth Jones, The Sunny Green Garden Corp.; Emerald V. Troxel, Trox Manufacturing Co.; Dean Doss, Vegetable Factory Greenhouses; Frank A. Bammel, Vis Queen Film Products Division; Richard L. Kuroski, Wonder Garden; Thomas H. Alden, Woolfolk Chemical Works Inc.; L. H. Garrett, The W-W Grinder Corporation; W. H. Douglass, Wheeling-Pittsburgh.

Also, Norman F. Obeker, Cooperative Extension Service, University of Arizona; Kent B. Tyler, Cooperative Extension, University of California; Dan O. Exell, College of Agricultural Science, Clemson University; F. Aloysius Wood, University of Florida, Institute of Food and Agricultural Sciences; Henry G. Taber, Cooperative Extension Service, Iowa State University; Milo Burnham, Cooperative Extension Service, Mississippi State; Dermot P. Coyne, Dept. of Horticulture, University of Nebraska; L. C. Peirce, Department of Plant Science, University of New Hampshire; M. T. Vittum, Department of Seed and Vegetable Science, New York State Agricultural Experiment Station, Cornell University; R. W. Helper, Department of Horticulture, Pennsylvania State University; Michael J. Bresin, College of Agricultural Experiment Station, West Virginia University; O. B. Combs, Department of Horticulture, University of Wisconsin

INTRODUCTION

In writing several gardening books and in gardening avidly myself I have seen new products by the hundreds become available to help solve any number of gardening problems.

The frustrating part, however, was that while I knew there were a number of new items on the market, I could seldom find out just what they were or even where to buy them, for only a fraction of the available home garden products can be found in any one nursery or garden catalog.

Suppose, for instance, you read about a new corn variety and decide to try it. Often no one at the local nurseries has even heard of that particular variety. Now the only real way to find it is to send for as many individual garden catalogs as possible, then thumb through them looking for a seed source.

Or, you may be a beginning gardener and looking for a backyard greenhouse. There are dozens of types available today in a wide range of materials. Just where can you find the information you need to make a decision? For (until now) there was no central source that allowed you to make a comparison or even a complete list of manufacturers' addresses.

As we initially began to look for home-garden-supply manufacturers to include in this sourcebook, we discovered that there were hundreds of them producing literally thousands of products, many more than would be possible to include here. As a result we decided to present a roundup of each garden area and to include products that represent basic types.

With tractors, for instance, we tried to show what's available, from the simplest to the most complex, pointing out the basic differences between types along with the jobs each performs best.

With handtools, we explained the uses of each tool and the choices available; we also included a guide to a new-old phenomenon, the wheeled cultivator.

For transplanting we provided a summary of both commercial and noncommercial devices.

This format was also carried out in the vegetable section, chapter 7. There is tremendous varietal variation in most vegetable groups, yet many gardeners grow few varieties outside of the most common types.

With ordinary radishes, for instance, you have a choice of round red to one-third white to two-thirds white round to all-white long.

Eggplant is available in the familiar plump oval or long cylindrical varieties; colors range from purple to green, yellow, and white. And even zucchini comes in dark-green, medium-green, green-black, gray, yellow, white, and striped (cocozelle type) varieties.

This sourcebook allows the gardener, for the first time, to visualize the variation within each vegetable group and also charts the vegetable varieties available through over 100 seed catalogs.

The sourcebook itself is intended primarily as a guide to help you determine what's available and to allow you to make your own decision as to what's best for you.

If you are considering the purchase of a rototiller, you might decide from the sourcebook that both general front end and rear end tillers are too heavy but that a compact tiller is exactly what you need. Having made that decision, you should send for literature from several manufacturers listed in this sourcebook. Then, using the dealer addresses these manufacturers provide, actually look at some machines. By this time, using both the sourcebook and manufacturer's information, you should be able to make a decision as to which one is best for you.

Gardening itself is great fun as well as a practical way to provide yourself with vegetables. This sourcebook is designed to take some of the work off your shoulders. It will show you the wide range of products available, provide you with some basis for making a decision, and in general help make all phases of vegetable gardening a truly enjoyable experience.

1

VEGETABLE GARDENING TODAY

Not since the Victory Garden era of World War II have so many people been bitten by the vegetable gardening bug. By the end of the 1970s over 40 million gardens were being planted yearly in the United States. Plots of land just about everywhere—rural fields, suburban backyards, big-city vacant lots—have been cultivated by a new generation of gardeners.

This chapter presents the fundamentals of raising vegetables, emphasizing the importance of planning to a bountiful harvest. In addition community gardening and other group efforts are described.

The boom continues

The size, shape, and dimensions of vegetable gardening today are certainly not the same as they were when the current boom began in the early 1970s. At that time one out of every four vegetable gardeners was brand, spanking new. Today only one out of every 15 gardeners is just starting out.

That, of course, doesn't mean that a tremendous number of new gardeners won't be turning over their first shovel full of dirt in the 1980s. It does mean, however, that America today has a great many experienced vegetable gardeners who are looking to extend their experience, to try new things.

Why is the vegetable gardening boom still going full speed ahead?

The reasons are somewhat complex. The first is almost surely money. Families seeing their grocery bills rise out of sight are turning to their own vegetable garden for a little relief.

Second, vegetables from your own garden do indeed taste better than those bought from the supermarket. Corn, for instance, reaches a peak of sweetness, then holds it only two to five days. Besides that, the minute you pick corn, the sugar in the ear starts to turn to starch. Other vegetables hold their peak taste only a short time after picking, too.

In addition, we are so dependent today on the rest of society for our needs, there's something highly satisfactory and reassuring about being able to say, "I grew it myself." No strikes, no shortages, can intervene. Gardening is also therapeutic. While many people have tremendous pressure in their lives, just a few hours working in the garden, as one psychologist explains, relieves much tension and pressure.

Indeed, gardening is an avocation that gives pleasure to millions. For those who would like to start a vegetable garden of their own, it is first necessary to know a half-dozen fundamentals.

Six basic steps to a more productive garden

Planning your garden

The first step to a more productive garden is selecting the location. Be sure to pick a spot that will receive six to eight hours of sunlight per day. The soil should be fertile, well-drained, and located several feet from trees and other vegetation that might rob your plants of nutrients. Start your garden in January or February by laying it out on paper. Select your favorite vegetables from seed catalogs or garden shops. Then, using a sheet of graph paper, sketch in the garden's vital statistics.

Garden size depends primarily on space available. Ideally, the plot should be no less than 100 square feet (10 by 10 feet). With a garden this size, you can plant as many as 15 different types of vegetables, including corn, lettuce, beets, radishes, carrots, tomatoes, and green beans. If your family is large and the space is available, a garden 25 by 50 feet, when properly tended, can provide all the fresh vegetables five people are likely to eat in an entire season.

When plotting your rows, it is best to run them from north to south to maximize sun exposure. Place tall plants at the north end so they don't shade other vegetables in your garden. Large plants should also be placed against a fence whenever possible. Fences make nice trellises for tall plants like cucumbers and green beans. And don't forget to leave adequate spacing between rows. About 18 to 20 inches will leave sufficient room for your tiller when cultivating time arrives.

How much of each crop to plant will depend, in part, on your plans for canning or freezing. If you want just enough for immediate consumption, 25 feet or less of each vegetable will probably be enough.

Selecting the tools

After you've determined the size and "lay" of your garden, you're ready to collect the tools you'll need to do the job. To minimize the time and effort you'll spend, proper tool selection is vital. (See Chapters 4 and 5.)

For the small garden (less than 100 square feet), only the basic tools will be needed—spading fork, rake, hoe, trowel, tape measure, garden hose, string, and label stakes. If your garden is larger, you should also think about investing in a rotary tiller.

Preparing the soil

Local weather conditions usually dictate the best time for you to begin tilling. Dig up a trowelful of dirt and squeeze it with your hand. If it packs solidly, the soil is too wet. If it crumbles, the soil is too dry. If it just holds together nicely, conditions are right for tilling to begin.

To give proper richness and texture to the soil, commercial fertilizers or manure should be applied, using a tiller or a shovel till the ground is a workable consistency. (See Chapter 2.)

After the initial tilling or digging job is completed, rake or harrow the soil. Break up any larger clumps that may be left, but do not granulate the soil. Fine soil will crust after a hard rain, making it difficult for plant sprouts to push through.

Planting

Different types of vegetables need to be planted at different times because some will withstand cool temperatures and some will not. As a rule, the best time to plant sensitive crops is usually two or three weeks after the last freeze in your area. For more specific information on proper planting times, contact your county extension office or local garden shop.

After you've determined the proper planting time, you're ready to begin the actual planting process. Check seed packets for any special instructions, then stake out your garden area. Set up stakes at either end to ensure straight rows. Then, begin making your rows with a hoe or tiller and furrow opener accessory.

Plant the seeds and cover them with a thin layer of soil. Firm the soil with your hand or foot. Then label each row stake with the empty seed packet.

Consider planting companion crops of early- and late-maturing plants in the same row. For example, radishes can be planted with carrots, and harvested and replanted before the carrot plants mature.

Green beans, tomatoes, cucumbers, and certain other plants require only a third to half the normal space when properly staked or trellised. Staking and trellising should be considered, especially in smaller gardens.

Garden care

For higher yields and tastier vegetables, correct garden care is essential. Proper care includes watering, cultivating, mulching, and fertilizing. For maximum growth, your garden should receive no less than one inch of water per week, about 120 gallons per 12-by-15-foot area (see Chapter 8). Water between furrows until rows are soaked. It's far better to water thoroughly once a week than to water lightly every third or fourth day. A weekly soaking allows plant roots to grow deeply into the soil. Then, if a drought should occur, the plant's deep root system lets it draw from the "water table" for continued growth.

Cultivate your garden whenever the need arises with a tiller or a hand cultivator.

Proper mulching and fertilizing also improve plant yield. Compost placed between the rows helps prevent weed growth, conserves moisture, and provides added nutrients for the soil (see Chapter 3). Fertilizer stimulates root growth and produces fleshier, healthier fruit.

Postharvest tilling

Working the soil in the fall pays big dividends the following spring. Use a rotary tiller or spading fork to turn under surface refuse—weeds, stalks, and dead leaves. A tiller used in fall also accelerates the breakdown of soil-building materials that occurs naturally during the winter. That means richer, more workable soil the following spring.

That's one classic method of establishing and maintaining a vegetable garden. Other ways have been developed, and are worth consideration by all gardeners.

The gardening method explosion

So popular has vegetable gardening become today, that not only are millions of new gardeners growing vegetables, but dozens of different gardening methods are springing up all across the country. These methods differ in one way or another from our conventional way of planting vegetables in wide rows in a fairly large garden. Here are a few:

Depressed bed method

One- to two-foot-wide beds are planted between two ridges with two to three rows of vegetables planted in each bed. Organic material is dug into each of these beds with a spading fork. Advantages: The soil in the beds stays moist longer, and the beds are protected from the winds by ridges in between.

Reference: *Organic Gardening in the West* by Robert F. Smith (Sunstone Press, Santa Fe, N.M.).

Intensive gardening

A good method for city gardeners who have only small, flower-bed-type spaces. After intensive cultivation utilizing compost and manure, seeds are broadcast across the bed, utilizing all the space. Vine crops, including squash and watermelons, are grown in the air on a trellis. This method produces a tremendous yield while requiring about 50 percent less labor and water.

Reference: *The Postage Stamp Garden Book* by Duane G. Newcomb (J. P. Tarcher, Inc., Los Angeles, Cal.).

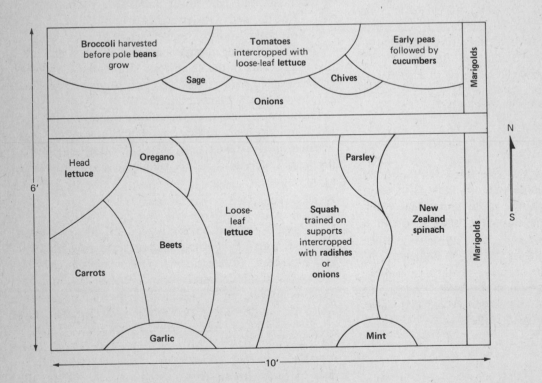

A small, intensive garden that any city gardener can grow. Although only 6 by 10 feet, this one is big enough to supply many of the needs of a family of four.

An intensive garden in containers, with pots on shelves to utilize wall space.

Raised bed method

Beds approximately 20 feet long and 5 feet wide are made up by double-digging in large amounts of compost or aged manure, then adding bone meal and wood ash. Seeds are broadcast across the beds so that the plant leaves touch as they grow. This creates a mini-climate under the soil that helps hold moisture and reduce weed growth.

Reference: *How to Grow More Vegetables Than You Ever Thought Possible on Less Land Than Anyone Can Imagine,* by John Jeavons (Ecology Action of the Mid Peninsula, Palo Alto, Cal.).

Vertical vegetable gardening

Utilizing limited patio areas, vegetables are now being grown in upright vertical containers. Here are a few:

The vegetable tree is made of wire filled with planting mix, along an eight-foot-high board with tomatoes at the bottom, cucumbers above, then radishes and carrots. Vegetable pot trees are baskets supported on a five-by-seven-foot post that has been anchored with bags of sand. Also there are many types of roll-around bookcase vegetable planters being used. (See Chapter 10 for details.)

Reference: *Gardening Shortcuts* (Ortho Books, Chevron Chemical Co., San Francisco, Cal.).

Wide-row gardening

Wide-row planting is planting in extra-wide rows of up to three or more feet. Vegetable seeds are then broadcast across the rows.

Reference: *Wide-Row Planting, The Productive Miracle* by Dick Raymond (Garden Way Publishing Co., Charlotte, Vt.).

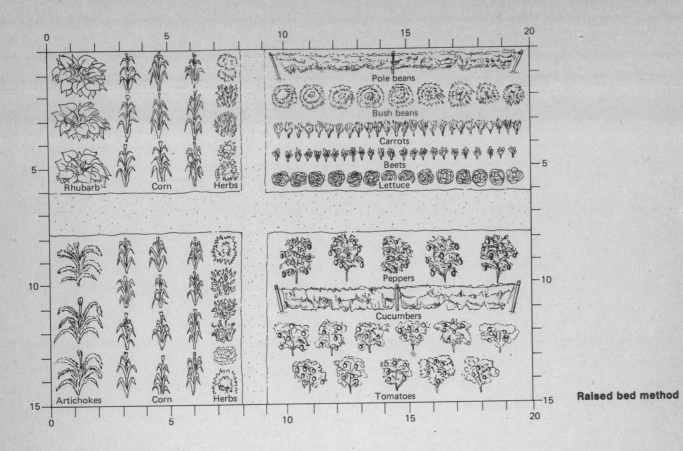

Raised bed method

Which method is for you? That depends on your gardening conditions. But if your time and space are limited, consider either intensive or wide-row gardening. If you are interested primarily in organic gardening, and want to try a more productive method, consider either the raised bed or depressed bed method. If you live in an apartment or townhouse with a patio, try container vegetable gardening. There are, of course, many other methods besides these—one of the great joys of gardening as you become more experienced will be to experiment with the many methods and to decide for yourself just which one suits you best.

The Mittleider method

The Mittleider method is an efficient garden system developed by Jacob Mittleider in which vegetables are grown in raised beds filled with a lightweight growing medium. The beds are fed each week with a special fertilizer.

HERE'S HOW TO DIG A RAISED BED

Cover the area first with a six-inch layer of rotted manure or compost. Then (1) dig one spade's depth and set it aside. Loosen one more spade's depth. (2) Use soil from second trench to fill first trench. Loosen bottom soil each time, and mound soil as you dig it out. (3) Finish bed by filling last trench with soil dug from first trench. Bed will be mounded and aerated. Rake fine before planting.

When finished sprinkle on a dusting of bone meal, an inch of rotted manure and some wood ashes. Turn these materials into the top 3 to 6 inches, rake the mound smooth and soak the soil with a gentle spray.

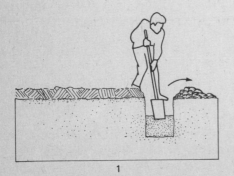

1

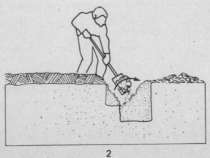

2

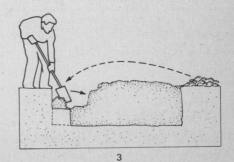

3

The standard Mittleider beds are built of 1-by-8-inch redwood or cedar, 30 feet long, 4 feet wide, and 8 inches deep. These beds are generally filled with a 50/50 mix of either fine sand and peat moss or of perlite and peat moss.

Before planting, mix 4 pounds each double superphosphate and sulfate of ammonia, 2 pounds each of magnesium sulfate and potassium sulfate, and 2 ounces of boron. Spread 5 pounds of gypsum over this and mix all of it into the soil.

Order prepared fertilizers from:

Grow Box 2047
Lomita Blvd.
Lomita, Cal. 90717

Wilkens Enterprises
Box 13238
Oakland, Cal. 94661

Hydro Greenhouse Systems
2 Binnacle Lane
Mt. Harmony, Md. 20836

The method is explained in the book *More Food from Your Garden* by Jacob Mittleider (Woodbridge Press, Santa Barbara, Cal. 93100).

How much is your garden really worth?

Surprisingly, even a small garden is worth quite a bit. A few years ago the National Garden Bureau worked out the production from a "small" conventional 25-by-15-foot backyard plot. At that time the total amount saved came to $284 at 1974 prices. Today that same garden is worth $376.60 and going up.

The costs were basically as follows: fertilizer and insecticide, $8; nursery transplants, $9; seedlings, $10.40; for a total of $27.40.

Choosing a garden site

Selecting the right site for your vegetable garden is important. Here are a few points to consider:

1. Select a site with loamy or sandy loam soil instead of clay whenever possible (see Chapter 2).
2. Choose a garden spot that receives at least six hours of direct sunlight a day (eight or ten hours is ideal). Vegetables should be planted away from buildings, trees, and other objects that shade the garden. If part of your garden is in the shade, plant that part with leafy vegetables such as lettuce, spinach, and similar plants.
3. Don't plant your garden near trees—their roots can compete with vegetables for water and nutrients. Generally the tree roots take food from the soil in a circle as far out as the tree's widest-reaching branches; plants usually do poorly within that circle.
4. Place the garden on high ground rather than in a depression at the base of a hill. Low spots warm up slowly in the spring. High ground allows vegetables to escape borderline freezes.

SAVINGS

VEGETABLE	SPACING OF ROW	YIELD	RETAIL VALUE	SAVINGS
*Cucumbers (6 plants on trellises)	2 ft.	60 cucumbers	@ 30¢	$18.00
*Tomatoes (9 plants)	2 ft.	100 lbs.	@ 60¢	60.00
*Zucchini (5 plants)	2 ft.	40 lbs.	@ 42¢	16.80
*Bell Peppers (9 plants)	2 ft.	40 lbs.	@ 80¢	31.20
Cabbage (2 plantings)	2 ft.	24 heads	@ 59¢	12.00
Lettuce (2 plantings)	1½ ft.	48 heads	@ 59¢	28.32
Beans (2 plantings)	2 ft.	25 lbs.	@ 45¢	11.25
Chard	1½ ft.	48 lbs.	@ 69¢	33.12
Beets (2 plantings)	1 ft.	36 lbs.	@ 40¢	14.40
Carrots (2 plantings)	1 ft.	36 lbs.	@ 58¢	13.68
Spinach (2 plantings)	1 ft.	12 lbs.	@ 69¢	9.36
Radishes (2 plantings)	1 ft.	24 bunches	@ 39¢	18.76
Parsley	1 ft.	48 bunches	@ 39¢	18.76
Green Onions (sets)	½ ft.	24 bunches	@ 32¢	7.68
Leeks	½ ft.	28 bunches	@ 69¢	19.32
*Broccoli followed by	2 ft.	24 heads	@ 69¢	16.56
*Cauliflower		12 heads	@ 85¢	9.20
Peas followed by	2 ft.	15 lbs.	@ 45¢	6.65
*Brussels sprouts		60 pints	@ 70¢	42.00
*Use hybrid variety			TOTAL	$376.60

5. Locate the garden away from low or soggy areas where water stands in puddles after rains.
6. Use contour rows or terraces on hillside gardens. Rows run across a slope help catch the rain.
7. Do not plant your gardens in a windy location.
8. Your garden should be close to a water supply. This eliminates having to drag a hose long distances. Also, try to put the garden as near your tool storage as possible.
9. Locate your garden fairly near the back door. This makes it easier to reach for weeding, watering, planting, picking and other chores.

Community Gardening

If you don't have space for your own garden, group gardening may well be your path to growing your own vegetables.

A few years ago, surveys indicated that over 30 million Americans would like to grow their own food but couldn't because of lack of space. Since that time, literally hundreds of communities have begun garden projects almost everywhere across the United States.

The group garden, itself, is simply a piece of land divided into individual plots that are rented or given to people who don't own their own land. In any project there may be as few as six gardeners or as many as several hundred.

In the Troy–Albany–Schenectady, New York, area, for instance, gardeners rent plots in sites coordinated by the Capital District Community Gardens, Inc.

In Burlington, Vermont, the Burlington Parks Commission divided a half-acre site into 24 plots at Cliffside Park. To supplement this the Burlington Parks Commission ran ads in the local paper asking for free garden plots. The Cliffside project attracted a wide cross-section of people, including retirees, a stockbroker's wife, medical students, businessmen, and others.

In Boston, Fenway Gardens, composed of 400 15-by-30-foot plots, was established a number of years ago in the Back Bay area. There is no charge for gardening here, but the gardeners are encouraged to become members of the Fenway Garden Society.

"Without these gardens," says the Administrative Secretary of the Boston Park Department, "a lot of people in the city simply would never get out of the house."

Besides communities and nonprofit organizations, many business organizations also sponsor community gardening projects. In Louisville, Kentucky, the Citizen's Fidelity Bank recently began a project that attracted over 3,000 gardeners. "These gardens," the bank estimates, "saved over a quarter of a million dollars based on retail food prices."

VACANT LOT COMMUNITY GARDENING

Vacant lots like this one all across America are being put to use in the communities to help produce vegetable crops.

Urban Gardening Program
S.E. Corner, Broad and Grange Streets
Philadelphia, Pa. 19141

COMMUNITY GARDENING

Crops like these are grown by community gardeners everywhere. The Urban Gardening Program in Philadelphia uses a variety of vacant lots right in neighborhoods, some privately owned and abandoned, some made available by their owners. This particular program is being handled through the Philadelphia County Extension Service.

Urban Gardening Program
SE Corner, Broad and Grange Streets
Philadelphia, Pennsylvania 19141

Numerous large companies also offer group gardening opportunities for their employees. Dow Chemical Company employees, for instance, have been gardening on company land for 34 years, and at RCA's David Sarnoff Research Center, employees share 120 garden plots that are plowed in the spring by the company.

In many cases these group gardens are sponsored or coordinated by the City Parks and Recreation Department. In others they are backed by local businesses, the YWCA, churches, and many other organizations. In Appleton, Wisconsin, the Sacred Heart Church's garden project rented 7 acres of land, (tagged "The Papal Gardens,") from a local farmer and divided it into 259 10-by-100-foot plots. And in Asheville, North Carolina, an enthusiastic local gardener convinced the YWCA to transform a weed lot into a community garden project for retired people.

In some cases University Extension Services, various local government agencies, and even the Department of Health, Education and Welfare got involved, giving expert advice and money. And nationally, Gardens-For-All, a national nonprofit organization with offices in Charlotte, Vermont, publishes information, conducts research, and provides consulting services to community garden projects all across the country.

Community gardening, then, is literally busting out all over and becoming bigger and bigger each and every year. If you are interested in joining one of these projects in your own area, call your local Park and Recreation Department. If they do not sponsor a gardening program, they will be able to refer you to a group gardening project within your own community.

2

SOIL

Soil for growing vegetables is not just an accumulation of dirt and rock. It is a combination of organic material, living organisms, air, water, and minerals. An ideal soil for vegetables contains 50 percent solid matter and 50 percent pore space, with water occupying about half of the latter area.

Basically there are three types of soil—clay, sand, and loam.

(Some classifications also include silt, an intermediate grade between clay and sand, consisting of gritty, hard-packed particles. We will follow that system in our discussion.)

Types of soil

Clay is composed of fine, flat, waferlike particles that fit together tightly and take in water slowly. Chemically, clay is primarily silicon and aluminum in composition, with small amounts of sodium, magnesium, iron, calcium, and potassium.

Once the clay particles absorb moisture, they hold it so tightly that it is almost impossible for plants to get any use out of it. Beyond this, there is no space for the air to penetrate. When clay dries, it is difficult to work, and plant roots have a hard time penetrating downward.

Rubbed between your fingers, wet clay soil feels smooth, soft, and slippery.

Sand has particles at least 25 times larger than the largest clay particles. Pure sand, while high in mineral content, contains almost no nutrients and has almost no capacity to store moisture. Air penetrates sand deeply, and water moves through too rapidly, dissolving away many of the nutrients.

Sand thus dries out quickly and sometimes reflects enough heat to damage vegetable crops. Most sandy soils contain enough clay and silt to retain some water and nutrients.

Rubbed between your fingers, sand feels grainy and gritty.

Silt is a kind of intermediate stage between clay and sand. Silt particles pack down hard, almost like clay, but they are considerably larger. Their size is about halfway between the size of sand and clay particles. Silt topsoils are often found over dense layers of clay. They are not often fertile.

Rubbed between your fingers, silt feels a bit slippery, with a grainy texture.

Loam is made up of clay, sand, and a good supply of decomposed organic material called humus. The grains have good structure built by the combined action of root growth, insects, worms, and bacteria. This type of soils drains well, yet retains enough water for good plant growth. Air can circulate freely, and there is plenty of room for roots to grow. Some loams that have one-third clay content or more are quite similar to clay.

Very few soils are ready to grow vegetables; most soils need to be worked before they will yield as they should. If soil has a high clay content, or if it's got too much sand or silt, it's got to be improved. Fortunately, it is possible to change the structure, drainage, and circulation of most types of soil by the addition of organic material and inert materials such as gypsum. Although the former is dealt with from a "purist" point of view in Chapter 3, Organic Gardening, it would be foolish to ignore it in this chapter. And because it is just about the first alternative a gardener should consider, organic additives will be first on our list.

Organic additives

In clay soils, the coarse organic particles hold the compacted soil particles apart, breaking up the heavy soil. The fine organic particles help hold the clay particles together in small crumbs. This improves the drainage, allows the soil to "breath," and adds nutrients.

Organic material added to sandy soil holds water and nutrients where plants can use them. Organic matter also keeps sandy soils from warming up quickly and prevents damage to vegetables. In order to be effective, at least one-third of the final mix must be organic.

In addition, the minute organic material is added, microorganisms in the soil begin to break it down into forms plants can use. The rate of decomposition and the products of decay depend on the material itself.

There are four general types of organic soil conditioners:

Manures: Good water- and nutrient-holding ability, useful for changing soil structure. Manures can be obtained directly from a farm or purchased in sacks as a commercial product. Fresh manure should be allowed to rot before it is used in the garden. Commercial dried and packaged manures often have fairly high levels of soluble salts.

Peat moss: High in water- and nutrient-holding ability, fair for changing soil structure. The better peats come from Canadian bogs. They are long-lasting but provide little or no nutritive value.

Wood by-products: Fair in water- and nutrient-hold-ing ability, excellent for altering soil structure. These by-products include leaf mold, wood shavings, sawdust, and ground bark. These have a high ratio of carbon in relation to the amount of nitrogen present, which means that the nitrogen is used up by the micro-organisms in the decay process, making it unavailable to growing vegetables. Thus, nitrogen must often be added to these mixtures. Frequently commercial wood by-products have nitrogen added in the manufacturing process.

Organic by-products: (rice hulls, cottonseed meal). Poor water- and nutrient-holding ability, good for altering soil structure at low cost.

Partially decomposed organic material (compost), which is discussed at length in Chapter 3, has good moisture-holding and nutrient-holding ability. It quickly adds humus to the soil, along with nutrients in usable form.

Which additive you utilize in your garden depends on your own soil conditions and preferences. In general, sandy soils benefit from spongy materials like peat that hold water and nutrients well. Clay soils benefit most from bulky additions such as bark, hulls, and similar materials that separate the clay particles.

Inorganic additives

Inorganic additives generally are used in heavy clay soils to break up the soil structure and to allow greater penetration of air and water. You can utilize inert substances, which mechanically hold the particles apart, or chemical conditioners (see chart).

Clay soil can be broken up by the addition of gypsum (calcium sulfate). Clay in its natural state generally becomes packed and airless because an excess of sodium in each clay particle strongly attracts water. As the water drains away, the particles are left tightly packed. Gypsum removes the sodium by changing the sodium ions for calcium ions. The clay particles are then soon separated into large crumbs with ample pore space. Gypsum should be spread on the soil surface at the rate of about 50 pounds per 1000 square feet. Sand added to clay will not improve it, will not prevent it from baking hard.

Acid-alkaline soil

Soils are often acid (sour) or alkaline (sweet). This is expressed in terms of pH (the degree of alkalinity or acidity) on a scale of 1 to 14—7 is neutral, below 7 acid, above 7, alkaline. Most vegetables—with some notable exceptions like tomatoes—do best in neutral soils (see chart, page 14).

ORGANIC SOIL CONDITIONERS

TYPE	STRUCTURE-MODIFYING ABILITY	OTHER ADVANTAGES	NUTRIENT & WATER-HOLDING CAPACITY	USES
Activated sludge, garden compost	Organic sludge and compost are useful for modifying soil structure	Adds nutrients to soil	Good	Useful in clay and sand
Manures	Fair	Has high nitrogen content, but must be well rotted	Fair	Useful in clay and sand
Leaf Mold	Fair	Should be well decomposed; adds usable nutrients	Fair	Useful in clay and sand
Sawdust	Good	Untreated is high in carbon, low in nitrogen, can be purchased with nitrogen added	Fair to good	Useful in sand
Rice hulls	Fair	Add nitrogen 1/5 lb. per 10 cu. ft.	Poor	Useful in clay
Bark	Granular, easy to use; helps break up heavy soils	Needs nitrogen if untreated—1 lb. per 10 cu. ft.	Poor	Useful in clay

PEAT AND PEAT MOSS

TYPE	IDENTIFYING CHARACTERISTICS	PHYSICAL PROPERTIES	CHEMICAL PROPERTIES	ADVANTAGES	DISADVANTAGES
Sphagnum peat moss (includes related moss peats)	Light yellow to brown; extremely fibrous; readily identifiable; whole plant remains	Least decomposed or raw; highest moisture-holding capacity; lowest bulk density	Highest acidity; lowest ash content; lowest nitrogen content; highest in organic matter	Highest water-holding capacity; lowest volume weight; high acidity; desirable for acid-loving plants such as conifers; very sterile—free from plant disease and noxious weed seeds	Tends to decompose faster than other types; problems in mixing with soil because of light, fibrous structure; difficult to wet; high acidity can injure acid-intolerant plants; tendency to blow away
Reed-sedge peat (Also called fibrous peat)	Dark brown to reddish brown; variable in fibrosity; identifiable plant remains	Most favorable state of decomposition for immediate soil benefit; intermediate moisture-holding capacity and bulk density	Low cellulose content; high in organic matter, mild acidity; low ash content; high nitrogen content	Two to three times the nitrogen content of sphagnum; contains organic acid in its original moist condition; mixes smoothly with soil; free of weed seed; does not suffer the rapid, uneconomic decomposition of sphagnum	Does not hold quite as much moisture as sphagnum; bacterially active when applied
Peat Humus	Very dark brown to black; advanced state of decomposition; few if any fibers; no identifiable plant remains	Very low moisture-holding capacity; highest bulk density; almost completely decomposed	Highest nitrogen and ash content; variable acidity; lowest in organic matter	Lowest but most stable organic matter	Very dusty when dry; drying difficult to apply; may have impaired rewettability; may contain noxious weed seed

INORGANIC SOIL CONDITIONERS

MECHANICAL	SOURCE	FUNCTION
Pumice	A ground volcanic stone full of minute cavities	Holds apart massed clay particles
Sand		Useful when applied in large quantities
Vermiculite	Exploded mica	Holds 3-4 times its weight in water

CHEMICAL OR COMBINATION		
Gypsum	Naturally occurring calcium sulfate	The calcium in gypsum is capable of replacing the sodium ions in clay soils that make clay particles pack so hard; when the calcium ions replace the sodium, the particles group, forming large pore spaces
Lime sulfur (sold as Calcium polysulfide)	Sold as calcium polysulfide	Acts in a manner similar to gypsum; the most effective lime sulfur has a wetting agent that causes a deeper soil penetration
Soil sulfur		As the soil warms up, the sulfur breaks down into sulfuric acid and reacts with calcium carbonate in the soil to form soluble calcium sulfate

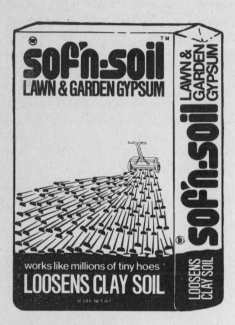

◄Gypsum loosens clay soil to let air and water penetrate, improves soil conditions for deep root growth, increases the effectiveness of fertilizers, and adds sulfur and available calcium.

Cascade Soil-Aid is a finely ground bark composted for several months with nitrogen added. This product is representative of many of the new bark products. It is extremely useful in breaking up heavy soils.

Soil can be conditioned and improved by the addition of a good peat mixture. Sandy soil lets water and nutrients leach through. Clay soil is compacted and keeps water and nutrients from penetrating. Peat holds water and nutrients in suspension in sandy soil, loosens and aerates compacted clay soils.

Questions and answers about gypsum and soil

Q. How does gypsum loosen clay soil?

A. Through electrochemical action. The calcium ions ($Ca++$) in gypsum neutralize the negative charges on the clay particles dispersed. Following neutralization, the particles can group together (flocculate) into a more granular form.

Q. When can gypsum be applied?

A. Any time of the year, but spring and fall are best, to take advantage of seasonal moisture. Moisture is essential to achieve the desired soil-conditioning effect.

Q. How deep will gypsum loosen clay soil?

A. Gypsum will loosen clay soil to a 3-6-in. depth if merely spread on the surface and watered in. To achieve greater depth and faster loosening action, gypsum must be cultivated into the top layer of soil. For particularly heavy clay soils, a three-year program may be necessary to obtain desired results.

Q. Does gypsum permanently loosen clay soil?

A. No. Gypsum keeps soil conditioned only as long as enough soluble calcium is available to keep the clay particles flocculated. For more permanent loosening, peat moss or other organic matter should be added along with the gypsum.

Soils become acid by the leaching of calcium and magnesium ions and their replacement by hydrogen ions. This occurs naturally in regions of heavy rainfall.

Soils turn more alkaline as calcium, manganese, and sodium ions accumulate and replace hydrogen ions. This condition occurs because of low rainfall and poor drainage. It is also prevalent in areas with native limestone deposits.

Sometimes you can tell whether the soil is too alkaline just by looking at it. Symptoms of alkalinity are yellowing leaves on vegetation, stunted growth, and burning of leaf margins. Often alkaline soils are too salty. In extreme cases heavy brown or white salt deposits are left on the soil surface or on the edges of water ditches.

In the case of acid soils the surface signs are not obvious or evident, even to the trained eye.

The surest way of telling whether or not your soil is too acid or too alkaline is with a pH test. There are three ways in which this test can be made. First, you can take some samples of your soil and have them tested by the State Cooperative Extension Service. Usually the agent in your county can arrange to have this done free or for a small fee. You can also send these soil samples to a commercial laboratory for testing. There are many labs throughout the country that make this service available, including the following:

Prescription Soil Analysis
P.O. Box 80631
Lincoln, Neb. 68500

Perry Laboratory
23416 Summit Rd.
Los Gatos, Cal. 95030

Soil and Plant Laboratory, Inc.
P.O. Box 153
Santa Clara, Cal. 95052

You can also purchase a soil test kit at your local nursery or similar outlet and test the soil yourself. The procedure consists of filling a small glass container partly full of fine soil, then adding the testing solution. The result of this mixture is compared with an easily read color chart. Anyone who can read and compare colors can produce practical results. Kits range from a simple test of pH (about $3.00) to elaborate soil test kits that test for all major, secondary, and trace elements ($100.00). Small kits (about $15.00) which test for the major nutrients (nitrogen, phosphorus, and potash) are satisfactory for most home gardens.

To counteract acid soil, ground limestone is an effective agent, and in some areas it is used extensively. Dolomite lime contains both calcium and magnesium. Hydrated or burned lime is sometimes used, but it leaches away rapidly and can burn your hands. To correct alkaline soil, add gypsum, soil sulfur, or aluminum sulfate.

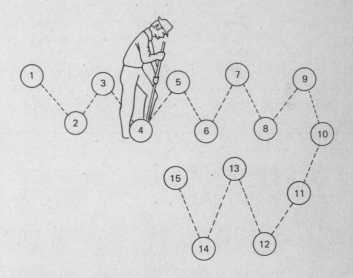

How to take a soil sample

1. Select 8 to 15 sample spots throughout the garden area. A zig-zag pattern is the best.
2. Take a soil sample from each area 8 inches deep with a soil probe or a garden spade.
3. Discard the top 1 inch of surface.
4. Place the composites in a plastic bag and mix thoroughly.
5. Take one cup of the mixed soil composite and put in a small plastic bag for shipping if you are shipping to a lab.
6. If you are making your own tests, select your soil from the composite.

pH scale

```
      0——
       -
      1—— Hydrochloric acid
       -
      2—— Lemons
       -
      3—— Grapefruit
       -
      4—— Tomatoes
       - Very strongly acid
      5—— Strongly acid
       - Medium acid
      6—— Slightly acid
       - Very slightly acid
Neutral  7——                          } Soil
       - Very slightly alkaline
      8—— Slightly alkaline
       - Medium alkaline
      9—— Strongly alkaline
       - Very strongly alkaline
     10——
       -
     11—— Ammonia
       - Washing soda
     12——
       -
     13—— Lye
       -
     14——
```

Note: A soil solution with a pH of 5 is ten times as acid as one having a pH of 6 and one hundred times more acid than a soil solution of 7.

SELECTED SOIL AND pH TEST KITS

LaMotte Chemical Products Company, Chestertown, Md. 21620, offers many sophisticated test kits including greenhouse, hydroponic, and complete nutrient test outfits. The following are best suited for the home gardener:

Model B: Tests for soil pH (acidity-alkalinity). A measured amount of the soil sample is mixed in a test tube with the liquid reagent provided. The color developed in the test tube is compared with a color chart. Tables furnished. $2.95
   Available from the following catalog firms: 23, 37, 62 (see page 00 for company names and addresses)

Model S: Tests for pH, nitrogen, phosphorus, potassium (potash). This combination soil test kit contains reagents to make a total of 40 tests. Color charts show low, medium, and high readings. Instruction booklet interprets test results. $11.95
   Available from the following catalog firms: 23, 37, 62

Model L: Tests for pH, nitrogen, phosphorus, potassium (potash). Deluxe kit with enough reagents for 30 pH tests, 15 nitrogen tests, 20 phosphorus tests, and 15 potassium tests. Measurements are made in graduate plastic test tubes.
   Available from the following catalog firms: 23, 37, 62

Sudbury Laboratory, Inc., Sudbury, Mass. 01776, manufactures a number of soil test kits. The following are recommended for the home gardner:

Home Garden Kit, Model D: 70 tests for nitrogen, phosphorus, potash, and acidity. Has color-coded bottle caps and dropper inserts. $8.75
   Available from the following catalog firms: 9, 10, 12, 31, 45, 49, 56, 57, 66, 67, 72

TESTING YOUR SOIL

The procedure is simple with a basic testing kit.
1. Fill a small glass container partially full of fine soil.
2. Add the proper testing solution according to the kit instructions.
3. Compare the results of the mixture to the easily read color chart.

Popular Garden Kit, Model H: Makes approximately 90 tests for nitrogen, phosphorus, potash, acidity; chart shows the needs of grasses, flowers, and vegetables. $13.75

    Available from the following catalog firms: 9, 10, 19, 28, 29, 45, 47, 49, 52, 57, 66, 67, 72

Green Thumb Kit, Model T: A more complete version of the popular garden kit. Tests for nitrogen, phosphorus, potash, and acidity. $20.95

    Available from the following catalog firms: 9, 10, 12, 31, 45, 49, 56, 57, 66, 67, 72

Horticultural Kit, Model B: A good kit for larger gardens, tests for nitrogen, phosphorus, potash, acidity. $37.25

    Available from the following catalog firms: 10, 45, 47, 66

Deluxe Kit, Model A: The deluxe kit is used by farmers, greenhouses, nurseries. Makes approximately 200 individual tests for nitrogen, phosphorus, potash, and acidity. $51.95

    Available from the following catalog firms: 10, 47, 57, 66

Valley Soil Test Kit: Kit includes complete instructions, test tubes, funnel. Enough for 20 or more tests for pH, nitrogen, potash, and phosphorus. $4.50

    Available from the following catalog firms: 18, 39

OPTIMUM PH RANGE FOR VEGETABLE CROPS

6 to 8	asparagus, beets, cabbage, muskmelons
6 to 7.5	peas, spinach, summer squash
6 to 7	celery, chives, endive, rhubarb, horseradish, lettuce, onions, radishes, cauliflower
5.5 to 7.5	sweet corn, pumpkin, tomatoes
5.5 to 6.8	snap beans, lima beans, carrots, cucumbers, parsnips, peppers, rutabagas, winter squash
5.5 to 6.5	eggplant, watermelon
4.8 to 6.3	potatoes

CHANGING SOIL PH

FROM	TO	ADDT'L. LBS./100 SQ. FEET	
		LIMESTONE	SULFUR
4.5	6.5	175	
5.0	6.5	140	
5.5	6.5	100	
6.0	6.5	66	
7.0	6.5		4
7.5	6.5		20
8.0	6.5		38

Soil nutrients

Plants need nutrients for growth. Three elements—oxygen, carbon, and hydrogen—come from the air and water. The other 13 nutrients are found in the soil. Three of these 13 are important factors: they are nitrogen, phosphorus, and potassium. Another three of the 13 are secondary: they are calcium, manganese, and sulfur. Then there are seven micronutrients: they are zinc, iron, magnesium, copper, molybdenum, boron, and chlorine.

The three major nutrients mentioned are needed by most vegetables in fairly large amounts. They have a strong effect on the growth of stems, leaves, roots, and fruits. So you must make sure that your soil has sufficient supplies of nitrogen, phosphorus, and potash. Among the secondary nutrients, calcium promotes early growth, magnesium is an important component of chlorophyll, and sulfur is a constituent of protein. All are needed for healthy growth. Although the micronutrients are needed only in very small quantities, they are nevertheless important, and should not be overlooked.

Most garden soils are not perfect—they are generally deficient in one or several of the basic nutritional elements. So for maximum production of healthy vegetables it is generally necessary to provide some kind of fertilizer to the soil.

Selecting the right fertilizer

Selecting the right fertilizer from the dozens of plant foods available can be confusing. Basically five different kinds are utilized in vegetable gardens.

Dry: Chemical fertilizer.

Powdered: A combination of materials in powdered form. They provide vegetables quick access to nutrient material, but blow away easily and leach out quickly.

Pelletized-granular: The same as powdered, but the fertilizer is compressed into pellets. They are easier to spread, and the nutrients are released more slowly as the pellets break down.

Time-release: The fertilizer pellets are coated with resin or a similar substance. The nutrients slowly diffuse through the "resin." When watered, the surface is worn away much like licking a lollipop. There is no danger of overfertilizing, but one application is generally enough for vegetables for an entire season. Time-release fertilizers are especially good for slow-maturing crops such as melons and winter squash.

Liquid: Liquid fertilizers are absorbed through the leaves, stems, and branches as well as through the roots. They can be sprayed or sprinkled on the vegetables. They come as concentrated powders or concentrated liquids that are diluted with water.

To add to the confusion different kinds of fertilizers are prepared for different soil conditions and vegetables. Some manufacturers, for instance, put out as many as 12 different formulations. Most are composed of nitrogen, phosphorus, and potassium with trace elements.

Vegetable fertilizer formulations are generally based on the following:

Nitrogen promotes leaf growth, stimulates vegetative development for cabbage, lettuce, spinach, and collards.

Phosphorus promotes strong root growth, hastens maturity, and aids in seed and fruit development.

Potassium (potash) is necessary for new cell division in roots and buds and is important to fruit quality. Corn ears sometimes don't fill out when a plant is low in potash. Potash is also important to the ripening of tomatoes and for the development of root crops such as beets and potatoes.

The numbers you find on a fertilizer container refer to the percentage of nitrogen (N), phosphorus (P), and potassium (K) found in that particular fertilizer (in that order). A 5-10-5 fertilizer contains 5 percent nitrogen, 10 percent phosphorus, and 5 percent potassium. In a 100-pound bag of this fertilizer there would be 5 pounds of nitrogen, 10 pounds of phosphorus, and 5 pounds of potassium.

Manufacturers make up different formulations depending on use: A good general fertilizer suitable for spring fertilizing might be 5-10-5 or 10-10-10. A fertilizer meant for potatoes might have the formulation 0-20-20, and one meant especially for tomatoes might be low in nitrogen, high in phosphorus, and medium in potassium such as 5-10-5.

The following nitrogen materials are also utilized by home gardeners—ammonium sulfate, ammonium nitrate, urea sulfate, ammonium nitrate, nitrate of soda, ammonium phosphate, and calcium nitrate.

Sidedressing

In order to achieve optimum growth, many crops such as asparagus, corn, and tomatoes need additional amounts of nitrogen in the form of ammonium nitrate during the season (see chart for amounts and times). Do not allow fertilizer to come in contact with plant leaves and stems. Apply ammonium nitrate in a band along the side of the row or around transplanted crops, 4-6 inches away. Water lightly if rain is not expected.

ALL YOU NEED TO KNOW ABOUT PLANT NUTRIENTS . . . AND MORE

MAJOR NUTRIENTS

Nutrient	Function	Symptoms of soil Nutrient Deficiency
Nitrogen (N)	Produces a dark green vigorous leaf color, vigorous root system, feeds soil microorganisms	Leaves yellow, yellow-green, stunted growth
Phosphorus (P)	Stimulates early root formation, gives rapid start, hastens maturity, provides disease resistance; important for development of flowers, fruit, and seed	Leaves have purple or red appearance
Potassium (K)	Important in the manufacture of sugar and starch; influences leaf and root system development; increases vigor and disease-resistance	Leaves look dry or scorched at edges

SECONDARY NUTRIENTS

Nutrient	Function	Symptoms
Calcium (Ca)	Necessary for manufacture and growth of plant cells, promotes early root growth	Plants stunted, leaves wrinkled
Manganese (Mn)	Speeds maturation, aids in photosynthesis and nitrogen metabolism	Patches of yellowing in leaves
Sulfur (S)	Maintains dark-green color—constituent of protiens	Pale-green, yellowing

MICRO-NUTRIENTS (Trace Elements)

Nutrient	Function	Symptoms
Iron (Fe)	Promotes chlorophyll production; catalyst in enzyme system	Yellowing leaves, green veins
Magnesium (Mg)	Forms chlorophyll and sugar; important for seed development	Chlorosis (yellowing) of leaves
Copper (Cu)	Enzyme activator essential for chlorophyll formation	Multiple budding
Zinc (Zn)	Necessary for normal chlorophyll production and growth	Small, yellow leaves
Boron (B)	Needed for calcium utilization and normal cell division	Leaves yellowish red
Molybdenum (Mo)	Important in the utilization of nitrogen	—
Chlorine (Cl)	Essential for proper plant development	—

SIDEDRESSING FERTILIZER-AMOUNTS AND TIMES

VEGETABLE CROP	OZ. PER 10 FT. ROW, AMMONIUM NITRATE 33-0-0	TIME OF APPLICATION
Asparagus	3½	Before growth begins in spring
Beans and peas	1½	After heavy bloom and set of pods
Beets, carrots, sweet potatoes, watermelons	None	Sidedressing of nitrogen not needed
Broccoli, cabbage, cauliflower	1½	Three weeks after transplanting
Cantaloupe, cucumber	1½	One week after blossoming begins
Corn	1½	When plants are 12-18 inches tall
Eggplants, peppers	1½	After the first fruit sets
Kale, mustard, spinach turnip greens	1½	When plants are about a third grown
Lettuce, parsnips, turnips	1½	Two weeks after transplanting, four weeks after sowing seed
Onion (mature)	1½	One to two weeks after bulb formation
Potato	2½	After tuber formation starts
Tomato	1½	One to two weeks before first tomato ripens

Fertilizer formulations of three companies

Companies vary considerably in the nitrogen, phosphorus, potassium formulations used in making up particular kinds of fertilizers. Here is a comparison between the different types of plant foods manufactured by Rain Bird, Chacon Chemical Corporation, and 3M Co.

	RAIN BIRD TIME-RELEASE PLANT FOOD	CHACON LIQUID PLANT FOOD	"PRECISE" TIME-RELEASE PLANT FOOD
Tomato food	14-18-14	5-10-5	6-18-6
Vegetable food	14-17-12	5-10-5	12-6-6
Rose food	9-6-12	2-10-10	8-12-4
Azalea/camellia	17-5-11	2-10-10	——
Flower food	15-14-10	0-10-10	6-12-6
Bulb food	10-21-10	——	——
Tree & shrub	21-9-5	——	20-10-10
House plants	19-6-13	4-4-2	——
African violets	18-8-13	——	8-11-5
All-purpose	14-14-14	10-10-5	12-6-7

Application of dried fertilizers

If you have not had your soil tested, you can apply a general fertilizer containing nitrogen, phosphorus (P_2O_5), and soluble potash (K_2O) rather than a specific analysis for each vegetable. These three grades give excellent results with most garden crops: 6-12-12, 10-10-10, 5-10-15.

You can either broadcast the fertilizer before planting and work it into the soil or apply it in bands at seeding time. If you broadcast the fertilizer, work it into the soil fairly soon, either mechanically or by hand.

To band a fertilizer, first determine where you are going to plant the seeds or plants. Then mark the row with a small furrow or a string tied from one end of the row to the other. Dig a shallow trench 2-4 inches to one side of the row and 2-4 inches below where the seed is to be placed. Place the fertilizer in the bottom of the trench and cover it with soil.

SOURCES OF SOIL ADDITIVES

BARK

Boise Cascade, Wood Products Division
P.O. Box 50
Boise, Id. 83728

Greenlife Products, Inc.
Subsidiary of Chesapeake Corp. of Virginia
West Point, Va. 23181

Mead Paygro
P.O. Box 221
Dayton, Oh. 45401

DG Shelter Products
Vita Bark
P.O. Box 60158
Sacramento, Cal. 95860

CHEMICALS

Leffingwell Chemical Company
111 S. Berry St.
Brea, Cal. 92621

SOURCES OF SOIL ADDITIVES (Continued)

COMPOST

DG Shelter Products
P.O. Box 60158
Sacramento, Cal. 95860

GYPSUM

American Pelletizing Corp.
P.O. Box 3628
Des Moines, Ia. 50322

United States Gypsum Company
101 S. Wacker Drive
Chicago, Ill. 60606

LIMESTONE

American Pelletizing Corp.
P.O. Box 3628
Des Moines, Ia. 50322

Faesy & Besthoff, Inc.
143 River Rd.
Edgewater, N.J. 07020

Vermont Marble Co.
Ground Products Division
61 Main St.
Proctor, Vt. 05765

MINERAL SOIL CONDITIONERS

Engelhard Minerals & Chemicals Corp.
Menlo Park
Edison, N.J. 08817

Set Products, Inc.
8501 Freeway Dr.
Macedonia, Oh. 44056

ORGANIC HUMUS

Early Bird Nursery Products
Ralston Purina Co.
14T Checkerboard Square
St. Louis, Mo. 63188

Humus Organic Products, Inc.
P.O. Box 520
Bernalillo, N.M. 87004

PACKAGED COW MANURES

Greenlife Products Co.
Subsidiary of Chesapeake Corp. of Virgnia
West Point, Va. 23181

Mead Paygro
P.O. Box 221
Dayton, Oh. 45401

PEAT MOSS

Atkins & Durbrow, Ltd.
Box 55
Port Colborne, Ont. L3K 5V7 Canada

Conrad Fafard, Inc.
Box 3033
Springfield, Mass. 01101

PEAT MOSS (Continued)

Greenlife Products Co.
Subsidiary of Chesapeake Corp. of Virginia
West Point, Va. 23181

Huber Peat Co.
Box 3006
Houston, Tex. 77001

Leoni's Power-o-Peat
Box 956
Gilbert, Minn. 55741

Michigan Peat Co.
Box 66388
Houston, Tex. 77006

Mosser Lee Company
Millston, Wisc. 54643

Western Peat Moss Ltd.
Vancouver, B.C., Canada

VERMICULITE - TERRALITE

Grace Horticultural Products
W.R. Grace Co.
62 Whitmore Ave.
Cambridge, Mass. 02140

Leoni's Power-o-Peat
Box 956
Gilbert, Minn. 55741

Michigan Peat Company
P.O. Box 66388
Houston, Tex. 77006

PERLITE

Carefree Garden Products
Box 383
West Chicago, Ill. 60185

Grace Horticultural Products
W.R. Grace Co.
62 Whitmore Ave.
Cambridge, Mass. 02140

Leoni's Power-o-Peat
P.O. Box 956
Gilbert, Minn. 55741

Sources of time-release fertilizers

Carefree Garden Products
Box 383
West Chicago, Ill. 60185

Chevron Chemical Co.
200 Bush St.
San Francisco, Cal. 94104

Holland Bulb Co.
6441 Johnson Circle Blvd.
Portland, Ore. 97206

Rain Bird Corp.
7045 N. Grand Ave.
Glendora, Cal. 91740

Ringer Corp.
6860 Flying Cloud Dr.
Eden Prairie, Minn. 55343

S & D Products, Inc.
Box 66
Prairie du Chien,
    Wisc. 53821

Sierra Chemical Co.
1001 Yosemite Dr.
Milpitas, Cal. 95035

3M Co.
3M Center
St. Paul, Minn. 55101

Unifeed
10 Burlington Ave.
Wilmington,
    Mass. 01887

Sources of dry fertilizers

Amchem Products, Inc.
Brookside Ave.
Ambler, Pa. 19002

American Cyanamid Co.
Agricultural Chemicals Div.
Box 400
Princeton, N.J. 08540

Bio Con
Division Searle
Agriculture, Inc.
Box 993
Hereford, Tex. 79045

The Bishop Co.
Box 317
Lebanon, Pa. 17042

Butler's Mill, Inc.
5180 Naranja St.
San Diego, Cal. 92114

H. D. Campbell Co.
Farm Products Division
Campbell Bldg.
Rochelle, Ill. 61068

Chacon Chemical Corp.
2600 Yates Ave.
City of Commerce,
Cal. 90040

Chevron Chemical Co.
Ortho Division
200 Bush St.
San Francisco, Cal. 94104

Ciba-Geigy Corp.
Agricultural Division
Box 11422
Greensboro, N.C. 27409

Continental Chemiste Corp.
2256 W. Ogden Ave.
Chicago, Ill. 60612

Creative Sales, Inc.
200 So. Main
Fremont, Neb. 68025

Elanco Products Co.
Division Eli Lilly Co.
Box 1968
Indianapolis, Ind. 46206

Encap Products Co.
Green Garde Division
P.O. Box 278
Mount Prospect, Ill. 60056

Faesy & Besthoff, Inc.
143 River Road
Edgewater, N.J. 07020

Germain's, Inc.
Box 3233
Los Angeles, Cal. 90058

Greenlife Products Co., Inc.
Box 72
West Point, Va. 23181

H & M Fertilizer, Inc.
Box 1542
Fort Stockton, Tex. 79735

Hercules, Inc.
910 Market St.
Wilmington, Del. 19899

A. H. Hoffman, Inc.
Box 8
Landisville, Pa. 17538

Holland Bulb Co.
6441 Johnson Circle Blvd.
Portland, Ore. 97206

Hyde Park Products Corp.
10 Cottage Pl., Box 320
New Rochelle, N.Y. 10802

International Spike, Inc.
462 E. High St.
Lexington, Ky. 40508

J & L Adikes, Inc.
182-12 93rd Ave.
Jamaica, N.Y. 11423

Lebanon Chemical Corp.
Box 180
Lebanon, Pa. 17042

Leeming/Pacquin
Division Pfizer, Inc.
235 E. 42nd Street
New York, N.Y. 10017

Charles H. Lilly Co.
(Lilly/Miller)
7737 N.E. Killingsworth
Portland, Ore. 97218

Milorganite Division
Box 160
Oak Creek, Wisc. 53154

Northrup King & Co.
1500 Jackson St. N.E.
Minneapolis, Minn. 55413

Olin Agricultural Products
Dept.
Box 991
Little Rock, Ark. 72203

Organic Compost Corp.
Box 217
Germantown, Wisc. 53022

Patterson Green-Up
Chemical Co., Inc.
1400 Union Ave.
Kansas City, Mo. 64101

Plantabbs Corp.
Timonium, Md. 21093

Plant Marvel Distributing
Co., Inc.
624 W. 119th St.
Chicago, Ill. 60628

Pro-Lawn Products, Inc.
Box 1358
Syracuse, N.Y. 13201

Ringer Corp.
6860 Flying Cloud Dr.
Eden Prairie, Minn. 55343

Why ammonium sulfate?

1. Supplies both nitrogen and sulfur needs in one application.
2. All nitrogen is in the ammonium form, which resists leaching.
3. Sulfur is in the sulfate form, so that it is immediately available to plants.

USS Granular Ammonium Sulfate

Agri-Chemicals Division
United States Steel
P.O. Box 1685
Atlanta, Ga. 30301

VEGETABLE FERTILIZER REQUIREMENTS

Vegetables fall into three categories with regard to their fertilizer requirements. If you have a large garden, you can group vegetables according to their requirements. This makes fertilizing easier.

HEAVY FEEDERS	MEDIUM FEEDERS	LIGHT FEEDERS
Artichoke	Asparagus	Beet
Cabbage	Beans	Carrots
Celery	Broccoli	Radishes
Onion	Cantaloupe	Rutabagas
Sweet Potato	Cauliflower	Turnips
Tomato	Corn	
	Cucumber	Very Light
	Eggplants	Southern Peas
	Herbs	
	Kale	
	Mustard	
	Okra	
	Peas	
	Pumpkin	
	Rhubarb	
	Swiss Chard	
	Watermelon	

Beans and Peas help improve soil fertility. The bacteria living in the nodules on the roots of legumes take soil nitrogen in unusable forms and combine it with sugars from the legumes to produce ammonia, a nitrogen compound that plants can use. Legumes actually conserve and restore soil.

Sources of dry fertilizer (Continued)

Rockland Chemical Co.,
Inc.
Box 809
W. Caldwell, N.J. 07006

Ross Daniels, Inc.
1720 Fuller Rd., Box 430
W. Des Moines,
Ia. 50265

Roto Grow Co.
118 Monell St.
Pen Yan, N.Y. 14527

S & D Products, Inc.
Box 66
Prairie du Chien,
Wisc. 53821

Science Products Co., Inc.
5801 N. Tripp Ave.
Chicago, Ill. 60646

O.M. Scott & Sons Co.
Marysville, Oh. 43040

Seaboard Seed Co.
Box 117
Bristol, Ill. 60512

Smith-Douglass
Division Borden Chemicals
Box 419
Norfolk, Va. 23501

Sta-Green Plant Food Co.
Box 540
Sylacauga, Ala. 35150

Stanford Seed Co.
Box 366
Buffalo, N.Y. 41240

Stim-U-Plant, Inc.
2077 Parkwood Ave.
Columbus, Oh. 43219

Swift Agricultural
Chemicals
Vigoro Division
111 Jackson Blvd.
Chicago, Ill. 60646

Swiss Farms, Inc.
3700 Prudential Tower
Boston, Mass. 02199

3M Co.
3M Center
St. Paul, Minn. 55101

Unifeed
Division Diamond Crystal
Salt Co.
10 Burlington Ave.
Wilmington, Mass. 01887

United States Gypsum Co.
Chemicals Division
101 S. Wacker Dr.
Chicago, Ill. 60646

USS Agri Chemicals
Division U.S. Steel
P.O. Box 1685
Atlanta, Ga. 30301

Vaughan-Jacklin Corp.
5300 Katrine Ave.
Downers Grove, Ill. 60515

Wilson & Geo. Meyer &
Co.
270 Lawrence Avenue
S. San Francisco,
Cal. 94080

Dexol Industries
1450 W. 228th St.
Torrance, Cal. 90501

Encap Products Co.
Green Garde Division
P.O. Box 278
Mount Prospect, Ill. 60056

Green Thumb Products
Corp.
Drawer 760
Apopka, Fla. 32703

Hercules, Inc.
910 Market St.
Wilmington, Del. 19899

Holland Bulb Co.
6441 Johnson Circle Blvd.
Portland, Ore. 97206

J & L Adikes, Inc.
182-12 93rd Ave.
Jamaica, N.Y. 11423

Lebanon Chemical Corp.
Box 180
Lebanon, Pa. 17042

Leffingwell Chemical Co.
111 S. Berry St.
Brea, Cal. 92621

Leeming/Pacquin
Division Pfizer, Inc.
235 E. 42nd Street
New York, N.Y. 10017

Leoni's Power-o-Peat
Box 956
Gilbert, Minn. 55741

Chas. H. Lilly Co.
(Lilly/Miller)
7737 N.E. Killingsworth
Portland, Ore. 97218

MacAndrews & Forbes Co.
Third St. & Jefferson Ave.
Camden, N.J. 08104

Mrs. Meyers Country
Garden Plant Food
1610 Rollins Rd.
Burlingame, Cal. 94010

Organic Laboratories, Inc.
5050 Westheimer
Houston, Tex. 77027

Organic Nutrients, Inc.
8909 Elder Creek Rd.
Sacramento, Cal. 95828

Patterson Green-Up
Chemical Co., Inc.
1400 Union Ave.
Kansas City, Mo. 64101

Plantabbs Corp.
Timonium, Md. 21093

Plant Marvel Laboratories
624 W. 119th St.
Chicago, Ill. 60628

Pro Lawn Products, Inc.
Box 1358
Syracuse, N.Y. 13201

Ra-pid-gro Corp.
88 Ossian St., Box 13
Dansville, N.Y. 14437

Science Products Co., Inc.
5801 N. Tripp Ave.
Chicago, Ill. 60646

Sta-Green Plant Food Co.
Box 540
Sylacauga, Ala. 35150

Sterns Garden Products,
Inc.
Box 888
Port Washington,
N.Y. 11050

Stim-U-Plant, Inc.
2077 Parkwood Ave.
Columbus, Oh. 43219

Sudbury Laboratory, Inc.
Sudbury, Mass. 01776

Swift Agricultural
Chemicals Corp.
111 W. Jackson Blvd.
Chicago, Ill. 60604

Swiss Farms, Inc.
3700 Prudential Tower
Boston, Mass. 02199

Vaughan-Jacklin Corp.
5300 Katrine Ave.
Downers Grove, Ill. 60515

3M Co.
3M Center
St. Paul, Minn. 55101

Sources of liquid fertilizers

American Cyanamid Co.
Agricultural Chemicals Div.
Box 400
Princeton, N.J. 08540

Atlas/Hamar
865 Lind Ave. S.W.
Renton, Wash. 98055

The Bishop Co.
Box 317
Lebanon, Pa. 17042

Black Leaf Products Co.
667 N. State St.
Elgin, Ill. 60120

H. D. Campbell Co.
Farm Products Division
Campbell Bldg.
Rochelle, Ill. 61068

Chacon Chemical Corp.
2600 Yates Ave.
City of Commerce,
Cal. 90040

Chevron Chemical Co.
Ortho Division
200 Bush St.
San Francisco, Calif. 94105

Clinton Nursery Products,
Inc.
Box 510
Clinton, Conn. 06413

Ross Daniels, Inc.
1720 Fuller Rd.
West Des Moines,
Ia. 50255

Soil test sampling augers

Haynes Mfg. Co., Inc.
Box 1275
Livingston, Tex. 77351

The Highsmith Co., Inc.
Grassroots Division
Box 25
Fort Atkinson, Wisc. 53538

Johnson's Industrial
Supply Co.
1941 Karlin Dr.
St. Louis, Mo. 63131

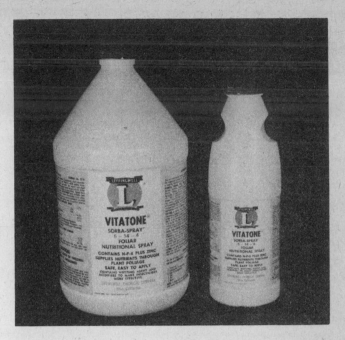

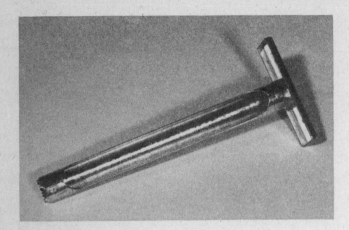

SOIL SAMPLER

This soil probe is designed to gather a cross-sectional core down through the plow zone and display it so abnormalities may be checked before it is put into a sample bag. Made of 16-gauge galvanized steel with a serrated edge, the probe will cut through hard, dry, or even frozen soil.

The Highsmith Co., Inc.
Grassroots Division
Box 25
Fort Atkinson, Wisc. 53538

FOLIAR FEEDING

One of the concentrated liquid fertilizers developed exclusively for foliar feeding. In areas where plant nutrients are unavailable because of the highly alkaline soils, liquid fertilizers are easily absorbed through the foliage. Vitatone Sobra-Spray contains the trace element zinc in addition to nitrogen, phosphorus, and potassium.

Leffingwell Chemical Co.
111 S. Berry St.
Brea, Cal. 92621

LIQUID FERTILIZER

This particular fertilizer comes as a concentrated powder which is diluted with water. Many companies now produce different formulations for use with different kinds of plants.

Sierra Chemical Co.
1001 Yosemite Dr.
Milpitas, Cal. 95035

SPECIALIZED PLANT FOODS

Many companies have their own mixtures of plant food for special uses. Stern's Miracle-Gro is widely available and has been used by gardeners with great success for many years.

Stern's Garden Products
Box 888
Port Washington, N.Y. 11050

3

ORGANIC GARDENING

Organic gardening is not new, it's not a fad left over from the 1960s. Before the age of industrialization and chemicals, every gardener was in some sense an organic gardener. This type of farming went into eclipse when the market became flooded with synthetic preparations, which were thought to be the cure for everything from Japanese beetles to crabgrass. Many of these chemicals worked pretty well at first, but as time went on it became apparent that many of them had unacceptable side-effects and diminishing effectiveness. At that point there was a renewed interest in natural, organic gardening.

The most important features of organic gardening are related to care of the soil and management of pests. In some ways these two subjects are intertwined, based on the following set of facts: healthy plants resist insects and disease better than unhealthy plants; one of the best ways to grow strong plants is to take good care of the garden soil; and to maintain the soil in excellent condition, it must be supplied with the nutrients found in such organic matter as compost.

Soil care will be the main subject of this chapter. Since mulching is an important aspect of soil care, especially in organic gardening, that subject will also be covered here. But all the material on bugs, diseases, weeds, and other garden plagues will be dealt with in Chapter 9, Pest Management.

Organic soil care

Reduced to its basics, organic gardening is a system of maintaining the soil's fertility by replenishing it, not with chemicals, but with organic materials in the form of humus and compost. Organic gardening works in accordance with a life cycle wherein soil, water, plants, and animal life all work in harmony, one having a part in the nourishment of the others.

When decomposed plant and animal remains are returned to the earth, they help produce good soil structure and good aeration. This in turn results in good drainage and good water and nutrient retention. Plants thrive in this environment, with the oxygen provided in the good, loose soil structure being used by the microorganisms therein to burn organic matter, releasing carbon dioxide and nutrients needed by the plants.

As previously noted, organic gardening is almost as old as the earth itself. Our current system, however, was developed early in the 20th century by Sir Albert Howard, an English agricultural expert working in India. It was not until the 1940s that this system reached the United States, introduced by Jerome I. Rodale. He attracted a loyal group of followers who believed in the importance of good soil.

Developing good soil

A soil in which vegetables can thrive generally contains about 50 percent solid matter and 50 percent pore space. Moisture should occupy about half the pore space, air the other half. Most of the solid matter, about 43-45 percent, should be mineral; the other 5-7 percent should be animal and vegetable organic material.

Most garden soils start out being either too sandy or too clayey. Sand has too much air, clay has too little, and both lack organic material. When this lack has been corrected by the addition of compost or similar material, the soil will become a rich source of nutrients for plants.

Organic matter is composed of a number of elements, most particularly carbon and nitrogen. Bacteria in the soil use the nitrogen in breaking down the carbon. This bacterial action proceeds normally when the ratio of carbon to nitrogen is about ten to one. When the organic material is higher in carbon and lower in nitrogen, the bacteria "borrow" nitrogen from the soil, depriving the growing plants. A symptom of this is yellowing of leaves.

There are several ways to avoid this problem. For one thing you can add nitrogen to the soil, perhaps in the form of manure, at the same time as you are adding nitrogen-poor organic matter. Or you can add organic material to the soil before you plant, so that any carbon/nitrogen imbalance will have been corrected by the time you're ready to plant. Perhaps the best method of all—and the one used by millions of gardeners—is to make compost outside the soil, in a separate bin or pile. The organic material is then broken down before it is turned into the soil.

Compost

Organic waste that has been allowed—in some cases, encouraged—to decay is called compost. When you put compost into your soil, your plants can immediately make use of the nutrients it contains.

There are a number of ways you can obtain compost. You can make it yourself, in a large pile, in a bin or a can, or in a commercial unit manufactured for this purpose. In addition, readymade compost can be purchased in sacks from nurseries and garden-supply stores.

To make your own compost is a fairly simple matter. First, every garden produces quite a bit of organic waste—leaves, decaying plants, weeds, hedge trimmings, etc. Second, every kitchen produces suitable compost material, such as vegetable and fruit scraps, eggshells, coffee grinds, and the like (but don't use meat, fat, bones, etc.). Instead of throwing away all of this garbage, tote it all to one corner of the yard, where you will begin your compost pile.

There are various ways of constructing the compost pile, or bin, just as there are various recipes favored by gardeners in different parts of the country. Before we get into them, it is desirable to consider the five basic principles of decomposition, which is the essence of composting:

1. The smaller the particle size, generally the faster the decomposition, because bacteria can then attack more surface area faster. If the leaves, stems, and other materials are shredded into small pieces before being added to the compost pile, they'll decay quicker and be ready sooner.

2. The bacteria in the pile need nitrogen. If there is too much organic material (carbon) in proportion to the available nitrogen, the bacteria will not work as fast, and the decomposition will go slowly. The evidence of this will be poor heat production in the compost pile. You can correct this by adding nitrogen in the form of fresh manure or blood meal here and there throughout the pile.

3. A compost pile must heat up for good bacterial action to occur. The degree of heat depends on the size of the pile. If the pile isn't high enough, it will loose heat and bacterial action will slow down. Too high a pile is also bad because it will then be compressed, shutting off too much of the air supply to the bacteria.

4. Every pile needs moisture for decomposition to take place. A moisture content of 40-50 percent is about right; more than this cuts down on the oxygen available to the bacteria. You can keep your pile at about the right moisture content by making sure that it remains about as wet as a squeezed-out wet sponge. Just put your hand in the pile and feel (watch out, however, for it can be really hot—about 130-160°F). If it doesn't seem moist enough just add water with a hose until it has the right consistency.

5. A compost pile also needs turning. Using a manure fork or a shovel, turn it so that the top and side materials become the center. This allows air penetration and also brings raw matter to the center where more action is taking place.

COMPOSITION OF SOME COMPOST MATERIALS

COMPOST MATERIAL	NITROGEN % N	PHOSPHORUS % P_2O_5	POTASSIUM (POTASH) % K_2O
Banana skins (ash)	—	3.25	41.76
Cantaloupe Rings	—	9.77	12.21
Cattail reeds	2.00	.81	3.43
Coffee grounds	2.08	.32	.28
Corncob ash	—	—	50.00
Corn stalks, leaves	.30	.13	.33
Eggs, rotten	2.25	.40	.15
Feathers	15.30	—	—
Fish scraps	2.0-7.5	1.5-6.0	—
Grapefruit skins	—	3.58	30.60
Oak leaves	.80	.35	.15
Orange culls	.20	.35	.21
Pine needles	.46	.12	.03
Tea grounds	4.15	.62	.40
Wood ashes	—	1.00	4.0-10.00

When finished, or "ripe," the materials placed in the compost pile will have been converted into a crumbly brown substance with the fragrance of good earth. It's then ready to use. The volume of organic materials will have decreased. As decomposition proceeds, most piles shrink to about half their original size.

Building a Compost Pile

There are many different ways you can make compost, depending on how much space you have, how much compost you need for the garden bed, and how elaborate a layout you're inclined to construct. Following are five general setups you can use in building up a compost pile, from a simple plastic bag to a permanent group of bins.

Plastic bag compost

1. Buy a dark-colored plastic bag, the kind used to line 20- or 30-gallon garbage cans.
2. Inside, put a 2-inch layer of soil or peat moss.
3. Add randomly any kind of waste kitchen materials (as noted before) and maybe occasionally garden wastes.
4. When full, set the bag out in full sunlight for about three weeks. The compost will then be ready to use.

Garbage can method. Here is a longer but more customary method of composting. Using a garbage can, though, makes it somewhat unusual.

1. Buy a galvanized garbage can (a 20- or 30-gallon size), and punch several small holes in the bottom.

Put the can up on a few bricks, and place a pan underneath to catch any liquid that might drain out from the moisture contained in the decaying garbage that you will be adding.

2. Put a 3-inch layer of soil or peat moss on the inside bottom of the can.
3. If you like, buy some red worms—the fishing kind —and add them to the soil at the bottom.

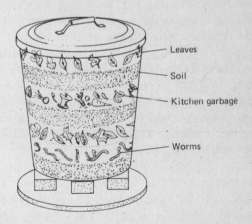

4. Add 2-3 inches of kitchen garbage, then a 2-inch layer of grass clippings and leaves, another layer of kitchen garbage, a layer of grass clippings and leaves, and so on until the can is full.
5. Put the lid on the can. The ripe compost will be ready in about 3 or 4 months. If you start the can in the fall, the compost will be ready to add to your garden by spring. (You don't need to worry about the moisture content of this kind of pile, nor does it need to be turned.)

Conventional compost pile

1. Clear off a 5- or 6-foot-square ground area.

2. On top of the cleared area put down a 6-inch layer of fairly coarse material—twigs, brush, a few corn stalks, sunflower stalks, and so on. This provides ventilation underneath the pile.
3. Start building the main body of the heap in layers. Put down a 6-inch layer of vegetation materials—grass clippings, leaves, weeds, vegetable remains, organic garbage, and so on. On top of this greenery, add a 2-inch layer of fresh manure. (You can also add a thin layer of limestone to improve bacterial action and hasten the decomposition.)
4. For every two or three layers of vegetation (and manure), add a 1-inch layer of soil. This soil contains bacteria that will help break down the organic material. Now wet down the pile until it is just moist, not saturated.
5. Repeat this procedure until the pile reaches a height of about 5 feet.
6. When finished, add a thin covering of soil to the pile to help seal in the moisture. You must, however, also keep air flowing throughout the pile in order to keep the bacterial action high. Thus take a stick or thin pole and punch vertical holes into the top of the pile, reaching all the way to the bottom. Make the holes about 2 or 3 feet apart.
7. Always keep the moisture content of the pile at 40-60 percent—about the consistency, as I've said, of a squeezed-out wet sponge. Check the moisture by feeling inside the pile with your hand, and then add water whenever necessary. Watering may be required every 4 or 5 days in hot weather.
8. Except for watering, let the pile sit undisturbed for 2 to 3 weeks. Then turn it, putting the material from the top and sides into the middle. Turn it again at 3-week intervals. When the inside materials turn brownish and crumble on touch, you can be sure that the compost is ready for your garden. This usually takes 3½ to 4 months.

The University of California quick method. In 1954 the University of California at its Organic Experimental Farm developed a composting method that's great for impatient types because the compost is ready in just 14 days. The decomposition is speeded up by shredding the materials and mixing them all together so that the bacteria have many surfaces to work on at once.
1. Mix together one part fresh manure and two parts other compost ingredients (leaves, grass clippings, cut-up corn stalks, table scraps, and so on). You can obtain fresh manure from a local riding stable or from a nursery. It must be fresh, not processed, manure, however.
2. Using a rotary lawnmower, shred everything completely. (You have to catch everything in a bag,

naturally.) Simply put down a small pile of materials and run the lawnmover over it. Then put down another pile and repeat the process. Better yet, use a power shredder; but, in any case, the materials must be shredded into very small particles for this method to work well.
3. Mix everything together, and form the mixture into a 4-foot-high, 4-by-6 foot heap.

Now here's what to expect.

4. By the second or third day the middle of the pile should have begun to heat up to about 130-160° F. If it hasn't, add more manure.
5. Turn the heap on the fourth day. Make sure that it's warm and moist. Simply put your hand inside, but be careful because it can be quite hot. If it doesn't feel moist to the touch, again, about like a squeezed-out wet sponge, add some water.
6. Turn the heap again on the seventh day.
7. Turn it once more on the tenth day. The heap should now have started to cool off, for it's almost ready.
8. It's ready on the fourteenth day. It won't look like fine humus, but the materials will have broken down into a dark, rich, fairly crumbly substance. You can let it rot further if you wish, or you can use it in your garden right away.

Compost bins. You can make a good compost bin with a few boards. Twelve pieces of board—each 12 inches wide, 1 inch thick, and 30 inches long—will work fine. Just take four of the boards and nail them together to make a frame or bottomless box. Using the remaining boards, make two more frames. You then set one frame on the ground and stack the other two on top of it to make a big bin. Now all you do is chop everything up with your lawnmower and throw it in. You then proceed, using whatever composting method suits you—either the "The Big, Conventional Pile" or "The University of California Quick Method."

You can steadily multiply these bins or piles easily by simply taking off the top frame after the compost has sunk below its level. Place it on the ground beside the other two and start to fill it with new materials for compost. As the compost in the first bin subsides some more, you take the second frame off and put it on your new bin. When finished, your original bottom frame goes on top of your new bin, forming a three-frame compost bin again.

A compost bin actually can be made from almost anything. Just make it about 3 feet high and about 2½ feet square. A neighbor of mine nailed four window screens together with a screen over the top to keep out flies. There are lots of other ways.

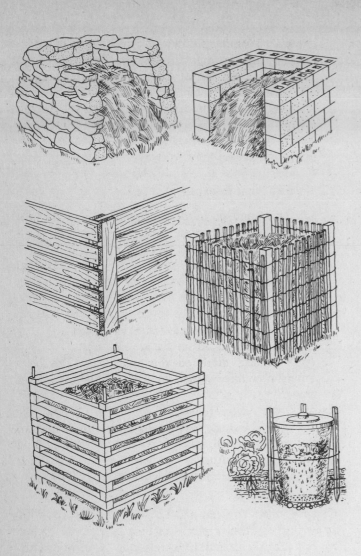

EASY-TO-BUILD COMPOST BINS

Top: Rough-stone construction; cement-block bin;

Middle: New Zealand box, boards slide out; picket-fence bin;

Bottom: Lehigh-Keston unit; trashcan set into ground with perforated bottom.

Improving soil with fall leaves

Rather than throw away or burn fall leaves, collect them with a sweeper-shredder or a power lawnmower with a lawnmower bag. You can then:

1. Sheet compost by tilling the leaves into the garden soil with a rotary tiller. If you till the leaves into the soil in the fall, they will be decomposed by spring. Sprinkle fertilizer (10-5-5) over the leaves at the rate of about 10-15 pounds per 1000 square feet of garden. The nitrogen will feed the decay organisms.
2. Compost in a heap utilizing one of the methods shown here. A compost starter will help speed up the process. Work into the soil in the spring.

The B.D. compost starter

This is a concentrated mixture of several cultivated strains of beneficial oil bacteria, enzymes, and plant-growth-promoting factors. These bacteria have been isolated from the most fertile humus soils. Under the proper condition of moisture, aeration, and organic matter, the B.D. Compost Starter will:

Quickly decompose raw organic matter and wastes by breaking down into simpler compounds.

Reassemble these simple compounds into complex, lasting substances—humus.

Fix nitrogen from the air and make it available.

Increase the availability of minerals in the soil and transform unavailable minerals into their available form.

Hold the soil and improve its structure.

Prevent leaching and washing away.

The Pfeiffer Foundation, Inc.
Laboratory Division
Threefold Farms
Spring Valley, N.Y. 10977

Commercial compost makers

There are basically three types of commercial compost makers on the market: bins; upright, canlike containers; revolving drums. Three- to four-foot-high bins can be made of plastic or wire fencing. They usually come with a booklet. They cost about $15.00 and can be ordered from any of the following firms:

Farmer Seed & Nursery Co.
Fairbault, Minn. 55021

Henry Field Seed &
  Nursery Co.
Shenandoah, Ia. 51603

Kelly Bros. Nurseries, Inc.
Dansville, N.Y. 14437

Olds Seed Co.
P.O. Box 7790
Madison, Wisc. 53707

Reuter Seed Co., Inc.
320 N. Carrollton Ave.
New Orleans, La. 70119

Upright can type. A round, canlike container made of heavy plastic has individual sliding panels with round holes for ventilation. This container is fed from the top, and finished humus is taken from the bottom. A good feature of a can like the Rotocrop is that it doesn't have to be filled all at one time. "Start with at least 12 inches of materials," the company says, to provide enough bulk for heating up. Thereafter add materials at least once a week whenever you have collected enough materials for a 2-3 inch layer. Ultimately you can add fresh material at the top, remove mature compost at the bottom.

Rotocrop, Inc.
94 Aero Park
Doylestown Pa. 18901

Drum types. These are simply a drum with a turning handle, and vents to allow air to enter. The tumbler is filled with shredded material (shred with a rotary type lawnmower, catching in a bag or a shredder/grinder); flanges inside insure that compost tumbles as rotated (1-5 times a day). This turning and shredding speeds up decomposition, to about 14 days. Available from:

Gardening Naturally, Inc.   Kemp Shredder Co.
Stockbridge Industrial Park   1118 Kemp Bldg.
Route 102   Erie, Pa. 16512
Stockbridge, Mass. 01262

Other organic nutrients

In addition to compost, many organic gardeners also feed their plants other organic nutrients to improve vegetable growth. Such waste materials as peanut hulls, seaweed, manures, cottonseed meal, and wood ashes are good sources of the basic nutrients plants need. As explained previously, the three most important elements for healthy plants are nitrogen, phosphorus, and potassium. In the following tabulation are listed some major sources of these nutrients that are readily available to organic gardeners:

Nitrogen

- Blood meal is 7-15 percent nitrogen and can be applied in liquid form.
- Cottonseed meal is 6-9 percent nitrogen and is especially good for acid-loving plants.
- Fish meal and fish emulsion contain up to 10 percent nitrogen, along with some phosphorus.
- Activated sewage sludge, the solid product of sewage treatment, is high in nitrogen and provides a wealth of trace elements.

Phosphorus

- Bone meal is 22-35 percent phosphoric acid, with up to 5 percent nitrogen.
- Phosphate rock is a finely ground rock powder that has about 30 percent phosphoric acid and many trace elements.

Potassium

- Granite dust is about 8 percent potash and may contain trace elements.
- Wood ashes of hardwood contain about 10 percent potash, of soft wood about 5 percent.

AVERAGE PLANT FOOD CONTENT OF ORGANIC FERTILIZER MATERIALS

Organic Materials	%N	%P_2O_5	%K_2O	Availability	Acidity
Basic slag	-	8.0	-	quickly	alkaline
Bone meal	3.5	22.0		slowly	alkaline
Castor pomace	5.0	1.8	1.1	slowly	acid
Cocoa shell meal	2.5	1.0	2.5	slowly	neutral
Cotton seed meal	6.0	2.5	1.5	slowly	acid
Dried blood	12.0	1.5	0.8	moderately	acid
Fish meal	10.0	4.0	-	slowly	acid
Green sand		1.0	6.0	very slowly	neutral
Ground rock phosphate	-	33.0	-	very slowly	alkaline
Guano	10.0	4.0	2.0	moderately	acid
Horn and hoof meal	12.0	2.0	-		neutral
Milorganite	6.0	2.5	-		neutral
Peat and muck	1.5-3.0	0.25-0.5	0.5-1.0	slowly	acid
Seaweed	1.0	-	4.0-10.0	slowly	neutral
Sewage sludge	2.0-6.0	1.0-2.5	0.0-0.4	slowly	acid
Soybean meal	7.0	1.2	1.5	slowly	neutral
Wood ashes	-	2.0	4.0-10.0	quickly	alkaline

Animal manures

Many animal manures are moderately rich in nitrogen, phosphorus and potassium. However, they are not as potent as chemical fertilizers. Generally you should use rotted manure, not fresh. The bacteria in your soil will need extra nitrogen to break down fresh manure and may divert some of the nitrogen from your plants. Moreover, like organic materials that have been composted, manure that has already rotted or decomposed is in a form your plants can use more easily. You can obtain rotted manure by placing fresh manure in a pile, covering it with a thin layer of dirt, and letting it stand a few months.

Do not buy steer manure, because it is high in salt content and generally offsets any benefit that the manure might have. Although these salts can be leached out by watering the steer manure, this leaching also washes out the nitrogen.

Hen, horse, sheep, and rabbit manures are known as "hot manures" because of their high nitrogen content. Cow and hog manures are called "cold manures" because they are fairly low in nitrogen, thus break down slowly. See chart for other manures.

COMPOSITION OF ANIMAL MANURES

MANURE TYPE	N	P_2O_5	% COMPOSITION K_2O	Ca	Mg
Fresh Cattle	0.53	0.29	0.48	0.29	0.11
Fresh Chicken	0.89	0.48	0.83	0.38	0.13
Fresh Horse	0.55	0.27	0.57	0.27	0.11
Fresh Sheep	0.89	0.48	0.83	0.21	0.13
Fresh Swine	0.63	0.46	0.41	0.19	0.03
Dried Cattle	2.0	1.8	2.2	—	—
Dried Sheep	1.4	1.0	3.0	—	—

MANUFACTURERS AND DISTRIBUTORS OF ORGANIC PRODUCTS

MANUFACTURER-DISTRIBUTOR	PRODUCT
Atlas/Hamar Co. 865 Lind Ave. S.W. Renton, Wash. 98055	Fish emulsion
BioCon Corporation Hereford, Tex. 79045	Tilleez cow, sheep manure
Chacon Chemical Corp. 2600 Yates Ave. City of Commerce, Cal. 90040	Fish emulsion
Dexol Industries 1450 West 228th St. Torrance, Cal. 90501	Compost maker, fish emulsion
Encap Products Co., Green Garde Division P.O. Box 278 Mt. Prospect, Ill. 60056	Fish emulsion
Falsy & Besthoff Inc. 143 River Rd. Edgewater, N.J. 07020	Bone meal, natural organic garden food 5-5-5
The Charles H. Lilly Co. (Lilly/Miller) 7737 N.E. Killingsworth St. Portland, Ore. 97218	Bone meal, blood meal, blood and bone meal, compost maker, cottonseed, super rich all organic plant food: contains crab meal, hynite leather meal, bone meal
The Organic Garden Center 193 Marinwood Ave. San Rafael, Cal. 94903	Cocoa bean hulls, cottonseed meal, fish meal, biodynamic compost, fish emulsion, bone meal, blood meal, kelp meal, seaweed concentrate, other organic materials
Organic Laboratories 5040 Westheimer Houston, Tex. 77027	Organic seed and soil treatment, organic plant food, Cop-ocide fungicide
Ortho Chemical Company 575 Market St. San Francisco, Cal. 94150	Bone meal
Premier Brands, Inc. Premier Peat Moss Corp. 350 Madison Ave. New York, N.Y. 10017	Organic compost
Ringer Corporation 6860 Flying Cloud Dr. Eden Prairie, Minn. 55343	Brown leaf and grass clippings compost maker
Science Products Company Inc. 5801 N. Tripp Ave. Chicago, Ill. 60646	Liquid sea weed
DG Shelter Products Vita Bark P.O. Box 60158 Sacramento, Cal. 95860	Organic compost
Stim-U-Plant, Inc. 2077 Parkwood Ave. Columbus, Oh. 43219	Fish emulsion
World Garden Products, Ltd. World Building First & Seaview East Norwalk, Conn. 06855	Soil of the Sea

MAIL ORDER ORGANIC SUPPLIERS

SUPPLIER	PRODUCT
Comstock, Ferre & Company 263 Main St. Wethersfield, Conn. 06109	Natural Organic Plant Food
Farmer Seed & Nursery Co. Faribault, Minn. 55021	Sea-Born, Norwegian Seaweed; liquid sea weed; fish fertilizer compost bin and tablets
Earl Ferris Nursery Hampton, Ia. 50441	Fish emulsion

MAIL ORDER ORGANIC SUPPLIERS (Continued)

SUPPLIER	PRODUCT
Henry Field Seed & Nursery Shenandoah, Ia. 55021	Fish emulsion, fish meal, fortified bone meal, fortified blood meal
Gurney Seed & Nursery Co. Yankton, S.D. 57078	Dried blood, fish emulsion, compost maker
Joseph Harris Co., Inc. Moreton Farm Rochester, N.Y. 14624	Compost maker tablets, liquid sea weed
H. G. Hastings Co. Box 4274 Atlanta, Ga. 30302	Fish emulsion
Herbst Brothers Seedsmen, Inc. 1000 N. Main St. Brewster, N.Y. 10509	Fish emulsion
Mellinger's 2310 West South Range North Lima, Oh. 44452	Compost maker, compost kits, fish emulsion, green sand, rock phosphate, cottonseed meal, milorganite, cattle or sheep manure, dried blood, bone meal, organic garden food
The Meyer Seed Company 600 S. Caroline St. Baltimore, Md. 21231	Compost builder and maker, blood meal, bone meal, cow manure, cottonseed meal; Electra organic food, Fertrell organic fertilizers, rock phosphate
The Natural Development Co. Box 215 Bainbridge, Pa. 17502	Adco compost maker, liquid plant food from the sea, Sudbury Sea Power, organic plant food
Nichols Garden Nursery 1190 North Pacific Hwy. Albany, Ore. 97321	Liquid sea weed, "QR"-herbal compost maker
L. L. Olds Seed Co. P. O. Box 7790 2901 Packers Ave. Madison, Wisc. 53707	Bone meal, compost, compost bin, dried blood, fertilife compost, fish emulsion, fish meal, liquid sea weed
Geo. W. Park Seed Co. Greenwood, S.C. 29647	Ferto sticks, Instant Liquid cow manure
W. H. Perron & Co., Ltd. C.P. 408 Ville de Laval Que. H7S2A6 Canada	Fish emulsion, bone meal, organic plant food, Fertosan compost acceleration, chicken manure
Reuter Seed Co., Inc. 320 N. Carrollton Ave. New Orleans, La. 70119	Compost maker, fish emulsion
R. H. Shumway Rockford, Ill. 61101	Dried blood, bone meal, fish emulsion
Stokes Seeds, Inc. Box 548 Buffalo, N.Y. 14240	Soil of the Sea, Sudbury Sea Power
Geo. Tait & Sons, Inc. 900 Tidewater Dr. Norfolk, Va. 23504	Bone meal, dried blood, cottonseed meal, organic garden food

---

Homemade organic fertilizer

This brew utilizes fresh chicken manure—which can be dangerous because of the high ammonia content. It is perfectly safe for vegetables, however, if handled properly. Place a shovelful of fresh chicken manure into a cloth bag. Submerge the bag in a bucket containing 2½ gallons of water for 2-3 days. Store mixture in an airtight container. To use, dilute 12 ounces of liquid in one gallon of water.

The ever-present earthworm

By burrowing, feeding, and excreting, earthworms let air and moisture in and break up the soil particles. They usually don't go very deep, but the minute that plant roots start going down, earthworms go with them making the soil better.

The gray pink worms (Helodrilus caliginosus and Heloarilus trapezoides) are important to your garden. The red one (Eisenia foetida), the fishworm, is not so good—it wants to fool around in damp spongy places instead of getting down to work. This red worm is, however, good for compost piles.

The earthworm improves the soil by swallowing it and later expelling it in the form of castings. The earthworm takes in the soil, grinds it up, mixes it with calcium carbonate, pulverizes it, sends it on through to the intestine to be digested by enzymes and then excreted. The final earthworm castings contain nitrogen, phosphorus, and potassium, the three elements that vegetables need the most.

Chemical fertilizers seem to decrease the number of earthworms in the soil, killing them or driving them off; ammonium sulfate is particularly harmful. Many insect sprays also are toxic to earthworms.

Earthworms are good soil builders. But you can't put earthworms in infertile or hard clay soils and expect results. When possible, dig up earthworms from other parts of the yard.

Value of earthworms

Chemical analyses of parent soil without earthworms and the same soil after being worked by earthworms have shown an increase of the following:

CHEMICAL NUTRIENT	% INCREASE
nitrate of nitrogen	500
available phosphorous	700
exchangeable potassium	1,200
exchangeable calcium	150
organic carbon	200

Where to buy earthworms

Avra Valley Bait Farm
Route 9, Box 593 W-1
Tucson, Ariz. 85704

Bar-D Worm Ranch
Box 15242 F
Santa Ana, Cal. 92705

Big Red Ranches, Ltd.
8200 Hickman Mills Dr.
Kansas City, Mo. 64132

Bronwood Worm Gardens
Bronwood, Ga. 31726

Clear Creek Farms
5300 Clark Rd.
Paradise, Cal. 95969

Double S Worm Ranch
5587 Wilson Lane
Paradise, Cal. 95969

Dunlap Bait Farms
Route 1, Box 125
Cape Girardeau,
   Mo. 63701

Earth Builders
31031 11th St.
Neuvo, Cal. 92367

Green Acres
1579 Bandoni Ave.
San Lorenzo, Cal. 94580

N & B Enterprises
P.O. Box 3265
Santa Fe Springs,
   Cal. 96070

New Earth Worm Farm
Route 2, Box 297C
Mena, Ariz. 71853

North American
   Bait Farms
1207A S. Palmetto
Ontario, Cal. 91761

Organic Gardeners
42506 25th St. West
Lancaster, Cal. 93534

Our People's Co-Op
2232 6th Ave.
Clarkston,
   Wash. 99403

Pacific Worm Growers
   Association
P.O. Box 1572
Oroville, Cal. 95965

Triple F Worm Farms
P.O. Box 521
Grass Valley,
   Cal. 95945

Ventura Wormgrowers
   Association
P.O. Box 3119A
Camarillo, Cal. 93010

Wieting Worm Farm
Route 1-B
Three Lakes,
   Wisc. 93010

Worm Enterprises
1624 W. Edinger
Santa Ana, Cal. 92626

Different organic methods

There are many variations within the organic gardening community. Some organic gardeners garden in moderation: that is they generally utilize compost and organic fertilizers, but sometimes they also utilize a few chemicals in controlling insects. On the other hand you find gardeners who treat organic gardening like an exact science. Between these extremes are several other variations:

Biodynamic gardening. A rather strict discipline of gardening in balance with nature. Based on the principles of Rudolf Steiner developed in the early 1900's Compost is constructed according to a formula and a bacterial starter is used. For more information contact, Three Fold Farm, Spring Valley, N. Y. 10977.

French intensive method. An extension of the biodynamic method, developed by Alan Chadwick, an Australian master gardner. Vegetables are planted equal distance from each other across raised beds rather than in rows, at such spacing that the leaves overlap on maturity creating a microclimate. The method generally produces about four times as many vegetables as conventional methods, takes one-third less water and requires less weeding. Contact Ecology Action of the Midpeninsula, 2225 El Camino Real, Palo Alto, Cal. 94036.

Mulching

It used to be called "trash gardening," this practice of spreading peat moss, hay, or some other material— generally organic, but not always—over the garden

Green manuring

Green manuring is the process of growing and turning under foliage crops solely for their fertilizing and soil conditioning values.

Plants with long tap roots tap deep buried nutrients and trace minerals, break up the soil, and return to earth nutrients that are used in growing.

Plants utilized as green manure are generally grasses, grains, and legumes . . . ryegrass and buckwheat. These plants generally grow rapidly and produce a lot of organic material quickly. Legumes fix nitrogen . . . this is, microbes in the soil are attracted to their roots and extract nitrogen and convert it into forms usable by plants. To make sure the nitrogen-fixing microbes are present it is recommended to inoculate legume seeds. The inoculant comes in a dark powder and is available from a number of seed firms.

Some sources of untreated seeds

D. V. Burrell Seed Growers Co.
Rocky Ford, Col. 81607

Johnny's Selected Seeds
Organic Seed and Crop Research
Albion, Me. 04910

The Natural Development Co.
Box 215
Bainbridge, Pa. 17502

Nichols Garden Nursery
1190 North Pacific Hwy.
Albany, Ore. 97321

Stokes Seeds, Inc.
Untreated beans, corn, peas
Box 548
Buffalo, N.Y. 14240

soil. Within the last 20 years, however, mulching has taken on new respectability, as experience has shown how valuable it can be in many environments.

In general, mulches modify and protect the growing environment, especially the soil, of plants. Mulches conserve soil moisture, keep soil temperature moderate, help control weeds (and thereby help prevent root injury from hoeing and cultivation, which are often unnecessary after mulch has been applied), maintain good soil structure (and thereby help prevent erosion), and improve soil fertility. An examination of each of these benefits will help readers to see how mulches might be of help in their own vegetable plots.

Benefits of mulching

Conserves soil moisture. All mulches generally slow down evaporation of water from the upper 6-8 inches of soil. Since they shade the soil (but not the plants) from the sun, evaporation is reduced by a good 70-90 percent. In addition, mulching tends to foster the distribution of water evenly throughout the soil area that it covers.

Moderates soil temperature. Mulching tends to insulate the soil from the weather conditions "outside," and thus helps prevent baking, freezing, etc. In addition, organic materials and some inorganic mulches like paper and materials with shiny surfaces reflect or inhibit the sun's rays. This reduces the temperature of the covered soil as much as 10 degrees below that of the surrounding, exposed soil.

Controls weeds. Organic mulches that are at least two inches thick will generally inhibit weed growth. Many weeds simply can't make it through the mulch to get at light and air. However, persistent perennial weeds will come through most organic mulches, and so must be pulled by hand. Inorganic mulches, especially black plastic, virtually eliminate weeds.

The full-time mulch

Mulching can be a permanent proposition. As soon as your vegetables come up and look vigorous, spread a hay, straw, grass, or leaf mulch 8-10 inches thick everywhere, between the rows and around all plants.

Next season, don't till the soil; just push back the mulch and make the row plantings. Then, when the plants have sprouted, push the mulch back around them. The soil beneath this permanent mulch will stay loose and friable. Add more mulch the second year to maintain a 4-7 inch depth.

A disadvantage is that soil under the mulch stays cool. This delays planting of the warm-weather plants.

Enhances soil structure. Soil frequently develops a surface crust because of the compacting pressure from rain or from sprinkler irrigation. A mulch breaks this water pressure and allows the earth's pore spaces to remain open. In addition, mulch slows water runoff and thus helps to hold the soil in place. (A subsidiary benefit is that mulch holds maturing vegetables off the moist ground and thus helps to prevent premature rot.)

Improves soil fertility. Organic mulch decomposes slowly, thus functioning as a kind of time-release fertilizer for the soil it covers. Each day a little bit of organic matter is added to the soil, improving its texture and providing it with nutrients.

Disadvantages of mulching

Despite what you may think from reading the preceding paragraphs, mulching is not the perfect answer to all the gardener's problems. For one thing, if the soil is not in very good shape, a mulch may do more harm than good by keeping it hidden from view. For another, organic mulches are high in carbon, and the microorganisms breaking them down will use up some of the soil's nitrogen in the process. So one must add a fertilizer rich in nitrogen to restore the balance. There is also a danger that in damp areas certain kinds of mulches will provide the perfect home for slugs and similar pests. Inorganic mulches, like black plastic, have their disadvantages, too, which will be enumerated below.

Thus, mulches are not perfect. Nothing is. But used properly, mulches can be of great benefit to both large and small gardens.

Organic mulches

Almost any organic material will make a usable mulch (see chart on next page), if it provides some insulation and is porous enough to permit moisture and air to get through to the soil. Organic mulches have an almost immediate effect on the garden. Aeration is improved in clay soils, as is water-holding capacity in sandy soils. As organic material decomposes, it plays an important role in soil granulation, too.

In addition to the standard products, many unusual mulches such as rice hulls are often available locally at reduced prices. To find any of the materials listed in the accompanying chart check your nurseries, newspapers, stables, woodworking plants, and any type of fiber processing plant. You can find many possibilities by checking the telephone yellow pages. In addition, by writing the manufacturers listed on p. 35 you can find the local dealers for manufactured mulches.

ORGANIC MULCHING MATERIALS

ORGANIC MULCHES	RATING	APPLICATION	REMARKS
Bagasse-baled crushed sugar cane	Good	Apply 2-3" thick	By-product of sugar manufacturing; great water-holding capacity
Buckwheat hulls	Fair	Apply 2" deep	Lightweight, high in potash, lasts several years
Chunk bark	Fair	Use small bark chunks, only used infrequently in vegetable gardens	Makes a durable mulch that stays in place well; especially effective used in combination with polyethylene film
Cocoa bean shells	Fair	Spread at least 2" deep	Has a cocoa odor
Coffee grounds	Poor-Fair	Apply lightly	Slightly acid
Compost	Excellent	Take partially decomposed grass clippings and plant tops from your compost bin	Save the more decomposed compost to place directly in the soil
Corncobs (ground)	Good	Apply 3" thick	Inexpensive, will decay and add nutrients; decaying action utilizes nitrogen, add a nitrogen fertilizer
Cornstalks (chopped)	Good	2" deep	Add nitrogen fertilizer
Lawn clippings	Good	Mow grass before the seed ripens to prevent the introduction of weeds and grass seed into the garden; apply green clippings in a thin 1-2" layer; cultivate into the top of the soil	If applied too thickly, green clippings build up heat and give off an objectional odor
Leaves	Good	Put on lightly; better if put through a shredder	Blow away, decompose slowly
Manure	Excellent	Apply partially decomposed	Fresh manure can burn plants; packaged steer manure can contain salts and weed seeds
Mushroom Compost	Good		Often available from commercial mushroom growers
Pecan shells Peanut hulls Rice hulls	Good	As purchased, apply 1-2" deep	Inexpensive; becoming more available commercially; long lasting; high in nitrogen
Peat moss	Good	Use the larger size particles; wet down before spreading	If peat moss completely dries out, it tends to blow away, allowing water to run off the surface
Pine needles	Fair to good	Can be used on vegetable gardens	A light, attractive mulch good for acid-loving plants; does not alter the soil pH
Sawdust	Good	Add nitrogen to the soil before applying; new sawdust is high in carbon, low in nitrogen and will draw nitrogen from the soil; 2" depth	Covers the soil well; some manufacturers of bagged sawdust add nitrogen to the sawdust before bagging
Seaweed	Excellent	Apply 1-2" thick	High in potash, good source of organic material
Straw, hay, cured grasses	Good	Add nitrogen, put on 2-3" deep	Long lasting; breaks down slowly; has a high carbon/nitrogen ratio; used for winter protection
Wood chips, shavings	Good	Add nitrogen to keep plants from turning yellow	Chips decompose slowly, can be obtained from local mills

Rules for organic mulching:

1. Apply fine organic materials at least 2 inches thick; coarse or fluffy materials should be 3 or 4 inches thick.
2. Don't apply mulch to seedlings. In certain climates it may keep them damp enough to rot. A wait of several weeks after setting out should be sufficient.
3. In general, keep mulch away from root crops; it may cause crown rot.
4. Watch out for insects. Mulch can provide a hiding-place for bugs and other troublemakers.
5. Don't apply a mulch until after the soil has warmed up.

Plastic mulching

Over the past several years agricultural experiment stations and manufacturers have conducted extensive research on the use of plastic (polyethylene) film, aluminum foils, brown asphalt paper, and other materials as a mulch for vegetable gardens. Many have proved effective.

Ordinary polyethylene film (black or clear), available in rolls three to six feet wide and 1 to 1½ mils thick, makes an excellent mulch (use the 1½-mil-thick plastic). Clear plastic heats up the soil about 10 degrees, black plastic 3 to 6 degrees. Clear plastic has been used effectively to promote the early germination of cool-season vegetables and to help warm-season crops reach maturity ahead of time. In addition, black plastic has been found extremely useful in increasing the growth of warm-season crops. Sky-blue plastic is also effective in heating up the soil and shows some insect-repelling properties.

Gardeners in hot climates also are now utilizing brown paper mulches and aluminum- and steel-coated plastic reflective foils to cool the soil. Reflective mulches have the added advantage of increasing the light on the lower leaves. Gardeners are also now utilizing aluminum foil mulch to cool the soil with a black nonplastic strip down the middle to warm the root zone.

Plastic mulch is excellent for crops that have trailing plants with fruit on the ground, such as melons, pumpkins, squash. Plastic is also good for peppers and eggplant. It keeps down weeds and keeps the fruit from spoiling.

The disadvantages: Polyethylene or paper mulches must be removed each season. Gulf States Paper Company, however, has developed a biodegradable paper mulch with a thin polyethylene coating that can be worked back into the soil.

In addition, Dixie Springs Agricultural Center in Illinois has experimented with biodegradable plastic film to determine its practicability. The present film seems to disintegrate too soon, but there is much hope for the future.

Kitchen foil mulch

Strips of ordinary kitchen foil will help improve light intensity and can be used to grow vegetables in the shady part of the garden. Simply lay the kitchen foil along each side of the plant row and cover the edges with soil to keep in place.

Since the foil will keep the soil temperature up to 10 degrees cooler in direct sun, it can be used to cool the soil for such plants as lettuce.

Experiments show it is also an effective control against aphids, which dislike reflected light under the leaf surfaces.

Newspaper mulching

Many gardeners insist that old newspapers make a good mulch. However:

Newspapers are mostly cellulose (the woody stuff of plants), and as this breaks down, it takes nitrogen from the soil. So nitrogen fertilizers must be added before the mulch is put on.

To stop weeds, use six sheets or more for each layer and overlap each adjacent sheet with half of the next one.

To keep the newspapers from blowing away, cover them with wood chips, bark, straw, or soil.

Put down when the seedlings are two to three inches tall. If the weather is cool, mulch makes the soil cooler and slows down germination.

When using plastic mulch, you can lay down a strip over a tilled row and then cover the edges of the plastic with soil. Use a tin can to cut holes for the plants.

Clear plastic mulches allow the short rays to penetrate and heat the soil during the day but prevent or slow the long rays from escaping at night.

Manufacturers of synthetic mulches

POLYETHYLENE MULCHES

Benson Maclean
Bridgeton, Ind. 47836

Central States Paper
and Bag Co., Inc.
5221 Natural Bridge St.
St. Louis, Mo. 63115

Cincinnati Cordage &
Paper Co.
E. Wayne & Scott St.
Lima, Oh. 45804

Coating Products, Inc.
580 Sylvan Ave.
Englewood Cliffs
N.J. 07632

Continental Extrusion
Corp. #2
End Blvd.
Garden City, N.Y. 11100

Dao Corp.
P.O. Box 659
Terre Haute, Ind. 47801

Dow Chemical Co.
Ag. Products Div.
Box 1706
Midland, Mich. 48640

E. I. Du Pont de Nemours
& Co.
1007 Market St.
Wilmington, Del. 19898

Ethyl Corp.
Vis Queen Division
Box 2422
Baton Rouge, La. 70821

Gering Plastics Co.
Kenilworth, N.J. 07033

Glick Twins
Pharr, Tex. 78577

Kordite Co.
Macedon, N.Y. 14502

Lamex, Inc.
Norcross, Ga. 30071

Peter & Co.
3618 Lexington Rd.
St. Mathews, Ky. 40200

Polygro Plastics, Inc.
Second and Depot Sts.
Bridgeport, Pa. 19405

Poly Tech
104 W. 94th St.
Minneapolis,
   Minn. 55431

Princeton Chemical
   Research, Inc.
Princeton,
   N.J. 08540

Rough Brothers
4229 Spring Grove Ave.
Cincinnati, Oh. 45223

Sinclair-Koppers Co.
Kopper Bldg.
Pittsburgh, Pa. 15219

X. S. Smith, Inc.
P.O. Box 272
Red Bank, N.J. 07701

Sound Screen Supplies,
   Inc.
2625 Grand Concourse
New York, N.Y. 10068

Staff Industries, Inc.
78 Dryden Rd.
Upper Montclair,
   N.J. 07087

Yoho & Hooker
523 Williamson
Youngstown, Oh. 44500

PAPER MULCH CONSTRUCTIONS

Anaconda Aluminum Co.
Mulch Division
Box 1654
Louisville, Ky. 40201

Fox Paper Co.
Box 15099
Lockland
Cincinnati, Oh. 45215

Mosinee Paper Co.
Mosinee, Wisc. 54455

St. Regis Paper Co.
Agricultural Service Station
West Nyack, N.Y. 10994

STEEL FOIL MULCH

U.S. Steel Corp.
Commercial New Product
   Development Division
Box 86
Pittsburgh, Pa. 15230

Types of plastic-synthetic mulches

Kraft paper (black and natural)
   Combinations
      Polyethylene coatings—clear, black
      Wax coatings—clear, black, aluminum, aluminum
      foil lamination
*Polyethylene (clear, smoke gray, black, white,
aluminum colored)*
   Combinations
      White binded to black
      Black sprayed with various colored paints
Foils (steel, aluminum)
      Steel foil tin plated
      Kraft paper with aluminum foil lamination
      Aluminum foil with 9-inch black center stripe

Shredder/grinders

For gardeners who want to make quick compost, make mulch, or condition the soil organically, a shredder/grinder is an invaluable tool.

For mulching and soil conditioning: Finely chopped vines, corncobs, hay, leaves, and manure make better mulch than coarse raw material, because their finer texture permits them to retain moisture more effectively.

For composting: A shredder both speeds and eases complete decomposition through bacterial action by reducing the size of the individual particles of matter.

Most models utilize steel tines (hammers) on a shaft that sweeps across grate bars or a perforated plate. The standard types are either fixed hammers (attached solidly to the shaft) or free swinging hammers. Inexpensive models utilize blades; other types include a rotating square gate and a grinding belt.

There is considerable variation in the size of the hopper, material used in the frame, and the quality of the hammers.

Some tractors and tillers also offer shredder/composter combinations. Also available are leaf mills, into which leaves are fed, chopped up by a blade, and collected in a bag for compression or use in compost.

Solid hammers

Advantages: Heavy, hammers will crush or break fairly heavy material. Usually less expensive.

Disadvantages: Will sometimes break or twist when processing heavy twigs or rocks. Rigid hammers often wrap heavy vines around hammer mills.

Swinging hammers

Advantages: Hammers will release on impact with heavy material and rocks.

Disadvantages: Hard to balance. Takes more power. Heavy strain and wear at pivot points.

SELECTED SHREDDER/GRINDER MANUFACTURERS

MANUFACTURER	NO. MODELS	TYPE	HOPPER	WET	DRY	SCREEN	BRANCHES	REMARKS
Fixed Hammer Type								
K-W Manufacturing 800 S. Marion Rd. Sioux Falls, S.D. 57106	7	Fixed hammer, high-carbon steel —4 cutting edges per hammer	20 or 30" flared	*	*	Shredder roller bars ¾" perforated screen standard ¼, ⅜, ½ & 1" screens optional	to 1½"	10 & 20" shredder grinders from 4-hp. and 7-hp. models; also 10" shredder/ grinder without engine
Speedy Shredders Winona Attrition Mill 1009 W. 5th St. Winona, Minn. 55987	8	Hammer mill, heavy-duty welded steel	Hoppers 12 x 12", 15½ x 20½" & 17 x 20"	*	*	Special wet screen—¾" rack/screen standard, finer screens optional	Small	Models come with 3-hp. or 8-hp. motor or without for tractor or accessory power mount
W-W Grinder Corp. 2957 No. Market Wichita, Kan. 67219	many	High-quality hammer mill; hammers are high carbon steel	9½ x 30" to 36 x 52"	*	*	Inter- changeable shredding roller bars & grinding screen; 3 other screens from ⅛ to 2"	Grind shrub and tree trimmings from ⅜ to 3" depending on machine and power	Also manufac- tures large portable four-wheel models
Flail Hammer Swinging Type								
Kemp Shredder Co. P.O. Box 6275 Erie, Pa. 16512		Flail type	Top-opening			Screen	To 3"	Wet material sometimes clogs the machine
Concho shredder- grinder-chipper								
Lindig Mfg. Corp. 1875 West County Road C St. Paul, Minn. 55113	Several	Free swinging organic-split double shredding edge	16 x 22" top opening	*	*	Removable 1" screen standard; optional ¼-1¾"	With wood chipper attachment	Electric or gas; standard, tractor mounted or as a 4-wheel trailer
The Roto-Hoe Co. Newbury, Oh. 44065	3	Flail type; 1 model rigid tine type	Large hopper; side feed			¾" round perforated plate	1¼-2" heavy duty models	3½-8 hp.; heavy-duty construction; 4-wheel models

SELECTED SHREDDER/GRINDER MANUFACTURERS (Continued)

MANUFACTURER	NO. MODELS	TYPE	HOPPER	WET	DRY	SCREEN	BRANCHES	REMARKS
Other types								
Gilson Bros. Co. Box 152 Plymouth, Wisc. 53073	2	3-hp. model uses cutting blades	7 x 13¼"			Slotted steel grates	Up to ½"	Adjustable discharge door
		7-hp. model uses rotating square cutting bars	15 x 15" 18 x 20"			Cutter bar	Up to ½"	High clearance
		3½-hp. shredder	14" big mouth			Cutting chamber	Small	
Lambert Corp. 519 Hunter Ave. Dayton, Oh. 45303		3½ and 5 hp. vacuum type				None	Small twigs	Has shredder & hopper attachments
Royer Foundry & Machine Co. 158 Pringle St. Kingston, Pa. 18704		Uses a cleated belt	Deep batch hopper			None	Up to ½"	Gas and electric

SHREDDER

As the hopper is loaded the high-speed cleated belt goes to work shredding, tearing, tumbling, mixing, and aerating the material. The belt's speed and angle combine to drive the material forward and upward to an adjustable, spring-loaded discharge gate. Here shredded, thoroughly mixed material is discharged. Other material, too large to pass through the gate, is rolled back for more processing, and nonshreddables are tumbled back to the trash gate.

Royer Foundry and Machine Co.
Kingston, Pa. 18704

PROCESSING WET MATERIALS

Leaves and other wet materials can be put through this shredder by using a wet rack. Speedy Esquire shredders are sold only factory-direct and process up to 50 cu. ft. per hour.

Winona Attrition Mill Co.
1009 W. 5th St.
Winona, Minn. 55987

WOOD CHIPPER ATTACHMENT

The hammermill rotor in this Concho Shredder/Grinder/ Chipper pulverizes/grinds material into a blended mulch.

The Chipper Attachment . . . with its extra sharp blade . . . slices the wood into small chips. The branches are fed into the special sidemounted chipper chute. This chipper will process wood up to 3 inches in width.

Lindig Manufacturing Corp.
1875 West County Road C
St. Paul, Minn. 55113

LEAF PICK-UPS AND GARDEN CARTS

These machines simplify handling materials. Rake leaves to opening duct and they are sucked into the grinding chamber. Cart fits directly under the grinding chamber and material is loaded as it is processed.

W-W Grinder Corp.
2957 N. Market
Wichita, Kan. 67219

MILORGANITE

Prior to 1925, Milwaukee treated sewage as many cities still do, dumped it in the river and passed it along to someone else, and Milwaukee's rivers flow into Lake Michigan—the water supply.

After investigating several treatment methods, Milwaukee adopted and pioneered the activated sludge process. It was most efficient in removing solids and returning water of the highest possible clarity and purity to the lake. But it provided a huge quantity of solids that had to be disposed of in some manner.

Before the by-product could be sold its value had to be determined. The solids were 75% organic matter, high in nitrogen, and contained some phosphorus and a wealth of trace minerals. In the early 1920's the problem was given to a graduate student in soils at the University of Wisconsin named O. J. Noer. He tested the waste material as a fertilizer for growing all manner of food, fiber, and ornamental plants. Every crop grew beautifully. MILORGANITE, for Milwaukee Organic Nitrogen, was born.

Milorganite is a natural all-organic fertilizer that contains more of the basic fertilizer elements than good old barnyard manure and is richer in the vital trace elements than other garden fertilizers. Milorganite is clean, dustless, and free flowing. In fact it's everything a gardener could want: It's organic, the effects are long lasting, it is high in purity, easy to use and keeps indefinitely.

Milorganite Division
Sewerage Commission of the City of Milwaukee
8500 South Fifth Ave.
Oak Creek, Wisc. 53154

38

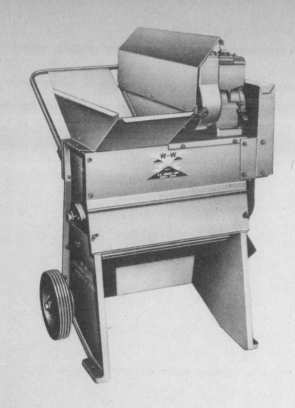

RIGID CYLINDER HAMMERS, A FAVORITE

This machine has a cylinder which turns at a high enough speed so that the hammer (tine) tips shatter, crush, break, tear, and shred material into fragments. The degree of fineness of the material is controlled by the length of time the material stays in the cylinder. A part of the cylinder has an opening, and material is grated by a perforated screen. When the material is fine enough to go through the screen perforations it escapes. The smaller the screen perforations the finer the grind.

W-W Grinder Corp.
2957 N. Market
Wichita, Kan. 67219

COMPOST MAKER

The Ringer Brown Leaf compost maker's formulated with an additional strain of fungi selected for leaf decomposition. It comes in flake form and is especially designed to work on leaves. Works with microbic action to turn leaves into rich brown humus in 60 to 90 days. Grass clipping and general compost maker are also available.

Ringer Corporation
6860 Flying Cloud Dr.
Eden Prairie, Minn. 55343

◀ FIXED HAMMER TYPE SHREDDER/GRINDER

This machine utilizes steel tines (hammers) on a shaft.

KW Manufacturing Co., Inc.
800 South Marion Rd.
Sloux Falls, S.D. 57106

39

▼ EARTHMAKER REVOLVING DRUM

This composter is designed for long life. The drum is 22-gauge galvanized steel, phosphatized and then painted with a permanent coating. (A) Dual tracks and wide, hard-rubber rollers center the drum and provide the necessary friction to prevent slippage while turning the drum. (B) The screened air and drainage vents are stainless steel. (C) A large crank handle makes revolving the drum an easy task. (D) The sturdy tubular frame is welded to control wobbling.

Gardening Naturally, Inc.
Stockbridge Industrial Park
Route 102
Stockbridge, Mass. 01262

COMPOST MAKER ▲

The Rotocrop Accelerator is a remarkable new PVC construction, compost bin from England, scientifically designed to convert cut grass, leaves, prunings, even kitchen leftovers, into rich, natural food for your garden—in weeks. *Simply drop garden waste in, shovel natural fertilizer out.*

Set up the Rotocrop Accelerator in your garden or backyard. Then "feed" it, weekly—and you'll have a never-ending supply of nourishing, free compost for a healthy, vibrant garden.

Rotocrop (USA), Inc.
94 Aero Park
Doylestown, Pa. 18901

The **EARTHMAKER**™ Revolving Drum Composter is designed and built to last for many, many years. The drum is 22-gauge galvanized steel, phosphatized and then painted with a special resistant paint.

4

HAND TOOLS

A tool is a tool is a tool . . . right? Wrong!

Scratch 12 gardeners and you'll find a dozen different opinions on which tools to use for a particular job. In addition, even in selecting something as simple as a garden shovel, you're faced with hundreds of choices.

As a result, many gardeners, even experienced ones, wind up with a shed full of tools that they never really use. These implements look good in the store, but when you get them out in the garden, they turn out to be worth very little indeed. Fortunately, with a little planning, and the information in this chapter, it's possible to avoid this waste of purchase money and storage space.

Choosing your tools

In figuring out what tools you need, the first thing to do is make a list of the jobs that have to be done around the garden—this chapter and others in this book ought to help you there. Second, estimate how frequently each job is likely to come up—this depends to a great extent on the size of your garden and the type of vegetables you plan to grow. Third, on the basis of these first two points, select only those tools that you need for the jobs you are likely to be doing, giving priority to tools that can be used for more than just one minor task.

In a typical garden the chores fall into four different categories: (1) digging and planting; (2) materials handling, i.e., moving stuff from one place to another; (3) raking; and (4) weeding and cultivating. Theoretically at least, you should be able to handle all these jobs with just a shovel, trowel, rake, and hoe—supplemented in many cases with a cart or wheelbarrow. That seems simple enough, but manufacturers today offer a wide variety of tools in each category, and this can make a gardener's choice difficult. A shovel, for instance, can be designed specifically for digging in rocky soil, can be reinforced for use in heavy-duty work over a long period of time, or can be made out of lightweight materials for the convenience of those gardeners who don't fancy themselves as weightlifters. There are of course many other variations on the basic shovel, just as there are hundreds of types to choose from among rakes, hoes, and other standard hand tools.

Two important considerations in the purchase of tools are quality and price. In most cases when one is high, so is the other—and low is equated with low, too. Some mail-order firms categorize their tools as good, better, and best, and price them accordingly. What the consumer should do is match the quality of the tool with the job that needs doing. If you've got a small garden and give your tools relatively light use, you should be able to get good service and value from a medium-priced tool. (Most writers are reluctant to recommend tools with the lowest price, simply because there's so much junk in the stores today. But if you run across a low-priced tool that looks and feels right, don't be afraid to buy it for your light-duty work.) If you have a large garden, however, and if you expect to give your tools lots of use, then give careful consideration to the more expensive, more sturdily constructed tools.

The following paragraphs will describe the wide variety of tools available for different jobs and will help you in making the important decision as to which tools you'll want to use in your own home garden.

Digging and materials-handling tools

Some gardeners use one tool for all their digging; others have a variety from which to choose. Before going any further there are some questions you should answer:

Will your use of the tool be light or heavy? Shovels are constructed in one of three basic ways—hollow back, closed-back, or solid-shank hot-tapered. The type of construction determines their strength, the amount of abuse they will take, and price.

Hollow-back shovels and spades derive their name from a ridge stamped into the center of the blade for strength and reinforcement. This type of shovel is generally least expensive and holds up well under light to moderate garden use.

Closed-back (or fast-back) shovels are completely closed in back by a strap welded over the conventional back area. This reinforces the blade and prevents drag and dead weight from mud and dirt. A closed-back shovel is stronger than a hollow-back shovel and is well suited for moderate to heavy garden use.

A solid-shank, hot-tapered shovel is forged from a single piece of steel. Blade and socket are one piece with no welds or seams—this is the strongest type of construction. There are several grades of solid-shank shovels designed for many different uses, from home-garden to heavy-duty industrial. These shovels are not cheap, but they will stand up for a long time under heavy use.

Do you need a shovel for digging, for moving materials, or for both? A standard round-point shovel will do an excellent job of digging and a passable job of moving peat moss and similar material. If you intend to move such items as sawdust, gravel, straw, leaves, and similar materials, you should consider buying one of the more specialized shovels or forks described below.

Do you have a soil condition that requires a specialized tool? You can handle light to medium soil with a standard shovel, but if your soil is extremely hard or if it contains lots of rocks or roots, consider a spade or a mattock. For cutting through roots you can purchase a shovel with a serrated rather than a standard blade.

Types of shovels

With the answers to the above questions in mind, you can now go through the following description of different kinds of shovels in order to find the model or models that will best fit your individual needs.

Round-point shovel. Most gardeners say this is the best all-round tool for digging, scooping, and shoveling. The blade is set at a slight angle to the handle. These shovels are manufactured with several variations. The clipped-point and caprock patterns, for instance, are flatter across the end than the standard models. Some gardeners believe that these blunter points dig better in moist, wet soil. Other types of shovels include the deep-bowl and the semiflat bowl, which vary in their capacity to carry earth and other material, and the irrigation shovel, which has a straight instead of an angled shank. Some people find it easier to use an irrigation shovel when digging holes or ditches with straight edges.

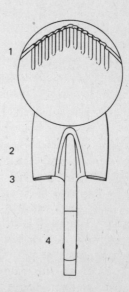

ROUND POINT SHOVEL

FEATURES

1. Serrated point.
2. Heavy-gauge blade.
3. Flat forward-turned steps.
4. Shockband.

At the back edge of the round-point shovel's blade (called a step), the shovel is cut off square—or part of the back edge may be extended beyond the shovel and turned backward, forward, or rolled to form a smooth step. These variations are called, appropriately, back-turn step, forward-turn step, or rolled step. They simply make it easier to place a foot on the back portion of the shovel for digging.

Anyone who has tried to cut through roots knows that it's an almost impossible job with a standard round-point shovel. However, with a serrated point, most problems of this nature are solved. A shovel with a serrated point will easily cut through hard soil, soil laced with masses of small roots, or roots one inch in diameter and larger. In addition, a shovel with a serrated point will clean out roots from ditches and other areas where you would normally have to use an axe.

Square-blade shovel. This shovel digs only moderately well, but it holds a good-sized load when you need to move soil, peat moss, and other materials. It is useful for picking up the last of a pile of rotted manure or similar material and for leveling areas around the garden.

Spade. Stronger than most shovels, a spade has an almost flat blade and straight sides. Many gardeners use it to dig and turn the soil, to work in fertilizers, manures, sawdusts, etc., to dig trenches, or to cut straight edges into the ground. A long-bladed spade is good for turning soil to a good depth or for digging deeply in one spot.

Scoop shovels. A deep blade for moving bulk materials such as bark, sawdust, gravel, and similar material is the outstanding feature of scoop shovels. They are available in many variations of sizes and weights. The blades are made of either aluminum (to make them lighter for heavier jobs) or high-carbon steel. They are generally hollow-backed in design and construction.

Forks and other tools

Spading fork. Better than a shovel for digging hard soil, rocks, or roots, a spading fork is also useful for loosening around plants and working in soil amendments. The standard model, which has 11-inch diamond-back-shaped tines, works well in most soils. The English pattern, which has inch-long square tines, is used for heavy soils. An 11-inch, six-tine clam fork with sharp rounded tines is also available for working with light soil.

Barn and manure forks. These round-tined forks are the equivalent of a scoop shovel. They're excellent for

moving light material such as leaves, partially decayed compost, manure, coarse straw, etc. The prongs pierce the mass and hold it together so that you can move a large pile in one piece. Round-tined forks come with anywhere from 3 to 10 tines; 4-6-tined models are used for most garden jobs. The more tines a fork has, the better it can pick up wet or heavy material. Heavy forks are available for picking up rocks and stones.

Mattocks. A modified pickaxe, the mattock is a double-bladed tool. One blade is shaped like a big, 3½-inch-wide chisel and serves to fracture hard soil and to perform other brute-force tasks in the soil. For the other blade you generally have a choice of a pencil-shaped pick end, which is good for chopping in rocky and clay soils, or an axe-shaped end, which can chop through the roots of such tough plants as bamboo or ivy.

Rakes

The rake is another seemingly simple tool that comes in an astounding array of shapes and sizes. This is an important tool, but so common that most people grab the first one they see on sale at the right price. That's often a mistake. It's easy to see from the following list that there are a number of different types of rakes to choose from, according to what kinds of jobs you have to do.

Level head. With its head fastened directly to the handle, this rake is useful for removing small clods of earth, twigs, and similar detritus. It has a flat side for leveling.

Bow design. A favorite of gardeners, so-called because the rake head is attached to the handle by a bow-shaped piece of metal. It has a spring action that helps in removing small clods of earth and the like.

Magnesium and aluminum rakes

Rakes made of magnesium and aluminum are lightweight yet extremely rugged. Such rakes can be manufactured 4 feet wide with 3⅜-inch teeth without becoming too heavy to handle easily. This extra width helps speed up the raking in larger vegetable gardens. A complete line of magnesium and aluminum rakes is manufactured by:

White Metal Rolling & Stamping Corp.
80 Moultrie St.
Brooklyn, N.Y. 11222

Floral. A small (usually about 8 inches wide), flat-headed rake useful in the garden for raking cultivated soil and for working in small beds.

Multipurpose. A large tool with triangular-shaped teeth on both sides; useful for cultivating soil and cleaning lawns.

Heavy-duty. These flat-headed rakes are designed for raking large stones or for smoothing asphalt. They can be useful in heavy soils or when putting in garden walks and paths.

Weeding and cultivating tools

Hoes

Traditionally an important tool for all gardeners, the hoe is easy to use in a number of different ways. There are many sizes and models available, each of which is designed for different jobs in the home garden. Following is a list of the most common types of hoes and their primary uses.

All-purpose garden hoe. The standard hoe, useful for turning up soil and for some weeding.

Warren cultivator hoe. A heart-shaped hoe with a point, that is useful for making short rows or hills to plant seeds. Turn the hoe point up and use the other face to hill dirt over new seeds.

Weeding hoe. Has a flat blade on one side and one or two prongs on the other; extremely useful for cultivating around plants.

Nurseryman's hoe. Resembles a standard hoe but with a tapered top; useful for many garden jobs.

Scuffle hoe. Has a flat blade that can be used to cut the tops off weeds by simply pushing the hoe along the ground or slightly underneath. Also comes with an open center, so weeds can be cut by either pushing or pulling.

Action hoe. Easy-to-use cultivator-weeder and edger, with a sharp double-edge blade that cuts weeds and grass in both directions. Will cut right up to edge of bricks and other material.

Cultivators

Overall, there are two kinds of cultivators—the small hand-type, which we'll deal with here, and the larger mechanical variety, which is described in detail just a bit further on in this chapter.

A cultivator is a pronged, forklike tool used to cultivate or turn over the dirt in the garden between plants. It is available as a 3- or 4-pronged curved-tine cultivator or as a 3-prong adjustable type. The cultivator will not slice off weeds that have gotten a good start, but it does an excellent job of loosening the soil. If used regularly, the cultivator will keep the soil open and prevent any weeds from growing.

Trowels

Some gardeners who manage to make do with the smallest number of tools claim that they get along very well without a trowel. Others consider these small, shovel-type tools a necessity. The evidence seems to favor the latter group. A trowel is handy for digging small holes in which hot-weather plants like tomatoes can be set out. And for quick, one-step transplants, the proper trowel is indispensable. Trowels are also useful for many other minor but necessary digging jobs.

When buying a trowel, be especially wary of shoddy construction. Blades or handles made of thin metal will almost surely bend or break.

There are essentially two types of trowels, the standard model and the *transplanting trowel*. The latter type is very useful in transplanting because plants can be removed from the containers in one quick motion, without injuring adjacent plants.

Three tips for keeping tools in shape

To remove rust from shovels and other hand tools, work them up and down in a bucket of sand mixed with old crankcase oil. This takes off much existing rust and helps keep new rust from forming.

To straighten bent spading forks, place a water pipe over the tine and move it back in place.

To sharpen on an electric grinding wheel, keep the blade moving on the wheel. To keep the built-up heat from destroying the temper of the blade, stop frequently to let the metal cool. Use a hand file to make the bevel smooth. When sharpening the tool with a hand file, file away from the body only. This method takes quite a long time, so you're better off working with a machine.

Garden hand carts

Garden carts have taken over where the wheelbarrow left off. Today's modern garden cart is so well balanced that it will handle bulky materials with complete stability and without a lot of musclepower. Unlike the wheelbarrow, carts allow you to move even the heaviest of loads with a minimum of effort.

Manufacturers have begun to make a wide variety of carts, from small-wheeled wedge-shaped models with a capacity of 4 cu. ft. to large 26-inch-wheel carts designed to carry anything from leaves to sacks of mulch to 4 or 5 bales of hay.

Some manufacturers provide these carts in the form of do-it-yourself kits. To assemble at home, some kits require additional materials such as plywood paneling. The saving on these kits is generally $15 to $20 off the standard unit price.

SELECTED GARDEN HAND CART MANUFACTURERS

MANUFACTURER	MODELS	FEATURES
Garden Way Research Charlotte, Vt. 05445	Three models with load capacities of 200, 300, and 400 lbs. All models available in kit form (plywood panels not included with kits)	Square front end keeps loads from tipping out forward; large wheels; cart tips down to allow easy loading; heavy-duty construction
Jackson Manufacturing Co. P.O. Box 1649 Harrisburg, Pa. 17105	Three models: Two small-wheeled, wedge-shaped handi carts, one yard cart with 16-inch bicycle wheels	Manufactured from heavy-gauge steel; the yard cart has a 4½-cu.-ft. capacity, semi-pneumatic rubber tires
Precision Products 2415 S. Grand Ave. East Springfield, Ill. 62708	Four hand cart models of the load-hop cart: one a 5½-and-6½-cu.-ft.-capacity cart with 16-inch spoke wheels; a 4-cu.-ft.-capacity cart with 10-inch wheels; and one 6½-cu.-ft.-capacity cart with 13-inch spoke wheels	Made of ¾-inch cold-rolled steel; extremely attractive
Vermont-Ware Richmond Rd. Hinesburg, Vt. 05461	Three models with 3-4-cu.-ft. capacity; 16- and 20-inch bicycle wheels; polymold model with lightweight polyethylene body; also manufactures a build-it-yourself kit (does not include a body box)	Regular Models have four-sided, tight-welded, all-steel body; polymold cart body is molded in a single unit—absolutely watertight

YARD CART

The balanced center of gravity of this yard cart makes it a lot easier to push around than a wheelbarrow. It is extremely handy for moving bags of fertilizers, a bale of peat moss, or similar big loads. This kind of cart is the coming thing for hauling garden materials since it is so easy to handle and so versatile.

Jackson Manufacturing Co.
P.O. Box 1649
Harrisburg, Pa. 17105

Cultivator Manufacturers

Ansan Tools & Mfg. Co., Inc. 7400 W. Lawrence Ave. Harwood Heights, Ill. 60656	Hand tiller with revolving discus	Esmay Products, Inc. P.O. Box 547 Bristol, Ind. 46507	Cult-A-Eze, low-wheel garden cultivator with attachments

Cultivator Manufacturers (Continued)

Lambert Corporation
519 Hunter Ave.
Dayton, Oh. 45404

High-wheel cultivator;
has a garden seeder
attachment

Planet Jr.
P.O. Box 58114
Los Angeles, Cal. 90058

Several types of high-
wheel cultivators

Rowe Enterprises, Inc.
Galesburg, Ill. 61401

Rotary cultivator with
tines

Tradewinds, Inc.
P.O. Box 1191 F
Tacoma, Wash. 98401

Rotary cultivator

Winona Attrition Mill Co.
1009 W. 5th St.
Winona, Minn. 55987

High-wheel cultivator

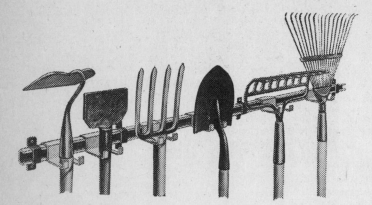

PLANT-RITE ROW SEEDER

This simple mechanical seeder plants your garden while you walk up and down the rows. Load the seed into the container and set the dial for lettuce, bush beans, spinach, or one of a number of other common vegetables. The seeder then distributes the seed evenly and at the required spacing for that particular vegetable. This saves seed by eliminating the need for thinning.

Esmay Products, Inc.
P.O. Box 547
Bristol, Ind. 46507

ALL-ON-ONE RACK

A space-saving way to organize large garden tools is with the Car-Mac "Hang-A-Tool." It can be installed quite easily in garage, shed, basement, etc., and is made of heavy-gauge steel with a baked enamel finish. Tools slip on and off easily. Once you get in the habit of using this or a similar rack, you'll find that your tool-storage area stays a lot neater and is easier to deal with.

Marathon-Carey-McFall
615 Lafayette Building
5th and Chestnut St.
Philadelphia, Pa. 19106

◄ SEED SOWERS

A wide variety of seed sowers are available today, ranging from a simple canvas shoulder bag with a hand crank to disperse seed, to galvanized steel shoulder models, to plastic or steel hoppers on wheels.

Also available are a hand-push disc row seeder, an unusual wedge-shaped corn, bean, or pea planter, and more elaborate two-wheel bicycle-type push seeders with a large hopper and a complex drive mechanism. The more sophisticated two-wheel bicycle-type models open the soil, plant the seed at the correct depth, space out the seeds by rotating the seeds in the hopper, press the soil firm, and space and mark the next row.

Some manufacturers also provide a seeder attachment for their high-wheel cultivators.

TOOL HANGERS

These small, inexpensive handle hangers solve the problem of how to store your garden tools almost anywhere. Simply slip the handle through the hook, and the weight of the tool holds it in place. These hooks can be installed in almost any out-of-the-way space.

Slip Seal Company
Long Beach, Cal. 90804

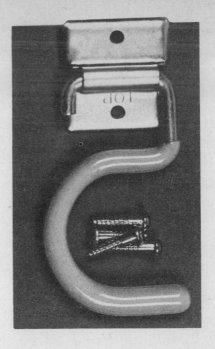

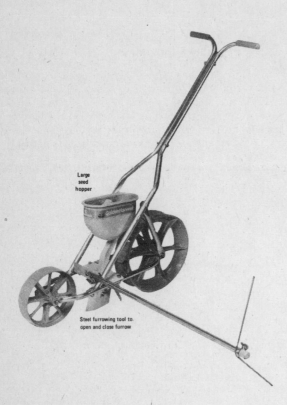

Large seed hopper

Steel furrowing tool to open and close furrow

◄ BICYCLE-TYPE PLANTER

These seeders do "all" the planting operations, from opening the soil to pressing it over the planted seed. Seeders come with up to 21 different plates that allow you to adjust the planting depth for any vegetable variety.

Lambert's Golden Harvest
  Garden Seeder
Lambert Corporation
519 Hunter Ave.
Dayton, Oh. 45404

Earthway
Precision Garden Seeder
Esmay Products, Inc.
P.O. Box 547
Bristol, Ind. 46507

Mechanical cultivators

Mechanical cultivators of many types, mostly powered by hand, are beginning to make a real comeback today, and will probably see even greater use in the near future. There are three basic types on the market —high-wheel (with an approximately 24-inch wheel), low wheel (with an approximately 12-inch wheel), and rotary.

High- and low-wheel types work in much the same manner as the old horse-drawn plow. But in this case you, not the horse, provide the power to push the blades through the soil. Although neither type is as easy to use as power equipment, both are better than hand tools. They can be used effectively in large vegetable gardens planted in rows.

Most cultivators come with several attachments similar to the attachments provided with power rototillers (see Chapter 7). For instance, there is a five-tine cultivator-weeder attachment that loosens the soil and cuts

the weeds, a moldboard plow that turns the soil and cuts the weeds, and a double-end shovel that forms furrows on either side. Some cultivators come with an optional sidewalk edger and a slicing hoe that cuts weeds below the surface and helps keep rows cleaned up. Most cultivators also have an adjustment that allows changes in cutting angle and depth.

Both the high- and low-wheel types operate in a similar manner. Because of the way the low-wheel design is balanced, most people find it more stable and slightly easier to use than the high-wheel type.

The rotary cultivator is quite different from the other types. Although it does a fine job of cultivating, it looks and works like a lawn mower. You simply push it through the garden. Revolving blades penetrate and break up surface soil, lifting it in layers over the cutter knife. Weeds are cut off below the surface.

STANDARD ATTACHMENTS

In addition to the 5 tine cultivator shown on the complete unit, standard attachments are:

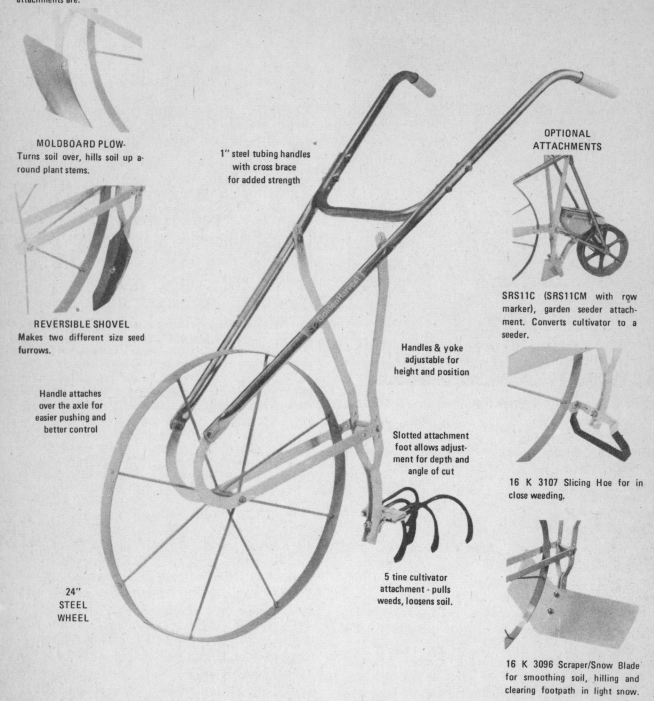

MOLDBOARD PLOW-
Turns soil over, hills soil around plant stems.

REVERSIBLE SHOVEL
Makes two different size seed furrows.

Handle attaches over the axle for easier pushing and better control

24" STEEL WHEEL

1" steel tubing handles with cross brace for added strength

Handles & yoke adjustable for height and position

Slotted attachment foot allows adjustment for depth and angle of cut

5 tine cultivator attachment - pulls weeds, loosens soil.

OPTIONAL ATTACHMENTS

SRS11C (SRS11CM with row marker), garden seeder attachment. Converts cultivator to a seeder.

16 K 3107 Slicing Hoe for in close weeding.

16 K 3096 Scraper/Snow Blade for smoothing soil, hilling and clearing footpath in light snow.

HIGH-WHEEL CULTIVATOR

This type of cultivator has been around for a long time, but it's making a fast comeback today, especially among energy- and ecology-conscious gardeners. It furrows, cultivates, weeds, cuts roots, and forms hills in tilled soil, all without a lot of work. You can also purchase a garden seeder that attaches right to this cultivator.

Lambert Corporation
519 Hunter Ave.
Dayton, Oh. 45404

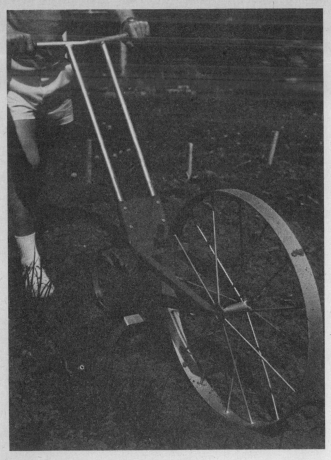

LOW-WHEEL CULTIVATOR

It's a lot easier to cultivate your garden with this gadget than using a hoe—and you don't have to bend over either. The Cult-A-Ease garden cultivator does a great job of getting rid of weeds and turning up the soil. It has a depth adjustment that varies from ⅛ inch to 3 inches and comes with a five-tine cultivator, a slicing hoe, and a furrow plow. Lift the release lever to change accessories.

Esmay Products, Inc.
P.O. Box 547
Bristol, Ind. 46507

THE SPEEDY GOPHER CULTIVATOR

All parts of this cultivator are welded steel. The depth control wheel is 2 inches wide and 8 inches in diameter. The handle height adjusts from 30 inches to 40 inches with an adjustable screw that is located immediately behind the front wheel.

Winona Attrition Mill Co.
1009 W. 5th St.
Winona, Minn. 55987

ROTARY CULTIVATOR DOES MANY JOBS

This hand cultivator weeds, hoes, cultivates, mulches, and levels, and it works just like a lawn mower. It will clean the row of weeds as fast as you walk. The action of the hoe points breaks the ground into small particles and turns under the surface materials. If you turn the cultivator over, the six-inch shovels penetrate the soil and break it up to an even greater depth.

Rowe Enterprises, Inc.
Galesburg, Ill. 61401

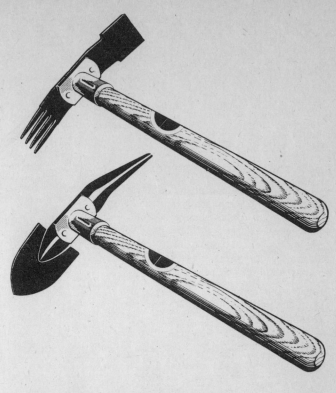

NEW GARDEN TILLER

The Ansan Gardevator with 128 steel points on 16 revolving discs is useful to cultivate your garden. This scientifically designed tiller leaves the soil fresh and pliable with no furrows or lumps. It is made so that mud and soil do not build up around the revolving discs.

Ansan Tool & Mfg. Co., Inc.
7400 W. Lawrence Ave.
Harwood Heights, Ill. 60656

WEEDER ROOTER AND PIC 'N PLANTER

These unusual hand tools have a number of uses in the vegetable garden. The weeder-rooter has a beveled straight edge on one side, and a fork on the other, making it a good tool for weeding in hard soil, removing rocks, and handling any number of close-quarter weeding and cultivating jobs. The Pic 'N Planter, with a small shovel on one side of the head and a pick on the other, can be used for digging holes for such transplants as tomatoes, peppers, and similar vegetables and for handling other transplanting and digging chores.

David W. Epstein & Company, Inc.
22711 Cass Ave.
Woodland Hills, Cal. 91364

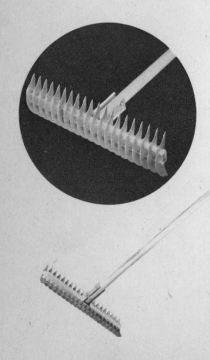

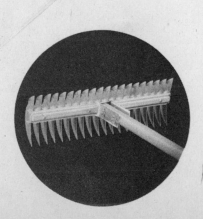

ADJUSTABLE DOUBLE-EDGED RAKE

This new idea in rakes is worth a look. Turn the head one way, it's a lawn and garden rake. Turn it over and it's a garden tool for pulverizing the soil around trees and bushes, for seed beds and other garden uses. It's also self-cleaning. Pull and it's full, push and it's clean.

Ansan Tool & Mfg. Co., Inc.
7400 W. Lawrence Ave.
Harwood Heights, Ill. 60656

◀ **HOE DOWN**

This one doesn't look like an ordinary hoe and it isn't. The unusual contoured blade cultivates, weeds, edges, hoes, spaces, and scallops to make it a versatile second hoe In any vegetable garden. Carbon-steel cutting blade and hardwood handle make it a durable tool.

David W. Epstein & Company, Inc.
22711 Cass Ave.
Woodland Hills, Cal. 91364

SMALL TOOLS FOR ALL PURPOSES

You can get some idea of the variety of tools available from this photograph supplied by a major manufacturer. All the tools in the top row are heavy-duty; in the bottom row are the same tools in lightweight, less expensive form. From left to right, the tools are: digging trowel, transplanting trowel, hand cultivator, digging fork, weeding hoe, pointed hoe, hand rake, and V-shaped weeder.

True Temper Corp.
1623 Euclid Ave.
Cleveland, Oh. 44115

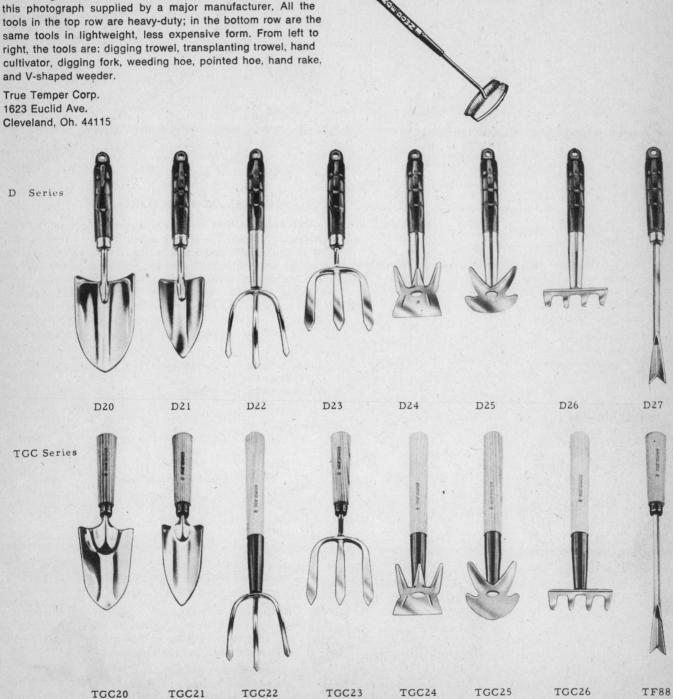

D Series

| D20 | D21 | D22 | D23 | D24 | D25 | D26 | D27 |

TGC Series

| TGC20 | TGC21 | TGC22 | TGC23 | TGC24 | TGC25 | TGC26 | TF88 |

5

POWER TOOLS

Everyone who now has or is thinking of taking on a large vegetable plot should examine the wide range of power tools currently available. These tools multiply by many times the amount of work a gardener can do.

In this chapter we will present a representative selection of the best power tools currently on the market. The first major category, rototillers, is of greatest interest to vegetable gardeners. The second category is the largest: Tractors are made by dozens of different companies, and there are thousands of different attachments. A third major category, shredder-grinders, has been covered in Chapter 3.

The uses of power tools

In the right places and at the right times, power tools can be invaluable to the home gardener. With a power rototiller, for instance, you can break up and pulverize large quantities of soil with relative ease. Cultivation becomes much less back-breaking, and you can even furrow a hill! With a garden tractor you can haul large amounts of material around the garden, and with the proper attachments you can disc-plow cultivate, grind compost, plant, and do many other garden chores. With the proper power tools a gardener can effectively manage a vegetable planting three or four times the size that can be handled by a gardener working only with hand tools. Even in the periods when gasoline and other sources of power are in short supply, it is still worthwhile to consider purchasing the right kind of power tools. If you've got a good-size plot of land, the amount of your own energy that these tools can conserve is far more than the relatively small amount of oil they'll burn up. But a decision to buy in this area must be a personal one, after looking at the objective data and deciding what's best for your own garden.

Rototillers

The principal purpose of the rototiller is to break up the earth—to till the soil—in preparation for planting.

There are two basic types of tillers, front-end and rear-end. The difference between them is simply that one has the tines in front of the wheels, the other has them in back of the wheels. Front-end tillers are powered through the movement of the tines. An adjustable drag bar is used to make the tines dig in, and the operator can use this to control both speed of the tiller and depth that the tines dig. In rear-end tillers power is applied through the wheels. The weight of the machine is distributed so that the tines dig in without pressure from the operator.

Front-end rototillers

ADVANTAGES:

1. Lighter and generally less expensive than rear-end.
2. More maneuverable, can turn in less space, making it easier to work in garden beds.
3. Good digging capability. Takes fewer passes to get the soil in good shape.

DISADVANTAGES:

1. Since wheels pass over soil that tines have tilled, some compacting occurs.
2. Not easy to control without strength and effort. Jumps and bucks in heavy soil or when rocks are hit.

Rear-end rototillers

ADVANTAGES:

1. Easy to operate. Can be guided with one hand. Good for people without the strength necessary to run a front-end model.
2. More efficient for breaking ground in heavy soils and over large areas.

DISADVANTAGES:

1. Generally more expensive than front-end, although not prohibitively so.
2. Less maneuverable than front-end.
3. Digs only six to nine inches deep.

Characteristics of tillers

There is a wide variation among tillers in their horsepower and engines, speed, size, type of tines, tilling width and depth, handles, and available accessories. The greatest choice is found among front-end tillers, where many different models are on the market. Rear-end tillers tend to be somewhat similar in construction, varying in horsepower from 4 to 10; front-end models have from 2 to 8 hp.

Engines. Offered in two- or four-cycle models. The former are fueled by oil and gas mixed together; the latter have separate gasoline and oil chambers, like an automobile. Another choice is between gear drive and chain drive; the latter is more expensive initially, but is up to 35 percent more efficient.

Speed. The less expensive machines are one-speed, good for average-to-loose soil and for cultivation. Two-speed operation helps in deep digging and is faster in churning soil and in mixing several ingredients. A few expensive tillers have four speeds, one each for heavy, medium, and light soil, and for cultivating.

Size. Small, medium, and large are the obvious variations here. Of interest is a relatively new idea, the compact tiller. With foldable handle, this type can be easily transported in a car trunk or stored in a small space. Excellent for tilling easy, workable soil, but not good enough for heavier work.

Tines. There are generally three choices—spring-steel, bolo, and slasher—for different uses. Spring-steel tines are all-purpose, made of special heat-treated steel that absorbs the impact of stones and rocks. They can penetrate hard soil, blend in organic material, and do a good job of bordering and cultivating. Bolo tines are narrow and curved, good for deep tilling and shallow weed control. Slasher tines provide brute strength for tough soil and roots.

Tilling width and depth. Many models give you only one width (often 20 inches), while others have adjustable widths from 6 to 32 inches. (One model has expansion tines to 5 feet!) On most front-end models depth capability varies from 7 to 12 inches. Most machines are adjustable, utilizing adjustable wheels, a depth stick, or a combination of both. On some models the depth can be controlled from the handle while tilling.

TILLING PATTERNS FOR MOST EFFECTIVE RESULTS

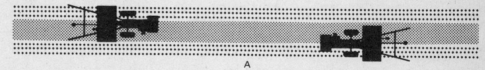

(A) For tilling a new garden overlap half the tiller width, or even one-fourth the width, on each pass.

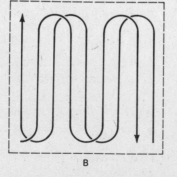

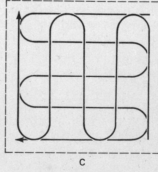

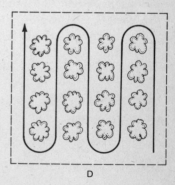

(B) This pattern is best with previously worked soil.
(C) This pattern is best for unplowed ground.
(D) This pattern is best for cultivating.

Handles. In addition to the folding handles on compact tillers, other models have tilt handles, allowing the operator to walk alongside, not behind, the tines and thus not leave any footprints in the newly cultivated soil. And some handles can also be adjusted up and down.

Accessories. A wide and ever-increasing variety of attachments are offered. With some your tiller can be converted into a tractor for plowing, cultivating, leveling, and even snow removal and other such jobs.

Tilling clay soil

Since clay is extremely hard, start tilling at a very shallow depth. On each succeeding pass, go down a couple more inches until you reach the depth you want. It is difficult to work clay when it is wet. If you do, it will lump together and become extremely hard as it dries out. An especially heavy clay soil may be quite slow to dry out below the surface. To solve this problem, till to a depth of 3-4 inches, let the plot dry out for a day, then till deeper.

COMPACT TILLERS

MANUFACTURER	MODELS	DRIVE SPEEDS	TILLER WIDTH	TILLER DEPTH
Ariens 655 W. Ryan St. Brillion, Wisc. 54110	2 hp. & cultivator, 3 hp. compact, tiller, 63 lbs., folding handle bars	Worm gear	Adjustable 12-28"	6"
Atlas Tool & Mfg. Co. 5151 Natural Bridge Rd. St. Louis, Mo. 63115	2 hp., 65-72 lbs., handles fold flat, lock in several positions	Chain drive	7-18"	6"
Feldmann Engineering 639 Monroe St. Sheboygan Falls, Wisc. 53085	Budget compact, 2 hp.; Compact, 2 hp., 58 lbs.	Chain drive	6-18"	To 4"
Gilson Bros. Co. Box 152 Plymouth, Wisc. 53073	2 hp., 51 lbs.	Worm gear and chain drive	Worm gear—6-18"; chain drive—7-22"	To 6"
MTD Products, Inc. 5389 W. 130th St. Cleveland, Oh. 44111	2 hp., chrome handles fold flat, 60 lbs.	Chain drive	14"	0-6"
Roper Sales 1905 W. Court St. Kankakee, Ill. 60901	3 hp. mini-tiller, 2 hp. mini-tiller, handles fold flat	Chain drive	11½-20-22" 10-15"	To 6" To 5"
Simplicity Mfg. Co. 500 N. Spring St. Port Washington, Wisc. 53074	2 hp., 58 lbs., handles fold	Chain drive	6-18"	0—6"
Toro Co. 8111 Lyndale Ave. S. Minneapolis, Minn. 55420	2 hp., folding handle	Chain drive	11-22"	To 8"
White Outdoor Products 2625 Butterfield Rd. Oak Brook, Ill. 60521	(Roto Boss 200) 2 hp.	3-step chain reduction, 4-cycle	18"	5"

FRONT END TILLERS

MANUFACTURER	MODELS	DRIVE SPEEDS	TILLER WIDTH	TILLER DEPTH
American Honda Motor Co., Inc. Box 50 Gardena, Cal. 90247	2 3½-hp., chain drive	A., 2 forward speeds; A2., 2 forward speeds with reverse	Adjusts to 36"	7"
Ariens 655 West Ryan St. Brillion, Wisc. 54110	4-5-6 hp., jet tillers	Worm gear; Model 624SR has 2 speeds forward, 2 reverse; other 1 speed and reverse	24"; 12-34" with extension kit	To 9"

FRONT END TILLERS (Continued)

MANUFACTURER	MODELS	DRIVE SPEEDS	TILLER WIDTH	TILLER DEPTH
Allis Chalmers Box 512 Milwaukee, Wisc. 53201	3-5-8 hp., worm gear	3-hp. model forward; others forward and reverse	24"; 35" with extension	6-7"
Atlas Tool & Mfg. Co. 5151 Natural Bridge Rd. St. Louis, Mo. 63115	3 worm gear models, 3-5-8 hp., 2 chain drive, 3 & 5 hp.	Some models have one speed forward; other models have forward & reverse, 2 speed forward, 1 reverse	24 & 26"	6-7"
Auto Hoe, Inc. Box 121 DePere, Wisc. 54115	3-4-5 hp., belt drive	One speed	10-14"; 12"	
Bolens-FMC 215 S. Park St. Port Washington, Wisc. 53074	5 & 3½ hp. worm gear, 3 & 5 hp. chain drive	5-hp. worm-gear model has forward/reverse; all others one speed forward	17-24" gear can be reduced to 9"; 21-29" chain can be reduced to 12"	
Dayton Electric Mfg. 5959 W. Howard St. Chicago, Ill. 60648	3-5-5-8 hp.	3-5-8 chain drive, forward & reverse; 5 hp. shaft drive, forward & reverse	3-hp., 18"; others 26"	8"
John Deere John Deere Rd. Moline, Ill. 61265	3½ & 6 hp., worm gear	Forward and reverse	24" reducible to 13"	7"
Detroit Tool P.O. Box 232 Lebanon, Mo. 65536	Soil Blender			12"
Feldmann Eng. & Mfg. 639 Monroe St. Sheboygan Falls, Wisc. 53085	3½-5-5-hp., worm gear	5-hp. models have both forward and reverse; 3½-hp. forward only	5-hp.—10 or 28" tilling width; all others 12-26"	7"
Ford Tractor & Implement Co. 2500 E. Maple Rd. Troy, Mich. 48084	3½-5-8 hp. gear models, 5 hp. chain drive	8-hp. has 2 speeds, forward & reverse; 5-hp. has forward & reverse; all others forward only	12-20-26"; 40" with extensions	6" on 3½-hp. 7" on all others
Gilson Brothers Box 152 Plymouth, Wisc. 53073	3-3½-5 hp., 8 hp., worm-gear drive	3½-hp., forward & reverse; 5-hp. has 2 forward, reverse; 8-hp., 4 speed & reverse	12-20-26"; extension to 40"	to 8"
Hahn Inc. Outdoor Products 1625 N. Garvin St. Evansville, Ind. 47717	3½-4-5 hp., worm gear	3½- and 4 hp., forward only; 5 hp., forward & reverse	20-24"; extension to 38"	7"
Heald Inc. Box 1148 Benton Harbor, Mich. 49022	5-hp. ground hog chain drive	Some with forward only, some with forward & reverse	24"	7"
International Harvester 401 N. Michigan Ave. Chicago, Ill. 60611	Worm gear	Forward only	25" down to 14"	8"
Jacobsen 1721 Packard Ave. Racine, Wisc. 53403	3-5 hp. chain drive	Forward	14-26"; 38" with extension	to 12"
Magna American Corp. Box 90 Raymond, Miss. 39154	5 hp. chain drive		12-22-24"	

MASSEY-FERGUSON CHAIN-DRIVE TILLER

This chain-reduction drive delivers up to 30 percent more power. Utilizes a 3-hp. Briggs & Stratton 4-cycle air-cooled engine, double-reduction chain drive, single forward speed, free-wheeling forward and reverse. Utilizes 13½"-diameter one-piece double-ended tines and has a 24" tilling width, to 37" with extensions. Digging depth adjustable to 9".

Model MF 253

Massey-Ferguson, Inc.
1901 Bell Ave.
Des Moines, Ia. 50315

POW-R BOY 5-HP. TILLER

The weight of this tiller is over the tines. Utilizes a Briggs & Stratton engine with a worm gearbox. Has a recoil starter. Tiller has a 24" cutting edge.

Model BHDT 124

Hahn, Inc.
1625 N. Garvin St.
Evansville, Ind. 47717

SOLO GARDEN TILLER

This is probably the most unusual garden tiller on the market—it has no wheels. Its 4½-hp./SAE two-cycle Solo engine has a preset rev adjustment that automatically adjusts to a variable load. This tiller has a V-belt transmission that connects to the rotor shaft by a worm drive with oil-bath lubrication. Rotor has three optional widths: 10", 16", and 24". Fingertip-easy to start.

Model 505

Solo Motors, Inc.
P.O. Box 5030
5100 Chestnut Ave.
Newport News, Va. 23605

FRONT END TILLERS (Continued)

MANUFACTURER	MODELS	DRIVE SPEEDS	TILLER WIDTH	TILLER DEPTH
Massey-Ferguson, Inc. 1901 Bell Ave. Des Moines, Ia. 50315	5 hp. worm gear, 3-5 hp. chain drive	Forward & reverse	28" reduced to 13"; 41" with extension	9"
McDonough Power Equipment McDonough, Ga. 30253	(Snapper) 3-4-5 hp. chain drive, 5 models	Forward & reverse		
Mono Mfg. Co. P.O. Box 2787 Commercial St. Station Springfield, Mo. 65803	3½-5 hp. worm gear, 5 hp. chain drive	5 hp., forward & reverse; 3½ hp., forward only	13-26"	
MTD Products, Inc. 5389 W. 130th St. Cleveland, Oh. 44111	2 worm gear, 3½-4 hp. vertical, 3 worm gear, 5-5-8 hp. horizontal, 4-4-5-5-8 hp. chain drive	Forward & reverse Forward & reverse Some have 4 speeds & reverse	to 26"	0-8"
The Murray Ohio Mfg. Co. P.O. Box 268 Brentwood, Tenn. 37027	3-5 hp., chain drive	1 forward only; 2 forward & reverse	14-26-28"	7"
Roper Sales 1905 W. Court St. Kankakee, Ill. 60901	4-5-8 hp., chain-& gear-driven (hydrid drive)	4 hp., forward; 5½ hp., forward & reverse; 8 hp., 2 forward & reverse	14-26-28"	7-8"
Simplicity Mfg. Co. 500 N. Spring St. Port Washington, Wisc. 53074	3-4-8 hp. worm gear	Forward only	26"	0-7"
Solo Motors, Inc. Box 5030 Newport News, Va. 23605	6 models, 4½-5½ hp., 7 hp. agricultural, pro tiller, chain drive	Single-speed & dual-speed models	10-16-22-24"	
The Toro Co. 8111 Lyndale Ave. S. Minneapolis, Minn. 55420	4 gear drive, 3½-5 hp., 2 chain drive	Forward & reverse	26" with extension to 38"	7"
White Outdoor Products 2625 Butterfield Rd. Oak Brook, Ill. 60521	(Roto Boss 500) 5 hp., double chain	4 speeds	14" diameter; 26" width; self-sharpening tines	8"

AUTO HOE

The spokes are welded on a collar secured to a shaft by a square head. The shovels overlay and don't miss a single weed. The point of the shovel is the cutting edge. The crook in the spoke allows the shovel to enter the ground at a perfect angle pulling the hoe forward.

Auto Hoe
Lost Dauphin Dr.
DePere, Wisc. 54115

BOLENS 5

With a 5-hp. Briggs & Stratton engine, there are both chain-drive and gear-drive models. Utilizes 14" slasher tines with a 24-35" tilling width reducible to 13".
A number of accessories are available, as illustrated.

FMC Corporation
215 S. Park Ave.
Port Washington, Wisc. 53074

MONO WORM GEAR TILLERS

This one has heavy-duty construction and a heavy diecast gear case. Powered by a 5-hp. Briggs & Stratton engine with a worm gear. Has special-alloy, heavy-duty, self-sharpening tines with a tilling width from 13-26". The depth-gauge control lets you adjust for deep tilling or light, shallow cultivation.

Model TH-50

Mono Manufacturing Co.
P.O. Box 2787
Commercial St. Station
Springfield, Mo. 65803

MURRAY CHAIN DRIVE—FORWARD/REVERSE

Powered by a 5-hp. Briggs & Stratton engine, chain drive with forward and reverse. Tiller has 14", 7-gauge bolo-type tines, 14", 26", and 28" adjustable cut width, adjustable depth bar, removable wheels, and an accessory furrow opener.

Model 7-1230

The Murray Ohio Manufacturing Co.
P.O. Box 268
Brentwood, Tenn. 37027

GILSON COMPACT TILLER

Can be used to break ground and till a uniform seedbed in the spring, to cultivate all summer long, and to cut and blend mulch in the fall. Has 2-hp. belt drive, spring steel 9″ diameter tines, four easy-to-adjust tilling widths from 6″ to 18″. Features a grip-type control that automatically engages the tiller drive when you grip the handle. Folds down in seconds without tools for easy car-trunk transport. Weight: 57 lbs.

Gilson Brothers Company
Box 152
Plymouth, Wisc. 53073

REAR-END ROTO TILLERS

MANUFACTURER	MODELS	ENGINE	SPEEDS	TRANS-MISSION	TILLING WIDTH	REMARKS
Ariens Company 655 West Ryan St. Brillion, Wisc. 54110	Rocket	7 hp., 4 cycle 5 hp.	2 speeds forward, 2 reverse	gear	20"	Swing handle; heavy-duty welded steel frame; separate tine clutch
Central States Mainline Box 348 London, Oh. 43140	Mainline Plainsman Mountaineer Lady Bug	8 hp. 8 hp. 8 hp. 5 hp.	3 forward 1 reverse	all gear	20"	Industrial quality engines; converts to a cycle bar mower
Garden Way Mfg. Co., Inc. 102nd St. & 9th Ave. Troy, N.Y. 12180	Horse	7-hp. manual start—Kohler Industrial 6-hp. Tecumseh manual or electric	fw rev	worm gear	20" 20"	Choice of: bolo, pointed pick, cultivating tines; a favorite of home gardeners
	Pony	4-hp. Clinton			14½"	
Giant Vac Mfg. Co. South Windham, Conn. 06266	826 B 826 K 1036 B	8 hp. aluminum 8 hp. cast iron 10 hp.	forward neutral reverse	all chain	20 to 36"	Rugged, well-balanced machines
Howard Rotavator Howard, Ill. 60033	Gem	Wisconsin 9.2 or 15.2 hp.	3 sp for safety rev	gear	20-24-30"	Handlebars adjust up and down & side to side
	350	Kohler 6.2 hp.	4 sp for safety rev	gear	16-23"	Handlebars adjust up and down & side to side
Oregon Mfg. Co. 6920 S.W. 111th Ave. Beaverton, Ore. 97005	Mang (Models 95 and 91)	Models 95-91 9-hp. Wisconsin; 10-hp. electric start Robbin		gear box	15"	Built for extra ruggedness
	Mang Jr. (Models 1000 and 2000)	7-hp. Kohler or Briggs-Stratton		gear box	21"	Short-coupled for close quarters
Precision Valley Mfg. Co. Springfield, Vt. 05156	Yellow bird	3-hp. Briggs-Stratton			13-18" optional	Low cost; weighs only 90 pounds
Roto Hoe Garden Tools 100 Auburn Road Newbury, Oh. 44065	990 910 190	6-hp. Tecumseh 5-hp. Tecumseh 3½-5-hp. Tecumseh	4 sp fw rev	chain drive	18-24" 12-24"	Attachments: tillers, snow throwers shredder, cultivator
Yard Man Co. Box 2741 Cleveland, Oh. 44111		8 hp.	5		26"	adjustable handle

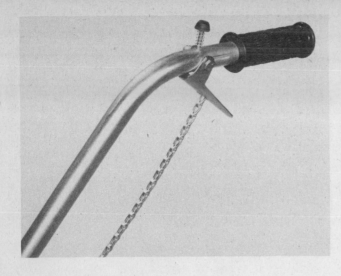

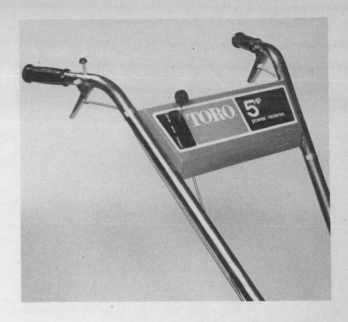

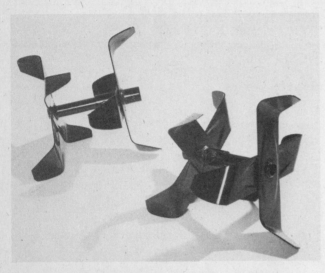

ACCESSORIES AND FEATURES

These photos of Toro Company products illustrate some of the features available on rototillers. From top, clockwise: Instant stop-and-go handle grip ensures good control; two-speed control lever; tiller depth adjustment moves from 1-8"; oil-lubricated drive with precision bearings; self-sharpening 13-gauge steel tines.

The Toro Company
8111 Lyndale Ave. S.
Minneapolis, Minn. 55420

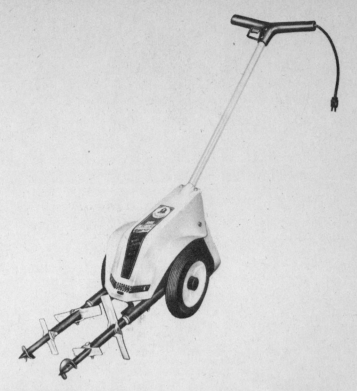

SOIL BLENDER

This unusual electric soil blender uses counter-rotating augers to break the ground from 1-12" deep. It digs, mixes soil, tills, hills, and cultivates. It is especially useful for mixing in fertlizer and organic materials, and can be used as a power shovel to break up hard, unyielding ground.

Garden Maid, Inc.
P.O. Box 912
Lebanon, Mo. 65536

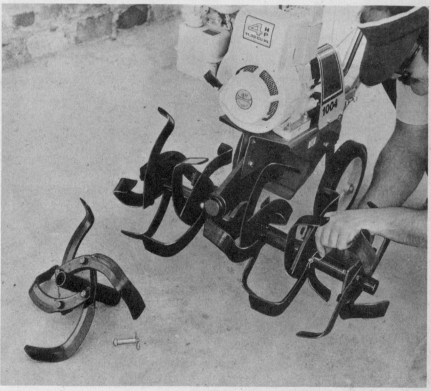

TINE WIDTH

The tilling width of most tillers can easily be extended with extension tines.

Allis Chalmers
Lawn and Garden Equipment
Box 512
Milwaukee, Wisc. 53201

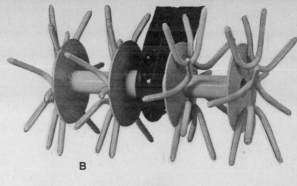

A

B

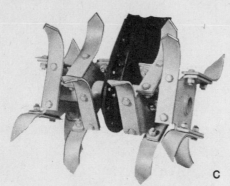

C

D

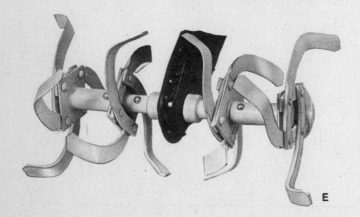

E

DIFFERENT TYPES OF ROTORS

Here are (A) scoops, each of which removes a 4" core of soil; (B) fingerlike rotors for a stirring action; (C) pick rotors to be used in clay and other hard soils; (D) bolo rotors for mulching and cultivating; and (E) slasher rotors, for breaking new ground (they minimize "wrapping" of weeds).

Merry Manufacturing Co.
Marysville, Wash. 98270

ROTO HOE

Choose the speed on this rear-wheeled model 810 by pulling on the shift rod. With four speeds forward and one reverse, the tiller will go as slow as ½ mph in first gear or as fast as 2½ mph for transporting.

Roto Hoe
100 Auburn Rd.
Newbury, Oh. 44065

GEAR BOX, MANG MODELS 91 and 95

The strain and shock of tough tilling is distributed among eight sprockets and heavy-duty roller chain. All moving parts are sealed in oil to give trouble-free performance.

Oregon Manufacturing Co.
6920 S.W. 111th Ave.
Beaverton, Ore. 97005

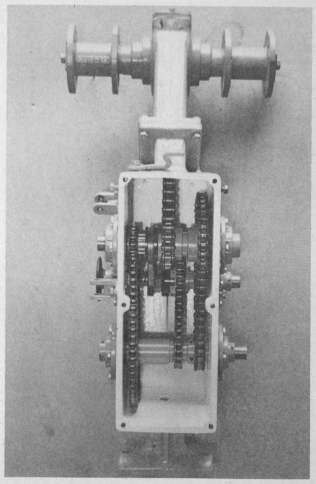

BIG GIANT TILLER

This rugged unit is propelled by a 10-hp. engine designed for tough jobs. The heavy-duty tines efficiently pulverize the soil. This machine can go through 20″ rows, and expand quickly to 36″ width with extra tines.

Giant Vac Mfg., Inc.
South Windham, Conn. 06266

HOWARD ROTAVATOR

The Gem model develops up to 15.2 hp., has three forward speeds and a wide range of operating speeds. The safety reverse provides ease in handling in confined areas. The handlebars are adjustable either up and down or side to side.

Howard Rotavator Co., Inc.
Harvard, Ill. 60033

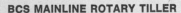

BCS MAINLINE ROTARY TILLER

This rotary tiller is mancfactured by BCS of Milan, Italy. It is self-propelled and has three speeds forward plus a reverse gear. It is powered by an 8-hp., four-cycle engine or an optional 5-hp., four-cycle engine. The engine is mounted low, where the weight makes it easy to operate on uneven or hilly terrain. The standard rotor width is 20 inches.

Distributed by
Central States Mainline
Box 348
London, Oh. 43140

EDKO WALKING TRACTOR

The Edko Walking Tractor features a heavy-duty frame, a rugged 5-hp. Briggs and Stratton engine and a number of attachments that make the tractor a year-round workhorse. These include a 7″ moldboard plow, a 6-prong cultivator, a furrow opener, a 40″ push blade, and a disc plow.

Edko Manufacturing, Inc.
2725 Second Ave.
Des Moines, Ia. 50313

JOHN DEERE ROTARY TILLERS

These tillers mix and mulch thoroughly to a 7″ depth. The 324 is powered by a 3½-hp. engine. Turbo tines can be set for 13-24″ tilling widths. The 624 develops 6 hp. and tills a 34″ path with optional extension tines.

Deere & Company
John Deere Rd.
Moline, Ill. 61265

WALK BEHIND TRACTOR

This unusual garden tractor is diesel powered and has no plugs, points, magneto, or carburetor. The steering handle bar column is adjustable for height and capable of rotation through 180 degrees with the possibility of quick locking into 4 positions. Quick-change implements make this tractor into a mower, sprayer, rototiller.

Ferrari
6104 Avenida Encinas
Carlsbad, Cal. 92008

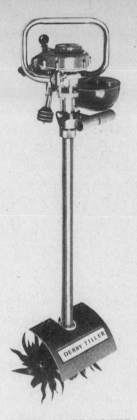

TILLER/WALKING TRACTOR KIT

Build your own tiller with this semi-kit from Heald. Utilizes a 5-hp. Briggs & Stratton engine with a chain drive. This unit tills, cultivates, and plows; converts easily to a walking tractor.

Heald, Inc.
P. O. Box 1148
Benton Harbor, Mich. 49022

DERBY TILLER/POWER HOE

This easy-to-use Derby tiller and power hoe tills gardens up to 20 by 100 feet, cultivates or weeds from 1 to 2 acres. Can be used single-handed.

Derby Tiller/Power Hoe
P.O. Box 21
Rumson, N.J. 07760

Lawn/garden tractors

Garden experts say you should consider four points when deciding whether or not to purchase a lawn garden tractor.

1. Can you afford it?
2. Do you have a lot of different jobs to perform?
3. Are you growing vegetables seriously in large quantities?
4. Is it impossible to find inexpensive labor in your neighborhood?

Garden tractors with their attachments can perform many functions. They are good for seed bed preparation, tilling, cultivating, planting, and more. They can be used as mowers, and they are helpful in leaf and grass disposal, utilizing sweepers, vacuum units, composters. They are good for grading; they will load materials, haul, spray, dig, and do many other chores.

There are, of course, many models on the market. Here are some points and the variations to consider when purchasing a tractor:

Horsepower. In general, there are three broad categories: Tractors with under 10 hp. are used primarily for tending a yard under one acre and for light snow removal; those with 10-14 hp. are good for preparing a good-sized vegetable garden and are able to handle a variety of cultivating equipment; those with 16-20 hp. are designed for heavier-duty, large garden work, and utility chores.

Transmission controls. Tractors in the 10-14 hp. category usually have gearshift transmissions. Some have 3-4 speed transaxles or, combined with a high/low range selector, 6 speeds forward, one speed backward; one model allows a variable control speed in each range without clutching. Tractors in the 16-hp.-and-above class normally offer hydrostatic drive, which is like automatic transmission. There is just one lever, which is forward and backward. One tractor model has a foot-operated hydrostatic pedal that requires uniform foot pressure. A hand control mounted through the dash panel is generally the most convenient system.

Some tractors offer almost vibration-free operation achieved by proper balancing or isolating the engine on rubber mounts. Many new tractor models also have completely enclosed engines for reduced sound levels.

Interiors. Best is a welded steel, one-piece design. Some tractors have a two-piece frame that is bolted and riveted together.

Axles. Best are solid cast iron. Some models have hollow axles of shaped steel; this is not as durable.

Steering spindle. A 1-inch spindle is the mark of a well-built tractor. Steering spindles of ¾-inch diameter have less bearing surface for the front wheels to turn on, and heat builds up.

Operator's section. The station should be uncluttered, so you can get in and out without hindrance. Controls should be within convenient reach from the seat. Best are color-coded controls for easier identification. Seat should be padded with a high backrest. Brake and clutch pedals should be wrapped in rubber.

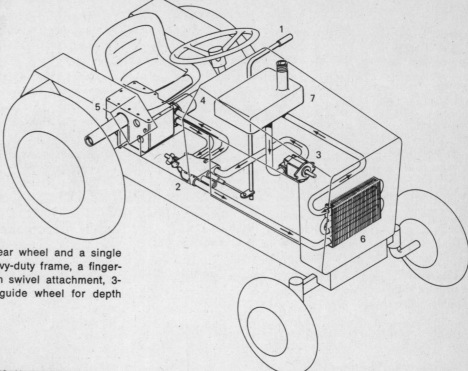

EDKO POWER WHEEL

This power wheel unit utilizes one rear wheel and a single front small guide wheel. It has a heavy-duty frame, a finger-tip belt idler, adjustable tool bar with swivel attachment, 3-position handle, and an adjustable guide wheel for depth control.

Edko Manufacturing, Inc.
2725 Second Ave.
Des Moines, Ia. 50313

CASE HYDRIV TRACTOR

A single system powers not only the tractor, but also the attachment lift, the tiller, the loader, and other hydraulic implements.

1. Cushion control level. Push it forward to go, pull it back for reverse. It's linked to a valve, so the farther you move it the faster you go.

2. Control valve directs flow of oil from pump to hydraulic motor for control of direction. It also regulates volume of oil for control of speed. Built-in relief valve prevents overloading and protects entire system.

3. Hydraulic pump connected to engine develops constant, powerful oil flow to drive tractor and attachments. No belts, shafts or pulleys.

4. Hydraulic motor with built-in torque multiplier transmits power to heavy duty transaxle.

5. Dual range transaxle is geared with a "high" for light loads, "low" for heavy loads.

6. Heat exchanger provides ample cooling capacity for toughest operating conditions.

7. Oil reservoir stores cooled hydraulic oil.

GARDEN TRACTORS

MANUFACTURER	MODELS HORSEPOWER	TRANSMISSION	POWER TAKEOFF	FRAME	AXLE
Allis Chalmers Corp. Box 512 Milwaukee, Wisc. 53201	608 IT—8 hp.	Transaxle, 3 forward, 1 reverse	Single V belt front & center	Full-length steel	Solid
	808 S—8 hp. 810 GT—10 hp. 800 series	Transaxle, 3 forward, 1 reverse	Single V belt front, center, rear	"	"
	710—10 hp. 712—12 hp. 716—16 hp.	710, 716—6 speed forward, reverse; 712 —shuttle, reverse without clutching; 712, 716—single-lever hydrostatic	Center & rear cone clutch, front, engine crankshaft	"	"
Ariens Company 655 W. Ryan St. Brillion, Wisc. 54110	S8G—8 hp. S10G—10 hp. S14G—14 hp.	S8G—3 forward, reverse; others— forward & reverse	Front, center, & rear power except S8G	Solid structural steel	Heavy duty I-beam
	S12H—12 hp. S14H—14 hp. S16H—16 hp.	Hydrostatic, single-lever	Front, center, and rear power direct from engine	"	"
Bolens FMC 215 S. Park St. Port Washington, Wisc. 53074	G8—8 hp.	Transaxle, 3 speeds forward & reverse	Belt power takeoff	All-steel	Solid
	G9—8 hp. G10—10 hp. G12—12 hp. G14—14 hp.	Transaxle gear, 6 forward, 2 reverse	Power takeoff shaft under front axle	Tubular	Solid
	H14XL—14 hp. H16—16 hp. OT16—16 hp. HT20,19—9 hp.	Hydrostatic foot pedal		Tubular	Solid
J.I. Case Co. Winneconne, Wisc. 54986	108—8 hp. 210—10 hp.	Gear drive: 108—3 forward, 1 reverse; 210, 4 forward, 1 reverse		All-welded, twin-channel	Cast iron
	220—10 hp. 222—12 hp. 224—14 hp.	Hydrostatic, single-lever		All-welded, twin-channel	Cast iron
	444—14 hp. 446—16 hp. 644—14 hp.: loader-backhoe 646—16 hp.: loader-backhoe	Hydrostatic, single-lever		All-welded, twin-channel	Cast iron
Deere & Company John Deere Rd. Moline, Ill. 61265	100—8 hp.	Transaxle gear, 3 forward, 1 reverse		Full-length steel	Solid
	220—10 hp. 222—12 hp. 224—14 hp.	Transaxle; variable belt	Front-mounted PTO attachment	Full-length steel	Solid
	300—16 hp. 400—19.2 hp.	Hydrostatic		Full-length steel	Solid
Engineering Product Company PO Box 284 1515 E. Ellis St. Waukesha, Wisc. 53186	Jim Dandy 2 Power King—14 hp.	Borg-Warner: 3 speeds forward, 1 reverse, optional tandem transmission	Two takeoffs, forward belt drive—3 groove pulley, behind	Welded construction	Steel
Ford Tractor Operations Troy Mich. 48084	LT 80—8 hp. LT 10—10 hp.	Gear transmission with creeper gear	Front, power takeoff	Steel	Heavy front axle

GARDEN TRACTORS (Continued)

MANUFACTURER	MODELS HORSEPOWER	TRANSMISSION	POWER TAKEOFF	FRAME	AXLE
	LGT 100—10 hp. LGT 120—12 hp.	Gear Transmission with creeper gear	Rear & front power takeoff	Welded tubular steel	Cast iron
	LGT 125—12 hp. LGT 145—14 hp. LGT 165—16 hp.	Hydrostatic, dual-range, foot control		"	"
Ferrari 6104 Avenida Encinas Carlsbad, Cal. 72008	Model 85, diesel—45 hp.	7 speeds forward, 3 reverse	2- power takeoff	Heavy-duty	Floating-wheel
Gilson Brothers Co. Box 152 Plymouth, Wisc. 53073	53024 53026 16-hp. 53030	Gear transaxle, 4-speed, 53024, 53026, variable	Front—cast-iron drive pulley	Unitized	Steel-bar reinforcement
Gravely One Gravely Lane Clemmons N.C. 27012	810—10 hp. 812—12 hp. 816S—16 hp. 817—16½ hp.	Gear, 8 speeds	Optional front PTO	Reinforced, box beam	Pivoted front axle
Heald PO Box 1148 Benton Harbor, Mich. 49022	Yard Bronc—10 hp.	Transaxle, 3 speeds forward, 1 reverse	Mid-mount	One-piece welded	Solid steel casing
Homesteader-Anderson's Custom Trailer Mfg. Co. P.O. Box 207 Clinton, Ark. 72031	Homesteader—8 hp. Homesteader—16 hp.	Transaxle, 4 speeds	PTO	Heavy-duty, welded	Heavy-duty
International Harvester 401 N. Michigan Ave. Chicago, Ill. 60611	Cub Cadet: 1000—10 hp. 1200—12 hp.	All gear, direct sliding spur gear	Front, rear, mid power takeoff, electric PTO clutch	Steel channels	Cast-iron alloy
	1250—12 hp. 1450—14 hp. 1650—16 hp.	Hydrostatic, single-lever	"	"	"
	184Lo Boy18—5 hp.	All gear, 3 speeds forward, 1 reverse	"	"	I-beam, cast iron
Jacobsen Mfg. Co. 1721 Packard Ave. Racine, Wisc. 53403	1000—10 hp. 1200—12 hp.	Gear, four speeds, reverse	Optional rear power takeoff	Heavy-duty	Reinforced
	1250—12 hp. 1450—14 hp. 1650—16 hp.	Hydrostatic, dual-range, foot control	"	Steel frame	"Float-N-Pivot"
Kubota Tractor Corp. 300 W. Carob St. Compton, Cal. 90220	12½-30 hp., four-wheel drive, liquid cooled, diesel engine				
Massey-Ferguson Inc. 1901 Bell Ave. Des Moines, Ia. 50315	MF 1200—12 hp.	4-speed transaxle	Optional rear power takeoff	Unitized welded steel	
	MF 1450—14 hp. MF 1650—16 hp.	Hydrostatic, foot pedal	Middle, optional rear power takeoff	"	Heavy-duty
MTD Products Inc. 5389 West 130 St. Cleveland, Oh. 44111	147-760—10 hp.	Case, 3-speed transaxle	2 power takeoff belts	Heavy-duty channel	Pivoted front axle support
	147-860—10 hp.	4-speed transaxle	Side power takeoff	Unitized steel	"
	147-910—10 hp. 147-912—12 hp.	4-speed transaxle 16-speed overdrive	Auxiliary PTO as option for tiller and mower through universal drive shaft		

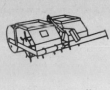

Brinly-Hardy roller aerator

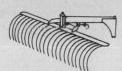

Arps mini-rake

Arps mini-blade

Amerind-MacKissic compost shredder

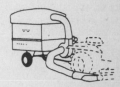

Kwik-way front end loader

Brinly-Hardy rear blade w/scarifier

Roxy-Bonner gang reel mowers

Haban sickle mower

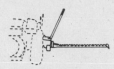

Kensico lawn aerator

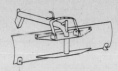

E-z rake vac sweepers

Amerind-MacKissic 22-gallon sprayer

Garber seeder spreader

Cozy Cab metal winter cab

Brinly-Hardy lift-type disc harrow

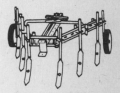

Brinly-Hardy row crop cultivator

Brinly-Hardy mold board plow

W-W Grinder Corp. grinder/shredder

Brinly-Hardy compactor rake

Brinly-Hardy power caster

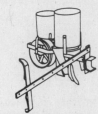

Brinly-Hardy Garden planter & fertilizer unit

Ohio Steel Fabricators mold board plow

Brinly-Hardy tool bar

Ohio Steel Fabricators cultivator

Ohio Steel Fabricators disc harrow

E-z rake 101 lawn thatcher

Nortech log splitter

ACCESSORIES FOR RIDING TRACTORS

There are hundreds of attachments available for tractors. Here are 26 different pieces of equipment manufactured by the Allied Equipment Company for Gravely tractors.

GARDEN TRACTORS (Continued)

MANUFACTURER	MODELS HORSEPOWER	TRANSMISSION	POWER TAKEOFF	FRAME	AXLE
MTD Products Inc. 5389 West 130 St. Cleveland, Oh. 44111	147-916—16 hp.	Standard 4-speed	Front, rear, mid	Heavy-guage channel steel	Heavy-duty cast iron
	147-918—16 hp.	16-speed overdrive	Front, rear, mid		
	147-990—16 hp.	Hydrostatic	For tiller & mower—through universal drive shaft; snow blower off front pulley	"	"
Murray Ohio Manufacturing Co. PO Box 268 Brentwood, Tenn. 37027	7-4297—10 hp. other-8 hp. models	3-speed transaxle	PTO	Steel	
Simplicity Manufacturing Co. 500 N. Spring St. Port Washington, Wisc. 53074	6008—8 hp. 6010—10 hp.	Belt drive, gear transmission	Front, rear	Welded heavy-gauge	Heavy bar axle
	7010	6 forward, 2 reverse	Center	"	
	7013 7016	Sliding spur gear	Center	"	
	9020	Hydrostatic	Front power takeoff electric, also rear PTO		
Speedex Tractor Co. Ravenna, Oh. 44266	820, 840—8 hp. 1020,1030—10 hp. 1430—14 hp. 1632—16 hp.	Automotive type	PTO	Solid welded chassis	
Wheel Horse Lawn & Garden Tractors 515 West Ireland Rd. South Bend, Ind. 46614	*B-series* B-60—7 hp. B-80—8 hp. B-100—10 hp.	8-speed unidrive transaxle, manual	PTO	Heavy-duty	Heavy-duty
	C-120 (8-speed)—12 hp.	8-speed manual	PTO	"	"
	C-120 (automatic) C-160 (8 speed)—16 hp. C-160 (automatic)	automatic 8-speed, unidrive transaxle Automatic	PTO	"	"
	D-160—16 hp. (twin cylinder)	automatic		"	"
	D-200—19.9 hp. (twin cylinder)	automatic	optional power takeoff	"	"
	D-250—19.9 hp. (four cylinder)	ten-speed transaxel, 4 forward speeds reverse, tow ranges	front, mid, rear	"	"
	B-145—Battery powered, six heavy-duty 6 volt batteries; plug in to recharge; three forward and two reverse speeds	manual		"	"
	C-185—A cruise control lets you choose either of two constant working speeds; seven speeds forward, three reverse, in each of four gear ranges	manual	36-volt PTO	"	"

GARDEN TRACTORS (Continued)

MANUFACTURER	MODELS HORSEPOWER	TRANSMISSION	POWER TAKEOFF	FRAME	AXLE
White Outdoor Products Division White Farm Equip. Co. Oak Brook, Ill. 60521	GT-1020—10 hp.	4-speed transaxle, with 4-speed shift; 16 speeds	center, direct engine, front, rear, gear box shaft driven	steel	deep-formed box-type steel
	GT-1620—16 hp.	4-speed transaxle with 4-speed shift; 16 speeds forward	center, direct engine driven, front and rear gear box, shaft driven	steel	deep-formed box-type steel
	GT-1650—16 hp.	automatic hydrostatic combined with dual range transaxle	front engine direct; center, rear shaft driven from PTO drive case	steel	cast iron
Yanmar Diesel Engine Co., Ltd. 1-11-1 Marunouchi Chiyoda-ku Tokyo, Japan	YM 135—13 hp., 2-wheel drive; YM 135D—13 hp., 4-wheel drive diesel	Constant-mesh/ selective-mesh gears combination, 6 speeds forward, 2 reverse	Rear PTO	heavy-duty	
	YM 155—15 hp. YM 155 D—2-wheel drive, 4-wheel drive	As above	"		

MANY SIZES AVAILABLE

Manufacturers like Massey-Ferguson offer tractors in many different sizes and styles. Massey-Ferguson garden tractors range in size from 8-16 hp., with both gear-driven transaxle and hydra seep drive, unitized welded steel frame plus many extra features.

Massey-Ferguson, Inc.
1901 Bell Ave.
Des Moines, Ia. 50315

1

2

GARDEN TRACTOR ACCESSORIES

Today garden tractors handle many specialized accessories. Here are a few:

1. **Cultivator.** This V tool bar mounts five 6″ sweeps and two 6″ half-sweeps along with two-gauge wheels. It works 6″ and 42″ rows and adjusts to plow both sides of a single row and half the middle, or the full middle and each side of 2 rows.

2. **Spring Tooth Harrow.** This attachment prepares rough seed bed by digging deep. It penerates hard soil conditions and pulls out weed and grass rot to leave soil loose, open, and clean. Comes with 7 coil spring teeth, each individually adjusted.

3

4

3. **Thirty-Six" Rotary Tiller.** Overlapping tines work up a thoroughly mixed and crumbled seedbed or work the soil between your crop rows. Enclosed ends and full width rear skirt keep the action inside.

4. **Moldboard Ten" Plow.** Turns over soil and sod. Covers weeds, and field residue. Leaves the surface lumpy to slow down water run-off and wind erosion. Adjustable draft control.

Allis Chalmers
Lawn and Garden Equipment
Box 512
Milwaukee, Wisc. 53201

HOMESTEADER GARDEN TRACTOR

This is a very different-looking garden tractor. Has great visibility in front of a 16-hp., 4-cycle cast iron Kohler engine. Utilizes a transaxle, with 4 speeds forward, one reverse chain drive.

Anderson's Custom Trailer Mfg. Co.
P.O. Box 207
Clinton, Ark. 72031

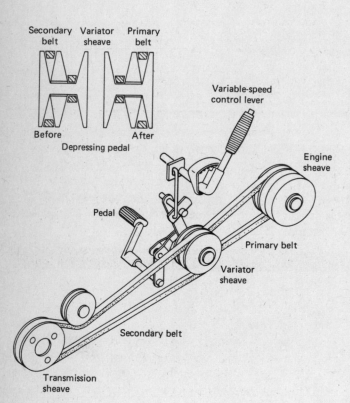

HOW VARIABLE-SPEED DRIVE WORKS

Speed of the primary belt is determined by engine speed, or throttle. Pulling back on the lever, or depressing the clutch pedal, moves the variator sheave forward. This forces the secondary belt deeper into the variator sheave and causes the belt to revolve around a smaller radius, thus reducing the speed at which the tractor is driven. Engine speed and power to equipment remain the same. Similar variable-speed drive systems have proved to be dependable and efficient through years of use.

6

TRANS-PLANTING

After a year or two of vegetable growing, many gardeners decide to get a step or two ahead of nature by planting seeds indoors during late winter and early spring. Later, when the weather has warmed up, they transplant their homegrown seedlings to the outdoor garden. By doing this they not only lengthen their growing season, they also avoid the expense and risk of buying seedlings from a nursery.

Many vegetables benefit from transplanting. For instance, it is very difficult to start such vegetables as tomatoes, eggplant, and peppers outdoors as seeds. Other vegetables such as lettuce, onions, melons, squash, and corn can be started indoors or outdoors.

The methods of transplanting

There are many techniques that can be used with transplants, and the most important will be discussed in this chapter. Warming the soil electrically can hasten the germination and growth of seeds indoors. Outdoors, coldframes and hotbeds can be used as intermediate stopovers between the indoor seedling bed and the garden—or, as the weather gets warmer, as places where seeds can be eased through the first weeks of life. The techniques of English cloche gardening can be used to protect tender seeds that have been planted directly in the garden soil.

Starting transplants inside

Many gardeners have not tried their luck with seedlings because they think the whole process is difficult and time-consuming. In fact, it's quite simple. To start, all you need is: (a) a growing medium, (b) warmth and moisture, and (c) adequate light. There are two general methods to choose from—the two step and the one step.

Two-step method

You can start quantities of plants in containers and transplant them later into individual pots. Plant initially in commercial plastic flats or half-flats, in shallow wooden crates, or in such household items as aluminum meat loaf pans, milk cartons cut lengthwise, large frozen food containers, cut-off gallon bleach containers, and the like. Following is an outline of the procedure:

Step 1:

1. Fill the container with vermiculite, commercial soil mix, or a homemade soil mix. Scrape off the excess

The two-step transplant method using a milk carton.

mix with a flat knife or stick, then press down the remaining soil lightly.

2. Make furrows with a pencil or similar tool.

3. When using large flats, water from above before planting seeds. With smaller containers, water from the bottom after planting. You can put one or two inches of water in a sink and place the container in it. When the surface of the vermiculite becomes moist, take the container out and allow it to drain.

4. Sow seeds directly from the package, about an inch apart. Sow more seeds than the number of plants you'd like to end up with. Then, when they come up, thin out the weak plants by clipping with a small pair of scissors.

5. Slip the trays into a plastic bag (a bread bag will do fine), and keep as close to 75°F. as possible. Don't water again until after germination—that is, after you see the little sprouts poking up through the soil —and after that add only enough water to keep the soil mix damp.

Step 2: When the first true leaves have formed (the first two leaflike growths are not leaves, the third and succeeding ones are), dig the seedlings out and put them into pots. When they are five or six inches high, you can transfer them into the garden plot or large container. But before you complete this step, you must be sure that the weather conditions are suitable. The time to transplant cool-season crops such as lettuce and celery is when the outside temperature averages 55-75° F. For warm-season crops such as tomatoes and peppers, the time to transplant is when the average

outside temperature is in the 65-80° F. range. (See the full discussion of cool- and warm-season crops on page 90.)

The one-step method

Seeds can also be sown directly into small pots or cubes made of biodegradable material. Generally it's one seed to a pot. After the plants have come up, and when the temperature is right for the particular vegetable, as indicated in the previous paragraph, you can plant each of these containers directly into the garden bed or larger container. Roots grow right through the walls of the pots and spread into the surrounding soil.

One of the major advantages of this procedure is that it avoids the root shock that happens to many vegetables when they are transplanted. (Large-seeded plants such as squash and melons should always be handled in this way; their root systems do not tolerate transplanting well.)

Pots and pellets

There are several kinds of small pots, pellets, cubes, and other small containers available for use in transplanting. Jiffy-7 pellets are compressed sterile sphagnum peat and soil with added fertilizer, all enclosed in a plastic net. The pellet expands to form a small container (1¾″ by 2″) when placed in water. The seed is planted directly in the pellet just before this watering. Jiffy pots are available in several forms: Jiffy-7 Standard, for direct sowing of vegetable seeds; Jiffy-7 Special, with a preformed ¼-inch hole, ideal for cuttings; Jiffy-7 Trays, prepackaged pellets in green plastic trays; and Jiffy-9, which is held together with a binder instead of a net.

Other brands include BR-8 Gro-Blocks, which are fiber blocks containing fertilizer; Fertl-Cubes and Gro-Blocks, which are made from a blend of mosses, plant food, and vermiculite and each of which has a depression for planting the seed; Peat Pots, which are made of fiber and should be filled with synthetic soil. These latter are square or round and come in multiple break-apart strips. Cell Pots or Paks are light plastic pots, filled with synthetic soil, for growing individual "pop-out" transplants. They are often used with a plastic tray, and are available as single cells or in units of 2, 3, 4, or 12 cells. There are also larger sizes.

Seed starter kits

Several companies now offer vegetable and herb starter kits. Each kit contains everything you need to grow healthy seedlings to transplant size. These kits vary from containers already planted with individual vegetable seeds to kits with cubes, fertilizers, trays, heating cables, and clear plastic tops to keep in the moisture (these latter are often referred to as indoor greenhouses; for some examples see Chapter 10).

Timing your Indoor planting

If you put your seeds in containers too early, the plants will probably grow too large for their containers. Thus, as you let them sit inside waiting for the proper time, they may grow weak. If, on the other hand, you plant your seeds too late, they will not be mature enough to go outside at the proper time. So you've got to know what you're doing; timing is crucial.

The two most important factors in the indoor-planting equation are the climate of your area and the time

POTS AND A HEATING CABLE

Three stages in the use of pots and a heating cable to grow seedlings. The seeds are planted; then, in a couple of weeks, they germinate and produce the first true leaves. Later, when the plants are five or six inches high, they should be transplanted to the garden—provided that the danger of frost has passed.

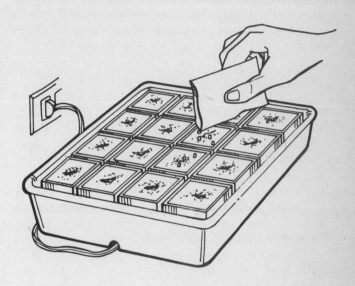

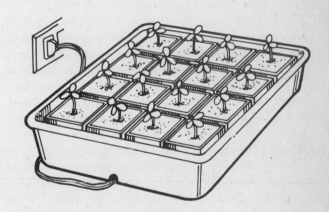

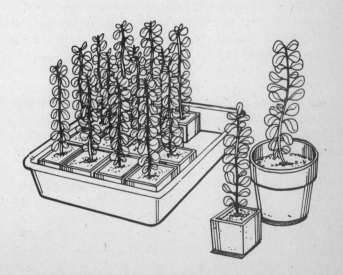

How important is the right soil mix for starting seedlings?

The soil mix used makes a tremendous difference in seedling growth. A recent study using tomato plants showed that seedlings planted in ordinary potting mix had the least growth in a six-week period. Plants grown in perlite and vermiculite did a little better. Seedlings grown in pure sand grew twice as fast as seedlings grown in potting mix, perlite, or vermiculite. Plants grown in either Cornell or University of California mix did best. In six weeks tomato plants grown in the Cornell mix reached six inches, while plants grown in potting mix were barely an inch high.

your seeds need for germination, leaf development, and growth. You should be able to get this latter information from the individual seed packets; for a general idea about early and late varieties of various vegetables, refer in this book to Chapter 7.

Take onions as an example. If your seeds take eight weeks to become mature enough for transplanting, and if the middle of May is the proper time in your area to set out onions, then start them indoors in the middle of March.

Hardening the transplants

Before actually planting the seedlings in the garden bed or in a patio or balcony container, you should get them used to outdoor conditions. Adjust the young plants by placing them outside, in their pots, around the middle of the day. Don't overexpose them, especially at first, but gradually increase the time they are left out in the fresh air. Be sure to bring them indoors whenever frost seems likely, especially overnight. In one way or another expose your seedlings to lower temperatures for about two weeks before setting them out in the garden bed.

Coldframes

One of the best devices to use in hardening your transplants is a coldframe. This is simply a structure with a clear lid designed to let in the sun's warming rays and to keep out cold air, wind, and other unfavorable weather factors. A coldframe actually controls three factors—light, humidity, and temperature.

Light. Plants generally need lots of light. Plan to locate your frame so as to take maximum advantage of available sun. Many gardeners utilize a southern exposure to increase the light. Others paint the inside of the frame white or put up a white wall to increase sunlight reflection. However, keep in mind that direct sun can cause overheating. If this seems to be a problem, try placing cheesecloth over the coldframe; in a very hot climate use a heavy material like burlap. You can also whitewash the glass to give your seedlings a gentle light, or you can build a lath panel for the top. On a warm day be sure to open the top of the frame for air circulation.

Humidity. Optimum humidity for seedlings is very high, about 80 percent. You will find that a layer of sand and gravel on the bottom of a coldframe increases drainage and helps to build humidity. But watch for heavy condensation on the glass—this indicates that there is too much moisture. To combat this problem simply raise the top for a few minutes each morning.

Temperature. You can keep a coldframe at the required temperature whether or not the sun does its job by using electric heat (which gets more expensive every year) or by taking advantage of the heating action of decomposition. To heat a frame naturally, place about 18 inches of green organic material (grass clippings, etc.) in a pit and set the frame on top. The bacterial action involved in the "rotting" of the green material will supply heat to the frame for a long time.

One fairly simple way to heat electrically is with a light bulb inside the coldframe. Then there is *electrical soil warming,* which offers several advantages for home gardening. First, the vegetables will germinate faster and thus get an earlier start. And gentle soil warming will produce healthier plants with fully developed root structures.

Soil warming by itself will not protect exposed plants from frost, but the controlled, even temperature of the soil will reduce the effects of temperature cycling when the nights are cool, and thus enable you to extend your outdoor growing season.

The heating cables that do the job of soil warming are offered in a variety of types. Generally, you have a basic choice between lead- and plastic-covered cables, but it goes beyond that. There are now cables, soil-warming mats, heated seed flats, heated sash beds, and even heated starter kits with the seeds and planter mix included. All these generally have a built-in thermostat that keeps the soil at a constant temperature.

An example of a group of plants helped greatly by being planted in a coldframe is the melons. You can make small frames or boxes, each one foot by one foot and three or four inches high, with a clear plastic cover. Place them in the prepared garden bed. Plant eight to ten seeds within each frame. Remove the plastic on warm days, replace it on chilly days and at night. Remove the cover entirely when the danger of frost has passed.

Cloches

A cloche is any sort of cover placed over your plants in the garden bed. The principle behind the cloche is to bring the protection to the growing crop instead of bringing the crop inside to a fixed frame or greenhouse or other protected environment. The highly efficient cloche system of gardening is used extensively in England, Holland, and parts of Japan, where food must be grown under unreliable or cool conditions. The cloche creates a more-or-less constant warm temperature and protects the plants from wind, rain, frost, and pest damage.

Commercial cloches made of clear or translucent plastic are just beginning to come on the American

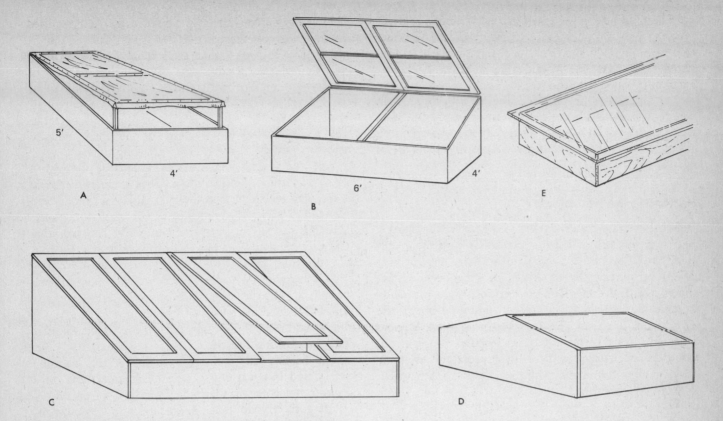

FIVE DIFFERENT METHODS OF BUILDING A COLDFRAME:

(A) Plastic nailed to frame. (B) Old windows over frame. (C) Multiunit construction. (D) Double-span frame. (E) Glass over box or frame.

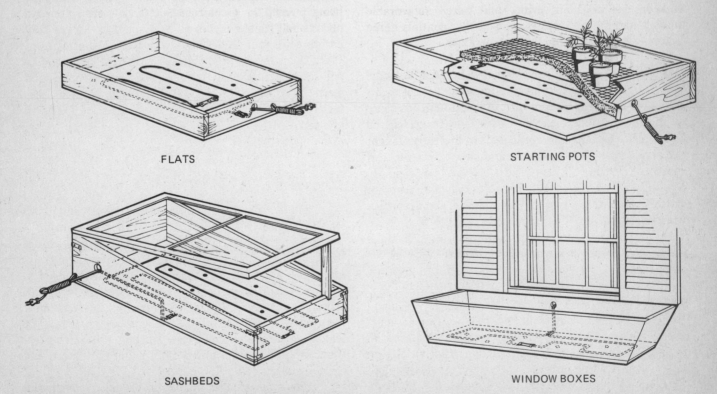

FLATS

STARTING POTS

SASHBEDS

WINDOW BOXES

FOUR FLATS WHERE HEATING CABLES CAN BE USED

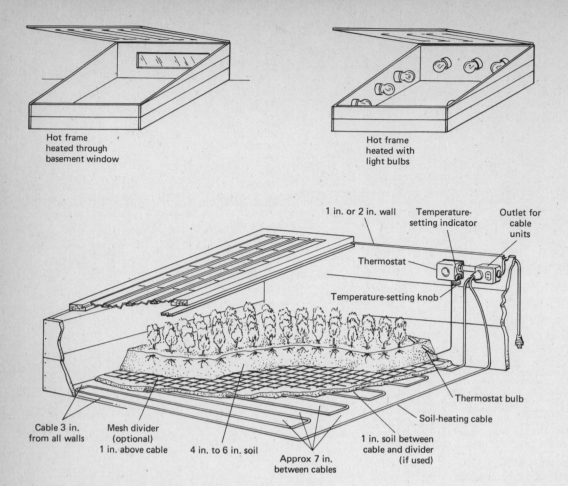

Hot frame heated through basement window

Hot frame heated with light bulbs

1 in. or 2 in. wall

Temperature-setting indicator

Outlet for cable units

Thermostat

Temperature-setting knob

Thermostat bulb

Soil-heating cable

Cable 3 in. from all walls

Mesh divider (optional) 1 in. above cable

4 in. to 6 in. soil

Approx 7 in. between cables

1 in. soil between cable and divider (if used)

WARMING YOUR COLD FRAME

Three ways of keeping a coldframe at the proper temperature. You can place it near a basement window, out of the cold but in the sun. Or you can use light bulbs, no more than 25 watts. Or you can construct a fairly elaborate setup, as diagrammed above.

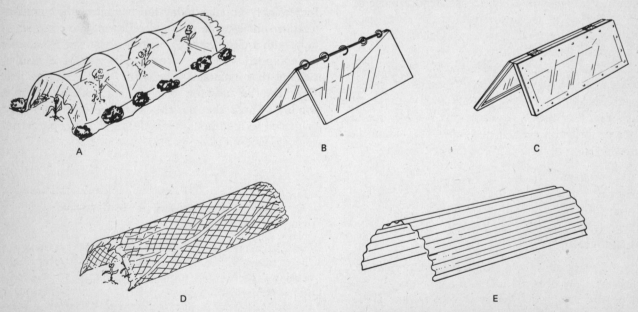

A

B

C

D

E

FIVE CLOCHES YOU CAN MAKE

Different types of cloches and tunnels can be used to protect plants in the garden. A) Wire clothes hangers twisted in proper shape and covered with plastic held down with rocks. (B) Clear plastic sheets held together with notebook rings passed through punched holes. (C) Wood frames held together with small hinges, covered with polyethylene. (D) Chicken wire covered with polyethylene. (E) Panel of flexible, corrugated plastic.

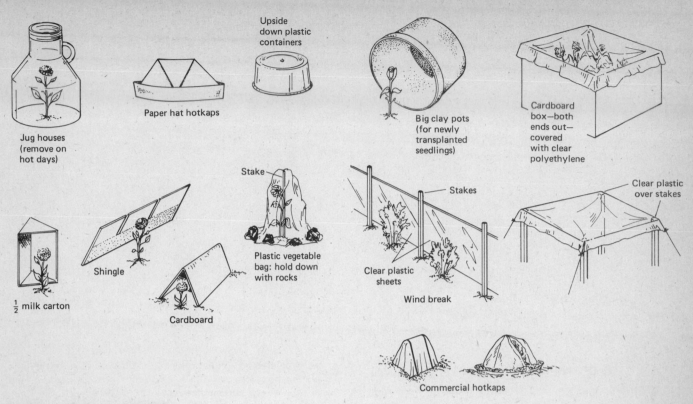

Jug houses (remove on hot days)

Paper hat hotkaps

Upside down plastic containers

Big clay pots (for newly transplanted seedlings)

Cardboard box—both ends out— covered with clear polyethylene

½ milk carton

Shingle

Cardboard

Stake

Plastic vegetable bag: hold down with rocks

Stakes

Clear plastic sheets

Wind break

Clear plastic over stakes

Commercial hotkaps

PLANT-PROTECTION DEVICES

market. You can also make your own at almost no cost (see drawings). Here are a few ideas: Bend a piece of corrugated plastic in an inverted U shape over your plants. Staple clear plastic on a wooden frame and hinge to form on A frame.

Another type of cloche is called a jug house. You can make these by cutting off the bottoms of gallon bottles and setting the bottomless jugs over your planted seeds. You can also buy commercially made waxed paper plant protectors, called hot caps. They come in standard and king sizes and in the larger hot tents.

Plastic tunnels

These are a variation of the cloche and simply consist of a sheet of clear plastic made into a row-long tunnel greenhouse by being stretched over wire hoops. These covers thus modify the climate of an entire row of vegetable plants. In addition they protect your crops from birds and hail, and usually bring harvest time ahead by as much as two weeks.

Mini-greenhouses

Increasingly popular today are commercially manufactured or home-made mini-greenhouses. These are small units with a clear vinyl cover over a planting box. Some are equipped with a thermostatically controlled heating element that maintains a constant 75° F. temperature. They can be used on balcony, roof, patio, or by a window. Those that do not have a heating unit must be placed so that they get sun during the day, yet do not cool off below the danger point at night.

Planting in peat kubes using an electrical soil warmer

Wet the soil thoroughly and plant the seedlings according to the directions of the seed package. The healthy seedlings with strong roots, well-developed stems, and full leaves will show the benefits of soil warming during the germination and early stages of growth. The seedlings in peat pots can be placed directly into prepared holes in your garden or into permanent pots indoors.

A

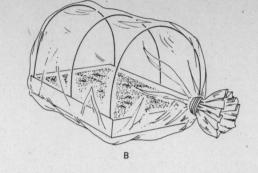

B

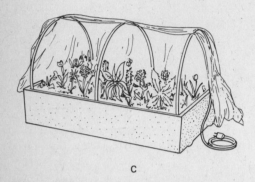

C

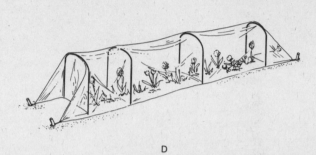

D

FOUR TYPES OF MINI-GREENHOUSES:

(A) A plastic bag wrapped around a group of pots, with the end tied securely. (B) Wire clothes hanger twisted into shape as indicated, then covered with plastic. (C) Polystyrene planter box with polyethylene cover; electrical cable buried in soil keeps temperature at 70°F. (D) Guard-N-Gro miniature greenhouse.

TRANSPLANTING AIDS (Continued)

ORGANIC STARTERS	SOURCES*
BR-8 Gro-Blocks	28
Fertil Pots	32 66 70 72
Fertil Strips	66
Fertl-Cubes	9 10 19 22 28 39 50 52 53 62 66
Gro-Blocks	38
Jiffy Flats	53
Jiffy Gro Pot Kit	62 67
Jiffy Pots	11 28 29 47 52 53 60 62 62A 66 67 70
Jiffy Strips	29 47 52 53 60 66 67 70
Jiffy-7 Peat Pellets	10 11 12 14 19 22 29 31 38 41 43 45 47 49 52 55 57 60 62 66 67 70 72
Jiffy-7 Trays (prepacked)	29 52
Jiffy-9 Peat Pellets	45 52 53 60 66 67 70
Kys-Kubes	31 45 55 70
Peat Pots	9 10 14 18 19 22 31 41 43 45 49 55 57
Peat Pot Strips	45 57
Sea-Gros (contains liquid seaweed)	60
Solo-Gro Seed Starter Cubes (seaweed added)	27 43 45 62
XL Seed Starter Cubes	45

ADDITIVES	SOURCES
Growth Stimulant (for Fertl-Cubes)	19
Seed Protectant (Thiram) (reduces seed decay)	11 12 52 55
Transplantone (hormone-vitamin plant starter) (reduces wilting on transplanting)	9 19 21 22 28 32 38 47 53 55 56 57 66

PLASTIC SEED STARTERS	SOURCES
Burpee's Deep Root 6-packs	10
Burpee's Deep Root 4-inch pots	10
Flats	45 72
Growing Trays	10 22 45 66 72
Jiffy Trays for Jiffy Strips	66 67 70
Moistrite Seed Starter Tray	29 45 66
Park's Easy Does It Containers	53
Park Trays	53
Perma-Nest Plant Trays	29 45 47 53 66
Plastic Cell-Paks	72
Poly Flats	31
Poly Trays	53
Round Pots	32 45 52 57 66
Square Pots	32 45 59
Tufflite Pots & Trays	53
Western Trays	57

*See list of suppliers, page 291.

TRANSPLANTING AIDS (Continued)

FIBER-WOOD SEED STARTERS	SOURCES
Fiber Pots	29
Garden Flats (fiber)	66
Garden Paks (fiber)	66
Kys-Pak (Flora-Paks) (asphalt & wood fiber)	10 28 29 45 52
Market-Paks	70
Wooden Seed Flats	31

ELECTRIC SOIL STERILIZER	SOURCE
Electric Soil Sterilizer	66

SOIL HEATING CABLES	SOURCES
Cox Heating Coils	47
Easy Heat	10 22 28 31 47
Electric Soil Heating Cable & Thermostat	66
Electric Soil Cable	35 53
General Electric with Thermostat	45 72
Gro Quick	11 19 38 45 52 72
Wrap-On	45 72

SOIL HEATING CABLE THERMOSTATS	SOURCES
Cox Thermostats	47
Wrap-On	45

HEATING TRAYS	SOURCES
Gro-Quick Combo	45 47 52 72
Heating Tray	53

SEED STARTER KITS	SOURCES
No Seeds	
Harris Seed Starting Kit	29
Jiffy-Gro Kit	28
One-Step Seed Starter Kit	53
Park's Seed Starter Kit	53
Seed Start Kits	22 52 66
No Seeds, with heating cable	
Bio-Gro Seed Starter Kit	53
Burpee's Early Start Kit	10
Jung's Gro-Mor Seed Starting Kit	38
With Seeds	
Fertl-House	10
Gourmet Herb Garden	49 52 60 62
Gourmet Oriental Vegetable Garden Kit	62
Indoor Salad Garden	43
Seed Start Vegetable Kits	10 19 28

VEGETABLE TAPES	SOURCE
Burpee's Indoor Vegetable Seed Tapes	10

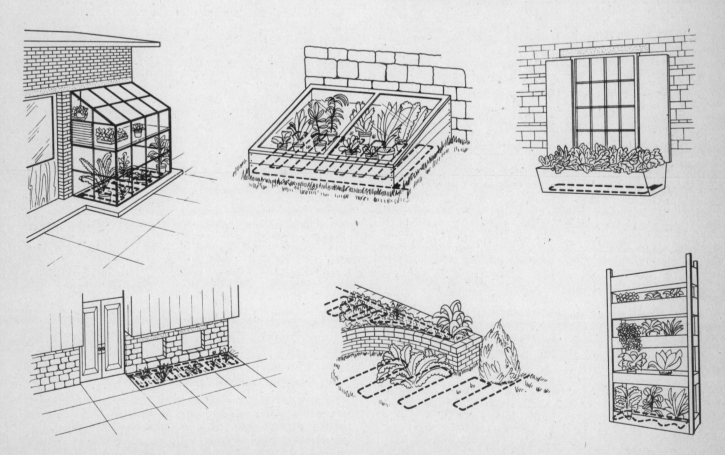

PLACES WHERE HEAT CABLES CAN BE USED

TRANSPLANTING AIDS (Continued)

MINIATURE GREENHOUSE WITH HEATING CABLES	SOURCES
Burpee's Electric Hothouse	10
Dean Foster Indoor Greenhouses (several)	23
Easy-Heat Greenhouse	10
Electric Greenhouse	22 28 62
Electric Thermostat Greenhouse	12 21 45
Gro-Quick Gro Varium	19 45

MINIATURE SEED STARTER INDOOR GREENHOUSES	SOURCES
Crytalite Greenhouse	45 53
Fertil Pot Miniature Greenhouse Kit	72
G.E. Seed Starter & Plant Lite Kit	62
Jiffy Hobby Greenhouse	45 49 60 62
Jiffy Seedstarter Greenhouse	9 12 19 28 38 47 49 52 53
Merry-Gro Plastic Greenhouse	47 49 53 66 72

OUTDOOR PLASTIC TUNNEL GREENHOUSES	SOURCES
Guard-N-Gro	22 28
Outdoor Greenhouse	53
Spring Jumper	45

COLDFRAMES	SOURCES
Burpee Garden Frame	10
Coldframes	22 28
Vent-o-Matic Automatic Coldframe	10 45 52 53
Hotbed Glass	47

OUTDOOR PLANT PROTECTORS	SOURCES
Hot Kaps	9 10 11 19 22 28 29 32 38 45 52 55 57 60 62 66 70 72 73
Hot Tents	45 57 60 66 70 72
King Tents	45
Tomato Gard	38 53

HOW TO PICK THE CORRECT CABLE SIZE

for larger areas use proportionately

LOWEST TEMP. READING F.	SQUARE FEET OF SOIL TO BE HEATED									
	1	2	3	4-5	6	7-8	9-11	12-16	17-22	23-25
Below 0°	6'	12'	24'	36'	48'	60'	80'	120'	160'	200'
0° to 15°	6'	12'	24'	36'	36'	48'	60'	80'	120'	160'
15° to 30°	6'	12'	12'	24'	36'	36'	48'	60'	120'	120'
Above 30°	6'	12'	12'	24'	24'	24'	36'	48'	60'	80'

Length of cable needed

PLANT GROWING TEMPERATURE RANGE

MINIMUM GROWING TEMP. F.	OPTIMUM TEMP. F.	MAXIMUM TEMP. F.	CROP
30°	75°	85°	Asparagus, rhubarb
35°	75°	85°	Garlic, leek, lettuce, mustard, onion, parsley, peas, spinach
40°	85°	90°	Beet, broccoli, brussels sprout, cabbage, carrot, cauliflower, celery, chard, collard, kale, kohlrabi, parsnip, potato, radish, rutabaga, turnip
50°	85°	100°	Corn
60°	85-90°	95-100°	Bean, cucumber, eggplant, melon, okra, pepper, pumpkin, squash
65°	80-85°	95°	Tomato

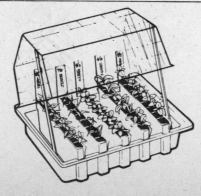

◄ JIFFY STARTER GREENHOUSE

This is a new way to start seedlings. Grow as many as 40 plants at one time. Even difficult-to-germinate seeds can be started with success. Keeps the soil from drying out and maintains a "closed" high-moisture-content "miniclimate."

Carefree Garden Products
Box 383
West Chicago, Ill. 60185

JIFFY POTS

These are fiber pots made of peat moss. Simply fill with synthetic soil. You can plant the entire pot directly in the garden. They come in several sizes.

Carefree Garden Products
P.O. Box 383
West Chicago, Ill. 60185

PERMA-NEST PLANT TRAYS

Excellent for starting vegetables. These trays made of strong high-impact polystyrene never harbor bacteria or harmful molds. They can be cold sterilized. You can use these many ways after seed starting: group your potted plants with consistent watering needs or root them.

Grower's Supply Company
P.O. Box 1132
Ann Arbor, Mich. 48106

GARDENING WITH A GUARD-N-GRO CLOCHE

The Guard-N-Gro cloche protects vegetables against rain, frost, and pests. It is insulated with a layer of sealed air cells to maintain an even, warm, humid climate.

It folds flat for easy storage and can be reassembled in seconds.

Guard-N-Gro Cloche Company
61 Cromary Way
Inverness, Cal. 94937

JIFFY HOBBY GREENHOUSE ▶

This includes everything you need for seed starting. All you need is a sunny corner, a balcony, or a window box. The Jiffy Hobby Greenhouse consists of a plastic growing tray and clear plastic bubble top that fits on the tray for controlled atmosphere and rapid germination.

Carefree Garden Products
Box 383
West Chicago, Ill. 60185

AUTOMATIC COLDFRAME

This coldframe powered by a thermal solar element will open itself at about 72° F., and closes at about 68° F. Keeps plants from being damaged by the heat built up in an ordinary coldframe.

Dalen Products, Inc.
201 Sherlake Dr.
Knoxville, Tenn. 37922

HEAT CABLES IN A FLAT (starting seeds)

Plants need consistent soil temperature if their seeds are to sprout quickly. A soil temperature maintained at approximately 74° F. will accomplish this. Simply insert a heat cable with thermostat directly in the bottom of the flat and cover with vermiculite or planting soil.

Wrap-On Co., Inc.
341 W. Superior St.
Chicago, Ill. 60610

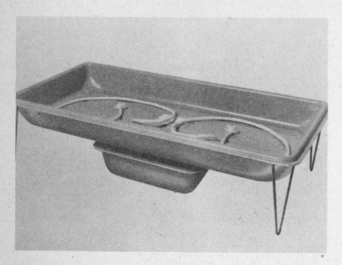

SEED STARTER

This starter tray waters itself. Has automatic wick-fed watering that eliminates seedling disturbance and surface crusting.

Grower's Supply Company
P.O. Box 1132
Ann Arbor, Mich. 48106

SEED STARTER KIT

The heating element and automatic thermostat are molded into the base of this high-impact PVC plastic unit. The starter kit comes with planting mix and a package of seeds. Simply fill with seed-starting soil and plant the seeds according to the directions on the package. When the seedlings are transplanted, simply wash the PVC flat in the sink.

Easy Heat
Lawn & Garden Products
U.S. 20 East
New Carlisle, Ind. 46552

7

VEGETABLE VARIETIES

A CATALOG OF SEED CATALOGS

The renewed interest in home gardening has kindled something of a revolution in the seed industry. In the last few years plant breeders have developed hundreds of new varieties of vegetables. Never before has the buyer/gardener been given such an abundance of top-quality seeds from which to choose.

Some of the new varieties mature in a shorter time and grow in a smaller space. Others grow larger and juicier, more delicious and more colorful than ever before. Plants are also being bred with stronger resistance to disease. The choice is so wide, it's confusing. Working with the charts in this chapter, however, the reader will be able to select the varieties that are just right for his or her home garden.

Some new varieties

Among the most popular of the new seeds on the market are the bush and semibush types of many vining vegetables. These are especially useful in small spaces. Also, it used to be that watermelons took up so much area that it was impossible to grow them in the average home garden. But today, with the development of the new icebox types, people are growing 3-10-pound watermelons on smaller, more compact vines.

Pot luck cucumbers, another example of a new vegetable group, are bred especially for containers, with each cucumber being almost the size of the entire vine! In addition there are many varieties of tomatoes that are just right for container gardening. You can also find new bush-type plants among squash (*Acorn Table King*), pumpkins (*Spirit*), and other vegetables—the trend seems to be just beginning. And as a result of the introduction of varieties with shorter growing seasons, gardeners in northern states and other short-season areas can now grow vegetables they had trouble with before.

How to buy vegetables from seed racks and catalogs

If you intend to plant fairly standard vegetables, you will probably want to buy your seed from a rack. There you have a chance to browse and compare. And reliable dealers will only stock seed that works well in their particular region. If you are looking for a large variety of seeds, for unusual kinds, for minivegetables or novelties, however, you will probably want to buy your seed through a catalog. Go through the catalog list on pages 241-243 and send for several. The vegetable charts included in this section are keyed to these catalogs.

Buying from seed racks. As noted, seed racks usually

contain varieties that perform well in your area. However, companies often include varieties with a national reputation that may not adapt well to your conditions. If you are in doubt about which variety to plant, check your local nursery or County Extension Agent before making a selection.

Check the seed package expiration dates. **Companies** usually change the seed seasonally, but in some cases old seed may stay on a rack. The date is your guarantee that the seed is fresh and viable. In addition, some seeds such as onion are short-lived and need to be planted as soon as possible.

Buying from seed catalogs. Order with caution from regional companies in distant states. The varieties they offer may not fit your area. The real value of a catalog is that a particular company often offers varieties available from no other source.

All catalogs feature new introductions each year. These are worth considering because each year seedsmen try to offer the best varieties possible. Catalog copywriters usually point out the varieties they feel have special qualities or that grow particularly well. Most seedsmen also offer novelties and catalog specialties.

Catalogs explain whether a variety is a hybrid with the words *hybrid* or *F₁ hybrid*—hybrids are a cross between two parents of different types, each with their own particular qualities. All American Selections (see page 92) are noted by the letters AAS. Catalogs also note which varieties are disease-resistant. (One of the best ways to eliminate any disease problem is to grow only disease-resistant vegetable varieties.)

Finally, always check the number of days to maturity (listed in the catalog). Order "early-to-harvest" varieties where summers are short, as in the northern states. In areas of hot and long summers you can stretch the season by planting both early- and late-maturing varieties.

Vegetable temperature requirements

Vegetables are basically divided into warm-season and cool-season crops.

Warm-season plants are those harvested for fruit, such as tomatoes, peppers, eggplant, beans, melons, and pumpkins. They need quite a bit of heat and fairly long days. Generally the average daytime temperature must rise over 65° for any of these plants to do well.

Cool-season plants do well in cool weather—generally between 45° and 65°. (But be careful, because frost will do them in.) These are the leafy and root vegetables such as beets, carrots, cabbage, spinach, lettuce, and broccoli. Peas are also a cool-season plant, even if the fruit is harvested. During the cool days these plants expend all their energy forming leafy and root materials. When the days warm up (usually much over 65°), they put their energy into producing seed. With such plants as lettuce and spinach this can be disastrous.

Thus, in planning a garden you must watch the heat requirements of the particular plants to know when to plant in your area. You can estimate this by using the frost map and charts in the U.S. Department of Agriculture booklet, *Growing Vegetables in the Home Garden,* sold for $1.75 by the Superintendent of Documents, U.S. Government Printing Office, Washington, D.C. 20402. However, there may be different microclimates within each region, depending on elevation, winds, etc. Thus, geographical points only a few miles apart may vary as to the date of the last killing frost by as much as 10 to 15 days. For more precision check your newspaper weather forecasts over a period of time.

The All-America Selections

The All-America Vegetable Selections are becoming more and more important each year. New seeds are tested by an organization that includes a council of judges and some 50 official test gardens across the United States. A great deal of time and effort is expended by these judges and the people who work in the test gardens in order to evaluate the new vegetable and flower varieties introduced by seed companies, state universities, and federal plant breeders in the U.S. and abroad. (Private individuals occasionally enter and win, too!)

Trial rows of All-America entries are grown side by side with popular varieties. From the 35-70 vegetable entries made each year, only three or four are given enough points to earn All-America medals—bronze, silver, or gold.

These varieties are especially adapted to home gardens. All winners taste good and must be superior vegetables. Judges pay special attention to the climatic adaptation and vigor. Each vegetable is adapted to a wide range of soil and climates.

It takes several years for seed companies to offer these varieties for sale. All-America Selections (AAS) are noted throughout the charts.

Two selections for 1980

Following are quotations from the descriptions of two AAS winners.

Pepper, Ornamental, HOLIDAY TIME, Bronze Medal. Developed by John Scarchuk, Coventry, Connecticut.

GOLD COAST
A New Variety of Okra

Julian C. Miller, Lloyd G. Jones and W. F. Wilson, Jr.

Mature Plant of Gold Coast

- Straight, dark green pod
- Excellent for freezing and local market
- Dwarf plant makes fruit easy to harvest
- Plant resistant to heat
- Fruits over a long period of time

Circular No. 57   June 1959
LOUISIANA STATE UNIVERSITY AND
AGRICULTURAL AND MECHANICAL COLLEGE
AGRICULTURAL EXPERIMENT STATION
Charles W. Upp, Director

Vegetable variety introduction

Plant breeders at the state experiment stations, the U.S. Department of Agriculture, and seed companies are constantly developing new vegetable varieties.

Of the many varieties produced only a few are deemed suitable for release to the public. Many are developed for large-scale commercial users, emphasizing such qualities as uniform size, good shipping qualities, disease resistance. Some varieties are suitable for home vegetable gardens. New vegetables are generally announced to commercial seedsmen by experiment stations with variety releases, as illustrated.

Produced by Pan-American Seed Company, P.O. Box 438, West Chicago, Ill. 60185

Holiday Time is the "baby sister" of the ornamental pepper family. Its tiny, nosegay-shaped plants grow to only 6 to 8 inches tall and 4 to 6 inches in diameter. Upright, tapered fruits like elongated thimbles are clustered in the center, surrounded by a halo of broad dark green leaves.

The edible hot peppers are yellow when young and turn orange and red as they mature. Purple splashes on the fruits add to the explosion of color. Although technically a vegetable, Holiday Time is more colorful than many annual flowers.

Pot plant growers will grow Holiday Time in 4-inch pots for fall and winter holiday sales and spring specials. Allow 14 to 16 weeks crop time in the northern U.S. Sow in the middle of June for 4-inch pots October 1st. No pinching is necessary. If pots are pinched, fruit coloring will be delayed by two to three weeks.

Holiday Time has such a high fruit-to-foliage ratio that the plants do best in protected situations when transplanted to the garden. Shade from the afternoon sun will prevent the exposed fruits from sunburning.

Squash, summer, GOLD RUSH Hybrid, Bronze Medal. Developed and produced by Petoseed Co., Inc., P.O. Box 4206, Saticoy, Cal. 93003

Gold Rush is a unique development in zucchini squash. The straight, uniform shape is typical zucchini. The fruit size, open plant habit, slow seed development, and ease of picking are all zucchini. The taste is zucchini. But the appearance is completely new— bright golden skin contrasting with a rich green stem, so smooth that it appears waxed. The interior is creamy white with excellent texture and zucchini flavor. New Gold Rush squash can be eaten alone or mixed with other summer squashes for colorful dips and cooked dishes.

Gold Rush has distinctive small plants, especially bred for intensive gardening. The deep-green, white-flecked leaves are so deeply "cut" that they resemble outstretched fingers. Sunshine can penetrate to the center of the plant to keep the soil dry and reduce spoiling of squash. All parts of the plants are easy to reach for insect control and for easy harvesting of the bountiful crop.

Gold Rush matures in about 50 days from seeds planted in the garden, and with its hybrid vigor will remain in top production for several weeks.

Occasional fruits of Gold Rush may develop a touch of dark green at the ends, which doesn't affect the flower but can be trimmed off with little loss. Late in the season, aphids may transmit mosaic to the Gold Rush plants, causing green mottled fruit.

Pick Gold Rush at lengths of 4 to 8 inches. Beyond that length, test the skin with your thumbnail and check the interior to see if the larger fruits need peeling or removal of seeds before eating.

ALL-AMERICA AWARD-WINNING VEGETABLE VARIETIES

VARIETY	AWARD	BREEDER OR INTRODUCER
Bean 'Executive'	Bronze	1963 Northrup, King & Co.
Bean 'Goldcrop'	Bronze	1974 USDA
Bean 'Greencrop'	Bronze	1957 A.F. Yeager
Bean 'Improved Commodore'	Bronze	1945 Cornell Seed Co.
Bean 'Puregold Wax'	Bronze	1948 Rogers Brothers Seed Co.
Bean 'Tender Pod'	Bronze	1941 W. Atlee Burpee Co.
Bean 'The Commodore'	Bronze	1938 Zwann & Van der Molen
Bean 'Topcrop'	Gold	1950 Dr. W.J. Zaumeyer
Bush Lima Bean 'Fordhook 242'	Bronze	1945 Dr. R.E. Wester
Beet 'Ruby Queen'	Bronze	1957 Northrup, King & Co.
Broccoli 'Cleopatra' Hybrid	Silver	1964 Dessert Seed Co.
Broccoli 'Green Comet' Hybrid	Gold	1969 Takii & Co., Ltd.
Broccoli 'Premium Crop' Hybrid	Silver	1975 Takii & Co., Ltd.
Broccoli 'Zenith' Hybrid	Bronze	1964 Dr. J.C. Jenkins
Brussels Sprouts 'Jade Cross' Hybrid	Silver	1959 Takii & Co., Ltd.
Cabbage 'Emerald Cross' Hybrid	Silver	1963 Takii & Co., Ltd.
Cabbage 'Harvester Queen' Hybrid	Bronze	1969 T. Sakata & Co.
Cabbage 'O.S. Cross' Hybrid	Bronze	1951 Takii & Co., Ltd.
Cabbage 'Red Head' Hybrid	Bronze	1972 Keystone Seed Co.
Cabbage 'Ruby Ball' Hybrid	Gold	1972 Takii & Co., Ltd.
Cabbage 'Savoy Ace' Hybrid	Gold	1977 Takii & Co., Ltd.
Cabbage 'Savoy Chieftan'	Silver	1938 Ferry-Morse Seed Co.
Cabbage 'Savoy King' Hybrid	Silver	1965 T. Sakata & Co.
Cabbage 'Stonehead' Hybrid	Silver	1969 T. Sakata & Co.
Cantaloupe 'Honey Rock'	Gold	1933 J.C. Robinson Seed Co.
Cantaloupe 'Samson' Hybrid	Silver	1965 Dessert Seed Co.
Carrot 'Gold Pak'	Bronze	1956 Ferry-Morse Seed Co.
Cauliflower 'Snow Crown' Hybrid	Silver	1975 Takii & Co., Ltd.
Cauliflower 'Snow King' Hybrid	Bronze	1969 Takii & Co., Ltd.
Corn 'Early Xtra Sweet' Hybrid	Bronze	1971 Illinois Foundation Seeds
Corn 'Golden Beauty' Hybrid	Silver	1955 University of Mass.
Corn 'Iochief' Hybrid	Gold	1951 Iowa State College
Cucumber 'Liberty' Hybrid	Bronze	1978 North Carolina State University
Cucumber 'Marketer'	Bronze	1943 Asgrow Seed Co.
Cucumber 'Saladin' Hybrid	Bronze	1979 Sluis and Groot
Cucumber 'Spartan Valor' Hybrid	Bronze	1968 Dessert Seed Co.
Cucumber 'Straight-8'	Gold	1935 Ferry-Morse Seed Co.
Cucumber 'Triumph' Hybrid	Bronze	1965 Petoseed Co., Inc.
Cucumber 'Victory' Hybrid	Bronze	1972 Petoseed Co., Inc.
Kohlrabi 'Grand Duke'	Silver	1979 Takii & Co., Ltd.
Lettuce 'Buttercrunch'	Silver	1963 Cornell University
Lettuce 'Butterking'	Bronze	1966 Canada & USDA
Lettuce 'Great Lakes'	Bronze	1944 Michigan Ag. Exp. Station
Lettuce 'Premier Great Lakes'	Bronze	1949 Pieters-Wheeler Seeds
Lettuce 'Ruby'	Bronze	1958 USDA
Lettuce 'Salad Bowl'	Gold	1952 USDA
Mustard 'Green Wave'	Bronze	1957 Sluis & Groot
Okra 'Clemson Spineless'	Silver	1939 S. Carolina Exp. Station
Parsley 'Evergreen' Double Curled	Honorable Mention	1940 Ferry-Morse Seed Co.
Parsley 'Paramount'	Silver	1936 Ferry-Morse Seed Co.
Pea 'Freezonian'	Bronze	1948 Rogers Brothers Seed Co.
Pea 'Victory Freezer'	Bronze	1948 Rogers Brothers Seed Co.
Pea, Edible Podded 'Sugar Snap'	Gold	1979 Gallatin Valley Seed Co.
Pepper 'Bell Boy' Hybrid	Bronze	1967 Petoseed Co., Inc.
Pepper 'Dutch Treat'	Bronze	1979 Sluis & Groot
Pepper 'Early Pimento'	Bronze	1943 W. Atlee Burpee Co.
Pepper 'Fordhook'	Bronze	1940 W. Atlee Burpee Co.
Pepper 'Sweet Banana'	Bronze	1941 Cornell Seed Co.
Pumpkin 'Spirit' Hybrid	Bronze	1977 Petoseed Co., Inc.
Radish 'Champion'	Bronze	1957 A.R. Zwaan & Son
Radish 'Cherry Belle'	Bronze	1949 A.R. Zwaan & Son
Radish 'Comet'	Silver	1936 Zwaan & Van der Molen
Spinach 'America'	Silver	1952 Sluis & Groot
Spinach 'Melody' Hybrid	Silver	1977 Royal Sluis
Squash 'Aristocrat Zucchini' Hybrid	Bronze	1973 Petoseed Co., Inc.
Squash, Bush Acorn, 'Table King'	Silver	1974 University of Connecticut
Squash 'Caserta'	Gold	1949 F.H. Woodruff & Sons
Squash 'Chefini' Hybrid	Bronze	1965 Petoseed Co., Inc.
Squash 'Early Butternut' Hybrid	Bronze	1979 Petoseed Co., Inc.
Squash 'Early Prolif. Straightneck'	Silver	1938 Ferry-Morse Seed Co.
Squash 'Fordhook Zucchini'	Bronze	1942 W. Atlee Burpee Co.
Squash 'Gold Nugget' Hybrid	Silver	1966 N. Dakota State University
Squash 'Greyzini Zucchini' Hybrid	Bronze	1963 Petoseed Co., Inc.
Squash 'Hercules Butternut' Hybrid	Silver	1963 Dessert Seed Co.
Squash 'Kindred' Hybrid	Bronze	1969 Northrup, King & Co.
Squash 'St. Pat Scallop' Hybrid	Bronze	1969 Dessert Seed Co.
Squash 'Scallopini' Hybrid	Bronze	1977 Petoseed Co., Inc.
Squash 'Sweet Mama' Hybrid	Bronze	1979 Takii & Co., Ltd.
Squash 'Waltham Butternut'	Bronze	1970 University of Mass.
Tomato 'Floramerica' Hybrid	Bronze	1978 University of Florida
Tomato 'Jubilee'	Bronze	1943 W. Atlee Burpee Co.
Tomato 'Pritchard'	Gold	1933 USDA
Tomato 'Spring Giant' Hybrid	Bronze	1967 Dessert Seed Co.

ALL-AMERICA AWARD-WINNING VEGETABLE VARIETIES
(Continued)

VARIETY	AWARD	BREEDER OR INTRODUCER
Tomato 'Small Fry' Hybrid	Silver	1970 Petoseed Co., Inc.
Turnip 'Tokyo Cross' Hybrid	Bronze	1969 Takii & Co., Ltd.
Turnip 'Just Right'	Silver	1960 Takii & Co., Ltd.
Watermelon 'Congo'	Bronze	1950 Drs. C.F. Poole & C.F. Andrus
Watermelon 'New Hampshire Midget'	Gold	1951 University of New Hampshire
Watermelon 'Sweet Favorite' Hybrid	Bronze	1978 T. Sakata & Co.
Watermelon 'Yellow Baby' Hybrid	Bronze	1975 Known-You Nursery & Seed Production Co., Ltd.

Midget vegetables

Over the last few years a number of vegetables have been developed that are as small as a fifth the size of the regular varieties. These midget vegetables mature earlier—generally 10 to 15 days earlier than the larger vegetables. Mini-cantaloupe, for instance, mature in 60 days compared to 90 days for larger varieties. This allows them to be picked sooner, and in some cases it is even possible to harvest a double crop during the regular season.

Of course, if you are looking for quantity, you'll have to grow twice or three times as many of these midget vegetables to obtain the same production that you would get from regular-size plants.

You can grow many of the midget vegetables both indoors and outdoors. Even corn can be grown behind a window when it gets to be only 3-4 feet high at the most.

In addition some of the midget vegetables are well suited to intensive gardening in flower beds and fit well in small outdoor spaces.

In the charts beginning on page 96, each vegetable category has a special list of the midget varieties, with short description and source. You will find midget cabbage, cucumbers, carrots, corn, eggplant, melons, tomatoes, and more. Of special interest are *Dwarf Morden Cabbage, Little Finger Carrot, Golden Midget Corn, Tiny Dill Cuke,* and *New Hampshire Watermelon.*

Oriental vegetables

Oriental vegetables are becoming more and more popular with American cooks and gardeners. Some of these vegetables have been around a long time and are listed in the regular seed catalogs. There are, however, two firms that specialize in Oriental vegetables:

Tsang and Ma International
15556 Laruel Street
San Carlos, Cal. 94070

Kitazawa Seed Co.
356 Taylor Street
San Jose, Cal. 95110

All vegetables have about the same growth cycle and pattern whether they are Oriental or Western varieties. One simple rule to follow is to grow leafy vegetables (such as Chinese cabbage and greens) in cool weather and to grow vegetables that bear mature fruits (melon-like gourds, eggplant, beans) in the hot summer.

Soak the seeds in water a few hours before sowing. This will expand them slightly and ensure that they are properly moistened. Always keep the soil moist but not soaked. To ensure maximum flavor, harvest your vegetables as soon as they are ready. Never let them become overmature or go to seed.

Some of the more important Oriental vegetables are described in the following section. Other Oriental varieties are included in the vegetable variety charts. The sources refer to the list on pages 241-243.

Asparagus bean (yard-long bean) *Dow Gauk*

Dow Gauk is a stringless, long green bean. It is mildly sweet without the strong green taste. The tender stem tips and leaves are delicious.

Plant seeds when the weather warms up—about ¾ inch deep, 5 seeds per foot. Space rows 5 feet apart. Seeds germinate in 9-10 days. When seedlings are 3 inches tall, thin to 6 inches apart. Harvest when the beans are 2-3 feet long. *Seed sources:* 16, 19, 22, 26, 27, 28, 36, 42, 43, 53, 62, 69, 73.

Burdock *(Gobo)*

This Japanese specialty is used in many Oriental dishes. The plant grows as a weed in many areas. It has long stalks, broad leaves, and sharp burrs. The root is edible—scrape, scald, and boil it.

Plant burdock seeds ¼ inch deep in a light-medium soil in a sunny location, 2-3 inches apart in 12-inch rows. Keep the soil that is in contact with the seeds moist during the entire germination period. *Seed source:* 50

Chinese cabbage

Chinese cabbage is an Oriental relative of regular cabbage. The Chinese cabbage most people think of has rather elongated, compact heads that resemble a bunch of tight celery with the leaves removed. Actually there are two basic types—heading (celery cabbage) and nonheading (mustard cabbage).

There are also two celery cabbage types—a tall and lean one, best exemplified by the variety *Michilli,* and the short, squat *Won Bok* type.

The nonheading types greatly resembles Swiss Chard (without the heavy stalks). Again you have a choice of two types—White Mustard Cabbage, *Pak Choy,* or

Green Mustard Cabbage, *Kai Choy*. There are many cultivated varieties of the Oriental mustards. The leaf size, color, and flavor varies. (See Mustards, below, for sources and also the charts on page 173 .

The heading Chinese cabbage has a delicate tartness and a celery crunch when cooked. The nonheading type is frequently found mixed in Chinese dishes in restaurants.

Plant seeds of the heading types about ¾ inch deep, 6 seeds per foot. Space rows 2 feet apart. Seeds germinate in 7-10 days. Plant seeds of the nonheading types 20 seeds per foot. Space rows 1 foot to 18 inches apart. Seeds germinate in 8-12 days.

Chinese celery (*Hueng Kunn*)

This celery is smaller and more delicate than the Western varieties. It is fragrant, aromatic, and delicious.

Plant seeds about ⅛ inch deep, 15 seeds per foot. Space rows 1 foot apart. Seeds germinate in 8-12 days. When the seedlings are 2 inches tall, thin to 4 inches apart. *Seed Source:* 69

Chinese chive (*Gow Choy*)

Gow Choy has a mild garlic flavor with a touch of onion taste. It has light-green, almost flat, awl-shaped leaves at maturity. You can make your first cuttings in about 4-5 months.

Plant seeds in spring in rich, moist potting soil. Plant seeds about ⅛ inch deep, 1 inch apart. Seeds germinate in 12-18 days. Thin when 3 inches tall. *Seed Sources:* 68, 69

Cucumbers

There are many varieties of Oriental cucumbers, all extra long.

Armenian Yard Long has distinctive long, curved fruits that often reach 2-3 feet in length. The vines are rampant growers and produce an enormous crop. *Seed Sources:* 16, 42, 50, 51, 57, 58.

China Long (Kyoto) is an extra-long, curved, light-green cucumber that grows 12-15 inches long. The vines are large and vigorous. *Seed Sources:* 12, 16, 26, 27, 29, 50, 66, 68

Japanese Long Pickling grows 12-18 inches long and 1½ inches in diameter. *Seed Source:* 66

Nagaoka Homogreen Hybrid is semiforcing, with fruit 8-9 inches long. *Seed Source:* 42

Sanjiaku Kiuri is a light green cucumber, 1½-2 feet long. *Seed Source:* 42

Serpent Cucumber produces long, slim fruits that sometimes reach a length of 4 feet and coil into realistic snakelike shapes. The taste is mild since it doesn't actually belong to the cucumber family. *Seed Source:* 9

Sooyow is an early, dark-green, highly spined and ribbed fruit 10-12 inches long. *Seed Source:* 42

Yamato (extra long Japanese) grows 18-24 inches long, is dark green in color, and has a smooth skin. This is a warm-weather plant. Plant seed 1 inch deep, 12 inches apart, in rows 48-72 inches apart.

Eggplant (Oriental or Japanese Long Eggplant)

The fruit of the Oriental eggplant is long and narrow and is harvested at about two-thirds of maximum size. They are usually steamed or cooked in mixed vegetable dishes.

Hybrid Millionaire is a late, long type with 10-inch fruits. *Seed source:* 42.

Hybrid Nagaoka (New Kissin) has 4-inch-long, 2½-inch-diameter, extra-early, dark-purple fruit. *Seed sources:* 16, 42, 50, 51, 57, 58.

Hybrid Nagaoka is a long, black, early eggplant that has 8-9-inch-long fruits, 2-2½ inches in diameter. *Seed source:* 42.

Chinese Long is a late variety that has long, purple fruit. Start seeds indoors about 10 weeks before you intend to plant outside. Eggplant is a warm-weather plant. When the plants are about 6 inches high, transfer outside 2 feet apart in rows 3 feet apart. *Seed source:* 36.

Oriental Greens

Aka Shiso has dark purple-red leaves with a strong aroma. It is used for garnishing, seasoning, and the coloring of pickled vegetables. *Seed source:* 42.

Ao Shiso is similar to Aka Shiso, but has green leaves. *Seed source:* 42.

Chinese Parsley (Coriandrum sativum), *Yuen Sai*, is known as the culinary herb coriander. It has a delicious fragrance. The young seedlings are harvested at the 6-8 leaf stage. *Seed source:* 69.

Chinese Spinach (Amarantus gangeticus), *Hinn Choy*, is not a spinach, but a vegetable green from China. The small, light, fuzzy, paddle-shaped leaves are slightly sweet. *Seed Source:* 69.

Chop Suey Green, Shingiku, a dark-green, aromatic, edible, leaf chrysanthemum. The large, tender leaves are used in cooking. Harvest when the plant is 4-5 inches tall. *Seed source:* 42.

Japanese Parsley, Mitsuba, aromatic greens with long, white stems and light-green leaves, are used in salads and some other dishes. *Plant* seeds about ¼ inch deep, 10-20 seeds per foot. Thin to 2-4 inches apart. *Seed source:* 42.

Kale

Chinese Kale (Brassica alboglabra), *Gai Lohn,* is broccolilike rather than kalelike. It has dark green leaves and stalks.

Plant seeds ½ inch deep, 10 seeds per foot. Thin when seedlings are 2 inches tall. *Seed source:* 69.

Mustard

(Many catalogs list mustard cabbage as mustard.)

Hakarashina has radish-shaped, dark-green, pungent leaves. *Seed source:* 42.

Mizuna (Kyona) has numerous narrow, slender stems with deeply indented, feathery leaves. The plant is resistant to cold. *Seed source:* 42.

Mustard Spinach (Komatsuna) is a quick-growing, tender, dark-green plant with glossy leaves that is often used in salads. *Plant* seeds ¼ inch deep, 10-15 seeds per row. Thin when seedlings are 6 in. apart. *Seed source:* 42.

Melon

(These are often gourds or squash.)

Aouri is 10-12 inches long, 4-4½ inches in diameter, with dark-green flesh and thick, white flesh. *Seed source:* 42.

Bitter Melon (Momordica charantia var chinensis), *Foo Gwa,* are heavily warted, long, dark green fruits. The bitter melon is not a melon but is more squashlike. The flavor is tangy. *Seed sources:* 42, 69.

Chinese Fuzzy Gourd, Mao Gwa, is a sweet, succulent, squashlike vegetable gourd. *Seed source:* 69.

Chinese Winter Melon, Doan Gwa, is a squash and belongs to the vegetable gourd family. It has white, succulent, tender flesh and grows on a vine like a pumpkin. *Seed source:* 69.

Japanese Pickling Melon, Oshiro Uri, has long, oval-shaped, light-green fruits that turn white at maturity. *Seed source:* 42.

Onion

Japanese Onion, Nebuka, grows thick with pure-white, blanched stems.

Plant seed ½ inch deep, 2-3 inches apart, in rows 12-24 inches apart. *Seed source:* 42.

Okra

Chinese Okra (Luffa acutangula), *Cee Gwa,* is not actually okra but a vegetable gourd. It is sweet, with tender flesh and crisp skin.

Plant seeds 1 inch deep, 3 inches apart, in rows 3 feet apart. Thin to 6 inches apart. *Seed source:* 69.

Pumpkin

Japanese Pumpkin is a flat, globe-shaped, ribbed, heavily warted fruit. It has a dark-green rind that turns to buff orange when fully mature. *Seed source:* 42.

Radish

Minowase is an early-type Oriental radish with a 1½-foot-long, pure-white, tender root. *Seed source:* 42.

Miyashige is a winter type with a 12-15-inch-long white root. It is crisp and mild. *Seed source:* 42.

Nerima is a winter-type radish with a 2-2½-inch-long white root that tapers at both ends. *Riso* is a winter type radish similar to *nerima. Seed source:* 42.

Sakurajima is a large, globe-shaped radish that sometimes reaches a weight of 30 lbs. or more. *Seed sources:* 36, 42, 50, 67.

Shogoin is a winter-type, globe-shaped radish that looks much like a turnip. *Seed sources:* 42, 50.

Tokinashi (All Seasons) is a late, slow-bolting type with a 1½-2-foot-long tapering root. *Plant* for a fall harvest. Plant seeds ½ inch deep, 3-5 inches apart, in rows 1 foot apart. *Seed source:* 42.

Sugar Peas

Sugar peas are used in many Oriental dishes: see the pea section under standard vegetables for varieties.

Turnip

Tokyo Market is a small, semi-globe-shaped, pure-white turnip. It is tender and has sweet flesh.

Plant seeds ½ inch deep, 1-3 inches apart, in rows 15-18 inches apart. *Seed sources:* 29, 31, 37, 42, 48, 50.

Gourmet vegetables

The exquisite taste of really fine food often comes from the vegetable world. Gourmet cooks know that the vegetable garden is a wonderful source of flavor, texture, and color. Often there is nothing that spices up a dish like a touch of chives or fresh basil . . . or cress in a salad.

The following gourmet vegetables (in addition to the Oriental vegetables) are included in the charts in this chapter.

Cardoon	Horseradish
Celeriac	Jerusalem artichoke
Celtuce	Leeks
Chicory-Endive-Escarole	Salsify
Corn Salad	Shallots
Cress	Spinach
Dandelion	Malabar
Florence Fennel	New Zealand

Novelties and show-offs

There are many vegetables with unusual shapes, sizes, and colors that are fun to grow in any garden, or by themselves in a container. Rainbow corn, for instance, has large ears with red, yellow, orange, and blue kernels that make attractive dried decorations: lemon cucumber, the size and color of a large lemon, is a real conversation piece; banana melons and 15-pound sakurajima radishes and other unusual vegetables are all garden show-offs. You'll find these and many more in the variety charts.

French varieties

French vegetable varieties are now quite popular in the United States. There are two companies which specialize in these varieties:

J. A. Demonchax
225 Jackson
Topeka, Kan. 66603

Le Jardin du Gourmet
West Danville, Vt. 05873

You can also obtain a large French garden catalog for $1.00 by writing:

Vilmorin in-Andrieus
Division Commerce International
49750 La Menitre, France

Choosing vegetables for your garden

This section catalogs the wide variety of choices available for each vegetable. With corn, for instance, you can grow a large-eared white variety or one with a small strawberry-shaped ear—and several hundred types in between. With some vegetables there are over 500 listed varieties.

This sourcebook has utilized a large number of catalogs to obtain the greatest number of varieties possible. In some cases seedsmen use different names for the same variety. In other cases, particular varieties may not be available from catalog sources. If these varieties interest you, inquire at local nurseries as to their availability.

Each variety listed in this section is followed by a series of numbers. These numbers are keyed to the suppliers listed on pages 141-143. Many of these catalogs contain a tremendous amount of information on gardening and particular vegetable varieties.

Each catalog has its own personality. Some of them, such as Burgess Seed and Plant Company, offer many unusual vegetables. W. Atlee Burpee Co. probably has the most complete catalog available, while Johnny's selected seeds has many unusual, hard-to-find seeds. R. H. Shumway Seedsman publishes a catalog with an "old-time" format that is great fun to look at and read.

Artichokes (Cynara scolymus)

Artichokes are bold, showy, silver-green perennial plants that really show off in a small garden or in a flower bed. This thistlelike vegetable can grow to a height of about 4 feet and spread as wide as 6 feet. The flower buds ripen into large thistle blossoms that can be used in dried arrangements. Once an artichoke plant has become productive, it will remain vigorous and productive for five to six years.

Harvesting: Initial harvest is the spring following the first planting. Cut the unripened flower heads before the bracts start to separate. Both the terminal buds and those on the side shoots are delicious.

HOW TO PLANT: Home gardeners will often find it better to buy root divisions from a local nursery. Early spring is the best time to plant. Place the division in a rich soil with the old wood stalk in a vertical position and the base of the new leafy shoot just above the ground. Space 3-4 feet apart, and leave 4-5 feet between rows.

Artichokes require the cool days of spring to produce an edible crop. Generally artichokes need a sunny location, but in hot-summer areas they do better in half-shade since early-summer heat causes the buds to open rapidly and become tough.

Where winters are severe, you can plant artichokes in large tubs or boxes and wheel them inside during the winter. In mild-winter areas cut the top back to 10-12 inches, tie the leaves over the root crown, and mulch.

You can also grow artichokes from seed. Sow seed indoors in peat pots four to six weeks before you intend to set them outside (when there is no danger of heavy frost).

ARTICHOKE

VARIETY	HEADS	REMARKS	SOURCES
Early Green Provence	Small, long heads	Early variety . . . narrow green scales	36
Green Globe	Large flower heads	Edible flower buds made up of thick fleshy scales and solid centers . . . best harvested when young . . . not reliably hardy . . . 4-foot plants with 6-foot spread	6 10 12 16 22 26 28 30 31 32 43 53 56 62 72
Grande Beurre	Large fleshy heads		68

Asparagus (Asparagus officinalis)

Asparagus is one of the most permanent, dependable, and earliest of all home garden vegetables. It is a perennial, cool-season crop that produces from March until June, well ahead of other vegetables. It can be planted almost anywhere in your garden or yard. Besides being a delicious food, it is as decorative as any ornamental. The only problem with asparagus is that it takes three years for it to come into full production. Generally, however, it is well worth waiting for. And once established, it will keep producing for up to 20 years.

Most asparagus strains grown in the United States today are selections from the *Martha* and *Mary Washington* strains developed in the early 1900s by the U.S. Department of Agriculture. All presently available asparagus strains produce plants with variable vigor, size, and disease resistance, but plant breeders are now in the process of developing more uniform plants.

The most popular strains among home gardeners are *Mary Washington* and *Waltham Washington*. The *Viking* strain is often suggested for gardeners in the northern United States, *U.C. 157* for the West Coast and California, and *Waltham Washington* for the midwest. Local selections of the Washington types are also available.

HOW TO PLANT: Starting with seed in the early spring, soak the seed in water for two days. Plant seeds a half-inch deep in rows 2 feet wide; thin seedlings to 3-4 inches between plants. Grow these seedlings a season, and the following year transplant to a permanent asparagus bed. Starting from crowns, buy year-old plants (or crowns) from seedsmen in the early spring. This will save a full year.

Dig a trench 1 foot wide and 8-10 inches deep, to any length that you like. Work from 2-6 inches of steer manure into about 6 inches of soil at the bottom of the trench. Space the crowns about 12 inches apart and cover with 2 inches of loose, fine soil.

Harvesting: As the young plants grow, fill in the trench little by little. Don't harvest any spears the first year. When the foliage turns brown in the late fall, cut the stems to the ground. The second year you can harvest the 6- to 8-inch-high spears for four weeks. Cut the spears at ground level or a few inches below the soil, but never closer than 2 inches to the crowns. In the early spring cultivate the bed and feed with a complete fertilizer. The third year you can cut spears for a full season (about six weeks).

ASPARAGUS

VARIETY	STALKS	REMARKS	SOURCES
Asparagus Paradise		Produces more per acre and a year earlier when started from seed	14 19 23 53 58
Argenteuil Early	Green with purple tips		15 44
Brock Imperial (hybrid)	Dark-green, plump, large, fiber-free	Moderately rust-resistant	16 28 32 53
California 500	Fine green; tight; almost free of purple tips	Particularly adapted to West Coast	16 22 23 51
California 711			23
Faribo Hybrid		Superior first-generation hybrid . . . produces heavier, bigger stalks	21
Giant Washington	Thick, green stalks grow large in size, yet remain crisp and tender	Can be eaten raw	38
Lakeland's Tender Asparagus	Long, straight stalks	Thrives in any U.S. area and in any type of soil	43
Limburgian Hybrid	Very tight heads		72
Mary Washington	Medium green with purplish tinge.	Produces plenty of spears . . . rust-resistant	3 10 12 14 16 18 19 21 22 23 25 28 29 30 31 32 34 45 46 47 48 51 52 53 55 57 58 62 67 72 73
Mary Washington Giant		Rustproof	52
Mary Washington Roberts Strain		Heavy yields	7 19
Mary Washington 500	Green stalks without purple overcast	Earlier, larger, more uniform strain of Mary Washington	11 48
New Roberts	Produces jumbo-size stalks	Excellent for home gardens . . . tender . . . good fresh or frozen	28
Regal Pedigree	Double the normal thickness		68

ASPARAGUS (Continued)

VARIETY	STALKS	REMARKS	SOURCES
Viking (Mary Washington Improved)	Heavy-green, thick stalks	Rust-resistant . . . excellent freezer	66 72
Waltham Washington	Dark-green, slight purple tinge	Top quality, with more shoots . . . excellent flavor	22 23 28 60
Xtra Tender (Green Candaigana)	Tender, fernlike tops and jumbo-size spears	Rust-resistant . . . easy to freeze or can	35

Beans (Phaseolus sp)

Beans are literally small food factories that give you your money's worth in your garden. They are rapid growers, give tremendous yields, and require little attention. When you start trying to make a selection, you'll find there are beans, beans, and more beans.

Snap beans (Phaseolus vulgaris) come in tall-growing (pole beans) and low-growing (bush snap beans) varieties. Both pole and bush beans vary in their color, type of growth, days to maturity, seed color, resistance to disease, and similar qualities.

Pole beans: Many garden gourmets say that the flavor is better in pole beans than in bush beans and that young pole beans are absolutely delicious.

Among green pole beans, *Kentucky Wonder* (Old Homestead) is a meaty, tender old favorite that produces brown seeds. *Blue Lake* has tender, dark-green, oval pods. *McCaslan* is thick, flat, and medium-green, has white seeds, and is used as a shelling bean as well as a snap bean. *Rattlesnake* has dark-green pods with purple streaks.

Yellow wax snap beans have buttery yellow pods. *Burpee Golden* has wide, flat yellow pods, and *Kentucky Wonder Wax* produces long, brittle, meaty, light-yellow pods.

Purple: These delicious pole beans grow purple, then turn green when cooked.

Romano (Italian Broad Bean) is a wide, flat bean that is a perennial favorite. Gourmet cooks swear by this bean.

Scarlet Runner Bean (*Phaseolus cocineus*) grows wild at high altitudes in Guatemala. Generally it is grown in the United States as a scarlet-flowered ornamental bean, but the pods are quite edible.

Bush snap beans: These beans produce 18- to 22-inch-high compact plants. They can be grown successfully in fairly short summer areas since they need only six to seven weeks to reach maturity. In general, the breeders of bush beans have concentrated on mechanical harvesting characteristics rather than flavor. There are also yellow wax, purple, and Romano varieties of bush beans, in addition to the green varieties.

Lima beans (Phaseolus lunatus). There are two types —pole, or climbing, and bush. Both pole and bush forms have plump-seeded (potata lima) varieties and small-seeded (baby lima) varieties.

The most popular plump-seeded pole lima, *King of the Garden,* has vines that grow to 8 feet or more. *Christmas Pole Lima* produces heavy crops from mid-season to frost. *Carolina* (a baby lima) has small pods that produce three to four small white seeds.

Of the bush limas *Fordhook 242* is a popular plump-seeded heavy yielder that will set pods under adverse conditions. *Henderson Bush Lima* is a very popular buttery baby lima.

Soybeans (Glycine soja) have been popular in China, Manchuria, Korea, and Japan since ancient times but have only been recognized as a home garden vegetable in the United States since the 1940s. There are a number of varieties: *Green Giant,* with large green pods, grows well in northern gardens. *Kanrich,* which is low in starch, produces a heavy yield on 24-inch bushes. *Panther* has black soybeans.

HOW TO PLANT:

Snap pole beans: 1½-2 inches deep, 4-6 inches apart in rows 36-48 inches apart.

Snap bush beans: 1½-2 inches deep, 4-6 inches apart in rows 18-30 inches apart.

Lima pole beans: 1½-2 inches deep, 6-10 inches apart in rows 30-36 inches apart.

Lima bush beans: 1½-2 inches deep, 6-10 inches apart in rows 24-30 inches apart.

Soybeans: 1½-2 inches deep, 2-3 inches apart in rows 24-30 inches apart.

Garbanzo: 1½-2 inches deep, 3-4 inches apart in rows 24-30 inches apart.

Fava beans: 2½ inches deep, 3-4 inches apart in rows 24-30 inches apart.

Plant snap, lima, and soybeans after the soil warms up in the spring. Lima beans require warmer soil conditions for germination and a longer growing season than snap beans. Fava beans grow well in cool weather. In mild-winter areas plant in the fall for a spring crop.

Fava bean—Broad beans, horsebeans, Windsor beans *(Vicia faba)*—is not a true bean but is related to vetch. Favas grow well in cool areas; shelled, the pods yield five to seven large beans each. *Long Podded Fava,* used as a substitute for lima beans in the north, produces flat, oblong beans in 7-inch pots . . . *Seville Long Pod* is an early, large beaned variety.

Other varieties: **Mung beans** are generally grown for sprouts but can be grown for the pods as well. Mung beans produce 3-inch curving pods that contain round white beans. **Horticultural beans** are large-seeded beans used in the green shell stage. The fiber is too tough for them to be cooked as snap beans. **Shell beans** are old favorites—kidney, navy, pinto, and others. Good cooks use them extensively.

Garbanzo—chick-pea, chestnut bean *(Cicer arietinum)* —is neither a pea or a bean. It produces one or two seeds in puffy little pods on bushlike plants. Garbanzo beans have a chestnutlike flavor.

Harvesting: Pick snap beans when the pods are fairly small—the flavor is better then. Keeping the plants picked helps extend the season.

Pick the pods of lima beans as soon as they begin to look a little lumpy and before they begin to turn yellow.

SNAP POLE BEANS

VARIETY	DAYS	POD SHAPE/COLOR	REMARKS	SOURCES
Blue Lake (White-seeded) (White creaseback)	55-66	Oval, 5½-6" long, dark-green pod	Has small white seeds . . . stringless . . . good fresh, for canning and freezing	10 16 22 29 30 31 32 34 38 49 50 51 52 53 55 56 57 58 62 66 67 71 73
Challenge	65	Long	Heavy cropping . . . red flowers	68
Champagne	62		White-seeded . . . grows 10 or more feet high . . . high quality	37
Dade	55	7-8" flat oval pods	Pure white seeds . . . stringless . . . famous in the South . . . resistant to rust and common southern bean mosaic	40 41 51 71
Genuine Cornfield	81	6-7" round, medium green pods	Seeds are buff with brown stripes . . . a good freezer, canner	31 51 71
Genuine White Half Runner	60		Good freezer . . . 3-foot runners	53
Green Isle Bean		6-8" pods	Heavy yields of white-seeded beans . . . good freezer, canner	21
GreenPak	60	5½-6" dark green	White-seeded . . . resistant to bean mosaic and New York 15 strain	70
Green Perfection	58	6"-long, round green pods	Early heavy yielder . . . resistant to common bean mosaic . . . good freezer, canner	70
Hastings White Cornfield	90		Vines are prolific, producing white-seeded beans that are tender and of high flavor	31
Kentucky North	64		Brown-seeded . . . distinctive flavor and texture	37
Kentucky White Wonder 191	60-68	6 x ½" thick, oval, silvery-green	Long, flat, white seeds . . . used as dry shell or snap bean . . . fair climber . . . grows 60-78" tall, medium-green plant	51 56 60 62 71
Kentucky Wonder (Old Homestead)	58-74	7-9" thick, oval, silvery-green	Produces brown seeds . . . meaty, tender, and stringless . . . good freezer	10 11 12 14 16 22 25 28 29 30 31 32 34 36 37 39 40 45 47 49 50 51 52 53 55 56 57 58 59 62 66 67 70 71 72 73
Kentucky Wonder (Rust-Resistant)	66	6-7" flat, oval, dark-green	White seeds . . . stringless . . . high quality when young . . . good for baking	10 11 14
McCaslan	65-66	7½" thick, flat, medium-green	White seeds . . . southern favorite . . . stringless . . . shelling as well as snap	31 40 41 51 62 67 71
Missouri Wonder	65	Long, medium-green	Seeds are mottled tan, brown striped . . . good for planting around corn	62 71
Morse's Pole 191	63	8-9" straight, oval, dark-green	White seeds, high yields	41
Oregon Giant Paul Bunyan Bean	63-68	Giant pod a foot long	Prolific climber	50 71

SNAP POLE BEANS (Continued)

VARIETY	DAYS	POD SHAPE/COLOR	REMARKS	SOURCES
Promo		Medium-large, dark-green	Stringless and white-seeded . . . early variety	72
Rattlesnake		7" long, round	Dark-green with purple streaks . . . good for home gardens	40 51
Romano (Italian Pole)	64-70	5½" wide, flat	Good for freezing, canning	10 12 14 16 22 29 30 32 39 49 50 51 52 55 57 60 62 71 72
Scarlet Runner	65-70	6" flat	Has scarlet-flowered vines that grow 10-12 feet	3 16 29 32 51 52 62 66 71 72
Selma (Zebra)		Light-green, striped with blue	Vines grow to height of 6 feet . . . tender, green, stringless	53
Speckled Cut Short (Corn Hull)		4" long, flat, green	Popular in South . . . good quality . . . fine for small gardens	62
Striped Creaseback (Scotia) (Nancy Davis)	70-72	6" round, light-green, purple-spotted	Old Cornfield . . . not stringless	62 67
Veithes Climbing	60	Very long, narrow, fleshy		69
Yard Long Bean (Asparagus Bean)	70-80	25-40" beans	Vines are vigorous growers, with excellent snap bean quality . . . small red-brown seeds . . . better when picked young	See page 93

POLE BEANS — Yellow and Purple

VARIETY	DAYS	POD SHAPE/COLOR	REMARKS	SOURCES
Burpee Golden	60	5½-6½", stringless	Tender, fiberless, meaty pods	10
Kentucky Wonder Wax Round Pod (Golden Podded Wax)	60-68	7-9" long, slightly curved, brown seeds	Long, brittle, meaty, almost stringless	3 10 22 30 31 38 47 51 52 62 66 71 72
Purple Pod	65	Red-purple stringless	Cooks green . . . meat is thick	22 28 56 72

BUSH BEANS

VARIETY	DAYS	POD SHAPE/COLOR	REMARKS	SOURCES
Apennine		5½" straight, green	Resistant to common bean mosaic and New York 15 . . . sturdy bush bean flavor	40
Astro Round Pod	50-56	Deep-green	Upright, vigorous, good in home gardens . . . resembles Harvester . . . good canner	3 32 41 48 51 57 71
Avalanche	50-57	Straight, light-green	Good for canning, freezing	53 70 71
Best Crop	52	6" medium-green, stringless	Resistant to common bean mosaic . . . good for cooler climates . . . meaty, flavorful	71
Black Valentine	70		Bushy	16 25 50 56 71
Black Valentine Resistant	50	6½" slender, dark-green	Mosaic-resistant	67
Bluecrop	54-57		Low failure rate, high performer . . . good in N.Y., Vt., Wi., Or., . . . white seeds . . . good fresh, frozen, or canned . . . can tolerate heat well	29 70 71
Blue Max	52-56	5½-6" dark-green	White-seeded . . . plants grow 15-17"	51 57
Blue Lake Bush	52-60	5½-6½" plump	White seeds . . . good flavor	3 11 12 16 53 55 58
Blue Lake Bush No. 141	55-59	6" dark, round, meaty	New variety . . . good size and yield . . . delicious fresh or frozen	31 52 56 62 66 67
Blue Lake Bush No. 274	58	5-6" dark-green	Plump, round . . . good fresh, frozen, or canned . . . resistant to bean mosaic, New York 15 virus	10 14 16 28 29 30 32 38 40 41 57 60 62 66 70 71 73
Bountiful Stringless	48-51	6-7" flat, green	All-purpose bean . . . good freezer	3 10 12 16 25 30 32 47 49 51 52 55 56 62 67 70 71
Burpee's Richgreen	56-58	5¼-6" extra-rich, green	Mosaic-resistant . . . color retained when cooked	14
Burpee's Stringless	54			14 16 30 36 47
Burpee's Stringless Green Pod	50	5-6" long, slightly curved, deep-green	Tender, brittle . . . good for canning or freezing	3 10 22 28 36 49 51 52 55 57 59 62 71 72

BUSH BEANS (Continued)

VARIETY	DAYS	POD SHAPE/COLOR	REMARKS	SOURCES
Burpee's Stringless Improved		5-6" dark-green	Resistant to common bean mosaic and New York 15 virus . . . popular with home gardeners	40 58
Burpee's Tenderpod	50	4½-5½" thick, round, curved, tip-green	AA winner . . . brittle, meaty, tender	10 49
Bush Romano	50-66	5-6" very long and flat (Italian type)	18" plants . . . fresh, frozen, or canned	11 16 28 30 34 38 41 50 55 57 60 66 70 71 72
Cascade	54	5-6" medium-long, dark-green	Resistant to common bean mosaic and New York 15 virus . . . good flavor	40 51 71
Catskill		5½-6" round	Resistant to common bean mosaic and New York 15	40
Commodore (New Dwarf Kentucky Wonder)	63	Dark-green, stringless		14 31 53 56 58 62 71
Commodore Improved	58	7½-8" curved (almost round), dark-green	Vigorous medium-sized plant . . . AA winner . . . good for home gardens	11 40 41 45 51 55 57 67 71
Contender	48-55	7" round, oval, medium-green, stringless	Bushy and vigorous . . . mosaic resistant . . . reddish-purple seeds . . . good for all climates	11 12 14 16 19 30 31 32 40 41 46 48 51 52 53 55 56 57 66 67 70 71 72 73
Early Contender	49	6-7" oval, stringless	Resistant to mosaic and powdery mildew . . . vigorous vines, tolerant to heat . . . buff-colored seeds	28
Early Gallatin	53	5-5½" dark-green, round	Resistant to pod mottle and New York 15 virus	40 51 71
Executive	53	5½-6" firm, meaty	AA winner . . . good for home gardens, canning, freezing	11 51 56 60 66 70
Gallatin	50	5-5½" medium-green, round	Tendercrop type . . . resistant to common bean mosaic and New York 15 virus	40
Gardengreen	55	5-5½" straight and round, dark-green	Tremendous yields . . . good fresh, frozen, or canned	28
Gator Green	53	Medium-green, long, slender	Patented	48 70 71
Giant Stringless	53	6½" round, light-green	One of the most productive varieties for home gardens . . . good for canning, freezing	62
Green Crop	51	6½-7½" long, dark-green	AA winner . . . white-seeded . . . brittle	10 16 22 37 40 48 49 51 66 70 71 72
Green Isle			Resistant to most diseases	51 57
Green Ruler	51	Long, very flat	Spreading bush vines . . . rich, beany flavor	29
Greensleeves	56	Round, dark-green	Good freezer	10 45
Harvester	56	5½-6" green, round, straight	White-seeded . . . 24" bushes . . . resistant to common bean mosaic and New York 15 virus . . . good canner	3 11 12 16 32 40 41 47 48 51 56 66 67 71 72 73
Harvest King	54		Used for cut and French style	51 57
Itasca	55	5½" medium-green	White-seeded . . . 18-21" upright bush	51
Lake Erie		4½-5"	Blue Lake type, mid-season . . . good canner, freezer	40
Lake Geneva		5½" long, blue-green	Mid-season . . . resistant to common bean mosaic and New York 15 virus . . . Blue Lake type . . . good canner, freezer	40
Lake Shasta		5-5½" dark-green	Compact, mid-season plant . . . Blue Lake type	40
Lake Superior		5-6" long	Mid-season, Blue Lake type . . . resistant to common bean mosaic and New York 15 virus	40
Lika Lake (new)	56	4" round, dark-green	Seeds develop slowly	49
Limelight	38	thick, fiberless, broad	Very, very early . . . rich sweet flavor	68
Miami		5" medium-green, straight	Resistant to mosaic and New York 15 virus . . . excellent for home gardens	40
Olympia		5-6½" mottled	Resistant to mosaic and New York 15 virus . . . good freezer, canner	40
Oregon	58	6½" dark-green	Flavor and quality of Blue Lake . . . stringless . . . good canner, freezer . . . resistant to Oregon rust	71

BUSH BEANS (Continued)

VARIETY	DAYS	POD SHAPE/COLOR	REMARKS	SOURCES
Pride of Iowa	53		Bushy vines 18" high . . . unaffected by strong winds . . . thick stalks	14
Processor	53-55	Medium-green, oval, round	Recent introduction . . . meaty, fiberless pods that are good for canning, freezing	71
Provider	50-52	5¼-6" round	Purple-seeded . . . heavy early yields . . . resistant to common bean mosaic and powdery mildew	29 37 40 47 48 51 66 67 70 71
Rainier	50	6" dark-green	White-seeded . . . perfect for canning, freezing	71
Rebel		5-5½" bright-green, straight	Resistant to mosaic and New York 15 virus . . . use fresh, good canner	40
Regal	57	6" long, bright-green	18-22" plants that are very productive . . . white-seeded	57
Richgreen	56	5½-6" extra-rich green, round, smooth	Resistant to mosaic . . . color is retained when cooked	10 49
Roma (Italian type)	53-59	4½" wide, thin, flat, green	White-seeded . . . resembles pole Romano . . . needs no support . . . use fresh or frozen	3 10 12 31 47 49 53 60
Slender White	56	5-6" medium-green	Plants are medium height and very productive . . . good freezer	32 71
Slimgreen	60	5-5½" light- to medium-green, round	Similar to Slender White . . . extremely heavy yielder . . . resistant to mosaic	32 40 71
Spartan Arrow	52	5½-6" medium-green, oval, straight	Heavy yields . . . good for home gardens	16 22 29 48 51 53 66
Spring Green	41	4-6" dark-green, round, stringless	18" upright plants . . . matures after Contender . . . tender, excellent for home gardens . . . good canner	66
Sprite Stringless	52	5-6" medium-green, straight	Vigorous, bushy-type plant . . . resistant to mosaic	16 40 51 66 71 72
Stringless Green Pod (Landreth's)	52-54	Round, green	Good canner	12 14 71
Super Market	50	6½" stringless	Bushy vine grows 16-18" high . . . tender, brittle . . . good fresh, canned, frozen . . . highest quality	14
Tendercrop Stringless	52-61	5-5½" straight, long, round	Dark-seeded, good yielder, fine flavor . . . good freezer . . . resistant to pod mottle, mosaic, and New York 15 virus	10 12 16 19 22 29 32 34 40 45 50 51 53 55 60 62 66 71
Tenderette	55	5½-6" long, rich-green, straight	White-seeded . . . stringless, fiberless . . . good fresh, cooked, frozen, or canned	22 28 32 47 48 52 53 62 67
Tendergreen Stringless (Asgrow Stringless)	52-57	6-7" pencil-round, dark-green	Resistant to mosaic . . . meaty, tender . . . good canner	3 12 14 19 22 28 31 36 38 39 45 47 49 52 56 68
Tendergreen Improved	53-56	6-7" long	Seeds are purple-mottled tan . . . extremely meaty . . . AA selection . . . mosaic-resistant	10 11 16 30 41 48 51 53 57 59 60 62 66 71 73
Tennessee Green Pod	54	6-8" flat	Not for northern states . . . mosaic resistant . . . early variety, meaty pods	31 40 41 51 56 71 73
Tidal Wave	54	6" dark-green	16-18" plants . . . white-seeded, fine freezer	71
Topcrop Stringless	48-52	5½-6" medium-green, stringless	16" plants are mosaic-resistant . . . AA selection . . . top yielder in home gardens . . . good canner, freezer	10 11 14 16 19 22 28 30 31 32 34 38 40 47 48 51 52 53 55 57 58 62 66 67 70 71 73
Wade Bush Stringless	54		AA selection . . . southern bean has red-brown seeds . . . good canned, fresh, or frozen	16 21 31 57
White Half Runner (Mississippi Skip Bean)	60	4"	Sweet snap or shell bean . . . good canned, fresh, or frozen	10 71
White Half Runner (Mountaineer)	52	Light-green, oval, round	Early half runner . . . use for string or shell	31 37 40 41 47 51 55 62 67 73

WAX BUSH BEANS

VARIETY	DAYS	POD SHAPE/COLOR	REMARKS	SOURCES
Admiral Wax	49	Yellow		14 66
Beurre De Rocquencourt (Mangetout)	46	6-7" yellow	Black-seeded . . . very early bearer	15 37
Brittle Wax (Round Pod Kidney Wax)	50-58	6-7" yellow stringless	White-seeded . . . vigorous vine . . . mild flavor that is good fresh, canned, or frozen	10 16 21 28 51 57 62 72
Cherokee Stringless (Valentine Wax) (Cherokee) (Golden All American)	49-58	6-6½" golden, oval	Black-seeded . . . resistant to mosaic, New York 15 strain bean virus . . . extremely popular AA selection	11 12 14 16 19 22 28 29 31 32 40 41 47 48 50 53 57 66 67 71 72
Earliwax	50-54	Yellow	Resistant to mosaic . . . good canner and freezer	40 57 70 72
Early Puregold	57-58	Yellow	White-seeded	72
Earlywax Golden Yellow	54	Slightly curved	Flavorful . . . good canner and freezer	71
Eastern Butterwax	44-53	4" long, yellow, stringless	Tender and thick-meated . . . excellent for freezing	29 72
Gold Crop Wax Bean	45-52	Shiny-yellow, stringless, long-podded	White-seeded . . . AA winner . . . good fresh, frozen, or canned	10 19 28 30 32 34 38 48 51 53 57 60 66 70
Golden Wax	50-60	Heavy, flat	Rust-resistant . . . good canner	22 39 46 50 59
Golden Wax Improved (Topnotch)	51	Long pod, flat, and stringless	Good for freezing or canning	3 12 14 16 28 30 32 51 52 53 55 56 58 71
Honey Gold	40	5½" long, stringless	Resists common bean mosaic . . . bush is 12-14" in height and is heavy yielder	66
Improved Butter Wax	54	6½" long	16" high bush is preferred in home gardens . . . good canner	28
Kinghorn Wax (Butter Wax) (Improved Brittle Wax)	50-56	6" long, creamy, yellow	White-seeded . . . vigorous vines . . . good canner, freezer	12 16 19 28 30 32 34 38 49 51 57 60 62 72
Moongold Wax	49-55	5-5¼" stringless	Disease resistant . . . grows 14" in height . . . early, plentiful crop	22 28 50 72
Pencil Pod Black Wax	53-65	Round, black, straight	Black-seeded . . . good for canning	3 12 16 30 39 45 49 51 52 55 59 60 62 72
Pencil Pod Wax (Butter Bean)	51-54	Yellow, stringless, straight, and round	Meaty . . . all-purpose	10 14 19 32 38 49 66 71
Rustproof Golden Wax	40-50	5-5½" flat, oval, stringless	White seeds with reddish marks . . . Rust-resistant . . . profuse . . . brittle	10
Sungold Wax	45-56	5-6" straight, yellow	Resistant to bean mosaic . . . good flavor . . . white-seeded	29 37
Sunrise Wax		4-5" yellow	Sturdy plant	40
Surecrop Stringless Wax (Yellow Pod Bountiful)	52	6-6½" yellow, large, flat	Heavy producer	10 45 49
Tenderwax	53			48

BUSH BEANS—Purple

VARIETY	DAYS	POD SHAPE/COLOR	REMARKS	SOURCES
Royal Burgundy	50	5½-6" curved	Medium-sized bush . . . freezes well . . . turns green after 2 minutes in boiling water	52 66
Royalty Purple Pod	50-68	5" curved	Many are early . . . bean beetles avoid it . . . good in colder soils . . . disease-resistant . . . buff-colored seed . . . good canned, fresh, or frozen	10 16 21 22 28 37 50 51 53 55 56 57 62 71 73

LIMA BEANS—Pole

VARIETY	DAYS	PODS/BEANS	REMARKS	SOURCES
Burpee's Best (Dreer's Improved Challenger) (Potato Lima)	87-92	4-4½ x 1¼" straight, broad, plump seeds	10-12 foot plant . . . strong climber . . . rich, tender pods with excellent flavor	10 47 49 67
Calico Pole Lima	78	3-4" speckled seeds	Prolific and vigorous	22

LIMA BEANS—Pole (Continued)

VARIETY	DAYS	PODS/BEANS	REMARKS	SOURCES
Carolina (Sieva Pole) (Southern Running Butterbean)	79	3-3½"smooth 3-4 small, flat, white seeds (dried)	Quick to bear . . . heavy yields . . . winter use	31 40 41 47 49 51 56 67 71 73
Christmas Pole Lima (Large Speckled Christmas) (Giant Florida Pole)	88	Purple and white seeds	Heavy crops from mid-season to frost . . . high quality . . . butter-flavored	31 50 51 53 56 67 71 73
Climbing Baby Lima	72	Medium-green; small seeds	8-10 feet tall . . . excellent eating . . . earliest of white limas	22
Florida Speckled Butter Bean (Speckled Butter Bean)	68-85	3½" white and purple beans	Popular, big yielder . . . 6-8 feet tall	22 31 40 41 51 56 58 62 67 71 73
Giant Podded		7 x 1½" extra large		47
Henderson's Early Leviathan Lima	70	3-5 large beans per pod	Strong grower . . . very early . . . bears until frost	38
Jumbo	90	8 x 2"	Vines bear from top to bottom	14
King of the Garden (White Pole Lima)	88-90	5 x 1¼" large, flat beans, 3-4 per pod	An old favorite that climbs 8 feet or more . . . good fresh or frozen	10 12 16 19 28 29 30 31 32 41 47 49 51 52 53 58 59 60 62 66 67 70 71
Prizetaker	90	6 x 1½"—3-4 giant beans per pod	Unique, excellent quality	10 43 45 49
Speckled Pole Lima	85		Has rich, nutlike flavor . . . yields a great crop year after year	19 55
Willow Leaf		3¼ x ¾" medium-green; dull-white, small seeds		51

LIMA BEANS—Bush, Small Seeds

VARIETY	DAYS	PODS/BEANS	REMARKS	SOURCES
Baby Fordhook Bush Lima	67-70	2¾ x ¾" dark-green	14" plant . . . small, thick-seeded	10 28
Baby Bush Lima (Evergreen Bush)	67-72	3-4 bright-green beans per pod	Very early . . . becomes creamy white when mature . . . stands hot weather better than most	28 38
Baby Potato Bush	60-65	3" pods	Excellent for table, freezing, or canning	66 67
Bridgeton	76	3" flat pods	Good freezer . . . resistant to downy mildew	29 31
Cangreen Bush Lima	65	3" pods	Stays green after cooked or canned . . . Henderson type . . . 16" plants	19 31 47
Clark's Green Salad	68	Small, flat, green	High quality . . . good for eating, freezing	53
Green Seeded Baby Henderson (Thorogreen Baby Lima)	67	2-4" plump, pale-green beans	12-14" plants . . . good canner, freezer	21 22 34 50 51 56 60 67 71 73
Henderson Bush Baby	65-81	2 ¾ x ¾" flat, slightly curved	Buttery baby lima . . . use as dried or canned	3 10 11 16 19 22 31 32 37 40 41 47 48 49 51 52 53 55 56 58 60 67 70 71 72 73
Jackson Wonder (Calico) (Speckled Bush)	65-83	3¼" mottled-purple seed	Most prolific of all bush limas . . . fully adapted to all parts of the south	28 31 37 40 41 51 52 53 55 56 58 62 67 71 73
Kingston	70	Green pods, 3-4 beans	Excellent freezer . . . 14-18" plant	10 59
Thaxter (All Green)	67	3-3¼" small, flat	15-16" plant . . . early canner . . . tolerant to downy mildew	32 40
Wood's Prolific	68	3½" green	Has tendency to throw out small runners	67

LIMA BEANS—Bush, Plump Seeds

VARIETY	DAYS	PODS/BEANS	REMARKS	SOURCES
Burpee Fordhook	75	4½ x 1¼" straight, dark-green	20" plant with 2-foot spread . . . fancy lima	10 47
Burpee Bush Lima	77		Buttery bean for table or freezing	39
Burpee's Bush Improved	75	5 x 1" slightly curved; large, flat, oval seed	Strong vines . . . clusters of 5-6 pods	10 11 12 14 21 25 30 45 47 49 51 52 57 58 62 66 67 71
Dixie Butterpea White	70-76	Seeds are white, almost round, and meaty	Strong, vigorous plants loaded with pods	31 41 51 55 56 67 71
Dixie Butterpea Speckled	76	Brownish-red seed speckled with darker brown	Similar to Dixie Butterpea White . . . excellent taste	41 51 56 71 73
Fordhook Bush Lima	70		Heavy-yielding strain . . . medium early	11 14 19 38 47 49 58 62 71
Fordhook 242	75-85	3-4" pods	AA selection . . . delicious fresh or frozen . . . heavy yielder . . . beans of choice quality	10 11 14 16 21 22 29 30 31 32 34 37 40 41 45 46 47 48 51 52 53 55 56 57 59 60 66 67 68 70 71 73
Giant Early Bush Lima		5-6" pods	1½-foot plant . . . good freezer	62
Giant Improved Bush	75	5-6" pods, slightly curved; 4-5 large seeds per pod	Bears from July until frost	19
Wonder Bush Lima	75	4-8 large seeds per pod	18-24" plant . . . pods are held off ground	38

BUSH SHELL BEANS—Soybeans

VARIETY	DAYS	PODS	REMARKS	SOURCES
Altona	100	Medium-size, green, shiny yellow when mature, with black eye	Dependable . . . early, thus good for northern gardens	37
Anika Early	95	2-2½" furry pods	Japanese development	29
Disoy	92-110	2-3" round pods	26" upright plants . . . eat green, dry, or freeze	28 31
Early Green Bush	85	4" green pods	16" upright bushes . . . should mature by end of August in most parts of USA and Canada	66
Edible Soy Bean	103	Oval, bright-green	Delicious cooked as green-shelled beans	16 19 21 22 28 55 68
Envy	104	Bright-green inside and out	Early . . . high-yielding	37
Extra Early Green	70		Early . . . high yielding . . . tender and tasty	42 72
Fiskely V	91	Small, buff-yellow	18" upright bushes . . . early as common dry beans . . . not high yielding . . . can be grown in northern and coastal gardens	37
Frostbeater	75	Large shining-green, 3 beans per pod	22" bush that is heavy producer . . . rich flavor . . . use as green shell also	10
Giant Green Soy	105	Large, green	The best edible . . . matures early for northern gardens	21 71
Hakucho Early	95		Very good variety . . . use as green shell or Limas	36
Kanrich	93-98		24" bush . . . heavy yields . . . can eat green, dried, or shelled . . . good canned and frozen . . . low in starch	14 30 50 66
Kim Edible Soybean	125		30-36" bush . . . heavy pod set . . . beans are large, with excellent texture and flavor	46 60
Panther (Japanese, Kuromame) (Oriental Black Soybean)	100-115	Black soybean	More easily digested . . . excellent flavor	37 50 71
Prize	85-105	Large, oval	Erect bushes . . . use as green shell . . . cook like limas . . . excellent for winter use	10 41 46
Tamanishiki	120		The best late variety	36
Traverse	111	Shiny-yellow beans	30-36" upright plants . . . good yields . . . fine quality . . . best in warmer seasons	37
Verde	85	Large, green	High in protein . . . good cooked, canned, or frozen	28

BUSH SHELL BEANS—Soybeans (Continued)

VARIETY	DAYS	POD SHAPE/COLOR	REMARKS	SOURCES
Yellow Soybean	105		24" upright plants . . . ideal for quick freezing . . . not recommended for northern climates . . . excellent for use as a green shell bean or dry	71

BUSH SHELL BEANS—Fava Bean (English Broadbean)

VARIETY	DAYS	POD SIZE/SHAPE	REMARKS	SOURCES
Aguadulce Very Long Pod			Very productive	15
Broad or Fava Long Podded	85-90	7" inedible, oblong, flat; light-green	Much hardier than other beans . . . use as substitute for lima in North	3 10 12 15 44 45 49 50 52 60 62 71
Broad Improved Long Pod	85	7" pods; flat, oblong beans	Use green shell or dry stage	29
Broad Windsor Long Pod	65	Large beans in long pods	Upright plants . . . slow-growing	66 72
Conqueror	78	Extra-long pods	Better yielder than Seville	72
Olga	70		Bush giving big yield	72
Seville Long Pod			Early variety with large beans	15 72
Three-in-One	68		Seed is smaller, but there are 3 times as many . . . white	72
Windsor	75	Extremely large, flat, fat bean	Upright on tall plants . . . frost-hardy . . . shelled out green or left to mature	37

BUSH SHELL BEANS—Kidney

VARIETY	DAYS	PODS/BEANS	REMARKS	SOURCES
California Red Kidney	100		Hardy and high yielding . . . large, red beans	66
Charlevoix Dark Red Kidney	110	Medium size, dark-red	Provides a tasty, thick broth in soups, stews, and chili	37
Dark Red Kidney	95	Large, flat, waxy-green pods	Used as a dry cooking bean	56 62
Light Red Kidney	112	Pinkish-mahogany, larger than Charlevoix	Well-known soup and stew bean	30 37 72
Red Kidney	95-100	Large, pinkish-red to mahogany bean, inedible 6" pods	20-22" tall plant . . . good baked, boiled, in soups, or in Mexican dishes	3 10 12 14 19 21 22 28 45 49 50 52 53 71
Redkloud	100		Early red kidney with some halo blight resistance . . . good yielder of fine quality	29
White Kidney	88	Large, white	Milder flavor than red kidney beans . . . delicious in minestrone soup . . . good baker	28 29 30 45 71

BUSH SHELL BEANS—Horticultural Bean

VARIETY	DAYS	PODS	REMARKS	SOURCES
Bush Horticultural No. 4	64		Compact vines that perform well in cooler climates . . . pink beans with dark-red markings . . . excellent freezer	29
Dwarf Horticultural (Long Pod) (Wren's Nest)	65	5-6", thick, flat	Carmine color at maturity . . . delicious green or dried	10 12 30 37 45 51 52 59 60 62 73
French Dwarf Horticultural	60-65		14-18" bush . . . can be used as green snap bean or dried . . . for table, canning, or freezing	3 12 28 29 30 49 60 66 70 71
King Horticultural	75	6" pods; straight, broad, stringless, green shell	Heavy-yielding pole type . . . may be eaten like snap beans	29 45 47 72
Ruby Dwarf Horticultural	60	5" pods; thick, flat, light-green	Used chiefly as green shell bean . . . seeds are chamois-colored splashed with carmine	57
Taylor's Dwarf Horticultural	64		Light-green, turning cream splashed red . . . used for green shell	31 40 41 47 56 66

BUSH SHELL BEANS—Navy

VARIETY	DAYS	PODS	REMARKS	SOURCES
Improved Navy	95		Pure-white . . . robust plant . . . original navy soup bean	19 62
Michiliti (Improved Navy Sanilac)			Glossy-white, full-oval . . . resistant to blight	21 72
Navy (Pea Bean) (White Wonder) (Soup Bean) (Sanilac)	85-95	Long, uniform	Off-green pods . . . favorite standard bean . . . heavy yielder . . . makes good bean soup	12 16 22 28 30 52 71
Purley King	70		Good baked . . . 20% protein when dry . . . 12" plants	68
Seafarer	90		Earliest navy . . . pleasant texture and flavor . . . seed is small, rounded, shiny-white . . . high yielding	37

BUSH SHELL BEANS—White

VARIETY	DAYS	PODS	REMARKS	SOURCES
Bonus Small White	85	Long, narrow pods	White . . . excellent baker . . . small bush	71
Great Northern White (Montana White)	90	Large, flat	Big white beans . . . cooks ⅓ faster than navy beans . . . heavy yielder . . . use in soup and baking	14 16 19 21 22 28 52 62 68 71
White Marrow	68-100	4½-5" inedible pods; flat, straight	Larger than regular navy . . . better for baking . . . highly overrated	10 30 45 62 66 71
White Mexican		Large pods	Sure cropper . . . white, nearly round seeds	62

BUSH SHELL BEANS—Red, Purple, Cranberry

VARIETY	DAYS	PODS	REMARKS	SOURCES
Cranberry Bean	60	Long, thick, flat	Splashed red at maturity	19
Lowe's Champion	65	Flat pods; 5-6 shell beans per pod	Purple bean . . . 18-24" bushes	3 8 37 71
Mexican Red Bean	85	Medium-green pods	14" bush . . . excellent baking qualities . . . excellent all-round bean	71
Red Beans	95		Heavy yields . . . full bean flavor used in chili, rice, or southwestern dishes . . . 2½' bushes	28
Speckled Cranberry Eggbean (Wren's Egg) (King Mammoth)		8-9" nearly round	Flesh-colored	62 71
Vermont Cranberry (Old Fashioned) (King's Early)	60-90		Medium-dark-red; mottled . . . good in soup	30 37 71
Wade Bush	58	6" pods	Light-purple bean . . . highly recommended for freezing	31 71

BUSH SHELL BEANS—Miscellaneous

VARIETY	DAYS	PODS	REMARKS	SOURCES
Adzuki	90-125		Japanese bean . . . small bushes . . . maroon . . . tender and delicious . . . high in protein	46 68 71
Berken	90		Nutritious . . . 2-5 days for sprouts	10 12 71
Black Turtle Soup Bean	85	Slender pods	Famous in the South . . . best grown as a dry bean	71
Flageolet Bean	100		French bean . . . 24" bush . . . pure white . . . excellent as a shelling bean	15 44 71 72

BUSH SHELL BEANS—Miscellaneous (Continued)

VARIETY	DAYS	PODS	REMARKS	SOURCES
Garbanzo	100	Small	Dried seeds are prepared by boiling or roasting . . . distinctive flavor . . . good cold in salads	10 53 71
Improved Pinto			Vines are heavy producers . . . pods are stringless at snapping stage . . . large, plump seeds	55
Marfax	89		Early, dependable yielder . . . popular baking bean in Maine . . . beans are brown, rounded	37
Mung Bean Oriental	120	Small, olive-green	Does well in warmer weather . . . excellent as sprouts	16 19 31 37 68
Pink Bean	85	Long, narrow pods	Medium-pink bean similar to Mexican Red . . . true bush bean . . . ideal for chili or soup	71 73
Pinto	85-90	4½-5"; 5-6 beans in each short, broad, oval pod	Popular for use as refried beans in Mexican cooking . . . light-buff background speckled with greenish brown	3 16 22 28 37 53 55 71 73
Santa Maria Pinquito	90		Pink bean	50
Yellow Eye	85-92		18" bush . . . good baker . . . popular dry bean used a great deal in Maine	3 30 37 71 72

Beets (Beta vulgaris)

Beets are a double-barreled vegetable because you can eat both the roots and leaves. Beets grow rapidly from seed, are disease-free, and aren't bothered much by insects. Beets are a little slow to sprout from corky seeds, but once up, they produce a lot of food in a small space.

Beets generally offer the home gardener a choice of shapes and colors; some beets are grown almost exclusively for greens.

The round ones: The majority of beets grown are dark, red, and round (although some of the semiglobe varieties are extremely popular). The favorite is *Detroit Dark Red*. This super beet is early (55-60 days) and sweet, excellent for canning or freezing. It is also available in a medium or short top. Other excellent globe-shaped beets are *King Red* and *Garnet*.

Semiglobe: A number of beet varieties are semiglobe with flattened tops. *Ruby Queen*, for instance, is an early-maturing, All American award winner that is excellent for processing. And the flattened *Early Blood Turnip* (60 days) has large, coarse tops that make wonderful table greens.

Long Cylindrical Beets, Too? Several beet varieties grow long like a carrot instead of round like the traditional beet. *Formanova* (55 days) has a six-inch-long cylindrical shape. Cooks say it is sweet and tender and especially good for slicing and pickling.

Yellow or White: Gardeners who like variety and novelty should try one of these. *Burpee's Golden Beet* has a spectacular orange skin and yellow flesh. It doesn't bleed like the red beets do. The tops are delicious cooked, and the roots are excellent pickled or in salads. *Albino White Beet* is globe-shaped and sweet.

Some beets, as mentioned, are grown primarily for *greens* rather than roots. *Lutz Green Leaf* has tender sweet leaves that can be used either large or small. The glossy green tops have a pink rib. And *Beets For Greens* have flattened, uneven roots and produce an abundance of greens.

Commercial agriculture makes use of the beet in many forms—the mangel-wurzel is used for cattle feed, and the sugar beet for sugar.

HOW TO PLANT: Plant seed a half inch deep in rows 12 to 18 inches apart. The beet seed is a compact ball with numerous tiny seeds. When the plants reach about 6 inches high, thin to 2-3 inches apart. In hot-summer regions plant beets in early spring or late summer. In cold regions plant in the spring as soon as the ground can be worked.

Harvesting: Pick some beets when they are about an inch in diameter. Let others grow to about 2 inches. Large, older beets generally become woody.

BEETS—Round

VARIETY	DAYS	COLOR	REMARKS	SOURCES
Asgrow Wonder	57			48 57
Best of All	50-53		Good beet	38
Boltardy				48 68
Burgundy Pickling	59	Red-wine	Strong top	62
Burpee's Red Ball	60	Dark-red	Tall tops . . . erect	10 45
Crimson	61			36 62
Dark Red Canner	59	Dark-red	Small . . . exceptional fine pickling	22
Dark Red Improved		Blood-red	Round and small	72
Detroit Dark Red	55-60	Dark-red	All-American . . . 12" dark, glossy tops . . . early and sweet . . . good for table, canning, or freezing	3 5 9 10 11 12 16 19 21 22 25 28 29 30 32 34 38 40 45 46 47 48 49 51 52 53 57 58 60 62 66 68 72 73
Early Blood		Red		58
Eclipse Cherry Beet	65	Dark-red	Oval and tender	58 62
Fire Chief	52-70	Deep-red	Tops have trace of red bronze . . . small root yields baby-size beets . . . tops make good canning	57 60 70
Formanova	55		Good fresh, canned, or pickled	37 53 57
Garnet	55-60	Garnet-red	13-15" medium-gloss green tops . . . flat glove	16 38 57
Iowa	56	Bright-red zones	Never cracks open	14
King Red	52	Dark-red	12-15" tops . . . green tinged with red . . . selected from perfected Detroit	14 28 51 66

BEETS—Semiglobe

VARIETY	DAYS	COLOR	REMARKS	SOURCES
Albino White Beet	50	White	Spinach greens . . . globe-shaped	66
Burpee's Goldenbeet	55	Golden	Small	10 19 66
Burpee's Red Heart	58	Dark-red	Tender flesh	10 45
Ceoavy Green Top	60	Dark-red	Bright-green tops . . . flattened	29
Crosby's Egyptian	42-50	Purple-red	Flattened . . . excellent for bunching	32 25 53 62
Early Blood Turnip	50-68	Dark-red	Turnip-shaped . . . good for home gardens	21 45
Early Wonder	48-55	Dark-red	16-18" tall . . . early . . . stores well, or use for table, canning, or greens	3 9 10 19 21 25 28 30 36 37 38 48 51 53 55 56 58
Extra Early Egyptian		Deep-purple	Flattened, small tops	62
Flat Egyptian		Dark	Round, flat	15
Golden Beet	55	Golden	Use in salads, pickled, or as greens	50 53 68
Green Top Bunching	53-58	Deep-red	Medium tops . . . early . . . resistant to mildew	48
Improved Early Blood Turnip	60	Bright-red	Flat tops . . . flattened globe	52 55
Long Season	80	Deep-red	Light-green tops . . . large, rough-looking . . . good greens . . . fine keeper . . . sweet and tender	29 30
Mangel Mammoth Long Red				12
Ruby Queen	52-55	Dark-red	Short top . . . AA winner . . . early-bearing . . . greens are excellent for processing	9 16 19 21 28 29 31 32 34 40 48 51 52 53 60 66 68 72 73
Smoothie		Deep-red	Small crown	40
Snow White		White		68
Winter Keeper	75-80	Dark-red	Remains crisp in storage	12

BEETS—Cylindrical, Baby

VARIETY	DAYS	COLOR	REMARKS	SOURCES
Baby Canning	54	Deep-crimson	Golf-ball-sized . . . perfect for pickling	19 28
Butter Slicer	58	Dark-red	Medium-long tops . . . good table beet	19
Crapavdine	65		Long, narrow, carrot-shaped	50
Cylindra	55-60	Dark-red	Uniform	10 22 28 42 62 70

BEETS—Cylindrical, Baby (Continued)

VARIETY	DAYS	COLOR	REMARKS	SOURCES
Cylindria Improved Formanova	58	Dark-red	6" carrotlike roots	52 66
Spinel Baby Beets			Early	22 32
Tendersweet	55	Dark-red	1½-6" tops . . . good greens	9

BEETS FOR GREENS

VARIETY	DAYS	COLOR	REMARKS	SOURCES
Beets for Greens			Large tops . . . roots flattened, uneven . . . early and quick-growing	3 29
Lutz Green Leaf	80	Purple-red	Top shaped	10 49 50
Swiss Chard			Large, upright, long-lasting	30

Broccoli (Brassica oleracea italica)

Broccoli is often called the gardener's best friend in the cabbage family. It is big and easy to grow, and one plant can produce a huge quantity of food. Unfortunately, broccoli is quite sensitive to heat. Just as you think it is growing mightily, a hot spell can force it right past the good eating stage.

Generally, broccoli varieties differ from each other by the type of "head" they produce and in the varieties of color and days to maturity.

Central Head—Many Side Branches: Home gardeners generally like their broccoli to have lots of side shoots in addition to the main head—that usually means a bigger harvest. Such varieties as *Calabrese,* for instance, give a long and heavy harvest because after the main head is cut, *Calabrese* continues to sprout continuously until it freezes.

Central Heads—Few Side Branches: For some gardeners and many commercial growers it's important to have a good-quality, large central head with fewer side branches. *Premium Crop,* for instance, is an extra-early variety that many gardeners love because it produces 8-9-inch light-green heads that stay firm and crisp a long time without producing side shoots. One of the newer varieties, *Green Hornet,* produces a large 7-8-inch head that develops quickly without side branches.

Branching, No Heads: Most gardeners have a hard time visualizing broccoli without a central head, but *Raab, Rapa,* or *Italian Turnip* produces nothing but side branches. Sometimes *Raab* is harvested simply for greens, but more often the tender stalks with the small florets are cut 8 or 9 inches long and bunched just like asparagus.

Purple and White: Everybody knows that broccoli sprouts are green, but several varieties produce purple heads that turn green when cooked. *King Robert Purple,* for instance, has a huge central head that turns emerald green when dropped in boiling water. And probably most unusual of all is *White Broccoli,* which produces white heads that look much like small cauliflowers.

HOW TO PLANT: Start from seed in peat pots or flats or purchase young plants from nurseries. Space the plants 18-24 inches apart in rows, and leave 36 inches between the rows. Plant from early spring to early summer.

Harvesting: Cut the heads while they are hard and green—never wait until the buds begin to crack. In many varieties the more you pick broccoli, the more new shoots will be produced.

BROCCOLI—Central Head, Side Branches

VARIETY	DAYS	HEAD SIZE	REMARKS	SOURCES
Calabrese	85	5-6"	Bluish-green, with many side branches . . . fine-grained heads . . . good for bunching, freezing	10 12 21 36 45 68
Cleopatra Hybrid	50-85	Large	Vigorous medium-size shoots . . . dark-green AA winner . . . cold- and drought-resistant . . . good fresh and frozen	16 25 31 52 53 57 66

BROCCOLI—Central Head, Side Branches (Continued)

VARIETY	DAYS	HEAD SIZE	REMARKS	SOURCES
Green Sprouting De Cicco	60-70	Large, flat	Many side shoots . . . tall, light-green . . . high-quality . . . freezer	3 10 16 20 47 49 53 57 66
Green Sprouting Calabrese (Italian Green) (Italian Green Sprouting)	70-85	3-5"	Bluish-green . . . sprouts continuously until freeze . . . good freezer	5 22 25 28 30 39 50 51 52 53 57 60 66 67 73
Green Umbrella Hybrid	50	Large 12"	Dark-green . . . vigorous grower, with many side shoots . . . good freezer	16
New Spartan	55	6-8"	Delightful flavor . . . frostproof . . . good freezer	8 19 22
Spartan Early	55	3-8"	Bluish-green . . . freezer	16 22 28 37 40 52 60
Waltham 29	74-80	Medium-large	Dark-blue-green . . . low, compact . . . grown for fall from New England to Florida . . . good fresh and frozen	3 11 16 29 32 37 40 41 47 48 66 67 70 72

BROCCOLI—Central Head, Few Branches

VARIETY	DAYS	HEAD SIZE	REMARKS	SOURCES
Blue Ocean Hybrid	Early	6" dia.	Well-rounded head, with tight buds . . . bright-green . . . medium-sized . . . fresh, freezing	40
Bravo Hybrid	Spring, summer	6-7" dia.	Medium-large, dome-shaped head . . . blue-green . . . good strain for eastern Canada	48 51 66
Crusader Hybrid	75-92	6-12"	Medium-large, dome-shaped, round head . . . smaller and more compact than standard size . . . flavorful, tender	34 38 48 51
Dandy	62		Deep-green heads . . . heavy yielder . . . good eating qualities	72
Duchess Hybrid	58	Large, compact	Very uniform in size	72
El Centro	60	Medium	Purplish cast, with a few secondary shoots . . . vigorous . . . well-adapted to east and south	16
Green Boy	85	1½ lbs.	Large, bright-green single head . . . nonbranching	32
Green Comet Hybrid	40-55	6-7"	Solid central stem . . . single-type large head . . . deep-blue-green . . . holds shape well . . . AA winner is disease-resistant	3 5 10 12 21 22 25 29 32 48 53 60 66 68
Green Duke Hybrid	69-88	Medium large	Uniformly round, dome-shaped heads . . . good freezer	11 48 51 53
Green Hornet	78	7-8"	Central head without side branches . . . bright-green . . . good for once-over . . . processing, marketing, or home gardens	66
Premium Crop	58-60	9-10"	Medium-blue-green . . . central heads with no side shoots . . . AA winner of excellent quality . . . disease-resistant . . . good fresh or frozen	10 19 21 25 32 34 53 66 68 70 72
Topper 43	80	Large	Dark-green . . . compact central head . . . medium spreading	16

BROCCOLI—Other Types

VARIETY	DAYS	SIZE	REMARKS	SOURCES
Christmas Purple Sprouting	Late		Good for freezing	68
Early Purple Sprouting	Early			68
King Robert Purple	57	Large head	Turns green when cooked . . . freezer	16 50
Raab or Rapa Italian Turnip	100		Branching, with no central head . . . rapid grower . . . cut before plants come into flower	32 66 67
White Sprouting	75		Heavy crop . . . white heads that look like cauliflower . . . mild flavor	50 68

Brussels sprouts (Brassica oleracea gemmifera)

This member of the cabbage family produces edible sprouts that look like tiny cabbages in the axils of the leaves. Brussels sprouts like long growing periods of cool weather. They're easy to grow if you live in the right climate. In most varieties, sprouts develop from the bottom of the plant upward, and one plant will keep producing until you wonder if it will ever stop.

With Brussels sprouts you have two basic choices —the standard-size plants, which grow to about 22 inches in height, and the dwarf and semi-dwarf varieties, which get to 12 or 15 inches. The most popular varieties are *Jade Cross Hybrid* (with richly blue-green, firm sprouts) and *Long Island Improved* (with round, dark-green, tight heads).

HOW TO GROW: Purchase plants from local nurseries or start seeds in peat pots, four to six weeks before your outdoor planting date. In cool-summer areas set out the plants in the garden, 12-18 inches apart, in rows 24-30 inches apart, as soon as the soil can be worked in the spring.

In other areas start plants in mid-summer so Brussels sprouts will mature during cold weather.

Harvesting: Pick the lowest sprouts each time you pick, and break off any leaves left below the "sprout." Don't remove the top leaves.

BRUSSELS SPROUTS

VARIETY	DAYS	SEASON	HEAD/PLANT TYPE	REMARKS	SOURCES
Achilles		Winter	Mid-sized		68
Amager Market	70	Early		Sprouts compactly set	14
Citadel		Late March	Medium-sized	Tight sprouts	68
Early Dwarf Danish	105			Sprouts are quite large on short plants	37
Early Morn	105	Early	Large, compact, pyramid, elliptical	Medium-green	66
Focus		Sept.-Jan.	Medium-sized	Dark-green	68
Green Pearl	120		Globe-shaped	Medium-green . . . upright plant that matures top to bottom	66
Improved Extra Dwarf	70		1" diameter	Thickly set	14
Indra	128	Early October	Globe, hard	Medium-green	66
Jade Cross E	90-97	Early Fall	Oval, upright, 24"	Dark-blue-green . . . good freezer	29 48 66 70 72
Jade Cross Hybrid	80-95	Fall	Oval, upright, 22"	Blue-green . . . AA winner that is heavy yielder . . . good freezer	5 9 10 12 16 25 30 31 32 34 52 53 55 60 66
Long Island	90-95	Winter	1½" cabbagelike heads	Fall frosts improve flavor	21 28 39 52 58 66
Long Island Improved (Catskill)	85-95	Fall	1¼-1½" base to top, 20" upright	Good crop with several pickings . . . good freezer	3 5 8 10 12 22 25 28 30 32 36 40 41 45 47 48 49 50 51 53 55 57 60 62 65 67 72 73
Peer Gynt				Dark-green . . . high quality . . . prolific	68
Semi-dwarf Paris Market			Solid, tight heads	Cold-resistant	15
Topscore	138	Early Nov.	Round, hard heads	Dark-green . . . very uniform . . . good freezer	66

Cabbage (Brassica oleracea capitata)

This great vegetable always looks so picturesque growing in a garden or flowerbed. And the red ones planted by themselves in a patio tub become tremendous showoffs. Cabbage produces in great abundance and is very hardy, withstanding temperatures down to 10 or 15 degrees.

In growing cabbage it is important to select varieties for the time of year you intend to grow. Decide whether you want to harvest cabbage in summer or late fall, then make your selections working back from the cabbages' maturity period.

Cabbages offer a delightful number of varieties for the home gardener. Cut fresh, they're delicious—a far cry from the strong-smelling, tight greenheads you buy in the supermarket. There are many choices you have by color, appearance, and shape.

Red Cabbage: Every gardener should try one or two of the red varieties, which vary from bright-red to dark-purple to almost-black. An extra-early variety, *Ruby Ball,* is delicious eaten raw and holds its sweet flavor well after cooking. Good cooks also like the standard red variety, *Mammoth Red Rock,* which stores well and makes a fine pickling cabbage. *Red Acre,* a small, purplish, round cabbage, holds well without bursting, and *Black Diamond* is almost black in color. There are many choices among the red varieties.

Savoy Cabbage: Gardeners love these cabbages for their dark-green leaves with the bubbly surface. *Chieftain Savoy* has a semiflat shape and is fairly resistant to heat. One of the newer Savoys, *Savoy King* (an All-American award winner), has a semiglobe shape and holds well without bursting.

Round: There are many varieties of round cabbages, varying from perfectly globe-shaped to slightly flat; they can be selected for early, mid-season, or late harvest. Most of these average from 3-8 pounds. Good cooks say that the new variety, *Green Parade,* has a deliciously crisp, tangy taste. This is a compact, globe-shaped, mid-season variety. *Golden Acre* is a medium-sized, early, round variety that is used extensively for slaw and sauerkraut and is a favorite of gardeners everywhere. And if you are looking for a heavy, hard-as-a-rock 16-pound cabbage, try *Jumbo*—it is especially good for cabbage rolls.

Flat: Many cabbage varieties vary from wide flat (Dutch Flat types) to almost egg-shaped (the drumhead types). Sometimes these flattened cabbages become huge and extremely heavy. *Late Premium Dutch Flat,* for instance, weighs approximately 10 pounds and has a large, flattened head. It grows extremely well in cool-summer regions and keeps well in storage. *Johnson's Drumhead* has a large, egg-shaped flat head that often weighs as much as 12-16 pounds.

Pointed: These are the heart-shaped Wakefield types that come to a point on one end. Generally they are small cabbages—*Early Jersey Wakefield,* for instance, weighs only 2-3 pounds, but has a wonderful flavor that sets off salads and cole slaw.

HOW TO PLANT: Sow the seeds a half-inch deep in flats or peat pots about six to eight weeks before you intend to set the plants outdoors. Space early varieties 12-16 inches apart in rows 20-24 inches apart. Space winter varieties 18-24 inches apart in rows 30-36 inches apart.

Harvesting: Pick cabbage heads as soon as the heads feel solid. If you let them mature on the plant, the core gradually lengthens until it bursts through the top and uncurls into a long stalk.

CABBAGE—Red

VARIETY	DAYS	SEASON	HEAD TYPE/SIZE	REMARKS	SOURCES
Black Diamond	90	2nd early	Almost black, medium	Comes from Holland	14
Improved Red Acre	85	Early			66
King Cole Red	72	Mid	Large, 6-7"	Disease-resistant . . . best for sauerkraut, canning, cooking, slaw	12
Mammoth German Red	100	Late fall	Large, solid, 6-8 lbs.	Purple-red color . . . good for slaw	50
Mammoth Red Rock	90	Fall-Winter	Globe, 8-9"	Stores and pickles well, use in salads	10 11 16 21 28 41 44 51 52 56 66 70
Meteor	80-85	Mid	Deeper than round, 6"	Bright-red color	51 66 72
Perfection	85		Large	Dark-red head	72
Red Acre	75-85	Early	Medium, 6-7", 4-5 lbs.		3 8 9 10 11 12 16 17 48 51 52 53 55 57 66 67 78
Red Danish Ballhead	92-97	Late	Round, firm, 4-6 lbs.	Good for storage	60 66
Red Drumhead	95		7-8"	Pickling type . . . yellows-resistant	38
Red Dutch Drumhead			Flat globe		47
Red Earliest of All		Early	Round, 3-4 lbs.		48
Red Head (hybrid)	80-85	Early	Round, 5-7", 4 lbs.	Deep-magenta	30 31 40 48 53 59 66
Red Hollander	95-110	Late	6½-7"	Similar to Round Red Dutch . . . yellows-resistant	16 48 51
Red Rock	100	Late	Round, hard	Good for cooking, salads, pickles	31
Red Storage	96	Fall	Globe-shaped	Use in coleslaw	66
Ruby Ball (hybrid)	65-72	Early	Ball-shaped, 5 lbs.	AA winner, Japan . . . cooked or raw	12 19 21 29 48 72
Wisconsin Red Hollander	100	Late	Medium-round, solid	Improved Red Rock . . . good for storage	62

CABBAGE—Savoyed

VARIETY	DAYS	SEASON	HEAD TYPE/ SIZE	REMARKS	SOURCES
American Savoy	85	Fall	Round, 3-5 lbs.	Drumhead type . . . deep-green	10 38
Chieftain Savoy	80-90	Late	8" flattened, 4-5 lbs.	Blue-green . . . AA Winner . . . good for coleslaw	8 15 16 17 30 31 41 47 48 51 52 57 67 70
Dark Green Savoy	85	Late	9", 3-6 lbs.	Dark-green . . . slow bolt	40
Green Globe Savoy	85		Uniform	Deep-green	72
Hybrid Novusa	70		Drumhead	Green	72
Ice Queen	80	Mid	Round, 4 lbs.	Dark-green	66
Marvin's Savoy	100	Late	Medium-large	Drumhead type	14
Perfection Drumhead	90-100	Late	Round, 9-10", 6-7 lbs.	Drumhead type . . . retains green color when cooked	10 38
Savoy Ace (hybrid)	70-85	Mid	Almost round, 4 lbs.	Deep-green . . . AA medal winner . . . good for sauerkraut, slaw, cooking	10 19 29 34 52 53 66
Savoy Early Vienna	85	Mid	Round, 3-5 lbs.	Dark-green	14
Savoy King (hybrid)	82-120	Fall	Semiflat, 4-6 lbs.	Dark-green . . . AA winner . . . vigorous grower	9 10 19 21 29 30 31 48 53 60 62
Savoy Late Drumhead	100	Late	Round, 3-5 lbs.	Dark-green	14
Savoy Winter King	90-100	Late	Round, 3-5 lbs.	Dark-green . . . extremely hardy	14

CABBAGE—Round, Early

VARIETY	DAYS	COLOR	WEIGHT/SIZE	REMARKS	SOURCES
All Head Early	78			Early season . . . best sort for those who plant one variety	14 16
Canada Kraut	66	Blue-green	4 lbs.	Early season . . . good for sauerkraut	66
CC Cross (hybrid)	45	Green	3 lbs.	Extra-early season . . . not yellows-resistant	70
Chogo (hybrid)	60	White interior		Round head	72
Copenhagen	68		5-6 lbs.	Early-season . . . all-purpose	19
Dessert's No. 126	65	Green			16
Earliana	60	Green	2 lbs., 4½-5"	Golden Acre type . . . early	10 53
Earlibird	66	Green, purpling outer leaves	4 lbs.	Badger Market type . . . early	66
Earlimart			4-7½ lbs.		40
Earlitimes			5 lbs., 5-8"		40
Early Dutch Round	70-72		4-5 lbs., 7" round	Second season . . . not yellows-resistant	8 12 16 40 41 48 66 67
Early Dutch Round Dwarf	71		4½ lbs., 7-8"	Produce soccer-ball-size heads	56
Early Copenhagen	65-70		6½-7 lbs.	Early season	16 66
Early Golden Acre	62		3 lbs.	Extra-early . . . small, round heads	21
Early Marvel	59-65	Dark-green	3-4 lbs., 5"		14 66
Early Spring	62		6 lbs.	Uniform dwarf growth . . . round, slightly flattened heads	14
Early Vienna		Blue-green	1½ lbs., 4½"	Early season	40
Early Wonder	60-62		3 lbs.	Extra-early season . . . solid heads . . . comes from Holland	72
Emerald Acre	61		3-4 lbs.	Extremely early season	66
Emerald Cross (hybrid)	65-67	Blue-green	4-5 lbs.	Early season . . . round heads . . . AA winner from Japan . . . Copenhagen Market characteristics	8 10 16 19 21 38 42 52 55 56
Extra Early			6½ lbs.	Mikado Seed growers	40
Ferry's Early Dutch Round	70-75	Blue-green	4-5 lbs., 7"	Early season	12 57 61 67 70
Golden Acre	60-65	Gray-green	3 lbs., 6-6½"	Extra-early season . . . resistant to diseases . . . slaw or sauerkraut	3 8 9 10 11 12 14 15 16 19 21 22 28 30 38 40 44 47 48 49 51 52 53 54 62 65 72
Hybrid No. 39	65		3 ¾ lbs.	Yellows-resistant . . . early	40 48

CABBAGE—Round, Early (Continued)

VARIETY	DAYS	COLOR	WEIGHT/SIZE	REMARKS	SOURCES
Jet Pak Y.R. (hybrid)	64-66	Blue-green	5-6" round heads	Purpling outer leaves . . . early	48 51 57
Stokes Early Hybrid	68	Green	3-5 lbs.	Early	66
Stonehead (hybrid)	50-70	Blue-green	3½ lbs., 6"	Extra-early . . . firm head . . . yellows-resistant . . . produces well in small areas . . . AA winner	9 10 11 12 14 30 47 51 52 53 57 62 70 72
Sun Up	64	Blue-green	20"	Early	22
Superette (hybrid)	66	Silvery-blue-green	3-5 lbs., 5½-6"	Second early season . . . yellows-resistant . . . performs best in New York and Florida . . . round, solid heads	57 72
Viking Extra Early	62	Blue-green	4-4½ lbs.	Early . . . Golden Acre type	66

CABBAGE—Round, Mid-Season

VARIETY	DAYS	COLOR	WEIGHT/SIZE	REMARKS	SOURCES
Badger Belle	80	Blue-green		Round head . . . resistant to yellows	16
Badger Blue Boy	85-90	Bright-blue-green		Round head . . . resembles Badger Ballhead . . . stores well	16
Copenhagen Market Late	70		6½" lbs.	Medium-large head . . . not yellows-resistant . . . good for sauerkraut	11 66 72
Globe	75-80		6 lbs., 6"	Yellows-resistant	48 56
Globe 62	80		5-7 lbs., 8" globe	Yellows-resistant . . . good for sauerkraut	40 52
Globelle	80-85	Deep-blue	6"	Grows well in the North . . . good for sauerkraut	16
Gourmet (hybrid)	68-75	Blue-green	3-5 lbs., 5-6"	Yellows-resistant	41 48 66
Great Round Dutch	70		4-5 lbs.	Favorite in the South	31
Greenback	74	Dark-gray-green	3-5 lbs., 7-8"	Yellows-resistant . . . short, flattened, round-shaped head—and firm	10 11 12 16 41 47 48 51 56 67 70
Greenboy (hybrid)	75	Gray-green	5 lbs., 7"	sauerkraut	21 48 51 70
Green Parade (hybrid)	75	Bright-green	7-8"		10
Green Storage	95-103	Green		Large round, flattened top . . . good keeper	66
Jumbo (Large Late Drumhead)	78-107	Green	12-16 lbs., 7½-9"	Not yellows-resistant . . . from Holland . . . good winter keeper	9 19 66
King Cole (hybrid)	68-70	Blue-green	4-6 lbs., 7-8"	Yellows-resistant . . . sauerkraut	16 41 60 66 67 72
Marion Market	70-80	Blue-green	5½-7 lbs., 8"	Yellows-resistant . . . early kraut	10 11 14 16 19 21 40 48 51 52 56 62
Market Prize	66-76	Blue-green		Medium-size heads . . . resembles Early Danish	17
Prime Pak	74		3-4 lbs., 5-6"		66 70
Rio Verde (hybrid)	79-82	Blue-green	5+ lbs., 6½-7"	Yellows-resistant . . . short, flattened, round-shaped head—and firm	17 47 48 57 70
Rio Verde No. 30	75			Slightly flat head	51
Round Dutch	75-78	Dark-blue	6-7"	Cold-resistant . . . does not store well	48 51
Roundup Y.R. (hybrid)	76-80		3-8 lbs.	Slightly flattened head . . . good for sauerkraut, coleslaw, and cooking	17 38 66 70
Shamrock	60	Blue-green	3½-4½ lbs.		48
Stokes Super Ace	68		3 lbs., 5½"	Golden Acre type	66

CABBAGE—Round, Late

VARIETY	DAYS	COLOR	WEIGHT/SIZE	REMARKS	SOURCES
April Green	99	Dark-green		Landgenfiker type . . . short stem	66
Autumn Marvel	90	Dark-green	3-4 lbs., 6"	Golden Acre type	66

CABBAGE—Round, Late (Continued)

VARIETY	DAYS	COLOR	WEIGHT/SIZE	REMARKS	SOURCES
Burpee's Danish Roundhead	105	Green	5-7 lbs., 7-8"	All-purpose cabbage . . . good winter keeper	10
Danish Ballhead	100-105	Dark-green	3-5 lbs.	Large, solid heads . . . does well in mountain sections . . . good keeper . . . good for salads, slaw, and sauerkraut	3 9 11 12 14 16 19 21 28 29 30 47 48 51 52 60
Eastern Ballhead	95	Green	6-7 lbs.	Slightly flat head	66
Hollander Short Stem	105	Medium-bluish-green	16 lbs., 6"		51
Penn State Ballhead	90-110	Whitish	8 lbs., 7-9"	Not yellows-resistant . . . good for sauerkraut . . . good winter keeper	10 12 14 16 17 21 49 51 66 72
N.K. Hollander	105		4 lbs., 6"	Stands cold weather well . . . good storer	67
Sanibel	90-92	Medium-green	5 lbs., 10-11"	Good fresh or stored; excellent for sauerkraut	38 48 51
Triple Green	99	Bright-green	Large	Landgezuker type . . . storage type . . . good for coleslaw and sauerkraut	66
Ultra Green	99	Bright-green		Good for coleslaw and sauerkraut	21 66
Wisconsin Hollander	100-110		8-9"	Flattened, globe-shaped heads	11 38 40 48 52 62
Wisconsin Ballhead	100		8 lbs.	Yellows-resistant . . . sauerkraut . . . late storer	62

CABBAGE—Round (2nd Early)

VARIETY	DAYS	COLOR	WEIGHT/SIZE	REMARKS	SOURCES
Badger Market	70-72	Dark-blue-green	2 ¾-3 lbs.	Round heads . . . yellows-resistant	16 41 66
Copenhagen Market No. 53			6"		40
Green Acre	62-68	Green	4½ lbs., 6½-7"	Similar to Golden Acre	14 16 21 66
Harvester Queen (hybrid)	60-80	Dark-gray-green	5 lbs., 6-7" globe-shaped heads	AA Winner . . . yellows-resistant	14 19 51 53 72
Hybrid No. 42	68		3-4 lbs.	Yellows-resistant	48
Market Topper	73	Blue-green	Solid heads	Adapted to eastern U.S.	17 29
Princess	66-70	Medium-gray-green	3-4 lbs., 6-6¾"	Yellows-resistant	51
Prizetaker (hybrid)	70	Blue-green	3½-4 lbs., 5¼ to 5½"	Yellows-resistant	48
Superior (hybrid)	67	Blue-green	3½-4 lbs.		29
Tastie (hybrid)	68	Blue-green	4½ lbs.	Round head . . . Closest substitute for stonehead	48 51 66 70
Wisconsin Golden Acre	67	Dark-blue	6"		48 52

CABBAGE—Round, Small

VARIETY	DAYS	COLOR	WEIGHT/SIZE	REMARKS	SOURCES
Baby Head	70-72	White	2½-3 lbs., 2½"	Not yellows-resistant . . . early Danish Ball Head type . . . miniature . . . late storage . . . slaw, salad, or cooked	16 19 66
Early Greenball	63	Green	2 ½ lbs.	Globe-shaped head, 4"	66
Early Shipper	60-65		2 ½ lbs.	Similar to Golden Acre	16
Morden Dwarf				Novel midget cabbage . . . 4" round head, from Canada . . . sweet, crisp, tender	11 21

CABBAGE—Flat

VARIETY	DAYS	SEASON	WEIGHT/SIZE	REMARKS	SOURCES
All Seasons	85-90	Late-mid	12 lbs., 10-12"	Yellows-resistant . . . good for winter storage, sauerkraut	14 16 28 49 53 67
Autumn King	105	Late	10-12 lbs., flat head	Dark-green . . . good for storage	62
Centennial Dutch Flat					31
Early Dwarf Flat	71	Medium-early	4-5 lbs.	Good keeper	21

CABBAGE—Flat (Continued)

VARIETY	DAYS	SEASON	WEIGHT/SIZE	REMARKS	SOURCES
Gurney's Giant	105		20-25 lbs.	Drumhead	
Johnson's Drumhead	105	Main crop	12-16 lbs., large, flat		14
Large Dutch Late Flat	100	Late	12-15 lbs., flat head		56
Late Flat Dutch	100-110	Late	Up to 15 lbs., 6" solid	From Europe . . . bluish-green . . . good winter keeper	8 14 28 51 65
Late Premium Dutch Flat	100-105	Late	8-14 lbs., 12"	Grows slowly	10 12 16 30 40 47 49 52 62 67 73
OS Cross (hybrid)	75-88		8-10 lbs. 4" flat-top	Blue-green . . . huge heads	67
Steins Early Dutch Flat	75-85	Early	5½-6 lbs., 8-9" nearly round	Good keeper	8 10 14 16 40 47 55 56 62 65
Wisconsin All Seasons	90-95	Mid	9 lbs., 10-12" flat, sloped	Blue . . . yellows-resistant . . . good winter keeper	16 40 52 56 62

CABBAGE—Pointed

VARIETY	DAYS	SEASON	WEIGHT/SIZE	REMARKS	SOURCES
Charleston or Large Wakefield (Long Island Wakefield)	70-75	Early	4-5 lbs., conical 8"	Dark-green	11 12 14 31
Early Jersey Wakefield	62-70	Extra-early	2-3 lbs., conical	Dark-green . . . raw or cooked	8 10 12 14 17 21 29 30 31 40 41 47 49 50 51 53 55 56 65 67 72 73
Jersey Queen	58-63	Extra-early	2-3 lbs., small, pointed	Disease-resistant . . . dark-green	21 28 38 52 62
Jersey Wakefield	70-75	Early	2-3 lbs., pointed	Good for slaw or boiling	19 53 72

CABBAGE—Potato

VARIETY	DAYS	SEASON	WEIGHT/SIZE	REMARKS	SOURCES
Cabatoes				Green cabbage grows above the ground, while potatoes grow beneath the ground	43

CHINESE CABBAGE—Heading, Long Type

VARIETY	DAYS	HEAD	SIZE	REMARKS	SOURCES
Burpee Hybrid	75	Cylindrical	13 x 8"	Medium-green . . . inner blanch heavily savoyed	10
Chihili	73	Elongated	18-20 x 3½"	White . . . fringed edges	3 14 62
Early Top No. 16		Cylindrical	5 lbs.		52
Michihili	70-75	Long, cylindrical	4 x 8"	Dark-green	9 10 11 12 14 16 22 25 29 30 31 41 42 45 47 48 49 51 52 53 55 56 57 60 66 68 72 73
Pe-tsai	75	Long	12"	Tender, blanched	12 16 50

CHINESE CABBAGE—Heading, Squat Type

VARIETY	DAYS	HEAD	SIZE	REMARKS	SOURCES
Aichi Hakusai			10-12 lbs.		42
Early Hybrid No. 25		Firm, husky		Slow to bolt	29
Hybrid No. 11		Cannon ball type; thick, early, firm			72
Nagaoka Hybrid No. 2	40	Tightly folded	6-8 lbs.	Slow to bolt	42
Nagaoka Pride				Summer, early June	42
Nagaoka WR Hybrid	60	Barrel-shaped, well-filled	6 lbs.		48

CHINESE CABBAGE—Heading, Squat Type (Continued)

VARIETY	DAYS	HEAD	SIZE	REMARKS	SOURCES
Nozaki Early		Barrel-shaped	5-7 lbs.	Green . . . spring, early summer	36
Springtime	60	Squat	10" head, 3-3½ lbs.	Heads slow to bolt	66
Summertime	70	Squat	6-8 lbs., 11" head		66
Wintertime	80	Solid	7-9 lbs., 10" head	September-October	66
Wong Bok	60-85	Solid, dumpy	6-7 lbs., 10" head	Completely bland	12 14 16 36 37 48 50 57 58 70
Wong No. 10 Hybrid	80	Tight, wide		Developed by Dessert	16

CHINESE CABBAGE—Nonheading, Green

VARIETY	DAYS	PLANTS	REMARKS	SOURCES
India Mustard (Gai Choy) (Brassica juncea var foliosa)	45		Chinese mustard green of the cabbage family . . . pungent mustard flavor. . . both leaves and stems are delicious. . . fast growing. . . does best in cool, humid climate	27 45 69 72
India Mustard (Dai Gai Choy) (Brassila juncea var rugosa)	65	Broad, thick stems and leaves; slightly hairy leaves	Broad-leaf mustard cabbage. . . more mustardy taste than Gai Choy . . . grows best in humid climate with lots of moisture	27 45 62 69

CHINESE CABBAGE—Nonheading, White

VARIETY	DAYS	PLANT	REMARKS	SOURCES
Aka Takana		Wide, white ribs, dark-purplish-red leaves	Pungent	42
Baktoy		Has prominent midrib	Resembles immense head of lettuce . . . tender and juicy	14
Bok Choy	50-60	Bulbous, with broad, white stalks and thick, green leaves	Leafy vegetable related to mustard . . . plants resemble Swiss chard . . . excellent for greens	41 68
Chinese Flowering White Cabbage (Pak Choi—Choy Sum) (Brassica parachinenis, baily)	60		Leaves are smaller, and heart (sum) is dominant . . . slightly sweeter than Bok Choy . . . grows best in cool, light, well-drained soil	27 45 69
Chinese White Cabbage (Pak Choi—Bok Choi) (Brassica chinensis var chinensis)	50-65	Outer leaves and stalks are slightly tangy	Belongs to loose-leaf cabbage family . . . gentle hint of mustard flavor . . . grows best in cool, moist soil	27 32 37 45 48 50 69
Crispy Choy, Loose-Leaved	45	8-12 greenish white stalks; 7-8" tall; spoon-shaped leaves	Mildly pungent flavor . . . fast-maturing	10
Japanese White Pac Choi	60	Deep-green, spoon-shaped leaves	Has good cold resistance . . . often picked for cooking as flowers appear . . . similar to Taisai	37
Mizuna (Kyona)	40	Numerous narrow, white stalks; deeply indented, feathery leaves	Highly resistant to cold	37 42
Pak Choi (Shakushina)		Smooth, rounded, open, green leaves; white leaf stems	Bolts easily on exposure to cold temperatures	42
Spoon Pak-Choi		White stalks formed in dense clumps; spoon-shaped, dark-green leaves	Better in warm climates—less tendency to bolt	26 36 42

CHINESE CABBAGE—Nonheading, White (Continued)

VARIETY	DAYS	PLANTS	REMARKS	SOURCES
Taisai	45-55	White, fleshy ribs, thicker at base; bright-green, spoon-shaped leaves	Used at any point of maturity—somewhat earlier in warmer weather	36 37

Cardoon (Cynara cardunculus)

Cardoon is in the same family as the artichoke. It is a handsome plant with silvery fernlike foliage and a large flower head with purple bristles. Cardoon, grown for its young leaf stalk, is a favorite with Italian and French cooks.

HOW TO GROW: Start seeds in peat pots and transplant outside when the plants are 5-6 inches tall. It is a cool-season vegetable requiring 120-150 days to maturity.

Plant cardoon 18 inches apart in rows 36 inches apart.

Harvesting: Cut the plants off just below the crown and trim the outside leaves. Cut the stalks in pieces and parboil them in salt water with a bit of lemon. It can be served in salads or as a hot vegetable.

CARDOON

VARIETY	DAYS	REMARKS	SOURCES
Ivory White Smooth		Spineless . . . broad, self-blanching stems	36
Large Smooth	110	Fine smooth-stalked strain . . . requires rich soil . . . favorite vegetable of the French, Spanish, and Italians . . . piquant flavor . . . stalks are blanched, then steamed or boiled	12 14 16 28 30 32 36 50 62 72 76 83 89 91
Spineless			48
Tenderheart		Plant early in greenhouse	25
White Improved (Cardon blanc ameliore)		Spineless variety with large ribs	15

Carrots (Daucus carota sativa)

Carrots offer the home gardener a tremendous number of choices—so many, in fact, that you can almost select a different kind of carrot for each and every mood. There are long, slender ones; medium, fat ones; short-top, shaped ones; even a bite-sized tender midget that's just right for parties. Here are the choices:

Long, Slender: These are the big, beautiful carrots that you generally see in the supermarkets and wonder why you can't grow them yourself. They grow to about 8 or 10 inches in length and are colored a bright, luscious orange. Examples are *Gold Pak,* which is long and slender, and *Imperator* (which has broader shoulders). There are a number of similar varieties to choose from.

Medium, Slender, Tapered: You'll find these in many home gardens, exemplified by *Danvers Half Long.* They are sweet and crisp.

Medium, Slender, Cylindrical: Exemplified by *Nantes,* this carrot looks like a big, blunt pencil.

Medium, Plump-Shouldered, Tapered: These are the fattish, blunt-shaped carrots that are extremely easy to grow in home gardens. Examples are *Royal Chatney, Goldenheart,* and *Spartan Bonus.*

Short and Fat: This particular type of carrot, *Ox Heart,* looks like it was made by a committee. It is so top-shaped that some gardeners think it looks more like a turnip than a carrot.

Midget Carrots: These tiny, bite-sized carrots make good snacks and terrific conversation pieces. They come as either short, thin, and tapering (*Bunny-Bite*) or short and pencil-shaped (*Finger-Stick*).

Round and Novelty Carrots: As a novelty every gardener should try golf-ball-sized round carrots, such as *Golden Ball* and *Planet.* They are easy to grow in shallow soil. And you'll want to try the long, slender Japanese carrots such as the 20-inch-long *Senko* and the white carrot, *Belgium White.*

HOW TO PLANT: Carrots grow best in stone-free soil. They also need deep, porous soil for optimum growth. Open up hard clay to a one-foot depth by spading in quantities of organic matter. As soon as the ground can be worked in spring, sow seed a half-inch deep a half-inch apart in rows one foot apart. Later thin to 2-3 inches apart.

Harvesting: Pick carrots when relatively small. Big carrots produce woody cores. For a special flavor, plant a few more than you'll need; then thin them when they're big enough to eat.

CARROTS—Long, Slender

VARIETY	DAYS	LENGTH/WIDTH	COLOR	REMARKS	SOURCES
Gold Pak	73-77	8½-10" x ¾-1"	Deep-orange	AA winner . . . good quality	5 10 12 21 22 25 28 30 31 32 38 40 48 51 52 55 60 62 66 70 72
Gold Pak Elite	60			Similar to Gold Pak	66
Gold Pak Improved	60	9-10"			66
Hipak	75	8-9"	Rich-orange	Choice quality	29

CARROTS—Long, Slender (Broad Shoulders)

VARIETY	DAYS	LENGTH/WIDTH	COLOR	REMARKS	SOURCES
California Bunching	75	8-9" x 1½"	Deep-orange		49
Dominator		10-11"	Intense-orange	Slender . . . excellent for processing	40
Fanci Pak	56	10½-11" x 1¼"	Deep-red-orange	Resists bolting	51
Hutchinson	80	12-15"	Deep-orange	Cylindrical	30
Imperator	77	7-10" x 1¼-1½"	Orange-red	Medium-dark-green tops	10 16 21 22 28 30 31 49 52 58 62 67 73
King Imperator	77	9-10" x 1½"	Deep-orange		48 51 57 66 72
Long Imperator	77	7-10" x 1½-2"	Orange	Indistinct core . . . fine-grained, tender, high quality	3 11 12 32 41 47 56 57 70
Long Orange	85	11" x 2"	Deep-orange	Fine-grained . . . table use	62
Short Top Imperida	75	8-10" x 1½"	Orange-red	Bunching carrot	62
Tendersweet	69-80	8-10" x 1½-2"	Orange-red	Sweet, tender, heavy yielder	9 12 19 22 28 34 45 52 53 62
Trophy Hybrid	78	7-9"	Orange	Sweet, brittle texture . . . quick, uniform growth	12 29
Ultra Pak	63	10"	Orange	Like King Imperator, but 2 inches shorter	66
Waltham Hicolor	74-80	8-12" x 1¼"	Deep-orange	Lack of green shoulders	16 40 47 52 57 66
Woodland		10-11" x 1¼"	Dark-orange	Slightly tapered	51

CARROTS—Medium Slender, Tapering

VARIETY	DAYS	LENGTH/WIDTH	COLOR	REMARKS	SOURCES
Danvers Half Long	73-85	6-8" x 2"	Deep-orange	Mild-flavored . . . tender, sweet, crisp	3 10 12 14 19 21 22 25 28 30 31 32 34 39 45 47 51 52 55 56 58 62 73
Early Cross 433 Hybrid	70	8½"	Deep-orange	Uniform in size and shape of roots	16
Park's Munchy Hybrid	70	8"	Orange-red	Sweet . . . retains color when cooked . . . good in salads	53
Primerouge	60	6"	Bright	Danvers type of French breeding	16 37
Sunset Hybrid		7½"	Intense	18" tops . . . Danvers type	21
Touche Hybrid		6-7"	Bright-orange	Superb quality and flavor	38

CARROTS—Medium Plump, Blunt End

VARIETY	DAYS	LENGTH/WIDTH	COLOR	REMARKS	SOURCES
Canuck	64	10-11"	Bright-orange	Northern conditions	66
Spartan Bonus Hybrid	70-77	5-7" x 2"	Deep-orange	Danvers type . . . excellent for juice or baby food . . . good quality and flavor	5 10 12 21 32 40 53 55 66
Spartan Delight	75	10-14" x 1¼"	Orange	Long and slender, nearly cylindrical	32 34 38 48 51
Spartan Fancy	63-67	10-13"	Uniform	Long and slender . . . richly colored exterior and interior	32 40 48 51 66
Spartan Sweet Improved	62	8½"	Bright-orange		66
Spartan Sweet	60		Deep-orange	Long and pointed . . . rich in caroten	72

CARROTS—Medium Plump, Tapering

VARIETY	DAYS	LENGTH/WIDTH	COLOR	REMARKS	SOURCES
Chantenay	68-72	5½-6" x 2-2¼"	Bright-orange	Stump rooted . . . tender, very sweet	3 9 12 14 15 36 45 52 56 62
Chantenay Long	68-72	7" x 2"	Deep-orange	Blunt roots . . . good quality and flavor	16 32 40 51 58 72
Coreless	70-72	6-7"	Rich-orange	No woody hearts . . . sweet	19 28
Goldinheart	70-72	5-5½" x 2¼"	Bright-orange	Tender, sweet . . . good canner or freezer	10 14 25 45 49
Gold King	68	7" x 2¼"	Red-orange	Blunt tip . . . smooth interior	51 57
Hybrid Gold			Deep-orange	Chantenay type	16
Morse's Bunching	65	8"		Sweet, tender . . . never becomes stringy	62
Red-Cored Chantenay	68-72	5½-6" x 2½"	Red-orange	Stump rooted . . . tender, sweet	16 21 22 28 30 31 32 37 38 39 40 47 48 50 51 52 57 58 66 67 68 73
Royal Chantenay	70	6½" x 2½"	Red-orange	Stump rooted . . . easily grown . . . well flavored	10 11 16 22 28 29 32 34 40 51 53 60 66 70 72
Royal Cross Hybrid	70	7" x 1¾"	Orange-red	Vigorous, uniform growing . . . good for cooking, canning, freezing	16

CARROTS—Medium Cylindrical, Blunt End

VARIETY	DAYS	LENGTH/WIDTH	COLOR	REMARKS	SOURCES
Amsterdam Forcing	72	Medium x Medium-large	Deep-orange	Early, forcing, stump rooted	14 72
Coreless Amsterdam	55	6-7"	Salmon-red	Long and sweet	66
Gold Coin	70	6½-7"	Orange-red	Very sweet, pleasant, scented flavor	14
Klondike Nantes	56	7-8"	Deep-orange	High sugar content . . . tender . . . good canner or freezer	21 66
Long Type Nantes	62	7-8"		Recommended for bulk storage	66
Morse's Bunching	65	7-8"		Sweet, tender . . . short tops	62
Nantes Half-Long Coreless	68-70	6-8" x 1¼"	Bright-orange	Tender . . . high-quality freezer . . . small top	3 9 10 11 12 14 21 25 38 53 57 58 62 66
Scarlet Nantes (Early Coreless) (Nantes Coreless)	68-70	6-8" x 1½"	Uniform orange	Sweet, fine flavor . . . good freezer	21 22 29 30 32 34 37 39 40 46 51 52
Super Nantes	62	8"	Bright-orange	Perfect cylinder . . . blunt ends	66
Sweetheart	70	6" x 1½"	Deep-orange	Very sweet, tender, brittle . . . blunt end	53
Touchon	70-75	6-7" x 1½"	Red-orange	Cylinder-shaped . . . excellent quality	14 15 21 50 51 66 72

CARROTS—Round

VARIETY	DAYS	LENGTH/WIDTH	COLOR	REMARKS	SOURCES
Golden Ball	58	2" round		Early	72
Gold Nugget	71	2-3" x 2"	Golden orange	Top shaped, golf-ball shape	21 28
Konfrix			Orange	Very round and very early ... flavorful ... ideal for forcing	68
Parisian Carrot	60	2" x 1½"	Deep-orange	Ripen early	27
Planet	55	1½"	Deep-orange	Beet-shaped	66

CARROTS—Small

VARIETY	DAYS	LENGTH/WIDTH	COLOR	REMARKS	SOURCES
Bunny Bite		1½" x ¾"		Tapering Chantenay type	60
Carrot Sucuram	70			Tapering baby carrot ... very sweet	50
Finger Stick	65		Rich-orange	Extra sweet Nantes type	19
Jungs First of All	65	3-4"	Deep-orange	Does well in almost any kind of soil ... tender, sweet, fine-grained Nantes type	38
Little Finger	65	3½" x ⅝"	Orange	Cylindrical, with small core and smooth skin ... Nantes type	10 72
Ox Heart (Guernade)	70-75	4-6" x 4"	Deep-orange	Short and fat ... good for home gardens ... tops are small, easily dug ... tender, good keeper	14 15 28 32 47 50 56 58 62
Short N Sweet	68	3½-4" x 2"	Bright-orange	Good in heavy soils ... tapering	10
Tiny Sweet	62-65	3"	Golden-orange	Good in salads, pickled, cooked ... tapering	9 21 28 53 62

CARROTS—Unusual Varieties

VARIETY	DAYS	LENGTH/WIDTH	COLOR	REMARKS	SOURCES
Belgium White	75		White	Mild ... add to salads	26 50
Imperial	77	3 feet x narrow	Salmon-orange	From Japan ... longest carrot known ... crisp and sweet	26
Kintoki Regular Strain	Spring	10"	Crimson	From Japan ... very tender	26 36
Senko	120	20"	Deep-orange	From Japan ... long roots ... fine flavor	36

Cauliflower (Brassica oleracera var. botrytis)

Cauliflower is one of those delicious vegetables that can sometimes be a bit finicky. This is a cool-weather crop for early-summer and fall harvest.

You have a choice of green and purple as well as the white types. Most of the white plants are variations of the super-mounding Snowball strain. These all generally have a large, deep, more-or-less dome-shaped head. Varieties also differ as to early or late maturity.

Snowball: *Snow King* and *Snow Crown* are fast-growing, early snowball types. *Self-Blanch* produces vigorous, curled, upright leaves that will self-wrap, shading the curds from the sun during the cool weather.

Both purple and green forms of cauliflower are popular novelties. Both change color to light green when cooked and taste exactly like white cauliflower.

Colored Plants: *Early Purple Head* (110 days) resembles cauliflower with a purple head. It is not necessary to tie the leaves over the head. *Chartreuse* (115 days) matures bright green. Cooks boast that it tastes better than regular cauliflower.

HOW TO PLANT: Where springs are fairly cool but frost-free, set out plants in early spring. But if summers are hot in your area, set out the plants in late July or August. For best results decide on the maturity date desired for your area, then work backward to the planting date.

You can start cauliflower indoors from seed in peat pots or flats—it generally takes about 50 days before the plants are ready to set out. You can also buy them locally from nurseries. Plant 2½-3 feet apart in rows 2 feet apart.

When the cauliflower begins to head, you must "blanch" the buds—that is, keep them from turning green by shielding the head from the sun. You do this by pulling a few outer leaves over the head, gathering the tops of the leaves together, and tying them loosely with a string or rubber band. For purple-headed or green cauliflower (as mentioned), blanching is unnecessary.

Harvesting: Pick cauliflower as soon as the heads fill out—otherwise they will lose quality.

CAULIFLOWER—Early

VARIETY	DAYS	HEADS	REMARKS	SOURCES
Abuntia	46	Crisp, white, medium	Highest quality	68
Bravo	48	Large heads protected by leaves		72
Daybreak	48	Large, white, not easily discolored	Grows vigorously, and every plant makes a head	19
Dwarf Erfurt	54	Large, white	Snowball type . . . oldest, yet most popular type	14
Early Abundance	47	Large, white, do not discolor	Extra-early	66
Early King	54	Large, white, 5" across	Large, much deeper, and more solid heads than Snowball	14
Early Pearl				16
Early Snowball (Snow Drift)	55-80	Medium-white, 6-7¼"	Close, compact heads . . . standard main crop	9 12 19 28 30 32 38 40 45 51 55 56 58 60 62 65 66 67 68
Master		Large, heavy, white	Uniform and productive	56
Pioneer		Large	Snowball type . . . very early heads of fine texture . . . hardy and frost-free	8 22 45
Snowball		9-14", solid white	Early . . . excellent for the South	3 14 30 55
Snowball Imperial		Large, deep, smooth white	Well-adapted to a wide range of conditions	57
Snowball M	58	Large, white	Noticeably uniform heads	16 70
Snowball 16		7-9" round, firm, snowwhite	Dwarf plant	14 16 47 51
Snow Crown (hybrid)	50-55	5-9" tight white; up to 2 lbs. each	Snowball type . . . AA Silver winner . . . good fresh or frozen	5 10 12 19 21 25 29 32 34 48 53 66 68 70
Snow Imperial	58	Deep dome, white	Has smooth texture . . . use fresh or frozen	29 32
Snow King (hybrid)	45-60	5½-9" flattish, creamy white, over 2 lbs.	Snowball type . . . AA winner . . . erect plants of good quality . . . heat-tolerant . . . good freezer	5 10 12 21 22 25 30 31 34 38 52 53 60 68 70
Super Snowball (Burpeeana) (Early Snowball A)	55-60	6½" dome	Dwarf plants very popular with home gardeners . . . freezes well	3 5 10 11 14 16 21 22 25 28 37 38 40 41 47 48 49 51 52 53 62 66 67 70
Snowball T-2		Large, deep white	Medium-large plants . . . heads are firm and smooth . . . extra-early	16
Tropical Snow 55	52	Medium	Not for spring sowing . . . very early, maturing before Snowball types	37
White horse	55	Uniform deep, snow-white, firm heads	Heads are finer and deeper than Snowball	66
Whitney Hybrid		Medium, globular white, firm and smooth	Early maturity . . . wide adaption to climates and soils	16

CAULIFLOWER—Early-Mid

VARIETY	DAYS	HEADS	REMARKS	SOURCES
Clou	67	6½" pure white	Earlier than Igloo	66
Dry Weather (Danish Giant)	67	2-3 lbs, snow-white, large heads	Needs little water	9 14 36 52 62
Ideal	60		Very fine heavy crop	72
Idol Original	62	Large, heavy, white	Suitable for growing in any soil	66
Monarch (Snowball)		Well-rounded, firm		16 32
Perfected Snowball	65	Solid	Main crop type	66 70
Snowball D	65	6½" medium-large, pure-white heads	Dwarf plants	51
Snowball E (Medium Early)	58-66	7½" large, white heads	Performs especially well in eastern states	11 16 73
Snowball Y	65-70	6½" medium-large, smooth and heavy	Very reliable under adverse conditions	5 11 16 20 40 51 54 66 72
Snowball X	60-64	Thick, firm, pure-white	Similar to Snowdrift . . . strong outer leaves	5 11 16 20 54 72
Snowmound	60	Medium-sized, white	Snowball improved . . . sturdy	66
Super Danamerica	66	Solid-white	Short stalk . . . medium-early	14

CAULIFLOWER—Early-Mid (Continued)

VARIETY	DAYS	HEADS	REMARKS	SOURCES
Super Junior	57		A Stokes seed introduction . . . excellent under adverse conditions	66
White Princess	60	Deep, uniform	Very dependable cauliflower . . . reliable under adverse conditions	70

CAULIFLOWER—Purple and Green

VARIETY	DAYS	HEADS	REMARKS	SOURCES
Chartreuse (Green Ball)	115	8½" bright-green heads	Tall, spreading plants . . . good freezer	16 66 68
Italian Purple Bronze				12
Purple Giant				16
Purple Head	80-110		Flavor like broccoli . . . turns green when cooked . . . good freezer	10 22 28 30 49 66 72
Royal Purple Head	85-95		Good freezer . . . flavor like broccoli	21 29 53
Sicilian Purple	85	Large, deep-purple heads	Mild flavor . . . good freezer	50
St. Valentine	70	Bluish-green	Broccoli type	51

Celeriac (Apium graveolens rapaceum)

Celeriac, a close relative of celery, forms rough, knobby, rounded roots that are peeled and used in soups and stews. The foliage of the celeriac is a beautiful deep green, and the dark-green stems are hollow. Sometimes celeriac is called turnip root. Most celeriac varieties are fairly similar. Two of the best are *Alabaster,* with large, thick roots, and *Giant Smooth Prague. Marble Ball* is a heavy yielder that is free of side shoots.

Harvesting: (1) Pull up the plant when the root has swollen to 3 to 4 inches wide and cut off the top; or (2) snip off the side roots and hill the soil over the swollen root as it is beginning to form. This partially blanches it. Harvest when the root is 3 to 4 inches wide.

HOW TO PLANT: In hot climates start in late summer from seeds or transplants. In mild climates you can set out seeds in early spring. To grow from seeds, soak seeds first, then plant in flats or peat pots. They germinate in about 10 days. Transplant when seedlings reach about 6 inches high. Work in fertilizer and space 6-8 inches apart in rows 24-30 inches apart. When the plants are about half-grown, feed them at regular intervals. Make sure celeriac receives plenty of water throughout its growing period.

CELERIAC

VARIETY	DAYS	PLANTS	REMARKS	SOURCES
Alabaster	120	Large, thick root grows to 4"	White flesh, similar to celery . . . good in vegetable soup	10
Balder L.D.	120	Ball-shaped	Fine inner color and texture . . . good Danish celeriac	37
Celeriac (Knob Celery)	110-120	Turnip-rooted celery; best when 2-3" across	Good boiled, in stews or vegetable soup, raw, grated . . . stores well	28 29 30 31 62
Giant Smooth Prague	110	4" turnip-shaped root, smooth	Soup flavoring	12 14 15 16 25 32 36 47 48 52 57 66 67 72
Globus	115		Wide variety of uses	68
Magdenburger		Large, white roots	Pure white interior	32
Marble Ball	110	Large, solid, big knobs	Yields heavily . . . free of side shoots	29
Paris Improved		Early, large, smooth		15
Prague Model Celeriac		Large	Larger than Giant Prague	14

Celery (Apium graveolens dulce)

Celery is not necessarily easy to grow, but it is worth the trouble. For it is truly a super vegetable, since the root, the stalk, and the foliage can be used in cooking. Celery is a heavy feeder and a heavy drinker. It only grows well in cool weather, and it needs a good rich soil. There are two basic types:

Green: The green varieties have green leaves, stalk, and stem. At one time, gardeners blanched all green varieties to make them white. This is not practiced much today since the newer varieties have an excellent flavor when green. *Giant Pascal* (134-140 days) has stringless stalks and keeps well. *Summer Pascal* is a compact plant with extra-thick stems, and *Utah 52-75* has a crunchy, crisp tender taste.

Golden-yellow: These types are generally self-blanching, with white stems and yellow-green leaves. *Golden Self-Blanch* has a crunchy, nutty flavor and blanches to a beautifully clear, waxen yellow. *Cornell 6-19* has an excellent flavor and a small to medium heart.

Harvesting: You can harvest younger stalks when the plants are still two to four weeks from maturity. Celery stores well in a cool place. Some gardeners leave fall surplus in the soil during early winter, piling dirt and straw around the stalks to protect against freezing.

HOW TO PLANT: Start seed indoors about 10 weeks before you intend to plant outdoors. Many gardeners start seed in closed containers (peat pots inside a plastic bag, for instance), to make sure the seedlings stay moist.

Plant outside, leaving 6-8 inches between plants in rows 24 inches apart. Celery grows best in cool weather. In mild-winter areas, then, celery can be grown as a winter crop.

If you want to try blanching, place a cardboard collar around each plant two weeks before harvest, then place soil or a heavy mulch around the collar. You can also wrap the plants from top to bottom with heavy brown paper held in place with rubber bands.

CELERY—Green

VARIETY	DAYS	SIZE	REMARKS	SOURCES
Beacon	100	9-10" tall	Early . . . short, dark-green strain	66
Burgess Fordhook	130	15-18" tall		9
Burpee's Fordhook	130	15-18" tall; stocky, compact	Always tender, crisp, and juicy . . . ideal for fall use and winter storage	10
Clean Cut	125	Tall and extra-heavy, with upright growth		29
Emerson Pascal		24-25" high	New . . . practically immune to blight . . . full-hearted . . . stems are thick, smooth, and round	14
Florida 683	120-125	22-24" high	Excellent heart formation . . . resistant to mosaic	16 32 40 66
Florimart	105	18" high	Broad-ribbed . . . taste is sweeter than the slow-bolting type	66
Fordhook Giant		Short and stocky	Dark-green in color . . . good flavor	73
French Celery Dinant			Unique celery that sends out a multitude of narrow, thin stalks . . . has fuller flavor than common celery . . . resistant to light frost . . . can be dried for winter use	50
Full Heart Pascal	100		Full heart . . . improved strain . . . early maturing	14
Giant Pascal (Winter King)	134-140	Tall, thick, solid	Stringless stalks . . . excellent keeper	3 9 10 12 14 25 28 30 31 39 51 52 57 58 62 67
Summer Pascal (Tall Fordhook)	115-125	26-28" tall	Extra-thick stems . . . vigorous and compact . . . resistant to blight	12 14 25 32 47 49 53 67
Summer Pascal (Waltham Green)	120-125	22-24" tall	Full-hearted . . . dark-green stalk, rounded and thick	16 29
Tall Utah	90	23" high, 11" rib	Long petioles . . . large heart . . . medium-green . . . head shape cylindrical and very compact	41 47 58
Tendercrisp	105	Upright, uniform	Long petioles . . . medium-green	66
Utah (Salt Lake)	125		Stocky, full-hearted, and compact . . . stems are thick, medium-broad, full-rounded . . . best for late use and storage	14 21 51
Utah-Pascal 15	125-130	24-28" high, 8-9" long	Full heart . . . plants are large and erect . . . dark green, deeply cut . . . for eastern and northern states	11 51 72
Utah 52-70	125-130	24-26" high, 8-9" long	Upright and compact . . . tender yet crisp, and of excellent quality	14 16 32 34 37 38 40 51 52 60 66 70 72
Winter Queen	125	24" upright	High-quality, late and long-keeping	14

CELERY—Golden Yellow

VARIETY	DAYS	SIZE	REMARKS	SOURCES
Cornell 16-19	100	18-22" high	Thick, well-rounded . . . main crop . . . Fusarium yellow resistant	16 66
Dwarf Golden Self-Blanching	85-100	18-22" high	Crisp, solid, stringless . . . compact . . . adapted to all areas	11 14 16
Florida Golden	118	22-24" high, 8-9" long	Thick, broad, blond	14
Golden Phenomenal		Tall	Exquisite flavor . . . blond-green leaves with strong, wide-ribbed stalks	36
Golden Plume (Wonderful)	85-118		Early, self-blanching, stringless	28 30 38 66
Golden Plume 4162	35	24-26" high, 7½-8½" long	Full-hearted	14
Golden Yellow Self-Blanching (American) (Fall Dwarf Strain)	80-118	20" high, 7" stalks	Compact . . . excellent for home gardens . . . popular for late crop	5 10 12 19 21 22 25 30 32 37 40 47 49 51 52 56 58 67 68 72
Golden Tall Self-Blanching	110	20-30" high	Earlier than dwarf strain . . . medium-thick stalks . . . delicate flavor	14 16 31 62
Processer		18" high	Compact	40
Resistant Golden Plume		25-27" high, 7½-8½" stalks	Resistant to Fusarium yellows . . . compact and straight, full hearts are thick, solid, and of fine quality	14

CELERY—Pink and Red

VARIETY	DAYS	SIZE	REMARKS	SOURCES
Pink Celery	120		From England . . . color remains after cooking	26
Red Celery	120		Adds color to salads and dressings	28

CELTUCE

VARIETY	DAYS	SIZE	REMARKS	SOURCES
Celtuce	45-85		Combines goodness of lettuce and celery . . . may be used as lettuce or "boiling" greens . . . chief value is the heart of the central stalk, which can be eaten raw	19 22 28 50 66 72

Chicory (Chicorium intybus)

Chicory comes in several forms: *Large-rooted Magdeburg* grows about 15 inches long with upright foliage. The roots grow 12-14 inches long (2-2½ inches thick at the shoulder) and are sometimes ground and blended with coffee.

Small-rooted Cicoria Catalogna, or Radichetta (Asparagus Chicory), is a rapid-growing annual that has the appearance of a dandelion plant with toothed, curled leaves. Both leaves and stalks are edible and have a faint asparagus taste. *Cicoria San Pasquale* (all seasons) is similar to *Radichetta* but has lighter-green and more finely cut leaves—use for greens.

Witloof Chicory (French or Belgian Endive) is a tall, leafy plant whose roots are harvested like parsnips, then forced to develop edible tops.

HOW TO PLANT: Sow seed a quarter inch deep, then thin to 4-8 inches apart in rows 18-24 inches apart.

How to Force Chicory to Produce Belgian Endive: All varieties can be used, but *Witloof* is the best choice. Sow seed as above in May or June (if sown too early, the roots will be too large for forcing). Dig the roots in the fall, and cut off the top 2 inches above the crown. Wash and trim roots to 9 inches long. Remove all the leaves except for the single central bud. Next, place roots with the buds pointing up in a 2-foot-deep bed of moist sand. Cover the roots with 6-10 inches of sand kept damp and at room temperature. Remove the blanched heads in 4-6 weeks by snapping them from the root. You can also place five or six roots in an 8- to 10-inch flowerpot filled with sand. Pack damp sand over the roots. Place a larger pot over the bottom one and cover the hole.

CHICORY

VARIETY	DAYS	REMARKS	SOURCES
Gebo		Slender, well-closed heads . . . heavy yields	32 66
Magdeburg (Coffee Chicory) (Large Rooted)	55-100	The only large-rooted variety . . . roots are long and tapered, and can be ground and used in coffee . . . grow 15" in height, 14-16" in root	12 16 36 47 68 72
Radichetta (Asparagus) (Catalogna) (Ciccoria)	52-75	Toothed, curled, and green . . . 3" wide tender stalks are small . . . cook like asparagus	12 14 16 29 30 32 40 50 66 68 72 91
Radichetta (F & P Strain)		Suitable for spring sowing	16
Rouge De Verone Chicory	85	Red-green color . . . good in salads	15 50
San Pasquale (All Seasons)	70	Light-green, finely cut . . . similar to Radichetta, but lighter-green . . . small, very tender	12 16 66
Sugarhat	86	Medium-green outer leaves . . . leaves are tender . . . sweet, yet tangy taste . . . good in tossed salads or cooked	10
Witloof (French Endive) (Large Brussels)	70-140	Fall and winter . . . solid heads, cluster of blanched leaves are 4-6" long . . . sharp flavor good in salads	10 12 14 15 16 25 29 30 36 47 48 49 50 52 62 66 72 77 84 91
Witloof Improved	110	Heads are 5-6" . . . leaf stalks are broad	15

Collards (Brassica oleracea acephala)

Collards are rather old as vegetables go, having been used as food for at least 4,000 years. In this country they have long been a favorite in Southern gardens with every Southern cook having a favorite receipe for hog jowls and collards. Today, they are rapidly taking their place along with the other delicious greens such as spinach, mustard greens, and kale (a close relative of collards).

Collards generally resemble a lanky, open-growing cabbage with smooth, dark-green edible leaves. They are usually regarded as nonheading, but several types form rather loose heads.

Vates, one of the favorite varieties, has broad, thick-textured, slightly curled leaves. *Morris Heading* has broad, wavy leaves that form loose heads.

HOW TO PLANT: Plant seed outdoors in late spring in cool-summer areas. In other areas plant in mid to late summer for a fall and winter harvest. The mature plants are frost-hardy. Sow seeds a half-inch deep, 1 inch apart in rows 24-30 inches apart. Thin 18-24 inches apart.

Harvesting: You can harvest the entire plant, or you can leave the first six to eight leaves to sustain the plant, harvesting the young leaves over a period of time.

COLLARDS

VARIETY	DAYS	HEIGHT	REMARKS	SOURCES
Georgia Green (Southern) (Creole)	70-80	2-3 feet	Nonheading . . . blue-green, crumpled leaves, with white vein . . . cook whole when young, or loose cluster of leaves at top	10 16 19 22 25 30 31 32 34 36 40 41 44 45 47 48 49 51 53 55 56 58 62 70 73
Morris Carolina Heading				47 51
Morris Heading	85	30-40"	Wavy green savoyed . . . slow bolt	12 17 40 56 67
Southern Short Stem (North Carolina Short Stem)	80	2 feet	Will thrive under conditions where cabbage is hard to grow . . . best nonheading	67
Taits Heading (Cabbage-Collard)	75		Heads fold in center . . . cross between Wakefield cabbage and Southern collard	31 67
Vates Nonheading	55-80	1½-2 feet	Smooth leaf . . . used for boiling greens . . . will stand light freezing	11 12 16 17 20 28 29 31 32 40 41 47 48 51 53 56 57 66 67 70 73

Corn salad (Valerianella olitoria)

Corn Salad, with pale-green, 3-inch-long spatula-shaped leaves, is generally sold in Europe as a mild-flavored green. It is an immensely tasty vegetable that is rich in vitamins and minerals.

HOW TO PLANT: Sow seed a half-inch deep, 4-6 inches apart, in 12-16-inch rows. It grows best planted in the fall for a quick crop. In milder climates it will grow all winter, if protected with hay or cornstalks.

CORN SALAD

VARIETY	DAYS	LEAVES	REMARKS	SOURCES
Big Seed		Large	Popular in Europe . . . early . . . use in salads	15
Broad Leaved (Winter Salad Plant)	45-60	Large, thick		12 67
Green Cambrai		Large, round	Cold-resistant	15 68
Green Full Heart			Compact and cold-resistant	15
Large Green Cabbaging	35		Large-seeded . . . dark-green leaves	14 36
Large Round Leaved	60		Grown for salads . . . very mild flavor	28 29 30 41 47 62
Valerianella				32

Corn (Zea mays)

What we call corn today is a far cry from the maize that the Pilgrims found the Indians growing when they first arrived in America. The reason: corn loves to crossbreed, and unlike some plants, every time one kind of corn is crossed with another, you get something in between. As a result, over the last 150 years corn hybridizers have developed countless varieties. Today you can plant yellows, whites, blacks, popcorn, tall varieties, short varieties, early varieties, late varieties, and everything else.

Yellow: There are literally dozens and dozens of yellow varieties available. The early yellows produce ears in 65-75 days. *Early Sunglo* has good vigor in cold weather and produces 7-inch ears on shoulder-high stalks. *Early Golden Giant* is usually listed as a main-season corn, but it is always one of the first ones ready, and *Golden Beauty* is especially valuable in short-season localities.

Of the main season varieties *Golden Cross Bantam* is the standard hybrid for good-quality golden-yellow kernels; *Iochief* produces two 9-10-inch ears on each stalk; *Jubilee* has deep, narrow kernels . . . all take 80-90 days to mature. There are also late varieties available that help stretch the season.

White: There aren't many white varieties compared to the yellow ones, but they've been around a long time. *Country Gentleman* (shoe peg), developed in the 19th century, has tiny narrow kernels crammed around the ears in no particular order. *Silver Queen* is one of the most popular white varieties. *Black Mexican* is black at dry maturity, creamy white at the edible stage.

Really Sweet: If you have a sweet tooth, try the supersweet, snappy-crisp varieties such as *Early Extra Sweet* and *Illini Xtra Sweet*. Most of these varieties must be kept away from other corn to reach full maturity.

Mixed-up Yellows and Whites: The ears of these varieties have a random mixture of whites and yellows. Favorites are *Butter and Sugar, Honey,* and *Cream and Bi-Queen.*

Popcorn: There are a number of varieties available; take your choice between white hull-less, yellow, calico, and *Strawberry,* a corn the color, shape, and size of a real strawberry.

Ornamental (*Indian corn*): This variety produces an endless array of color combinations. You can also buy them in solid colors. The *midget varieties* make good container or small space plantings. The only drawback is that the ears are only 4 inches long. Finally, for an unusual variety try *6 Shooter.* It produces six ears on a single stalk.

HOW TO PLANT: Wait until the soil has warmed to about 60 degrees. Plant corn in a block of at least three rows—never plant a single row. You can plant early, mid-season, or late varieties for a continuous harvest, or plant one variety every few weeks until about 85 days before the first frost.

Plant seeds 1-2 inches deep, 4-6 inches apart, in rows 30-36 inches apart, or plant in hills 3 feet apart, four-five seeds per hill. Later, thin to the three strongest plants.

Harvesting: Corn is hard to pick properly. You want to catch it in the milky stage. For best results take your thumbnail and squeeze a kernel. If it is just right, it'll squirt out a milky juice. Corn holds peak sweetness only four or five days, then the sugar starts to turn to starch. In addition the minute you pick corn the sugar starts to turn to starch. If you are really looking for top flavor, you must pop it in boiling water almost immediately.

CORN—Yellow, Early

VARIETY	DAYS	STALKS/EARS/ ROWS OF KERNELS	REMARKS	SOURCES
Ashworth	69	5' stalks 6" ears 12 rows	Selected from a composite of numerous early varieties . . . bright-yellow kernels . . . excellent flavor	37
Aztec	69	6½' stalks 7½" ears 14-16 rows	Glossy-green husks . . . deep, rich, golden kernels . . . excellent shipping variety	48 50 60 72
Blitz (hybrid)	64	6½" ears	Extra-early . . . high seedling vigor . . . grows strongly even in cool weather . . . medium-size kernels	29
Burpee's Golden Bantam	80	5½-6½" ears 8 rows	Delicious flavor . . . good for freezing on the cob	10
Buttervee	58	8-12" ears 12-14 rows	Tender, light, butter-yellow kernels . . . high sugar content	66
Earlibelle	71-77	7½-8" ears	Very high quality . . . bright-green husks	66
Earliking (hybrid)	63-66	5-5½' stalks 8 x 1¾" ears 12 rows	Early, high quality . . . scant foliage . . . produces few suckers . . . for home garden or market	11 31 34 38 47 48 51 52 57 60 66 70 72
Earlivee Hybrid	63	7" ears 12-14 rows	Bright-yellow kernels with good flavor and tenderness	60 66 72
Early Dawn	62	6-7" ears 8-12 rows	High-quality, deep-kerneled yellow corn . . . can be used frozen or canned	57
Early Golden Giant Hybrid	63	5' stalks 8" ears 14-18 rows	Large ears . . . main crop, but one of the first ready	10 21 28 31
Early Golden 113	65-68	8-10" ears	For early market . . . deep, tender kernels of good flavor	21
Early Sunglo (Hybrid)	63	4½' stalks 7" ears 12 rows	Tender and tasty for a long time . . . early vigor in cold weather	10 11 22 28 31 34 48 50 52 53 55 57 59 62 67 73
Early Sunshine (op)	65-70	7" ears 10-14 rows	Matures 5 days before Golden Bantam . . . golden-yellow, sweet, tender kernels	21
Faribo Golden Honey	68-70	12 rows	Matures a few days after Golden Early . . . long, tight husks protect ear tips	21
Faribo Golden Sugar	70-73	5' stalks 9" ears 10-14 rows	Medium-early . . . ideal for canning or freezing	21
First In	55-60	6' stalks 7-10" ears 8-10 rows	Usually bears 2 ears per stalk . . . golden kernels high in sugar	21
Fourth of July (hybrid)	63	7" ears 10-14 rows	Extra-early . . . richly golden ears	19
Garden Treat	58	6' stalks 12 rows	Produces high percentage of usable ears . . . high-quality, butter-yellow kernels	66
Gold Crest	67	5' stalks 7-8" ears 12 rows	Straight, even kernel rows . . . nearly 2 ears per stalk . . . heavy yielder . . . resistant to bacterial wilt	70
Golden Beauty (hybrid)	68-73	5½-6' stalks 7-8" ears 12-14 rows	AA winner . . . valuable in short-season localities . . . earliness combined with quality . . . sweet, tender, golden kernels	10 11 12 14 16 19 21 28 30 32 45 48 51 52 57 59 62 66 72
Golden Sunshine (op)	68	8" ears 10-12 rows	Extra-early variety . . . light-yellow, tender, and sweet	3 45 62
Gold Rush (hybrid)	66	6' stalks 8½" ears 12-14 rows	Tender, sweet, fine quality and flavor . . . earliness is useful to canners . . . does well in both North and South . . . tight husks, yellow ears	14 40 47 52 53

CORN—Yellow, Early (Continued)

VARIETY	DAYS	STALKS/EARS ROWS OF KERNELS	REMARKS	SOURCES
Gold Standard	73	5½' stalks 6½-7" ears 12-14 rows	Early, large-eared, yellow corn	37
Hy-Time	68	8" ears 16 rows	Very productive early-season corn . . . high-quality . . . good flavor for roasting, bar-b-que, freezing, or canning	57 73
Morning Sun (hybrid)	72	5-6' stalks 7-8" ears 14-16 rows	Large, early hybrid has proven to be outstanding	47 48 51 59 66 72
Northern Belle (hybrid)	74	6' stalks 14-18 rows	Rugged second-early variety . . . plump kernels, tightly packed . . . heavy yielder	29 66 68
Northernvee (hybrid)	61	7-7½" ears 12-14 rows	Excellent early vigor in cold soils . . . dark-green husks . . . a must for early home gardens	60 66 72
Polarvee (hybrid)	52-55	3½' stalks 6-8" ears 14 rows	Cold-resistant . . . matures 12 days before Early Golden 113 . . . grown in Alaska and Ontario	21 60 66 68
Pride of Canada (hybrid)	58	8" ears	Matures almost a week earlier than 4th of July . . . golden ears with excellent flavor	19
Royal Crest (hybrid)	60	5½' stalks 6-7½" ears 12 rows	Early . . . sweet, tender, fine eating qualities . . . golden kernels	14 32 34 51 57 59 66
Seedway Beauty	65	5-5½' stalks 7-8" ears 12-14 rows	Golden kernels of medium depth . . . dark-green husks	60
Seneca 60	64		Early corn of exceptional quality . . . suitable for home or commercial gardens	66 72
Seneca Beauty (hybrid)	65		High yields . . . nicely filled tips . . . adapted wherever Golden Beauty is grown . . . excellent in Canada	3 70 72
Seneca Dawn (hybrid)	66	7-8' stalks 14-16 rows	Excellent for home gardens and roadside stands . . . good for all areas . . . heavy husks	70
Seneca Explorer	65	5' stalks 7½" ears 12 rows	One of the best quality corns . . . cold-resistant	3 66 70
Seneca Star	66	5½' stalks 7-8" ears 14-16 rows	Vigorous plants . . . produces large, uniform ears	66 70 72
Seneca Sunbeam	62	4½-6' stalks 7½" ears 12-14 rows	Cold-resistant variety . . . very popular	66 72
Shawnee Chief	67	7½' stalks 7-7½" ears 14-16 rows	Excellent quality . . . husks are glossy, dark-green	48
Shorty	65	60" stalks 7" ears	Good flavor . . . deep, narrow kernels . . . good for home gardens	57
Spanncross (hybrid)	58	6½-7" ears 10-12 rows	Extra-early . . . highly resistant to bacteria wilt . . . somewhat cold-resistant . . . short and stocky plant with ears set low	30 52 66 72
Spring Gold	67	7" ears 12-16 rows	Small, tight, golden kernels . . . sweet and fine flavored . . . yields large crop	29 66
Stylepak	86	8" ears 18-20 rows	Wonderfully sweet and tender . . . bright-green husks protect the tip kernels from drying out	10 72
Sundance	69	7½" ears	Highly refined type . . . early . . . sweet flavor . . . bright, smooth husks have extra-long tip cover	29
Sunnyvee (hybrid)	64	12 rows	Excellent golden corn for first early home garden and northern areas . . . superior quality	32 60 66 72

CORN—Yellow, Early (Continued)

VARIETY	DAYS	STALKS/EARS ROWS OF KERNELS	REMARKS	SOURCES
Trucker's Favorite (hybrid)	68-115	14-18 rows	Popular with roadside stands . . . tender yellow kernels . . . excellent for roasting ears or freezing . . . there is also a white variety	28 56
Wisconsin 900 (hybrid)	79	5-6' stalks 12-14 rows	Early hybrid often produces 2 ears per stalk . . . excellent for sweetness and tenderness . . . good for home gardens	38 52
Yellow Dent (op)	85	6-7' stalks 9" ears 16 rows	Tender, yellow kernels . . . used primarily for roasting ears	53 55
Yukon Hybrid	75	7-7½' stalks 8-9" ears 16 rows	A good early hybrid with outstanding flavor . . . grows under adverse conditions	14 32 34 48 51 57 60 66

CORN—Yellow, Mid-Season

VARIETY	DAYS	STALKS/EARS/ ROWS OF KERNELS	REMARKS	SOURCES
Apache Hybrid	80	7' stalks 8" ears 16 rows	High-yielding, early to mid-season variety . . . bright golden kernels . . . sweet, outstanding flavor . . . tolerant to disease	14 60
Aristogold (hybrid)	85	8' stalks 9-10" ears 16-18 rows	High-quality . . . outstanding hybrid	70
Aristogold Bantam Evergreen	85-90	9' stalks 9-10" ears 12-14 rows	Good wilt resistance . . . outstanding yellow corn of the South	47 55 56 67 73
Ballerina (hybrid)		8" ears 16-18 rows	Mid-season market hybrid . . . deep-green husks provide excellent cover . . . picks easily . . . bright-yellow kernels	40
Barbecue	75	5' stalks 8-9" ears 10-14 rows	Tender, sweet, excellent quality . . . smooth, dark-green husks cover ears tightly . . . good for freezing	10 66
Bonanza	72-83	78" stalks 9" ears 16-18 rows	Good sugar content . . . among the highest quality corn	41 70
Burbank Hybrid	86	6½' stalks 7½" ears 16-20 rows	Sweet and delicious . . . husks cover ears well . . . excellent for freezing	10
Buttersweet (hybrid)		8" ears 18-20 rows	Mid-season variety . . . excellent husk cover . . . bright, medium-gold kernels . . . sugar is excellent and holds well	40
Candystick	75-80	18-24" ears	Thin cob eliminates cobby flavor when frozen on ear . . . 2 or more ears per stalk	21 53 57
Carmelcross (hybrid)	75	5-6' stalks 7-7½" ears 12-14 rows	Best second early hybrid . . . tender, yellow kernels . . . sweet and delicious . . . top quality and flavor	28 30 32 62 67
Carmelet Hybrid	72	7' stalks 8-9" ears 12-14 rows	Good eating quality . . . good husk protection . . . good for home gardens, roadside stands, and fresh market	60
Cheddar Cross Hybrid	88-90	6-7' stalks 8-9" ears 12-14 rows	Main crop variety . . . often bears 2 ears per stalk . . . top-rated, vigorous	38
Cherokee (hybrid)	79		Tolerant to a broad range of diseases . . . vigorous plants, well-suited for close spacing . . . bright-yellow kernels	70
Comanche Hybrid	72	14-16 rows	Tight, glossy, dark-green husks . . . well-suited for whole-ear processing	60
Elephant Ear Hybrid	84	7-8" ears 18-20 rows	Extra-deep golden kernels . . . very tender and sweet	28

CORN—Yellow, Mid-Season (Continued)

VARIETY	DAYS	STALKS/EARS ROWS OF KERNELS	REMARKS	SOURCES
Epic	83	7-8' stalks 7½-8" ears 18-20 rows	Nearly sucker free . . . excellent variety . . . vigorous plants	70
Fanfare	75	18-20 rows	Very high quality . . . replaces Seneca Carmelcross	72
Fairbo Butter Nugget (hybrid)	85-88	8-9" ears 8-19 rows	Pencil-thin cobs . . . tender, sweet, creamy-yellow kernels . . . perfect for freezing	21
Fairbo Golden Bouquet	75-78	9" ears 12 rows	A week earlier than Golden Bantam Cross	21
Fairbo Party Time (hybrid)	85-88	10-12" ears 12-14 rows	Big roasting ears	21
Field's Golden Delicious	85	16 rows	Tender, sweet . . . can be raised wherever ordinary corn is planted . . . good freezer	22
F-M Cross 66	79	8-9" ears 14-16 rows	Remains in edible condition for two weeks after crop is ready	48 70
Giant Golden Bantam	85	7-8' stalks 8-10" ears 8-10 rows	Deep-golden kernels . . . used fresh, canned, or frozen	38
Gold Cup (hybrid)	80	6½' stalks 7½" ears	Grown in Florida . . . sweet flavor	41 66
Gold Winner	79	8" ears 14-16 rows	High yields . . . dark-green husks are tightly wrapped . . . outstanding flavor	66
Golden Bantam (op)	78-80	6½" ears 8 rows	One of the sweetest yellow corns . . . excellent quality, canned or fresh . . . there is also an earlier variety of Golden Bantam	11 12 19 21 25 28 30 36 37 38 40 52 56 59 72 73
Golden Bantam Improved	84	6" ears 10-14 rows	2 ears per stalk . . . sweetest of all, and remains tender longer than regular Golden Bantam	31 48 50 58 62
Golden Cross Bantam (hybrid)	80-90	6-7' stalks 7½-8" ears 10-14 rows	Standard hybrid for quality . . . golden-yellow kernels . . . highly resistant to bacterial wilt . . . dark-green leaves	10 11 12 14 16 21 22 28 30 31 32 34 38 41 45 47 49 52 53 55 56 57 58 59 62 66 67 70 72 73
Golden Cross (hybrid)	82	6-7' stalks 8" ears 12-14 rows	Mid-season variety . . . good husk protection . . . tender, sweet kernels . . . stalks show tendency to produce suckers	40 51
Golden Cross VT	81	6½-7½' stalks 8-8½" ears 12-14 rows		51
Golden Fantastic (hybrid)	79	8½" ears	Stays in eating stage a long time . . . excellent growing habits	62
Golden Girl (hybrid)	75	7-8" ears	High-yielding . . . preferred by home and market gardeners . . . excellent quality and flavor	28
Golden Queen (hybrid)	92	8-9' stalks 8-9" ears 14-16 rows	Unsurpassed in quality and flavor . . . extra-rich in nutritional value . . . perfect for home garden or market	12 31 32 47 48 67 70
Golden Sweet "EH"	87	9" ears 14-16 rows	Ideal for home gardens . . . disease-resistant . . . extremely tender kernels . . . has excellent holding ability	22 66
Goldie (hybrid)	80	6½-7' stalks 8" ears 16-18 rows	Double-eared corn with a good protective green husk covering . . . has excellent holding ability	14 48 51 57
Hallmark (hybrid)	83	6½' stalks 8-9" ears 18-20 rows	Bright-yellow kernels . . . full-season processor	51
Harris Gold Cup	80	6½' stalks 7½" ears 14-16 rows	Small kernels of fine flavor . . . fine for freezing . . . tremendous yielder	29
Improved Carmel Cross	70	8½" ears 12-16 rows	Large cobs . . . excellent freezer . . . high quality	66
Ioana (hybrid)	87-89	6½' stalks 7½-8" ears 12-16 rows	AA winner . . . resistant to drought, wilt, and ear worms . . . good fresh, canned, or frozen	10 16 56

CORN—Yellow, Mid-Season (Continued)

VARIETY	DAYS	STALKS/EARS ROWS OF KERNELS	REMARKS	SOURCES
Iochief* (hybrid)	86-93	6½' stalks 9-10" ears 14-18 rows	AA winner . . . 2 ears on each stalk . . . Drought-resistant	10 11 12 14 16 19 21 22 25 28 30 31 32 34 38 40 45 47 48 49 53 56 57 59 62 67 70
Jubilee (hybrid)	85	5½-6½' stalks 8½" ears 16-20 rows	Mid-season variety . . . deep, narrow kernels . . . good freezer, corn on the cob or cream style	12 19 21 32 48 50 57 60 66 70 72
Kanner King (hybrid)	80-85	8" ears 12-14 rows	Main crop . . . yellow kernels . . . good canned or frozen	21
Mainliner EH	88	Tall stalks 8-9" ears 16-18 rows	Slow to convert sugars to starch . . . stays sweet and tender at maturity to allow a longer harvest period . . . excellent home garden type	10
Marcross* (hybrid)	75	5-5½' stalks 7" ears 10-14 rows	Vigorous, sturdy stalks, resistant to bacterial wilt . . . widely adapted in northern U.S. . . . also has earlier variety	16 28 62 66
Merit (hybrid)	84	8½' stalks 9" ears 20 rows	Main crop for processing or fresh market . . . tight dark-green husks . . . bright-yellow, sweet kernels . . . good tolerance to drought	14 30 47 48 49 66
Midway (hybrid)	86	8' stalks 9" ears 20 rows	Full-season hybrid for processing or fresh market . . . excellent yield . . . large ears— texture and flavor of superior quality . . . bright-yellow kernels	14
NK 75	75	6-6½' stalks 7-8" ears 15-16 rows	Good wilt resistance	47 48 57
NK 199 (hybrid)	84	6-8' stalks 8 x 2½" ears 14-20 rows	High-yielding main crop . . . bright golden color . . . excellent flavor	11 32 38 47 51 52 57 59 67 70 73
NK 51036	77	6-7' stalks 7½-8" ears 14-18 rows	For canning and freezing . . . very productive	51 57
Queen Anne	75	6-6½' stalks 7-8" ears 14-16 rows	Good wilt resistance . . . good market variety	47 57 70
Regal Bantam Evergreen (hybrid)	80	7½-8' stalks 8 x 2" ears 16 rows	Attractive golden kernels . . . good husk tip coverage reduces worm damage . . . exceptional performance and high quality	11
Reliance	76	6' stalks 8" ears 16-18 rows	Processor and fresh market variety . . . medium-yellow kernels	51 57
Roasting Ear Delight	63-70	7-8" ears	Fine eating corn	19
Seneca Chief (hybrid)	86	6½-7' stalks 8-8½" ears	Highly resistant to bacterial wilt . . . high-quality . . . excellent for freezing, table use, or market over a longer-than-usual season	3 11 14 29 30 31 32 52 53 66 67 70 72
Seneca Feather	78	84" stalks 7-8" ears 14-16 rows	Good flavor, deep kernels . . . for home and market use	3 57 72
Seneca Golden	72	5½' stalks 6-7" ears 10-12 rows	Mid-season variety . . . outstanding cold resistance . . . high quality . . . good flavor	57
Starlet Hybrid	75	7½' stalks 8-9" ears 16-18 rows	Medium-golden kernels . . . good eating quality . . . mid-season variety	60
Sugar Daddy (hybrid)	76	8½' stalks 16 kernel rows	Heavy yielding . . . sweet, tender . . . great variety for the home canner and freezer	34
Sugar King	78	6-7' stalks 8" ears 14-16 rows	Excellent quality . . . tender and sweet . . . deep and narrow, bright-yellow kernels . . . high-yielding, vigorous	14 48 51 57 66
Sunburst (hybrid)	72	5-6' stalks 8-9" ears 14-16 rows	Large ears . . . sweet, tender, and juicy kernels	28 48 70

CORN—Yellow, Mid-Season (Continued)

VARIETY	DAYS	STALKS/EARS ROWS OF KERNELS	REMARKS	SOURCES
Sunburst Improved (hybrid)	70	5-6' stalks 8-10 x 1¾" ears 14 rows	Tender, golden-yellow kernels well protected by tight, dark-green husks extending well beyond tip of ear	11 57 66
Sunshine State		8½" ears 16-18 rows	Sweet and tender . . . easy to pick	40
Sweetangold Hybrid	82	7½' stalks 9" ears 14-18 rows	Deep-yellow kernel of fine quality and flavor . . . tight, green husks . . . withstands adverse conditions . . . does well in the south	14 40
Sweet Tennessee (hybrid)		7¼" ears 18-20 rows	Mid-season variety . . . developed for areas where maize mosaic is a problem	40
Tasty	75	8" ears 12-14 rows	Exceptional flavor . . . tender and sweet kernels	53
Tasty Vee (hybrid)	76	7-8" ears 12-14 rows	Mid-season . . . light-colored husks . . . outstanding for tenderness and flavor	60 66 72
Tendergold (hybrid)	76	7-8" ears 10-14 rows	Sweet, delicious flavor, extra tender . . . stalks are resistant to bacterial wilt	19
Tendermost (hybrid)	80-90	7½-8' stalks 8" ears 14-18 rows	Deep-yellow kernels . . . very sweet . . . unusually small cobs . . . good freezer, canner . . . resistant to bacterial wilt	16 47
Wilhite Sweet Golden			Mid-season . . . good yield . . . worm-resistant	73
Wonderful	82	12-16 rows	Small, deep-golden kernels . . . ripens early mid-season . . . ideal for home gardens . . . good freezer	29
Wondergold Hybrid	83	7-7½' stalks 7½-8 x 2" ears 18-20 rows	Heavy yielder . . . bright-gold kernels, sweet and tender . . . good freezer, canner	14 57
Y-81	81		Main crop variety . . . outstanding for freezing and canning . . . stays in top eating condition for a long time . . . has nutty flavor	22

CORN—Yellow, Late

VARIETY	DAYS	STALKS/EARS/ ROWS OF KERNELS	REMARKS	SOURCES
Bantam Evergreen Hybrid	83-87	8-9' stalks 9-10" ears	Juicy, tender, sweet . . . freezes well	9 21 37 62
Burpee's Honeycross	87	8-9" ears 16 rows	Top-quality, high-yielding, wilt-resistant . . . tight husks protect ears from earworm and smut . . . sow to follow mid-season varieties	10 45
Iobelle	84	70" stalks 7½-7¾" ears 14-16 rows	A good-quality yellow corn	41
Kandy Korn EH (hybrid)	89	8½' stalks 8" ears 14-16 rows	High sugar content . . . does not require isolation from other corn . . . burgundy-red stalks . . . husks are combined bright-green and red . . . heavy yielder . . . excellent quality	11
Stylepak (hybrid)	85	8" ears 18-20 rows	Excellent flavor and tenderness . . . high yields . . . very deep, narrow, bright-yellow kernels	60 66
Sugar Loaf (hybrid)	83	6' stalks 8" ears 16 rows	Patented variety . . . high sugar content . . . used for freezing	51 57 59 73
Super Gold	90	7" ears 14-18 rows	Tender, good flavor . . . tight husks	73
Tendersweet (hybrid)	84	8-9" ears 14-16 rows	High quality . . . ears are well protected with dark-green husks . . . holds well in the field after reaching picking stage	60

CORN — Yellow, Late (Continued)

VARIETY	DAYS	STALKS/EARS/ ROWS OF KERNELS	REMARKS	SOURCES
Top Style (hybrid)	85	6½' stalks 8½-9" ears 18-20 rows	Excellent for canning and freezing . . . bright-yellow kernels . . . excellent flavor and tenderness	70
Tri Gold	84	8" ears 18 rows	Improved version of NK 199 . . . dark-green husks . . . husky plants	66

CORN—Yellow, Midget

VARIETY	DAYS	STALKS/EARS/ ROWS OF KERNELS	REMARKS	SOURCES
Faribo Golden Midget	60	30" plants 4" ears	Novel, corn . . . sweet, tender, and flavorful . . . high sugar content . . . good fresh or frozen	21 51
Golden Midget (op)	60-65	2-3' stalks 4-4½ x 1¼" ears 8 rows	Sweet, tender kernels . . . fine for freezing . . . ideal for minigardens	10 19 22 25 28 30 37 43 50 51 53 57
Golden Miniature (hybrid)	54	Dwarf plant 5" ears 12 rows	Vigorous . . . produces perfect cob	66

CORN—White, Mid-Season

VARIETY	DAYS	STALKS/EARS/ ROWS OF KERNELS	REMARKS	SOURCES
Silverliner	92	8½" ears	Standard mid-season white hybrid for market and home garden . . . tender, sweet kernels . . . good yield capacity	40
Silvermine	82	11-12" ears 14-18 rows	Exceedingly heavy yielder . . . resistant to worm damage . . . heavy, dark-green husks	41
Trucker's Favorite (op)	78	9" ears 16 rows	Large ears for roasting . . . hardy variety . . . there is also an early strain and yellow strain	14 31 40 41 53 56 58 67
Tokay Sugar (hybrid)	80	Bushy plants 6-7" ears 8-12 rows	Fine sweet flavor . . . pure-white kernels	12 32 46 50
White Delight	85	12-14 rows	Delicious . . . vigorous plant growth . . . free of smut	70
White Jewel	81	7" ears 14-16 rows	High-quality . . . resistant to bacterial wilt . . . deep, narrow, white kernels	70

CORN—White, Early

VARIETY	DAYS	STALKS/EARS/ ROWS OF KERNELS	REMARKS	SOURCES
Aunt Mary's (hybrid)	70		Extra-early . . . white table corn . . . especially sweet	31
Black Mexican	62	5' stalks 7" ears	Stands all kinds of weather . . . creamy white at edible stage . . . if left to mature, it turns black	28 36 37 62
Early Pearl	77	5" ears 12 rows	Tender kernels	30
Frosty Freeze	67		Finest flavored early white for on-the-cob freezing	19
Honey Cream	60	Dwarf plant 6-7" ears 10-12 rows	Delicious, and does not become tough or mealy . . . well suited to small gardens . . . good fresh, canned, or frozen	38
Improved Early Adams	75		An old-country favorite . . . prized for its roasting ears . . . keeps well	31

CORN — White, Early (Continued)

VARIETY	DAYS	STALKS/EARS/ ROWS OF KERNELS	REMARKS	SOURCES
Silver Beauty	84	7½' stalks 8" ears 14-16 rows	Early-maturing . . . fine-textured kernels	22
Silver Sweet (hybrid)	65	6' stalks 6" ears 10-12 rows	Early, tender, tasty . . . bright-purple husks . . . sweet	10
Spring White	66	7" ears 14-16 rows	Small, tight, pure-white kernels	29 66
Tait's Norfolk Market	75	6-7' stalks 9-10" ears 12 rows	Small, tight, pure-white kernel . . . usually 2 ears per stalk	67
Whipple's Early White	80	8-9" ears 16-20 rows	Deep, rather narrow kernels . . . very fine quality . . . often 2 ears per stalk	62

CORN—White, Late

VARIETY	DAYS	STALKS/EARS/ ROWS OF KERNELS	REMARKS	SOURCES
Burpee's White Evergreen	90	7-8' stalks 8-9" ears 16-20 rows	Retains flavor longer than most varieties . . . kernels keep whiteness and flavor when canned	10
Comet	84	6-6½' stalks 7-8" ears 14-16 rows	Good wilt resistance	47 60
Country Gentleman (Shoe Peg)	85-100	7-7½' stalks 8-9" ears	Sweet white kernels . . . good canner, freezer . . . dry grains are thin and narrow	10 11 14 19 22 28 31 34 37 47 49 50 51 52 57 58 62 67 73
Hickory King	75-100		Broad-grained . . . used for roasting or field corn . . . well suited for hominy	31 41 58
Howling Mob	85	7-9" ears 12-14 rows	Vigorous and productive . . . pearly-white grains	62
Illinois 14 x 11 (hybrid)	91	8' stalks 8" ears 16-20 rows	Vigorous . . . fine flavor . . . tips covered by husks	70
Keystone Evergreen		9" ears 18-20 rows	White-kerneled, medium sweet	40
Mexican June	110		Blue and white kernels . . . white at the eating stage . . . roasting ear	31 55
Midnight Snack	84	5½' stalks 7½" ears 14-16 rows	Blue-black kernels at dry maturity, but creamy white at eating stage . . . tender and sweet	37
Silver Cross Bantam (hybrid)	85	7-8' stalks 8-9" ears 14-18 rows	Silver-white kernels . . . tender, unusually sweet . . . dark-green husks . . . not resistant to bacterial wilt . . . widely adapted throughout the U.S.	16 73
Silver Treat	88	72" plants 6" ears 16 rows	Deep, pearly-white kernels . . . good quality . . . heavy yielder	57 66
Silver Queen (hybrid) (op)	94	8-9" ears 14-16 rows	Late variety of truly great flavor . . . snowy-white, tender kernels	3 10 12 19 21 29 30 31 32 47 48 49 53 57 59 60 62 66 67 70 72
Six-Shooter Sugar Corn	80	10 rows	Shoots as many as 6 ears per stalk . . . solid, meaty, sweet kernels . . . free of "cobby taste"	62
Stowell's Evergreen Hybrid	90-100	8-10' stalks 7½-8½" ears 14-18 rows	Deep, sweet kernels	10 11 16 19 21 28 30 36 37 40 45 47 49 51 52 57 58 62 67

CORN—Extra-Sweet

VARIETY	DAYS	STALKS/EARS/ ROWS OF KERNELS	REMARKS	SOURCES
Early Xtra-Sweet	71	5-6' stalks 7-9 x 2" ears 12-16 rows	Yellow AA winner . . . holds super-sweetness for a long time . . . isolate from other corns for maximum sweetness	10 19 21 22 30 31 38 45 52 53 56 60 66 68 70
Hi-Sugar (hybrid)	80		Pearly-white kernels . . . sweet, tender, and tasty . . . bred with extra-high sugar content	28
Illini Xtra-Sweet	85	8" ears 14-18 rows	Yellow . . . twice as sweet as others at harvest, four times as sweet 48 hours after picking . . . isolate from other corns	10 14 21 28 38 39 45 48 49 52 53 55 57 66 67 70 73
Sugar Loaf (hybrid)	83-85	6' stalks 8" ears 14-18 rows	Patented yellow variety . . . main crop variety . . . full isolation not required	29 51 57 59 73
Xtra Sweet	85	8" ears 14-16 rows	Golden kernels	19 22

CORN—Early, Bicolor

VARIETY	DAYS	STALKS/EARS/ ROWS OF KERNELS	REMARKS	SOURCES
Buttercorn	60-65	14-16 rows	Very tender, with the quality of Butter and Sugar	72
Faribo Sugar and Gold	55-60	50" stalks 7-8" ears 8 rows	Early . . . mixed yellow and white kernels . . . extra-high sugar content	21
Pride and Joy (hybrid)	72		Early, large-ear bicolor . . . one of the best flavored hybrids available	12
Ruby Gem (hybrid)	60	7-8" ears 10-12 rows	High-quality corn . . . burgundy stalks with burgundy husks . . . sweet	60
Sprite	69	7" ears 16 rows	Unusually refined appearance . . . tight-packed kernels	29
Sugar and Gold (hybrid)	67-74	4' stalks 6-6½" ears 8-10 rows	Yellow and white kernels . . . high-quality	3 30 60 72
Bi-Queen	92	8½" ears 14-16 rows	Late . . . high-quality . . . resembles Silver Queen . . . yellow and white . . . good tolerance to Stewart's wilt and northern and southern leaf blight . . . excellent home garden variety	10 12 32 48 60 70
Burgundy Delight (hybrid)	73	7-8" ears 12-14 rows	Tender, delicious kernels . . . burgundy stalks and husks	60
Butter and Cream (hybrid)	78	7" ears	Tender and juicy	28
Butter and Sugar (hybrid)	78-82	6' stalks 8" ears	Extra sweet . . . similiar to Honey and Cream	3 12 21 29 30 31 45 46 59 60 66 70 72
Harmony	73	7-7½" ears	Enjoy this bicolor corn from the beginning to the end of the season . . . close-packed, narrow kernels	29
Honey and Cream (hybrid)	78	6½-7½" ears 12-14 rows	Yellow and white . . . long, tight husks keep out earworms . . . extra-sweet	3 10 12 19 30 32 39 43 45 50 60 68
Peaches and Cream * (hybrid)	62-78	4½-6½' stalks 6½-8" ears 8-16 rows	Three strains—extra early, second season, and main crop . . . extra-tender and sweet . . . 80% golden-yellow and 20% white kernels	9 57 59
Pearls N' Gold (hybrid)	80	6½-7" ears	Delicious flavor . . . good, tender roasting ears	22 52 57
Silver and Gold (hybrid)	78	6½-7½" ears 12-14 rows	Both white and gold kernels on irregular rows . . . long, tight husks	62
Sweet Sue	88		Sweet, bright, close-packed kernels	29

CORN—Popcorn, White

VARIETY	DAYS	STALKS/EARS/ ROWS OF KERNELS	REMARKS	SOURCES
Early White Hybrid	90		Short ears, well filled . . . matures early enough for northern area . . . high-quality	72
Burpee's Peppy Hybrid	90	5-6' stalks 4" ears	Good in short-summer areas . . . deep, pointed, hull-less white kernels are large and tender when popped	10
Faribo Hulless White	90-95	3-4" ears	Every kernel will pop . . . almost as productive as White Rice . . . kernels are longer and hull-less	21
Giant White Hybrid	100-105		Big hull-less type . . . crisp and tender	28
Japanese Hulless	83-95	6-7' stalks 2½-4 ¾" ears	Hull-less . . . well-filled ears with deep, narrow, white kernels	10 14 28 45 51 57 73
Minihybrid White Hull-less	95-98		16% greater yield, 29% greater popping expansion . . . finest flavor, tenderness, and quality	21 62
Snow Cloud			Hull-less . . . high-quality . . . unsurpassed for popping expansion	38
Snow Puff White Hybrid		5½' stalks 5" ears	Early, hull-less . . . delicious, tender kernels	49 67
Tom Thumb (op) (Hull-less) (Dwarf Rice) (Squirrel Tooth) (Australian Hulless) (Bumble Bee)	85	3½" ears	Long, narrow, pointed kernels . . . no hard center when popped	52 62
White Cloud (hybrid)	95-110		Really good eating . . . pops up to large size . . . tender and fluffy . . . hull-less . . . short stalks produce heavy crop of small ears having deep, plump kernels	11 29 32 52 66
White Hull-less (hybrid)	85-100		Finest and best popcorn you can grow . . . grand flavor, most tender	19 22
White Rice (Snowball)			Standard variety used for many years . . . pops pure white . . . usually produces 2-3 ears to the stalk	62

CORN—Popcorn, Yellow

VARIETY	DAYS	STALKS/EARS/ ROWS OF KERNELS	REMARKS	SOURCES
Best Yellow	105		Fine popcorn of high volume . . . very popular yellow variety	22
Golden Queen	90	12-16 rows	Large golden-yellow, pearl-type kernels	39
Hybrid Gold	115-120		Pops to large, flaky, tender kernels of rich butter color . . . high popping volume	21
Purdue 410 (hybrid)	105		Yellow hybrid widely used for commercial popcorn . . . unusually large kernels . . . a heavy yielder	11 31 40 52 67
Rhodes Yellow Pop	117	6" ears	Good old-fashioned yellow popcorn	37
South American Golden Popcorn (hybrid)	95	12-15' stalks	3-5 ears on each stalk . . . good flavor	27 50 70
South American Hybrid (T.N.T.) (Late Yellow)	110		Produces heavy ears . . . pops large . . . popped corn has creamy yellow cast	14 51 53 56 57 62 67 73
South American Mushroom Hybrid	105	6-7' stalks 6-8" ears 14-16 rows	Orange-yellow kernels . . . good popping expansion . . . good eating	10 45
South American Yellow Giant	105-115	6-7' stalks 6-8" ears	Pops to large, flaky, tender kernels of a rich butter color	47 62
Yellow Hull-less (hybrid)	100		Exceptional flavor, tender and delicious . . . popping volume unsurpassed	19 28 73
Yellow Hybrid Iopop	100		Bright-yellow ears . . . excellent popping quality . . . deep kernels pop to large size	29 32

CORN—Popcorn, Other Colors

VARIETY	DAYS	STALKS/EARS/ ROWS OF KERNELS	REMARKS	SOURCES
Calico Popcorn	100		Brilliantly colored ears make fine decorations and pop well, too . . . colors run from white to yellows to blues and dark reds	28 66 73
Fiesta	100	4-5" ears	Ears are different colors . . . high volume popping . . . fine flavor	28
Fireside	85-90		Hip-high plants with miniature mahogany ears . . . tender and tasty	21 51
Strawberry Ornamental Popcorn (op)	100-105	2 x 1½" ears	Tiny, mahogany-red ears . . . used for popcorn or decoration	3 10 12 27 28 29 32 45 47 52 53 62 67

CORN—Dry

VARIETY	DAYS	STALKS/EARS/ ROWS OF KERNELS	REMARKS	SOURCES
Garland Flint	105	7-8' stalks 8" ears 8 rows	Some ears bright-yellow, the balance deep-red . . . earliest Northern Flint corn	37 46 48
Hominy Corn (op)			White kernels . . . used for hominy, cornmeal, or porridge	50
Indian Flint	105		Hard Flint corn . . . unsurpassed for grinding into cornmeal . . . multicolored ears	50
Longfellow Flint	118	10' stalks 10" ears 8 rows	Northern Flint type . . . kernels are orange	37
Rhode Island White Cap	115	8 rows	White flint corn of the Narragansett Indians . . . scattered red ears . . . recommended for northern gardeners, where seasons permit	37

CORN—Ornamental, Parching

VARIETY	DAYS	REMARKS	SOURCES
Indian Ornamental Corn (Squaw Corn) (Calico)	100-110	Large, decorative ears in an array of endless color combinations . . . popular in home gardens	11 12 14 21 27 29 31 32 47 62 66 67 70 73
Rainbow	112	Strictly decorative . . . rich color tones . . . used alone, or combined with gourds, foliage or pumpkins	10 32 46 49 52
White Crisp Parching Corn	85-88	Sweet, ideal for parching because of its microfilm skin . . . used in pioneer days as part of staples, traveling companion to hardtack	21

Southern cowpeas (Vigna sinensis)

Although they are called "peas," cowpeas are really more like beans in cultural requirements. There are several distinct types of pea, of which blackeye, crowder, and cream are the best known. As with beans, southern cowpeas may be classified as vining, semivining, or bush types. Also there are short-, mid-, and long-season varieties.

HOW TO PLANT: Plant 1½-2 inches deep, 2-4 inches apart, in rows 2½-3½ feet apart.

Harvesting: Harvest and shell peas before the pods turn yellow, or let the overly mature pods dry and shell the seeds.

COWPEAS—Blackeyed Peas

VARIETY	DAYS	PODS	REMARKS	SOURCES
Blackeye Southern Peas (Cowpeas)	60-85	6-8" long, smooth	Vigorous vines to 24" in size . . . use green in summer, dried in winter	22 28 34 45 47 48 52 53 57 71

COW PEAS — Blackeyed Peas (Continued)

VARIETY	DAYS	PODS	REMARKS	SOURCES
Blackeye No. 5		Long	Vines very prolific . . . easily snapped or shelled . . . excellent quality	55
California Blackeye	75	7-8" long, smooth	Fresh or dried . . . vigorous, heavy-yielding vines . . . resistant to pea diseases	10
California Blackeye No. 5		6-8" long	Resistant to pea diseases . . . semispreading . . . fresh or dried	11 67 73
Extra Early Blackeye	50	Straight, long	Bears heavy and early crop	14
Queen Anne Blackeye	56		Bushy and compact . . . good canner, freezer	67 71
Ramshorn Blackeye			Wilt-resistant . . . early-maturing heavy yielder	31
Tendersweet Blackeye Bush Type			10 days earlier than regular Blackeyes	14

COWPEAS—Brown Crowder Type

VARIETY	DAYS	PODS	REMARKS	SOURCES
Blackeyed Crowder			Fine-flavored snap pea . . . good producer	55
Blue Goose (Gray Crowder) (Taylor)	80	Long, large, speckled pea	Grows to height of 3 feet	67
Brown Crowder	74-85	Long, medium-round, green	Cream-colored seed . . . brown when cooked . . . vine type, Old Mississippi . . . good producer, with fine flavor and quality	28 31 48 53 55 67
Calico Crowder (Hereford) (Polecat)			Seed is maroon, red, and white . . . good flavor and quality	31 55
Colossus Crowder			Outstanding producer . . . easily picked and shelled	55

COWPEAS—Brown Crowder Type

VARIETY	DAYS	PODS	REMARKS	SOURCES
Crimson (Arkansas Pea)	75	Medium-size 6-7"	Outyields Purple Hull . . . excellent taste, good canner, freezer . . . bush type	71
Knuckle Purple Hull		Short, purple	Semivining . . . very prolific	31 55 73
Mississippi Cream Crowder			Large, plump, off-white, dark-eyed seeds	55
Mississippi Silver	64-70	6-6½" slightly curved; green-silver	Low, bushy plant . . . extremely prolific . . . easiest cowpea to shell	31 71 73
White Crowder			Has creamy-white seeds	53
White Purple Hull	85	Purple	Large, plump, off-white seeds . . . Pole cowpea bean . . . good freezer	31 71

COWPEAS—Cream

VARIETY	DAYS	PODS	REMARKS	SOURCES
Cream		Slender	Medium-large plants . . . very sweet flavor	55
Cream 8		Kidney-shaped	Bush-type	73
Cream 12		Round, smooth	Bush-type	73
Cream 40		6-8" kidney-shaped	Orange-eyed seeds . . . semibush	73

COWPEAS—Table Field Peas

VARIETY	DAYS	PODS	REMARKS	SOURCES
Austrian Winter				55
Big Boy			Large Southern field pea . . . prolific vine . . . tasty	31
Chinese Red Bean (Japanese Adjuki Bean)	85	Long, narrow, brown	Very high protein content . . . small bush type	71
Pink Eye Purple Hull	50-85	6-7" long, green	Excellent flavor . . . 18-24" vine that often produces two crops . . . good freezer	28 31 71 73

COW PEAS — Table Field Peas (Continued)

VARIETY	DAYS	PODS	REMARKS	SOURCES
Purple Hull	74	Long, well-filled, purple	Southern pea	48 55 73
Queen Ann	85		True bush . . . good in soup or stews, or baked	71
Six Week Browneye		Smooth, medium-size		73
Whippoorwill		Smooth seed, long		55 73
White Canada Field Peas			Use dry peas for soup, as for bean soup	52 53
White Lady		Round, green	Very prolific . . . tiniest and most delicate of field peas	31

Cress

Several kinds of cress are listed in the catalogs:

Watercress *(Nasturtium officinale):* You can grow watercress from seed. Sow in a small tray, then transplant to a pot or outside to the garden when the plants are 2 inches tall. Make sure they have a continuous supply of water.

You can also take cuttings from watercress bunches you buy in the supermarket. Plant the cuttings in a pot of sand or vermiculite, and place the pot in a container of water.

Garden Cress *(Lepidium sativum):* Also called curly cress and pepper grass, this annual looks like parsley.

HOW TO PLANT Plant a half-inch deep, 2-3 inches apart in rows 12- 16 inches apart.

For sprouts fill a Pyrex-type tray with vermiculite. Sprinkle cress seed over the vermiculite, then keep moist and place in the dark until the seeds unfold. Place in a window and leave until the plants are about 2 inches high.

Upland Cress *(Barbarea verna)* is a dwarf plant with slender stalks and notched leaves. It grows densely 5-6 inches tall and 10-12 inches wide. Sow seeds in rows 12-14 inches apart; thin to 4-8 inches apart and use the thinnings.

CRESS

VARIETY	DAYS	LEAVES	REMARKS	SOURCES
American (Land Cress)	60	Smooth, oval	Similar to watercress	14 32 68
Garden Cress (Curlicress) (Pepper Cress) (Land Cress) (Mountain Cress)	40-45	Curled, plain	Grows to height of 1 foot . . . fast growing . . . used in salads or as garnish . . . delicious for sprouts . . . fine-cut pungent . . . slow to bolt	10 12 14 15 16 25 28 29 30 32 36 38 45 49 50 52 53 57 60 62 66 73 76 91
Pink Cress		Pink, serrated	From India . . . mild, nonbitter flavor	26
Plain Cress			Fast grower	15 32 36
Salad Cress	10		Excellent in salads and sandwiches	10 49
Triple Curled		Coarse	Fairly tall	32
True Watercress	180	Small leaf		15 16 36
Upland Cress (Winter Cress)	60		Similar to watercress, but can be grown on any type soil	16 31 32 36 47 62 67 82 89 91
Watercress	50	Small, oval	Mildly pungent	10 14 25 30 31 45 47 49 50 52 62 67 76 77 84 86 91
Watercress Large Leaf	50		Mildly pungent . . . good strain for greenhouse culture	29 32 66

Cucumber (Cucumis sativus)

Cucumbers are members of the same family as melons, pumpkins, and squash. The vines for most varieties will spread over 6 feet. Each cucumber vine bears both male and female flowers. The first 10 to 20 flowers that are produced on any plant are males. After that there are 10 to 20 male flowers for every female. Cucumbers of course, come from only female flowers . . . so it takes awhile before most vines really get down to business.

The modern gynoecious varieties, however, have all female flowers. These varieties are popular because they start bearing fruit as soon as the first flowers appear. Seed packets always have a few seeds of a male pollinator mixed in.

Cucumbers have a thousand faces, and if you grow enough of them, you'll come up with every possible shape—smooth or warty, crooked or straight, balloon-shaped, cigar-shaped, and everything in between. Varieties are also bred for a number of other qualities, including disease resistance. This latter is extremely important, depending on the locality.

Cucumbers are divided into two families, *white spine* and *black spine*. The spines are miniature stickers that protrude from the warts when fruits are young. White spine cucumbers turn creamy white when completely mature; black spine varieties turn yellowish orange.

The extra-long cucumbers tend to be either oriental (such as the *Armenian Yard Long* and the *China Long*) or greenhouse type, such as the slender, bitter-free *English Telegraph.*

Generally the catalogs recommend one variety or another as a good slicing or pickling cucumber, but frequently you can use the same variety for both purposes.

Slicing varieties: These generally are fairly long and slender and have a sweet taste. The longer slicing varieties (8-11 inches long), such as the black-green-skinned *Longfellow,* are handsome cucumbers that grow well in home gardens.

The bulk of the slicing varieties are tapering and cylindrical, 6-8 inches long. *Marketmore 70* and *Victory* are disease-resistant, and *Ashely* can be used as a slicer or pickler.

Pickling varieties: These have shorter, blockier bodies that are more convenient for making whole pickles. The pickling varieties have a wide shape variation. *Burpee Pickler* is warted and blimp-shaped; *Spartan Dawn* is medium short; and the popular *Gherkin* is almost round and spiny.

In addition to these you can select burpless varieties (they don't give you gas), bush-type (that grow well in small spaces and containers), and apple, lemon, and white varieties.

HOW TO PLANT: Cucumbers are a warm-weather vegetable, so do not plant until the ground is warm. Plant in hills 4-5 feet apart, 1 inch deep, with five to six seeds per hill (pointed ends down). Thin to two to three evenly spaced plants per hill.

Or, plant 1 inch deep, 4 inches apart, in rows 4 feet apart. You will save space if you grow cucumbers up a wire or trellis.

Harvesting: Pick cucumbers any time while they are still green.

CUCUMBERS—Extra-Long

VARIETY	DAYS	SHAPE/SIZE/COLOR	REMARKS	SOURCES
Armenian Yard Long	65-75	1-3 ft. long, 3-4" around, gray-green	Unique fluting	16 42 50 51 57 58
China Long (Kyoto) (Japanese Climbing)	75	15-20 x 2", light-green with black spine	Especially adapted for climbing trellis and covering fences	12 16 26 27 29 50 66 68
Jumbo	65	18 x 3" dark-green, nearly black, with only a few spines	Long and slim	14 27
Sanjiaku Kuiri		1½-2 ft.	Should be grown with supported vines	42
Suijo Long	61	15"	Sweet flavor . . . popular for salads, bread and butter pickles, and mixed vegetables pickles . . . grows well in hot weather and sets early	37
Yamoto Extra Long	65	18-24" straight, dark-green, smooth skin	Best slicer	50
Zeppelin		10-12 lbs.	Outdoors or greenhouse . . . stays firm, juicy . . . can be thinly sliced, diced, or chopped	68

CUCUMBERS—Long, Slicing

VARIETY	DAYS	SIZE/SHAPE/COLOR	REMARKS	DISEASE-RESISTANT	SOURCES
A & C (WS) (Colorado)	64-68	10 x 2¼" deep-green	Fairly prolific . . . contains few seeds		12 14 21 31 32 62 73
Evergreen Improved	65	11 x 2½" glossy, dark-green	Vigorous plant . . . small seed cavity . . . remains crisp after picking		62
Extra Early Express	45	8-10"	Heavy crop . . . good slicer and pickler		14
Force Beauty Hybrid	45	10½-12" dark-green	Wonderful crop		72
Golden Harvest	52	9" dark-green	Extreme earliness . . . holds crispness long after picked		14
Improved Long Green (op)	60-70	12-14 x 2½" dark-green, black-spined	Vigorous vines . . . fine producer for home garden . . . favorite in South . . . warty		12 14 16 19 21 25 30 31 40 45 47 52 56 58 67 73
Long Market (BS)	65-70	8-11 x 2½" light-green black-spined, heavily warted	Used by home gardeners as both slicer and pickler . . . turns yellow at maturity		3 32 51
Marketer (WS) (op) (Early Green Market)	60-68	10 x 2¼" tapered, dark-green, white-spined	AA winner . . . heavy yielder . . . southern growers like this one		10 11 12 14 21 22 28 30 31 32 40 44 45 48 49 51 52 56 57 66 67 73
Sooyow		10-12 x 1½" ribbed and high spined	Almost seedless		36 42
Sunnybrook	60	9-11 x 2½" dark-green, white-spined	All-purpose		49
Supercuke (hybrid)		12" glossy, dark-green, straight, slim	Sweet, completely edible		34
The Longfellow	74	12-15 x 2½" dark-green, white-spined	Perfectly uniform . . . desirable indoors or out		14 21 25 36 52 62
Topsy (gyn)		12-16"	Outstanding . . . sweet and juicy taste		68
Windermoor Wonder (Long Green)	65	12-14"	Recognized as standard long, dark-green cucumber		66

CUCUMBERS—Medium, Slicing

VARIETY	DAYS	SIZE/SHAPE/COLOR	REMARKS	DISEASE-RESISTANT	SOURCES
American Climbing	58	9 x 2½" dark-green	Heavy, large-leaved, climbing vine . . . fruit has excellent eating quality . . . good slicer as well as pickler		62
Armour	65-70	Long, straight, dark-green, rounded ends	Does well in eastern Canada . . . suitable for home gardens	SCAB, MOS	16
Ashley (WS)	66	7½-8" x 2¼" dark-green, white spine	Vines are vigorous and heavily productive	DM	11 12 16 31 32 38 40 41 47 48 51 52 56 57 67
Atlantic Slicer (Hybrid) (gyn)	65-70	Long, smooth	Well adapted to northern and central states . . . suitable for home gardens	MOS	16
Ball Early Hybrid	58	White-spined	Heavy yield . . . size similar to Straight 8		5
Black Diamond					45
Burpeeana Hybrid	58	8 x 2¼" cylindrical, rounded ends	Vigorous		10 49
Burpee Hybrid	60	8 x 2¼" somewhat squared, dark-green, white-spined	Vigorous . . . can also be used in greenhouse	MOS, DM	5 10 14 19 25 45 48 50 52 66
Burpee M & M Hybrid	60	8" dark, glossy-green	Produces heavy crop . . . crisp, white flesh	MOS, MIL	10
Challenger (hybrid)	56-63	Long, slim, dark-green	Compact vines . . . fruit sets early	MOS	48 52 57 72

CUCUMBERS—Medium, Slicing (Continued)

VARIETY	DAYS	SIZE/SHAPE/COLOR	REMARKS	DISEASE RESISTANT	SOURCES
Cherokee (gyn)	60	7½ x 2¼"	Primarily used in the South	DM, PM, ANTH, ANG, LS	16 40 52 53 73
Comanche (hybrid)	50	Long	Early . . . vines give a summer-long harvest	SCALE, MOS, DM, PM	53
Crackerlee		8"	Nice shape and color	DM, PM	73
Damascus Hybrid (Emerald)		5-6" green	Popular in the Middle East . . . smooth and wartless skin . . . great production . . . fine flavor		15 50 53 57
Dominion Slicer (hybrid) (gyn)		Medium-size, dark-green	Adapted to northern states and Canada . . . plants are vigorous	SCAB, MOS	16
Early Fortune (WS)	58-65	9 x 2½" tapered at both ends, smooth skin with yellow-green stripe	Holds its intense, dark-green color and is heavy yielder . . . good slicer or pickler		14 28 32 36 51
Early Hybrid	56	8-9"	Does well indoors or out, from Texas to Canada		70
Early Marketer Hybrid	55	8½-9 x 2¼" cylindrical, very-dark-green	Extra-early	DM, MOS	11 56
Early Set No. 36 (hybrid)		8"	Excellent for commercial plantings		32
Early Surecrop (hybrid) (WS)	58	8½-9 x 2½" blunt end	Holds dark-green color well . . . suited to greenhouse, market, or home use . . . AA winner	DM, MOS	11 12 14 22 25 28 30 38 39 51 53 55 56
Fairbo Hybrid		8-9" blunt end	Extra-early		21
Gemini Hybrid (gyn)	61-65	7½-8"	Pick frequently	ANTH, SCAB, ANG, SL, DM, PM, MOS	3 11 16 29 30 32 38 40 48 53 55 57 60 66 67 70 73
Marketer Improved (WS)	70	7-8" tapered			47 66
Marketmore 70 (WS) (op)	60-70	8½ x 2¼" dark-green	Color does not fade in summer . . . excellent main crop	SCAB, MOS	5 10 11 12 29 32 37 38 40 45 47 48 51 53 56 60 66 70 72 73
Meridian (hybrid) (gyn)	54-64	8-8½" tapered	Specially adapted to northern growing conditions	MOS, SCAB	32 48 66 72
Mirella	60	7" plump, dark-green	Not scab-resistant . . . smooth-skinned Middle East type slicer . . . unusually sweet flavor	MOS	37
Mrs. Slicer (hybrid) (gyn)	57	8-9" smooth, deep-green	Crisp, tender, clear-white flesh . . . very few seeds		19
Mr. Slicer (gyn)	62	6-7" blocky	Slicer or pickler . . . small seed cavity . . . Cherokee strain		28
Nagaoka Homogreen		8-9"	Semiforcing		42
Niagara	63	8-10" smooth, cylindrical	Vigorous vines	MOS	14
Pacer	62	8½" cylindrical	Earlier Marketmore 70 . . . heavy bearer	SCAB, MOS	29
Palomar (WS)	60-66	9 x 2¼" dark-green	Heavy cropper . . . uniformly smooth	DM	14 16 32 40 48 51 56 66 70
Park's Comanche Hybrid	50			SM, SCALE	53
Poinsett	65	7½-8" cylindrical; rounded ends	Improved Ashley Clemson . . . heavy yielder . . . performs well in South	MOS, PM	10 11 14 16 32 38 40 41 47 48 51 52 53 55 56 57 67 70 73
Polaris	65-70		Vine is vigorous and productive . . . may not hold its color well under high temperatures	PM, ANTH, DM	16 31 56 57

CUCUMBERS—Medium, Slicing (Continued)

VARIETY	DAYS	SIZE/SHAPE/COLOR	REMARKS	DISEASE RESISTANT	SOURCES
Poona Keera		Small	From India . . . smooth, greenish-white skin . . . crisp and delicious, the whole thing can be eaten		26
Saticoy (hybrid)	60-65	6-7" blunt ends, dark-green	Holds color well . . . ideal for home gardens . . . long producing period	DM, SCAB, MOS	12 29 32 48 66 67
Shamrock	52	8" tapered both ends		PM, DM, SCAB, MOS	66
Slicemaster (hybrid) (gyn)	55	Dark-green and slim	Victory type, but earlier	SCAB, MOS, DM, PM, ANTH	5 25 28 48 57 70 72
Smoothie	70-75	Very-dark-green skin	Unusually small seed cavity . . . vigorous vines . . . excellent for home or market	DM	16 28
Smooth Set Hybrid (WS)		8 x 2½" tapered	Suitable for production under hot conditions	MOS	32
Spartan Green (hybrid) (gyn)	70-75	Smooth, blunt-end, cylindrical	Large, vigorous vines produce continuously, late into season	SCAB, MOS	16
Spartan Salad	56	Long, warted	Slicer or pickler . . . bears fruit over a long period . . . never bitter	MOS, SCAB, PM	38 52
Spartan Valor (gyn)	60-65	8½-9 x 2½"	AA winner . . . prolific	ANTH, MOS, SCAB	9 12 16 21 25 30 31 39 48 52 53 60 66 72
Stokes Early Hybrid	55	8-9" blunt, cylindrical, dark-green	Heavy yields . . . holds color well	DM, MOS	66
Stono	65	8 x 2½"	Vines are vigorous and produce heavily	Disease-resistant	14 16
Straight Eight (op)	60-67	7-8" blunt, cylindrical, white-spined	Small seed cavity . . . early . . . AA winner . . . very prolific . . . can be used as slicer or pickler		3 9 10 12 19 21 22 25 28 30 32 39 40 45 47 51 52 55 56 58 66 73
Straight 9		9 x 1½" dark-green	Vigorous vines yield well		28
Super Slice (hybrid)	64	9 x 2½" straight, cylindrical, dark-green, white-spined		CMV, SCAB	51
Tablegreen (op) (WS)	78	7½-8" straight, smooth, dark-green	Color slow to fade	LS, SCAB, MOS	16 22 47 48 51 57 66
Tamu Texlong		8-9" slender, straight, dark-green	Strong, vigorous vines	MOS	55
Tenderfresh	58	7-9" deep-green	Strong climber . . . not bitter	MOS	38
Tex Long	65	8-9"	Very juicy . . . mild flavor	DM, PM	28 41 73
Top Maker (hybrid)		6-7 x 2" smooth	Medium-early . . . easy to grow without trellis or support . . . vigorous vines	M, V	26
Triumph (hybrid) (WS)	62	7-8" tapered slightly at ends	AA winner of extra-high quality . . . heavy yields from vigorous vines . . . for home or market	MOS, DM	11 12 14 21 25 29 30 31 47 48 52 60 66 67 72
Victory (hybrid) (gyn)	60	7-8" dark-green, long, straight	Vigorous vines . . . AA winner	MOS, SCAB, DM, PM	5 10 11 19 21 25 28 29 30 31 32 34 40 47 48 52 53 55 56 57 60 66 67 70 72 73
White Spine (op) (WS)	60	8-9"			47
White Spine Improved	62	8-9 x 2½" deep-green	Stays in good eating condition for a long time		12 31

CUCUMBERS—Pickling

VARIETY	DAYS	SIZE/SHAPE/COLOR	REMARKS	DISEASE-RESISTANT	SOURCES
Addis	56	Straight, tapered at ends, dark-green, white-spined		ANTH, ALS, DM, PM, CMV	51
Alice Hybrid (gyn)	50-55	Black-spined		SCAB, MOS	16
Beit Alpha MR	56	Straight, round ends, medium-green, black-spined	Uniform size . . . medium-length vine . . . may be used as slicer or pickler	CMV	51
Boston Pickling	52-58	6"medium-long, rich-green	Good quality		3 12 30 37 73
Bravo (gyn)	50	Dark-green, white-spined, well-shaped, straight	High-yielding	Disease-resistant	22 28 60 73
Burpee Pickler	53	Medium-green, black-spined, warted fruit	Yields over a longer period	MOS	10
Calypso (gyn)	56	Medium-long, dark-green	High-yielding	MOS, SCAB, LS, ANTH, DM, PM	51
Carolina (hybrid)	49	Straight, blocky	Medium-size, vigorous plants	SCAB, MOS, ANTH, DM, PM	73
Chicago Pickling	59	6½ x 2½"squared ends, medium-green	Most widely used for pickling, but can be used for slices		21 25 38 51 52 56 58 62
Chipper	50-55	Blocky on ends, white-spined		PM, DM, ANTH, ANG, LS, MOS	16 51
Dixie Pickler (hybrid)	55	Uniform, cylindrical	Excellent disease tolerance . . . good brining ability . . . good yielder		57
Double Yield Pickling	50		Best variety for gherkins or dills		66
Earliest of All	59	6-7" straight, blunt ends	Highest quality flesh . . . very heavy bearer . . . good for home gardens		28
Earlipik (gyn)	54	5¾ x 2½" medium-green, blocky, white-spined	Early	SCAB, MOS, PM, DM	51 57
Early Quebec			Popular in Quebec city area		72
Early Russian		Small	Exceedingly early . . . prolific		3 72
Early White Spine (Fortune)	60	7-8" straight, squared ends, medium-green	Popular as "dill"		21
Everbearing	55	5" short, blocky ends	Keep picked, and will set vigorously		28 31 62
Explorer (hybrid) (gyn)	50-55	Straight, uniform, white-spined	Adapted to moist climates vigorous and productive	DM, PM, ANTH, ANG, LS, MOS	16 32 51 73
Fancy Pickling	50	5 x 2½" round-ended, dark-green, black-spined	Good-quality flesh . . . also good slicer		62
Frontier Hybrid (gyn)	50-55	Black-spined	Highly productive . . . vigorous growth	SCAB, MOS	16
Galaxy	60	Straight, tapered at ends; Medium-dark-green, white-spined		DM, PM, ALS, CMV, ANTH	51
Gherkin	60	2" chunky, covered with tender spines	Splendid flavor . . . vines are very productive		19 28 47 49 50
Green Beauty		Semiblocky, uniform, dark-green	Vines are vigorous growers and bear early	SCAB, MOS	38
Green Cluster	52	5½ x 2½" uniform skin is smooth, with few spines	Also good slicer		62
Green Spear (gyn)	55	Straight, medium-dark-green, white-spined			51 57
Green Star (gyn)	51	Cylindrical, blunt-ended, smooth, deep-green skin, white-spined	Produces abundance of pickles	SCAB, MOS	29

CUCUMBERS—Pickling (Continued)

VARIETY	DAYS	SIZE/SHAPE/COLOR	REMARKS	DISEASE RESISTANT	SOURCES
Grow Quick	48	Same shape as Chicago Pickling			62
Hilltop		Cylindrical, black-spined, warted	Well-shaped	Mildew	40
Hokus Original	59	Nonridged European type, white-spined	Stays solid when pickled	SCAB, MOS	37
Hycrop (hybrid)	54		Early . . . outyields other varieties		53
Liberator	56	6½ x 2½" white-spined, blocky,		SCAB, MOS	32
Mariner (gyn)	53	Cylindrical, blunt-ended, dark-green	Big yielder . . . excellent uniformity in all sizes . . . holds color in hot weather	PM, DM	29
Mincu	50	4 x 1¾" green, white-spined	Compact vines . . . early, heavy cropper		21
Miss Pickler (gyn)	50	Small, uniform	Tremendous yielder . . . small seed cavity		28
Model	55	Dark-green, white-spined	Widely used as pickling type in South		16 31 51
Mr. 17	57		Vines produce great yield . . . has become canner's choice for fancy pickles	MOS	19 51
N and K 805 (hybrid)	51	6½ x 3" near blocky, dark-green, black-spined	Prolific bearer . . . good briner		57
National Pickling	53	5 x 2½" cylindrical, blunt ends, dark-green			25 32 44 45 47 51 66 67
New Damascus	65		Both slicer and pickler	MOS	15 28
Northern Pickling	50		Not recommended in areas having mosaic . . . extremely early	SCAB	16 37
Ohio MR 17	57	7 x 2" dark-green	High-yielding, vigorous vines	MOS	10 73
Parisian Pickling	60		From France . . . good pickler and slicer		50
Peppi (hybrid) (gyn)	48	Dark-green, slightly tapered	Recommended for home gardens . . . very early	SCAB, MOS, DM	5 25 53 66
Perfecto Verde (gyn)	55	Straight, tapered at ends, dark-green, white-spined	A bit earlier than Earlipik	CMV, DM, ANTH, ALS, SCAB	51 57 72
Piccadilly (hybrid) (gyn)	56	6" straight, blocky	High yields		70 72
Pic-Nik	52	6 x 2½" dark-green	Extra early		28
Pioneer (hybrid) (gyn)	48-55	Medium-green, black-spined	Useful in northern areas . . . high yielder	MOS, SCAB, PM	5 11 12 16 25 30 32 48 51 53 57 66 73
Pixie	50-66	Medium-green	Prolific . . . recommended in areas where diseases are a problem	PM, DM, ANTH, MOS	16 32 51
Salty (hybrid)	50	Up to 5", dark-green, white-spined, doesn't hollow	Heavy yielder . . . excellent for canning	MOS, DM, PM, SCAB	5 12 25 28 31 34 48
SMR 58	56	6½ x 2½" medium-dark-green, black-spined	Excellent	SPOT, ROT, MOS	11
Snow's Pickling	55	4-5" cylindrical, dark-green	Can be used as slicer also		62
Southern Cross (hybrid) (gyn)	50-55	White-spined	Adapted to humid climates	PM, DM, ANTH, MOS, ANG, SL	16 32
Spartan Champion (hybrid)	50-55	Pale-green	Thick-walled, small seed cavity	SCAB, MOS	16 19
Spartan Dawn (hybrid)	49	6 x 2½" black-spined	Earliest of picklers . . . high early yields		9 14 16 28 32 52 53

CUCUMBERS—Pickling (Continued)

VARIETY	DAYS	SIZE/SHAPE/COLOR	REMARKS	DISEASE RESISTANT	SOURCES
Spartan Reserve (hybrid)	50-55	Light-green, prominently warted		SCAB, MOS	16
Spartan Salad (WS)	56	Long, green-warted	Not bitter		51
Sumter	56	Slightly tapered, blocky, medium-dark-green, white-spined		PM, DM, ALS, SCAB, ANTH	51
Tamu Triple Cross	56	Straight, slight taper to blossom end, dark-green, white-spined		DM, PM, SCAB, CMV, ANTH	51
Tiny Dill Cuke	55		Extra-early . . . grows on 2-foot vines		21 53
Trispear	55	Straight, slight taper, medium-dark-green, white-spined		CMV, SCAB, ANTH, ALS, DM, PM	51
West India Gherkin (Burr)	60	2-3" long, 1-1½" around, light-green	Very prolific . . . makes delicious pickles or relish		9 10 16 31 55 60 62 73
Wisconsin SMR 18	56	6 x 2½" black-spined	Best nonhybrid, all-purpose pickling cucumber		3 9 10 16 28 30 37 48 51 52 60 66 70 72
Wisconsin SMR 58	60	Medium size; medium- to dark-green; blocky	Very firm		16 38 40 41 48 51 66
Yankee (hybrid) (gyn)	50-55	Black-spined	High-yielding, very vigorous	SCAB, MOS	16

CUCUMBERS—Burpless

VARIETY	DAYS	SIZE/SHAPE/COLOR	REMARKS	DISEASE-RESISTANT	SOURCES
Burpless	62	8-12"	Not bitter	DM, PM	3 19 21 22 28 30 70
Burpless Hybrid	62	8-10", curved	Not bitter . . . Japanese	DM, PM	10 14 29 34 49 50 53 55 56 57 62 66
Burpless Hybrid No. 26 (WS)	50-70	9 x 1½" straight, dark-green, white-spined	Stake for best results	Mildews	5 25 39 51 52 72
Burpless Improved (hybrid)		8-10"	Peeling not necessary . . . best crops come when grown to climb fence or trellis		31 32 48
Burpless Muncher (op)	65	7 x 2¼" medium-green	Not scab-resistant . . . heavy producer	Mosaic	3 37 57
Burpless Tasty Green No. 26	62	10"	Crisp, delicious in salads		12 68
Green King (gyn)			An intensive and prolific cropping cucumber	PM, MOS, BAC, WILT	68
Green Knight Hybrid	60	7-8" dark-green	Thin skin . . . vigorous	Scab, mildews	10 45
Jet Set (hybrid) (Junior Burpless)		8"	Does well everywhere . . . highest quality . . . can eat skin and all	Disease-resistant	22 28 50
Sugar Slice (hybrid)	60	8" blunt, dark-green, white-spined	Uniform fruit . . . small seed cavity . . . bitter-free	M, MOS, LS, ANTH	32
Swallow Burpless (hybrid)	58	9"	Well-branched produces an abundance of slim fruit . . . smooth skin with a white spine . . . not necessary to peel	M	41
Sweet Slice (hybrid)	62	10-12" slightly tapered, dark-green, white-spined	Unusual sweet taste . . . bitter free	DM, PM, SCAB, MOS, ANTH	5 11 12 15 25 26 28 29 32 38 47 48 52 53 55 57 60 66 67 70 73
Tasty Green	60	7-10" smooth skin, dark-green	Can be used for greenhouse forcing, also sown directly into ground . . . stake for heavier crop	SCAB, MIL	14 60

CUCUMBERS—Bush (Container Culture)

VARIETY	DAYS	SIZE/SHAPE/COLOR	REMARKS	SOURCES
Baby Cucumber		4" pickler	Bushy vines are early and productive	22
Bush Whopper	55	6-8"	No runners	52 53
Little Minnie	52	4" blunt ends	2-foot bushes . . . keep picked, and vines will produce over long period	28
Midget		4"	Extremely early . . . ideal for pickling . . . 2-foot vines	62
Patio Pic (hybrid)	50-55		Pickler and slicer . . . extremely vigorous . . . performs well in hanging basket . . . scab, powdery, and downy mildew resistant	5 12 21 25 26 31 34 52 53 56 60 66 68 72
Pot Luck (hybrid)	50-55	6½-7" straight, green, white-spined	18-24" plants grow in pots or hanging baskets . . . mosaic-resistant	5 12 19 38 41 57 68 70

CUCUMBERS—Greenhouse Type

VARIETY	DAYS	SIZE/SHAPE/COLOR	REMARKS	DISEASE-RESISTANT	SOURCES
Brilliant (hybrid) (gyn)		16"	Bitter-free		66
English Telegraph		15-18" straight, slim, dark-green	Bitter-free		62 72
Faribo (hybrid) (gyn)		14-15"	Used as year-round crop		66
Femdan Hybrid		Smooth skin	Bitter-free . . . sets fruit quickly . . . requires extra fertilizer		32 68
Femfranc Hybrid (gyn)	77	Narrow, dark-green		Scab	32
Fertilia (gyn)		14"	Very productive	Spot gum	70
Gourmet Hybrid (gyn)		14-16"	Bitter-free . . . mid-season slicing type	Leaf spot, Gummosis	5 26 28 72 73
Highmark 11	60	8" dark-green		Scab, Mosaic	66 72
La Reine (gyn) (The Queen)		15-17" ridged, dark-green	Bitter-free		29 66
Pandex (hybrid) (gyn)		17" smooth, extra-long, bright-green			66
Rocket (hybrid) (gyn)		17"	Length and quality of La Reine		66
Sandra (hybrid) (gyn)		16"	Can be grown in any season		66 72
Sandrax (hyrid) (gyn)		16" slender, dark-green	Long-season		32
Seedless Supreme	75	12-14"	European forcing type . . . seedless unless pollinated	Disease-tolerant	5
Sporu Hybrid		45 cm, narrow, dark-green . . . 7-8 per plant			72
Telegraph Improved			Keeps crisp and fresh longer than original		68
Toska 70 (gyn)		14" deep-green	Bitter-free, extremely early		32 66
Uniflora D		14-15" dark-green	Stands up well in hot weather		66

CUCUMBERS—Other

VARIETY	DAYS	SHAPE/SIZE/COLOR	REMARKS	SOURCES
Crystal Apple		Apple-shaped when ripe; creamy-white skin	From New Zealand . . . very prolific . . . fine for home gardens	26 36
Lemon (BS) (Apple Shaped)	64	2½-3" round, yellow	Flat at stem end	12 14 16 29 37 38 49 50 51 55 57 60 66
White Wonder	65	8-10", ivory-white when mature	Vigorous vine . . . slice or pickle	51 52 62 72

Dandelion (Taraxacum officinale)

Believe it or not, the dandelion is a tasty green that can be purchased from a number of sources. It has a tangy taste that adds an interesting touch to salads, or it can be cooked and eaten like spinach. The leaves of the cultivated varieties are considerably larger than those of the wild ones.

DANDELION

VARIETY	DAYS	SIZE	REMARKS	SOURCES
Broadleaf	95	18-24" across	Large leaves, partially toothed . . . dark-green and prolific	32 50 91
Giant Broad Leaf				3
Montmagny (Green Improved)			Very early . . . thick-leaved, with full heart	15 57
Thick-Leaved	95		Large, thick, dark-green leaves are used for boiling . . . may be eaten raw . . . quick-growing	10 45 66
Thick-Leaved Improved			Stocky, very broad-leaved plants with heavy white rib	16 30 47 62 67

Eggplant (Solanum melongena)

Here's a garden showoff. Eggplants grow on tree-like bushes about 3 feet tall and produce beautiful fruit. The culture of eggplant is somewhat like that of a tomato; four plants will produce about 12 fruit, which can be stored in a cool place for several months.

The majority of eggplant varieties have purple to dark-purple fruit—either plump-oval or long-cylindrical. *Black Beauty* is the favorite in the plump-oval class, but don't forget the several dozen other excellent varieties. *Dusky* and *Royal Knight* are popular varieties of the long-cylindrical type.

In addition there are eggplants with green, yellow, and white fruit, plus several midget varieties—*Slim Jim* will grow in 6-inch pots.

HOW TO PLANT: To grow eggplant from seed, place seeds a third- to a half-inch deep in peat pots. It takes three weeks for the seeds to germinate and another eight to ten weeks before they are ready to set out. You can also buy plants from local nurseries. Plant seedlings 25 inches apart in rows 3 feet apart.

Harvesting: Pick your eggplants before they start to lose their glossy shine—after that they'll be tough. Be sure to keep picking the fruits as they become ready, so that the plants will continue to bear.

EGGPLANT—Oval

VARIETY	DAYS	SIZE	COLOR	HEIGHT/REMARKS	SOURCES
Beauty Hybrid	65-70		Glossy-black	Slightly smaller than Black Beauty . . . tolerant to fusarium	5
Black Beauty	73-80	Globular, broad, oval	Dark-purple	24-28" height	3 5 9 10 11 12 14 16 19 21 22 25 28 30 32 34 36 38 39 41 44 45 47 48 49 51 52 53 55 56 57 58 60 62 67 72 73
Black Bell Hybrid		Round, oval	Very glossy	28-30" height . . . excellent yields	48 56
Black Magic	73	Blunt, medium	Deep-purple	Tremendously prolific . . . highly recommended for home gardens	29
Burpee's Hybrid	70	Oval, medium	Glossy-dark	Tall, treelike . . . drought- and disease-resistant	10 48 49 66
Early Beauty Hybrid	62	Short, oval	Very-dark-purple	Prolific . . . early . . . 25" height	10
Early Hybrid	65	Slightly pear-shaped		Yields up to 40% heavier	66
Early Prolific (hybrid)	75-80	Medium, oval	Dark-purple	Bushy plants hold fruit fairly high above ground	16 31
Early Royal Hybrid	61		Deep-purple	Florida Market type . . . early	70
Faribo Hybrid			Deep-purple	Tall, semispreading plants	21
Florida Hybush (Fort Meyers Market) (Florida Special)	83	Egg-shaped	Dark	Vigorous, tall plants	12 25 31 32 48 56 57
Florida Market	80	Oval, 6½ x 9½"	Glossy-dark-purple	30-36" plant . . . productive . . . resistant to fruit rot	11 16 32 48 57
Hybrid Eggplant	80	Oval	Glossy-dark-purplish	Early . . . produces large crop . . . delicate, rich flavor	19
Hybrid No. 29	70		Deep-purple	Very productive	72
Hybrid Slicer	68	9 x 2"	Glossy-dark-purple	2-foot plants	9
Imperial Black Beauty	80	Egg-shaped	Dark-purple	18" high	66

EGGPLANT—Oval (Continued)

VARIETY	DAYS	SIZE	COLOR	HEIGHT/REMARKS	SOURCES
Improved New York Spineless		Egg-shaped	Deep-purple	Stalky . . . quite productive	14
Improved Purple Thornless	83	Large	Rich-purple	28-32" high . . . standard in the South	31
Large Fruited No. 25	65			Very productive	70
Midnite Hybrid		Pear-shaped	Deep-purple	28-30" high . . . AA winner	12 34 38 48
Mission Bell Hybrid	70-75	Deep, oval	Dark-purple	2½ feet high . . . high yields	5 11 12 25 48 52 53 54 55 62 67
New Orleans Market	85	Large	Dark-purple	2-2½ feet high . . . high yields	56
New York Improved (Large Purple)	80	Broad, egg-shaped	Glossy-purple	Large and uniform . . . 30-36" high	16 30 36
New York Spineless	83	Oval	Deep-purple	30-36" plants bear 4-5 smooth fruits	58
Pompano Market		Teardrop-shaped	Rich-purple	30-35" erect plants	40
Short Tom (hybrid)		Oval, 5 x 2½"	Dark-purple	Extra-early . . . good in short-season areas . . . continuous yielding	32 68
Small Fruited No. 1	60	Oblong	Velvety-blue		70
Special Highbush		Long, oval	Intense-black		17
Stokes Hybrid	70	1½ lbs.	Glossy-black	Tolerant to some diseases . . . extremely high yields	66

EGGPLANT—Long, Cylindrical

VARIETY	DAYS	SIZE	COLOR	REMARKS	SOURCES
Black Knight Hybrid	78	Uniform, long, slender	Shiny-black	32" tall, upright plant . . . high-quality	70
Black Jet	80	Long, slim	Jet-black	Strong plants hold fruit off ground	70
Blacknite	61-85	Elongated, 9 x 3½"	Glossy-black-purple	36" plants	5 32 66 72
Burpee's Jersey King Hybrid	75	Cylindrical	Dark-glossy-purple	High bush . . . excellent flavor	10 32 48 66 72
Chinese Long	125	Long, slender	Purple	Late . . . extra-good for South	36
Classic Hybrid	76	Long, slim	Purplish-blue	Vigorous vine	29
Dusky (hybrid)	56-68	Elongated 8 x 3½"	Dark-purple	36" plant . . . extremely early	5 21 25 28 29 32 48 52 53 57 60 66 72
Early Long Purple	78-80	12 x 3-4"	Dark-violet	Extra-early . . . heavy cropper	12 14 16
Florida Market (Cook's Strain)	82	Long, narrow	Glossy-blackish-purple	20-36" plants	41 47 70
Ichiban (hybrid)	65	Long, up to 12"	Purple	Early . . . more prolific than other eggplants . . . 36-40" plants	5 15 25 28 57 70
Kisuta Chunaga	110	5-6 x 2 "	Blackish-purple		36
Long Black		8 x 2½"	Purple-black	Earliest of long types . . . unusual quality . . . tender skin	70
Long Dark Purple	80	10 x 2 "	Shiny-velvet	22-26" erect plant	32 48
Long Purple Italian	75	Small, club-shape		Early	30
Long Tom Hybrid		7 x 1½"	Deep-purple	Short season . . . early . . . heavy yields	22 32 57
Long Tom No 4	60	7 x 1½"	Purple	Early . . . prolific . . . disease-resistant	41
Millionaire Hybrid		10"		Best of the late, long types	42
Nagoaka Long Black (hybrid)		8-9 x 2½"	Glossy-black	Early . . . prolific . . . tender skin	42 72
Parmigiana Hybrid	72	Cylindrical			50
Peerless (hybrid)	68	Long	Jet-black	Tall, vigorous plants . . . early	70
Purple Round Valance		Large, spherical	Dark-violet	Very early . . . high yields	36
Royal Knight (hybrid)	65	Long, slender 7-9 x 3½"	Glossy-purple	Tall, husky plants hold fruit off ground	11 32 48 56 66
Slice Rite (hybrid)	74	Oblong, cylindrical, 1 lb.	Shiny-black	Early-maturing . . . heavy cropper . . . highly disease-resistant	14 32

EGGPLANT—Non-purple

VARIETY	DAYS	SIZE	COLOR	REMARKS	SOURCES
Albino	68	Medium	Glistening-white	Bushy, medium-tall plants	70
Apple Green				Extra-early . . . nonacid . . . no need to peel	21
Golden Yellow	75	Lemon size		Cooked like other eggplant . . . fruit has excellent texture	50
Ornamental White		2½" fruit		2 feet tall	6
White Beauty	85	Medium	Snow-white	More flavor . . . earlier maturity . . . free of blemishes	21 53 62
White Italian	75	Average		Never bitter . . . milder flavor than purple	50

EGGPLANT—Small

VARIETY	DAYS	SIZE	COLOR	REMARKS	SOURCES
Early Black Egg	65	5" long		Unusually tender and flavorful	37
Morden Midget		Small	Deep-purple	Bushy plants earliest of all	21 53
Nagaoka New Kissin (hybrid)		4 x 2½" long, oval	Dark-purple	Extra-early	42
Purple Pickling	75	Small		Bears early, producing masses of tiny eggplant . . . use any pickling recipe	50
Slim Jim	65	4" long; sets in 3-5 fruit clusters	Purple	Novel eggplant that grows in 6" pots . . . excellent for pickling when young	5

Endive - escarole (Chicorium endiva)

The lacy, slightly bitter greens that look like lettuce are actually chicory. The frilly green, highly cut and curled, is endive. The less frilled, broad-leaved (Batavian type) with the white midrib is often called escarole. This one is rather bland in taste.

HOW TO PLANT: Plant a half-inch deep, 9-12 inches apart, in rows 12-24 inches apart. Both types are best for salads when blanched. Draw the outer leaves together, and tie with a string the last two-three weeks. Or . . . cover the plants the last two-three weeks with an upturned flower pot.

ENDIVE—Escarole—Not Curled

VARIETY	DAYS	LEAVES	REMARKS	SOURCES
Batavian Full Hearted (Deep Heart) (Escarole) (Florida Deep Heart)	85-90	Slightly crumpled, dark-green	12" spreading, white mid rib . . . well-blanched, tender heart	12 14 16 21 25 28 29 30 32 36 37 40 41 45 47 48 49 51 52 56 60 62 66 67 70 72 73
Batavian Special	80	Deep, broad, bright	Well-blanched, 16" spread . . . resembles Romain—earliest heading	37
Broad Leaved Batavian	90	Large, broad, slightly twisted	Well-blanched, full-hearted . . . 16" spread	3 10 15 16 31 32
Large Deep Limay	85	Wide	Deep heart	72

ENDIVE—Escarole—Curled

VARIETY	DAYS	LEAVES	REMARKS	SOURCES
Curled Large Green Head			One of the best varieties for summer	15 41
Deep Heart Fringed	90	Dark, curled	10-12" spread . . . extra-deep heart, well filled	14 16
Endive Curly Head	92	White-ribbed	Quite early . . . large . . . very deep-hearted	14
Endive White Curled (Moss Curled)		Bright-green	Well-blanched	14 16 49 62
Green Curled (Green Curled Ruffec) (Giant Fringed Oyster)	90	Finely cut, green, curled	16-18" spread . . . easily blanched . . . most popular curled . . . tangy flavor	3 10 14 16 21 25 28 29 30 31 32 34 38 40 41 45 47 51 52 53 55 56 62 66 67 72
Green Curled Pink Rib	90		18" spread . . . large plants	16 19 48
Premier Green Curled	95			48
Rosabella (Broad Leaf)	90	Deep-green, thick rib	16" spread	57

| Salad King | 75-100 | Curled, frilly, green | 22-24" spread . . . slow-bolting . . . popular variety | 9 11 12 16 22 32 40 46 47 48 51 53 57 60 66 72 |

Florence fennel (Foeniculum vulgare, dulce)

Florence Fennel is a gourmet vegetable grown for its bulblike base that is formed by the overlapping leaf stalks. The plant itself is an annual that grows to 2½ feet tall. There are actually two other kinds of fennel besides Florence Fennel. Common Fennel, *Foeniculum vulgare,* is a tall plant resembling dill that is grown for seeds and leaves; *Carosella, Foeniculum piperitum,* is grown for flavoring.

Harvesting: Pull the Florence Fennel plant from the ground when the bulbous base of the stalk measures 3-6 inches in length.

HOW TO PLANT: Sow the seedlings in rows 20 inches apart, then thin to 9-12 inches apart. Florence Fennel is a cool-weather crop. Plant in summer for a fall crop. In regions where the summer remains cool, you may plant in the spring.

As the plant develops its thick base of leaf stalks, pull the soil up around the base to blanch the stalks.

FENNEL

VARIETY	DAYS	REMARKS	SOURCES
Fennel-Copper			44 86 89
Florence Fennel (Finocchio) (Sweet Florence)	90	Enlarged, flat, oval leaf . . . 2½-foot growth . . . aniselike flavor . . . used in salad, raw or boiled . . . annual	10 12 15 16 25 28 29 30 31 32 36 37 44 46 47 49 50 51 52 60 62 66 68 72 78 79 82 83 84 85 86 88 89 90 91
Mammoth		Special, slow-bolting strain . . . adapted for fall crop	29
Perfection		A very large French variety . . . excellent	36
Sicilian Fennel		Superior to Florence Fennel . . . large and heavy, quick growth . . . easy to raise . . . flesh stalks	14
Silver Ball		Popular Swiss variety	36

Horseradish (Armoracia rusticana)

Horseradish is a centuries-old, tall, hardy plant native to Eastern Europe that is grown for its pungent root. Grated or shredded, it is added to many foods for flavor.

Harvesting: Lift the roots in October or November. Make cuttings from the base of the roots for planting the following spring.

HOW TO PLANT: Cut the top off square (of any 6-9-inch piece of root) and slant the bottom. Set the cuttings 2-3 inches below the soil surface, 7-9 inches apart, in rows 12-18 inches apart. When the leaves are about a foot high, remove all but one or two crown sprouts. Pull the soil back and rub off the side roots.

HORSERADISH

VARIETY	REMARKS	SOURCES
Bohemian Horseradish	Roots are large . . . flesh is snow-white . . . very hot to taste, yet mild	14 21 22 23 28 31 38 61 62 76 86 89
Maliner Kren	True Bohemian Horseradish . . . vigorous grower, which produces large white roots	10 35 60
Horseradish powder		84

Jerusalem artichoke (Helianthus tuberosus)

In many catalogs this is listed as an artichoke. It is not. The Jerusalem artichoke is a species of sunflower that grows from 6-10 feet high on a single stalk and produces 3-inch sunflowers. The round, knobby tubers produced by the roots are starchless. They can either be cooked like a potato or used raw in salads.

HOW TO PLANT: Cut the tuber into sections with one to two eyes in each section. Plant early—after danger of heavy frost has passed—4 inches deep, 1-2 feet apart, in rows 2-3 feet apart. When the foliage appears, hill the soil up around the plants.

Harvesting: Dig the tubers about six weeks after the flower petals drop. Store in a cool place. If any tubers are left in the ground, the plant can become a nuisance the following spring.

JERUSALEM ARTICHOKE (Sunchoke)

VARIETY	REMARKS	SOURCES
Jerusalem Artichoke (Sunchoke)	Tremendous yields of tasty tubers with nutlike flavor . . . good in salads, raw, boiled, baked, or creamed . . . excellent diabetic food	19 22 23 28 43 46 50 53 76 89 91

Kale (Brassica oleracea acephala)

Other members of the cabbage family may be a little hard to grow, but not kale. If you grow it in the right season, kale is a great home garden crop. The leaves are beautiful ranging from curled to fringed and from green to bluish purple. Cold weather doesn't seem to bother kale at all. In fact it is even crispier and more flavorful after being touched by a light frost. Thus, kale will furnish greens during late fall and early winter, when other leafy vegetables are scarce.

Borecole or *scotch types* have blue or dark-green leaves tightly curled. *Siberian types* have smoother, gray-green leaves with frilled edges and a spreading habit. *Ornamental kale* is deeply curled and ranges in color from green to white to lavender to red. It makes a good garden display in late fall and winter.

HOW TO PLANT: Sow seeds a half-inch deep, 15 inches apart, in rows 18-24 inches apart. Kale likes cool conditions. If the summers are cool, sow in spring. Otherwise sow seed in mid-summer so that plants grow in the cool days of the fall.

Harvesting: You can cut the outer leaves as they mature, or you can cut the entire plant. Generally, the inside leaves are more flavorful and tender than the outer ones.

KALE (Borecole)—Scotch Type

VARIETY	DAYS	LEAVES	REMARKS	SOURCES
Blue Curled Scotch	65	Finely curled, bluish-green	Low, compact plants	45 53
Dwarf Blue Curled Vates	55	Finely curled, bluish-green	Low, compact, short-stemmed plants . . . withstands below-freezing temps	10 12 20 29 31 32 34 40 41 47 49 51 52 58 60 62 68 70
Dwarf Green Curled Scotch (Bloomsdale) (Jamaica)	50-65	Large, finely curled	Extremely hardy . . . will withstand severe frost	3 9 14 16 21 25 28 30 37 47 48 57 66 72 73
Tall Green Curled Scotch		Deeply cut, curled, light-green	Very tender after exposure to frost	21 47 51 58 62 72

KALE—Siberian Type

VARIETY	DAYS	LEAVES	REMARKS	SOURCES
Blue Siberian (Sprouts)		Large, coarse, frilled edges, bluish-green	Largely grown in South . . . hardy and vigorous . . . 12-16" tall with a 24-36" spread	14
Curled Siberian	60	Bluish-green, curled	Hardy, rapid growing . . . slow to seed	67
Dwarf Siberian	65	Broad, thick, grayish-green, plumelike	12-16" tall with a 24-36" spread . . . hardy, stands cold especially well	10 31 49 50
Evergreen Gem	50	Heavily curled, deep-green with bluish sheen	18-24" high . . . prolific . . . dense growth, very spreading	14
Hanover Late Seeding (Long Seasons)	45	Dark-green, smooth	14" tall	47 67
Harvester L.D.	68	Short-stemmed, extra-curled, dark-green	Erect . . . will hold color through frosty weather	37
Konserva L.D.	60	Broad, moss-green, medium-curled, curls more in cool weather	30" tall . . . yield of fresh leaves is tremendous	37
Meyer's Brand (Late Seeding)	60	Dark-blue-green, frilled	26" tall	47

KALE—Siberian Type (Continued)

VARIETY	DAYS	LEAVES	REMARKS	SOURCES
Siberian (Dwarf German)	65	Dark-blue-green, frilled	14" tall . . . vigorous, sprawling growth	12 47 51 56
Siberian Improved	60-70	Large, thick, bluish-green, frilled	12-15" high . . . sprawling and extremely hardy . . . 36" spread	16 40 55 73
Spring (Hanover)	30	Light-green, smooth	16" tall . . . hardy, quick-growing	47 49

Kale—Other types

VARIETY	DAYS	LEAVES	REMARKS	SOURCES
Blue Leaf	110		Hardiest of winter greens	22
Chinese Kale	70	Dark-green	Mildly sweet and crispy . . . 12-14" tall	69
Marrow Stem Green Improved (Chou Moellir)			Very thick stems . . . and best of marrow-stem kales . . . high yields	36
Ornamental Flowering Kale			In early season leaves are green, but in fall they change to cream and to the red shades	14 28 38 48 72
Pentland Brigg	75		Very hardy	68

Kohlrabi (Brassica caulorapa)

Often called a turnip cabbage, kohlrabi produces an above-ground "turnip" in the middle of a profusion of cabbagelike leaves. When the plants are 6-8 inches high, the stems begin to swell just above the root line until the bulbs are 3-4 inches across. The swollen stem is delicious when eaten young and juicy. Cook just like a turnip.

Kohlrabis are green-white or purple. The flesh of both varieties is whitish. The most popular varieties are *Early White Vienna* and *Early Purple Vienna.*

HOW TO PLANT: Sow the seed two weeks after the average date of the last frost, and follow with several plantings two weeks apart. Sow seeds a half-inch deep in rows 18 inches apart, then thin the small plants to 4 inches apart.

Harvesting: Harvest when the "bulbs" are 2-2½ inches in diameter. Beyond this they become hard and have a bitter taste.

KOHLRABI—Purple

VARIETY	DAYS	SHAPE/SIZE	REMARKS	SOURCES
Blue Danish L.D.	66		Deep, red-cabbage color . . . a week later in bulbing than White Danish	37
Early Purple Vienna	60	Globe-shaped	Purplish skin, green-white flesh	10 12 14 16 19 21 25 28 30 32 34 48 49 51 52 62 66 72
Purple Vienna Short Top		Globe-shaped	Purplish skin, white flesh	36

KOHLRABI—White

VARIETY	DAYS	SHAPE/SIZE	REMARKS	SOURCES
Early White Vienna	55-60	Globe 8-10 x 2"	Light-green skin, creamy white flesh . . . dwarf plants . . . good freezer	3 10 11 12 14 15 16 19 21 22 25 28 29 30 31 32 41 44 45 47 48 49 50 51 52 53 55 56 57 60 62 66 67 72 73
Grand Duke (hybrid)	50	Semiglobe	White skin . . . very uniform size	32
Prague Special	44	Flattened	White skin . . . European type . . . very early . . . short leaves . . . uniform size . . . highly flavored and tender	14
Primavera White	50		Stays fiber-free for a long time . . . very early, quick growing	68
Vienna Green Short Top		2-3" globular	Light-green skin, white flesh . . . early	36
White Danish L.D.	60		Light-green bulbs . . . a good early Kohlrabi	37

Lettuce (Lactuca sativa)

What a vegetable! You can grow lettuce almost without effort, tucking it in anywhere. Lettuce is chockful of vitamins A and B, yet contains almost no calories. There are four types of lettuce:

Head lettuce: Fairly solid heads are produced, requiring 80-95 days to mature. Many of the heading varieties have been developed for commercial purposes. A number are variations of single types like *Great Lakes* and *Imperial*. Most stand the heat better than butterhead varieties.

Butterhead lettuce: Sometimes resembling a small cabbage, butterhead develops a well-folded head. The heart is tightly folded and blanches to a light, golden brown. It generally matures in 60-65 days. Some varieties are slow to bolt.

Romaine (Cos): With upright, cylindrical, folded heads, Romaine matures in 70-80 days. The interior leaves are usually self-blanching and white. A good change of pace for salads.

Looseleaf lettuce: This variety forms a very loose head that separates easily into individual leaves. It matures in 40-45 days. You'll find a wide range of leaf shapes and colors among the looseleaf types. Many gardeners grow several for variety. *Salad Bowl* has deeply lobed leaves that resemble endive. *Oakleaf* forms a tight rosette—the individual leaves have an oak-leaf shape. *Green Ice* is a startling dark-green color, with wavy, fringed leaves. *Early Prizehead* has bright-green leaves that are shaded brown. *Ruby* has intense red leaves.

There are also midget varieties available.

HOW TO PLANT: Sow looseleaf lettuce a quarter-inch deep; thin to 4-6 inches apart in rows 12 inches apart. Sow other types a quarter-inch deep; thin to 8-10 inches apart in rows 18 inches apart. All lettuce does not thrive in the hot summer. Plant in early spring and early fall. In summer plant in shady areas.

Harvesting: Pull the entire plant for cos, butternut, and head lettuce. Harvest looseleaf lettuce leaves individually as you need them. Some varieties are quicker to bolt (go to seed) than others.

LETTUCE—Medium Head

VARIETY	DAYS	SHAPE/COLOR	REMARKS	SOURCES
All-the-Year-Round			Best all-year-round variety . . . crisp and tender	68
Cornell 456 (W.S.)	85-90	Frilled and a little flat, dark-green	Developed to grow in the summer months in the Northeast . . . slow-bolting . . . very resistant to tip burn	16
Fairton	92	Deep-green, flattened	Upright growth habit . . . useful in wet areas . . . resists bolting . . . tolerant to tip burn and brown rib	32 40 66
Hanson Head (W.S.)	80	Broad outer leaves, yellow-green, frilled	Medium core . . . tolerant to tip burn	51
Merit (B.S.)	90	Short wrapper leaves, dark-gray-green	Uniform in maturity . . . large core	16 40
Minilake	80	Dark-green	Very solid and uniform	66
Minetto (B.S.)	75-80		Slow-bolting . . . uniform summer crop . . . resistant to tip burn . . . not recommended as a winter garden variety in southern zones	16 40 41 66

LETTUCE—Large Head   B.S.—Black-Seeded   W.S.—White-Seeded

VARIETY	DAYS	SHAPE/COLOR	REMARKS	SOURCES
Alaska (B.S.)	80-90	Dark-green	Late . . . slow-bolting . . . resistant to tip burn and anthracnose . . . good summer lettuce in the north	16
Bellevedere MC 39	59	Wavy, dark-green	Ideally suited to cooler coastal areas . . . extremely uniform	40
Calmar (W.S.)	90-95	Good wrapper leaves, dark-green	Resistant to downy mildew . . . adapted to the cool, humid coastal areas of California . . . excellent quality	16 40

LETTUCE—Large Head B.S.—Black Seeded   W.S.—White Seeded (Continued)

VARIETY	DAYS	SHAPE/COLOR	REMARKS	SOURCES
Caravan (W.S.)		Dark-green	Solid heads . . . well adapted to the winter growing areas of California	16
Climax (B.S.)	90-100	Large, bright-green wrapper leaves	Adapted for winter production in the southwest . . . vigorous grower	16 40
Forty Niner (W.S.)	85-90	Flat-ribbed, dark-green butts	Adapted for winter growing in California, and Arizona	16
Francisco (B.S.)	85-90	Well-frilled or crumpled, medium-pale to dark-green	Adapted to spring production in the California Salinas Valley . . . slow-bolting . . . resembles Great Lakes	16
Fulton (W.S.)	80-85	Crinkled	Produces firm heads . . . northern, firm-headed variety . . . crisp, tender, superb flavor	16 32 38 40 47 66
Golden State D (W.S.)	90-95	Smooth, flat, green	Rather large core . . . heart is cream-colored, firm . . . well adapted to West Coast	16
Great Lakes	90-100	Bright-green, large, erect, outer leaves	Resistant to tip burn, sunburn, and heavy rain . . : slow to bolt . . . New York type . . . AA winner	3 5 9 10 11 14 19 20 21 22 25 28 30 31 34 36 37 47 50 52 53 54 55 56 62 67 70
Great Lakes No. 66 (W.S.)	85	Frilled outer leaves, medium- to dark-green	Uniform in size and shape . . . very good for commercial plantings	16
Great Lakes 118 (W.S.)	85	Large outer leaves, glossy, dark-green	Suited for summer harvest in cool western coastal areas . . . early-maturing, uniform . . . shows resistance to tip burn	16 40 51
Great Lakes 366A (W.S.)	85-90	Lightly crumpled outer leaves, dark-green	Early-maturing	16
Great Lakes 407 (W.S.)	90-100	Large outer leaves, bright-green	Resistant to tip burn, sunburn, and heavy rain	14 16
Great Lakes 659-G (Mesa) (W.S.)	80	Extra-fringed outer leaves, dark-green	Firm heads with good tip burn tolerance . . . popular both North and South . . . early winter	11 16 29 40 48 51 55 58 60 70 72 73
Great Lakes 660 (W.S.)	85	Dark-green	Adapted to Southwest . . . well-formed heads	16
Iceberg (Giant Crystal Head)	80-85	Wavy, light-green tinged with brown	Hearts are crisp . . . does well in spring and summer . . . slow to bolt . . . does well in home garden	3 9 10 12 14 16 22 28 30 31 40 44 45 47 49 51 56 58 62 67 73
Imperial No. 101 G (W.S.)	85-90	Coarse, crumpled, dark-green	Vigorous . . . large, rather flat heads of excellent quality . . . does best in cool weather	16
Imperial No. 44	84	Heavily savoyed, dark-green	Slightly flattened head . . . tender . . . extremely compact, well-formed	10 67
Imperial No. 456 (Cornell)	80		Highly suitable for eastern use where heads are desired in July and August	30 72
Imperial No. 847	83	Dark-green	New York type for hot weather . . . heads well in mid-summer, does well both early and late	11 32 56 58
Ithaca (Improved Iceberg)	72	Frilled, glossy-green	Resistant to tip burn and brown rib . . . slow to bolt . . . iceberg type	29 32 34 37 60 66 70 72
New York (Wonderful)	70-80		3-4 pounds . . . good quality	14 19 36 56
New York No. 12	75		Makes fine, solid heads . . . will do well in well-drained ground anywhere . . . avoid low-lying muck lands	14 25 51 62
Oswego (W.S.)	80-85	Medium- to dark-green	Very slow to bolt . . . does well in northern muck soils . . . good tolerance to tip burn	16 40 60
Pennlake (W.S.)	75	Fairly smooth, medium-green	Fairly early . . . solid heads . . . AA winner . . . upland type	16 21 32 48 52 66 72
Phoenix (W.X.)	90-100	Thick, heavy	Exceptionally firm and solid head . . . particularly adapted to Arizona and California winter growing areas	16
Premier Great Lakes	75-80	Flattened, smooth, medium-green; no fringed margins	Resistant to tip burn and heat	10 16 31 48 66

LETTUCE—Large Head B.S.—Black Seeded W.S.—White Seeded (Continued)

VARIETY	DAYS	SHAPE/COLOR	REMARKS	SOURCES
Stokes Evergreen M.I.	95	Dark-green	Much hardier than Great Lakes 659 . . . popular in northern Ontario, Quebec, New York . . . cold-resistant	66
Valverde (W.S.)	80-85	Savoyed, wrapped leaves, medium-green	Downy mildew resistant . . . vigorous plant . . . cream-colored heart . . . well adapted to lower Rio Grande Valley	16
Vanguard	90-100	Broad wrapper leaves, dull dark-green	Adapted to West Coast and Central Valley of California . . . large core	16 40
Webb's Wonderful		Wrinkled	Tight, crisp head . . . distinct flavor . . . outstanding in wet and dry summers . . . slow to bolt	68

LETTUCE—Small Head

VARIETY	DAYS	SHAPE/COLOR	REMARKS	SOURCES
Common Green Cutting (W.S.)		Small, blond heads		36
Empire (B.S.)	80	Round, compact, yellow-green	Suitable for warm weather planting and northeastern area . . . very uniform in maturity	16 40 47

LETTUCE—Butterhead (Small)

VARIETY	DAYS	SHAPE/COLOR	REMARKS	SOURCES
Bibb (B.S.) (Limestone) (Kentucky)	60-70	Smooth thick, waxy-green	Bolts in hot weather	3 10 14 28 29 30 31 32 39 41 45 47 48 49 51 52 53 55 62 67 72
Bibb Forcing	60	Dark-green	Fine flavor . . . good for forcing	25
Bibb Slow Bolting (B.S.)			Withstands hot weather	12 32 57
Burpee Bibb Lettuce	75	Loosely folded, dark-green outer leaves	Inside blanches to golden yellow . . . no bitterness . . . slow-bolting	10
Mignonette Bronze (B.S.)	65	Frilled, medium-brown with dark-green tinge	Slow to bolt . . . blanches white	12 16 32
Mignonette Green (B.S.)	65	Deep-green	Grown largely in tropics	16 32 44
Summer Bibb (B.S.)	60-70	Thick	Vigorous grower . . . slow to bolt . . . same creamy, firm interior, typical of Bibb	16 29 31 47 56 60

LETTUCE—Butterhead (Medium)

VARIETY	DAYS	SHAPE/COLOR	REMARKS	SOURCES
Bohemian Head Lettuce	63	Light-green	Very early . . . slow to bolt . . . sweet, buttery flavor . . . soft texture	14
California Cream Butter	75	Crumpled, thick, dark-green spotted brown	Very hardy . . . buttery, sweet flavor . . . strictly for outdoor growing	14 62
Continuity (Crisp as Ice) (Harford Bronzehead)	65-70	Wavy, dark-green overlaid with red-brown	One of the best hot-weather garden varieties . . . slow to bolt . . . hearts are butter-yellow and of fine quality	12 21 28 30 50
Creamy Heart		Curled, bright-green	Hearts are a rich, golden yellow . . . crisp . . . fine producer, sure header . . . for home or market	22
Dark Green Boston	80	Smooth, tender, dark-green	Uniform and dependable under various conditions . . . excellent for home gardens . . . to be grown in spring and fall	10 29 32 40 41 46 47 48 51 66 70 72
Deer Tongue (Matchless)	80-90	Triangle shape, rounded tip, green	Stands heat . . . compact, upright growth . . . 8" across, 7" high . . . slow to bolt	10 14 30 45 49 50 52
Early Surehead		Medium-green	Extra-select, early strain . . . as easily grown as radishes	38
Fordhook	78	Crinkled, bright, glossy, deep-green	Creamy-yellow hearts . . . outstanding flavor	10
Hardy Green Winter (Hammersmith)		Crumpled, with straight edges	Heads in late fall, early winter . . . tight heads	62

LETTUCE—Butterhead (Medium) (Continued)

VARIETY	DAYS	SHAPE/COLOR	REMARKS	SOURCES
Hot Weather	63	Thick, slightly crumpled	Excellent summer variety . . . mildew-resistant . . . cabbagelike heads . . . excellent quality	14
May King	65	Light-green tinged brown	Creamy-yellow interior . . . hearts firm . . . used for greenhouse forcing	14 16 62
May Queen (W.S.)			Summer cabbage-type variety . . . good for spring planting	36
Resistant	54	Deep-green	Sweet-flavored . . . tender, blanched hearts	37
Summerlong	70		Compact, round heads . . . sweet, tender white hearts, even in hot weather	21
Tendercrisp	62	Crinkled, glossy, light-green	"Nutty flavor" . . . adapted to all areas where Bibb will grow	40 60

LETTUCE—Butterhead (Large)

VARIETY	DAYS	SHAPE/COLOR	REMARKS	SOURCES
Big Boston	70-76	Wavy, edges slightly brown, yellow center	Hard heads of superior quality	3 12 14 25 30 31 47 55 56 57 62
Buttercrunch (B.S.)	65-75	Smooth, green	AA winner . . . slow to bolt . . . tolerant of heat . . . fine for home gardens	3 5 9 10 12 14 19 21 22 25 28 29 30 31 32 34 37 39 40 45 46 47 48 49 50 51 52 53 55 57 60 66 67 68 72
Butter King	70-85	Wavy	AA winner . . . developed in Israel . . . 12-13- oz. heads . . . slow to bolt . . . does well in Midwest, even in hot weather	12 21 25 30 31 52 53 62 66 72
Hanson	80	Frilled, light-yellow-green	Hardy, broad, and thick . . . unsuited for wintering or forcing	14
Kagran Summer	54	Light-green	Heat-resistant . . . large heads . . . slow-bolting . . . large, firm hearts . . . does not tip burn	37
White Boston (Summer Unrivalled)	66-76	Smooth, wavy, bright-green	Free from bottom rot, tip burn . . . large, compact heads . . . unbeatable for forcing	12 14 32 41 47 51 66 67 72

LETTUCE—Midget

VARIETY	DAYS	SHAPE/COLOR	REMARKS	SOURCES
Midget Lettuce	55	Crisp, thick, juicy	Buttercrunch type . . . AA winner . . . compact heads	19 28
Sweet Midget Cos		5" tall, compact	Upright heads . . . sweet, greenish-white hearts . . . crisp and delicious	21
Tom Thumb	65	Small, tennis-ball-size, medium-green, crumpled	Centers are blanched a creamy-white . . . popular for indoor and window box planting . . . buttercrunch type	10 14 21 22 50 53 62

LETTUCE—Greenhouse

VARIETY	DAYS	SHAPE/COLOR	REMARKS	SOURCES
Dannie		Deep-green	Short-day lettuce . . . buttercrunch type for greenhouse winter crop	72
Deci-Minor	50		The best White Boston type for Sept.-Feb. greenhouse production . . . very responsive to short daylight periods . . . not for outdoor culture	66
Grand Rapids Forcing (Washington Strain)	45	Loose-leaf, curled, green	Most popular strain for winter greenhouses	66 72
Ostinata	60		Best Boston type for summer greenhouse production or hydroponic culture	66

LETTUCE—Romaine/Celery (Cos)

VARIETY	DAYS	SHAPE/COLOR	REMARKS	SOURCES
Crisp Mint	65-80		Excellent mildew and virus resistance . . . upright habit means all leaf is in good eating condition	68
Eiffel Tower (B.S.)	70	Tall/compact	More cylindrical than usual cos types	16
Little Gem (Sugar Cos)		Glossy-green	The heart is a mass of crisp, crunchy, blanched leaves with delicious, sweet flavor	68
Lobjoit's Green Cos (Dark Green Cos) (W.S.)	55-70	Extra-large, dark-green	Excellent quality . . . hard in texture, exceedingly crisp, sweet, and firm . . . does very well in summer	3 14 16 37 48 57 67 72
Paris Green (W.S.)	70	10-12" dark-green	Self-blanching, large heads	36
Paris White Cos (W.S.) (Trianon) (Valmaine) (Romaine)	70-83	Elongated, 10-12" tall	Crisp, sweet, yet piquant flavor . . . widely grown in North	9 10 14 16 21 28 30 31 34 36 40 41 49 50 51 55 56 62 66 72
Parris Island Cos	70-75	Large oval, 8-9", dark-green	Crisp texture and pleasing, mild flavor	12 16 25 29 32 40 41 47 48 51 57 60 66 70 73
Winter Density (W.S.)		Creamy-white interior	Round top, well-formed leaves . . . late-bolting in summer . . . cold-resistant	36 37

LETTUCE—Loose Leaf

VARIETY	DAYS	SHAPE/COLOR	REMARKS	SOURCES
Arctic King (W.S.)			Early-winter variety, but does not stand heavy frost . . . small, firm heads	36
Black Seeded Simpson	42-45	Broad, light-green, frilled outer leaves	Center leaves blanch almost white	9 10 11 12 14 19 21 22 25 28 29 30 31 32 34 36 38 39 40 41 44 45 47 48 49 51 52 55 57 58 60 62 66 67 70 72 73
Early Curled Simpson (W.S.)	45	Crumpled, light-green	Slow to bolt in hot weather . . . sweet, crisp, and delicious	12 19 21 28 30 51 53 57 58 62
Early Prizehead	45	Curled and crumpled, bright-green shaded brownish-red	Large, tender, loose heads . . . excellent flavor	10 19 30 52 62
Grand Rapids (Burpee's Greenhart)	40-45	Frilled, light-green leaves, deeply cut	Resistant to mildew and tip burn . . . slow to bolt	5 10 11 12 14 16 19 21 22 28 29 30 31 32 38 45 47 48 51 52 56 57 62 66 67 70 72
Grand Rapids No. 1	40	Densely fringed, light-green	Recommended for greenhouse culture . . . large, heavy heads . . . very uniform	14 16 25
Green Ice	45	Savoyed leaves with wavy and fringed leaf margins; dark-glossy-green	Used over a longer period than most leaf lettuces	10 45
Oak Leaf	38-50	Small, thick, medium-green	Leaves look like oak leaves . . . does not become bitter in hot weather . . . tender, long-standing	3 9 10 12 14 19 21 25 28 29 30 36 37 41 45 47 49 50 51 52 53 57 60 62 67
Prizehead (Jung's All Cream)	47	Large, loose, wrinkled	A bunching sort of good quality . . . sweet, tender and crisp	3 14 21 22 25 34 37 38 40 41 45 48 51 57 60 72
Ruby	47-65	Frilled, shaded with intense red	AA winner . . . sweet and succulent	10 12 16 19 21 28 29 30 31 38 50 51 52 53 58 66 72 73
Salad Bowl (B.S.)	45	Medium-size, waved, light-green	Deeply lobed, giving an endive appearance . . . slow to bolt . . . stands heat very well . . . excellent for home gardens . . . AA winner	3 5 10 11 12 14 16 19 21 22 25 28 29 30 31 32 34 37 38 39 41 45 47 49 50 51 52 53 55 57 60 67 70 72 73
Salad Trim		Purplish-red, crinkly	Sweet, crisp leaves	21 22
Slobolt Leaf (B.S.)	45	Crumpled and frilled	Continues to develop good, palatable lettuce during entire summer season without bolting	12 20 21 29 32 48 53 57

The melon family

Muskmelon (Cucumis melo cantalupensis)

The muskmelon (or cantaloupe) is an extremely popular vegetable for home gardens. The homegrown varieties are generally sweeter because you pick them ripe. Unlike some other fruits, muskmelons do not increase in sweetness when picked green. In fact, their sugar content begins to drop soon after picking.

Cantaloupes: The earlier-maturing muskmelon varieties are popularly known as cantaloupes, even though they are really muskmelons, just like the longer-season types. Many of the cantaloupe varieties are quite similiar in appearance to each other; differences show up in their outside skin markings, thickness of flesh, tolerance to disease, length of season and similar qualities. In recent years plant breeders have been busy developing muskmelon varieties especially adapted to the various climates around the United States. There are now some early-maturing varieties that will grow well in areas with short seasons.

Hale's Best Jumbo has a delicious sweet taste and a thick, salmon-colored flesh. *Hearts of Gold* is sweet and spicy and well netted, except for a narrow stripe between the ribs. *Burpee's Hybrid* has a heavy netting. *Main Rock* is one of the earliest varieties, and *Early Northern Queen* grows well in short-season areas. Compact varieties include *Far North* and *Midseason.*

In addition to the fairly minor differences mentioned above, some cantaloupe varieties are quite distinct from the norm.

Giant Cantaloupes: *Bender's Surprise* runs 10 pounds or more and *Turkey* weighs up to 18 pounds, but *Week's Giant Cantaloupe* has won all records at 22 pounds.

Green Flesh Varieties: Most cantaloupes have salmon-colored or orange flesh, but several varieties have green flesh. *Burpee's Fordhook Gem* has a long season and grows well in the north. *Green Nutmeg,* a heavily netted variety, is sweet and tasty.

Midget Varieties: There are now also several small cantaloupe varieties on the market. *Minnesota Midget* (60 days) bears extremely sweet 4-inch cantaloupes on small 3-foot vines. *Early Sugar Midget,* another 4-inch melon, has thick, very juicy flesh.

Unusual Shapes: A number of varieties don't look at all like melons. The *Banana Melon,* for instance, has salmon-pink flesh inside but outside resembles a giant banana. *Honey Gold No. 9* is a popular, golden egg-shaped Japanese melon that's about the size of a lemon.

Long-Season Muskmelons: These melons often require up to 115 days and a hot, dry season to mature. The climate adaptability of these melons has now been extended, however, with the introduction of earlier varieties that mature in about the same number of days as the "cantaloupe."

Casaba has white flesh and golden skin that is wrinkled when mature . . . the *Sungold Casaba* matures in 85 days and ripens in northern climates. *Crenshaw* melon has dark-green skin that turns yellow in parts on maturity. The salmon-pink flesh has a tasty, distinctive flavor. *Early Hybrid Crenshaw* produces 14-pound fruits in 88-90 days.

Honey Dew has a smooth, hard, creamy-white rind and a light-emerald-green flesh, and *Honey Mist* compares with the best. *Persian* has dark-green skin and deep-orange flesh.

HOW TO GROW: Muskmelons require a long growing season, thus are best grown in the South or Southwest. However, home gardeners in cooler regions will do fairly well with varieties adapted to northern climates—especially if they start seed indoors a month or two before planting outdoors. The vines need warm days and nights, so wait to plant until the soil has warmed to about 70-75 degrees. Plant in rows 1 inch deep, 12 inches apart, with 48-72 inches between rows. Or plant in hills, 4-6 feet apart each way, with 2-3 plants per hill. Later, thin to the strongest two plants.

Harvesting: "Cantaloupes" are ready to eat when the stems pull off easily—usually with the slight touch of the thumb. If they don't pull off easily, they should stay on the vine. You can also tell when they are ready because the skin begins to look like a cork net and the stem cracks a little way around.

For testing Crenshaw and Persian melons, smell the blossom ends. If the smell is fruity and sweet, the melons are probably ripe. Honey Dew and Casaba melons are ripe when the rinds have turned completely yellow.

CANTALOUPES—Large

VARIETY	DAYS	SIZE	FLESH	REMARKS	SOURCES
Bender's Surprise	90-95	8 x 7" oval, 10 lbs. or more	Deep-orange	Ribbed netting turns golden tint . . . unsurpassed in flavor and size . . . improves in flavor after picking	9 12 14 30 45
Improved Milwaukee Market (Schoon's Hardshell) (New Yorker)	83-88	5-8 lbs.	Red-salmon	Extra-hard shell on the order of Bender's Surprise . . . skin is yellow	11 14 16 25 28 48 51 52 57 70 73
Mammoth (Gurney's)	95	14-18 lbs.	Deep-orange	One melon feeds a crowd . . . very fragrant	28
Minnesota Honey		7-9 lbs., heavy, semioval		Fusarium-resistant . . . high sugar content	21
Old Time Tennessee Muskmelon				One of the largest melons grown . . . deep creases . . . delicious when fully ripe	73
Shumway's Giant Muskmelon	90	15-18 lbs.	Deep-orange	Slightly netted	22 43 62
Tip Top	85	round, large	Bright-salmon	Slightly ribbed and netted . . . ideal for home gardens	62
Turkey		long, oval, 12-16" 15-18 lbs.	Salmon	Slightly netted with light-green sutures . . . thick, firm flesh . . . better keeper than Old Time Tennessee	73
Week's Giant Cantaloupe		up to 22 lbs.			27

CANTALOUPES—Green

VARIETY	DAYS	SIZE	NETTING	INTERIOR	REMARKS	SOURCES
Burpee's Fordhook Gem	82	Medium	Fine silver	Green	Good in the North . . . usually a long season . . . prolific	10 49
Gold Lined Rocky Ford	85	5½ x 5", 2½ lbs.	Well-netted		Adapted to entire South for market or home use . . . thick, delicious flesh	31 56 67
Green Nutmeg	63	2-3 lbs., slightly oval	Heavily netted	Sweet green flesh	Good for home gardens	38
Israel (Ogen)			Wide sutures	Pale-green	Small seed cavity	73
Rocky Ford Green Flesh (Eden Glen) (Netted Gem)	84-92	2½ lbs., 5" oblong	Solid netted	Green	Rust-resistant . . . deep, fine-grained, sweet flesh	11 14 16 22 28 30 36 37 47 49 50 51 57 58 62 73
Rocky Ford Pollock	10-25	5 x 5½"	Abundant netting	Green	Home or local market	73

CANTALOUPES—Early

VARIETY	DAYS	SIZE	NETTING	INTERIOR	REMARKS	SOURCES
Alaska AAS (hybrid)	70	Large, football-shaped			Good for home gardens . . . pick when netting turns light-reddish-brown . . . super flavor	12 57 72
Ball 1776 (hybrid)	76	Nearly round, up to 5 lbs.	Heavy		Has performed well in every area . . . resistant to Fusarium wilt and powdery mildew	5
Canada Gem (hybrid)	78	Oval	Heavy	Deep-orange	Few days later than Gold Star . . . resistant to powdery mildew and Fusarium	66
Chaca	75	3-3½ lbs.			From France . . . distinct flavor . . . resistant to powdery mildew and Fusarium wilt	50 53
Chaca No. 1 (hybrid)	75	Slightly oval, 3-3½ lbs.	Open	Salmon	Tolerant to powdery mildew and Fusarium wilt . . . distinct, sweet flavor	5 21 22 28 55 60 70

CANTALOUPES—Early (Continued)

VARIETY	DAYS	SIZE	NETTING	INTERIOR	REMARKS	SOURCES
Charentais	74				French melon . . . flavor is supreme	15 50
Charentais Improved	74	5½", 3 lbs.	Ridged and smooth	Dark-orange	Flesh is 2½" thick	66
Charentais Sweetheart	74	5½"	Smooth	Dark-orange	European	21
Delicious 51	81-86	Slightly oval, 6-6½"		Salmon	Flesh is thick, crispy, sweet . . . can be grown on infected soil . . . resistant to Fusarium wilt	3 10 11 12 16 29 30 37 38 51 52 60 66 70 72
Dixie Jumbo (hybrid)	78-80	6 x 7"	Heavy	Salmon	Tolerant to powdery mildew and downy mildew . . . high in sugar content	5 11 41 70
Earlisweet Hybrid	73-75	5½ x 5½"	Medium	Salmon	Resistant to Fusarium wilt . . . good for home gardens . . . produces where others fail	11 19 48 52 57 72 73
Early Dawn	82	Oval, large	Fine	Richly colored	Its vigor and dependability make it a fine choice for first melons . . . resistant to powdery mildew and Fusarium wilt	29
Early Delicious	75	4-5 lbs.	Netted	Orange	Extra-early, good yielder . . . sweet	19
Early Northern Queen Hybrid	70	6 x 9", football shape			Well-suited for northern, midwestern, and western states . . . tops for areas of short season	70
Emerald Gem	80	Small, round 4-5"	Heavy	Yellow	Early, sweet, and productive	30
Farnorth				Salmon	Good in northern gardens	21 28 51
Golden Champlain	68			Salmon	Good for home gardens	28
Golden Honey	73		Heavy		Extremely early . . . Hale's type . . . mildew-resistant . . . heavy yielder	22
Golden Perfection	75	6 x 6½", 3 lbs.	Heavily ribbed	Golden	Sweet, fine texture . . . resistant to downy and powdery mildew and alternaria . . . good for home gardens	16 73
Gold Star (hybrid)	87	Oval	Heavy	Deep-orange	Very dependable . . . productive over a long season . . . tolerant to Fusarium wilt	29
Granite State				Orange	Very early . . . matures in the North	53
Hale's Best Jumbo	80-82	Long, oval, 7½ x 6", 4½ lbs.	Well-netted	Deep-salmon	Flesh is thick and sweet	11 12 14 16 19 25 31 34 41 48 51 52 55 56 57 58 67 70 73
Hearts of Gold (Hoodoo)	88-90	5 x 6", 3 lbs., nearly round	Well-netted	Deep-orange	Finest quality . . . sweet, spicy, fine-grained	10 11 14 16 19 22 30 32 47 51 62 67 73
Honey Rock (Sugar Rock)	77-85	5½", 3 lbs., almost round	Heavy	Salmon	Fusarium-tolerant . . . AA winner . . . sweet, finest flavor	5 10 21 25 28 30 31 32 38 45 48 49 52 57 62 66 72 73
Iroquois (Giant Early Wonder)	75-99	Oval, 7 x 6"	Coarse	Deep-orange	Popular, sweet . . . prolific strain . . . does well in northern half of U.S. . . . resistant to powdery mildew and Fusarium wilt	12 14 16 25 28 29 30 32 37 38 45 47 48 51 52 60 66 70 72 73
Luscious (hybrid)	75	Oval, 7", 4 lbs.		Orange	Uniform and vigorous growing . . . resistant to Fusarium wilt and powdery mildew	5 35

CANTALOUPES—Early (Continued)

VARIETY	DAYS	SIZE	NETTING	INTERIOR	REMARKS	SOURCES
Mainerock (hybrid)	75	Elongated, 6 x 4"	Medium	Salmon	One of the earliest hybrid available . . . excellent flavor . . . tolerant to Fusarium wilt	5 9 10 30 32 53 60
Midwest Extra Early Hybrid			Medium		Sets a large number of fruit per plant	48
Minnesota Honey		Large, 7-9 lbs., semioval	Heavy		Full-size melon for the north . . . Fusarium-resistant . . . high sugar content	21
Minnesota Hybrid		Oval, 7"		Deep-orange	Earliest of all hybrids . . . Fusarium-resistant . . . sweet	21
Osage	85	Oval, 6 lbs.	Slightly	Deep-salmon	Excellent for market or roadside stands	16 62
Penn Sweet	65	6", oval, 1½-2 lbs.	Slightly	Salmon	AA winner	62
Perfection	75	Round Medium-size	Well-netted	Salmon	Skin is strong	66
Resistant Joy (Golden Flesh)					Total resistant to powdery mildew and Fusarium wilt . . . replaces Charantasis	68
Saticoy (hybrid)	80-90	Oval, 4 lbs.		Deep-orange	Very productive in home gardens . . . tolerant to Fusarium wilt and powdery mildew	5 12 29 32 38 48 52 53 60 66 67 70 73
Star Headliner	84		Heavy	Deep-orange	High yield of heavy fruits	70
Sugar Salmon	70		Heavy	Salmon	Quality fruits in early season	66
Super Hybrid Muskmelon	85				Outstanding for its earliness, fine flavor, and texture . . . dependable, heavy yields . . . resistant to Fusarium wilt	19
Sweetheart Hybrid					Extra early for north country . . . very vigorous, easy to grow	21 50 72
Sweet Granite	80	Football-shaped, 3 lbs.	Moderate	Orange	Sure cropper in short seasons	21 37
Sweetie (hybrid)	65	Medium		Salmon	Highly resistant to melon diseases caused by high humidity	22 72

CANTALOUPES—Mid-season

VARIETY	DAYS	SIZE	NETTING	INTERIOR	REMARKS	SOURCES
Ambrosia Hybrid	86	4-5 lbs., 6-6½"		Salmon	Resistant to powdery mildew . . . very sweet, thick meat . . . small seed cavity	10
Burpee's Hybrid	80-82	4-4½ lbs., oval, 6-7"	Well-netted	Deep-orange	Vigorous vines . . . sweet, firm flesh	5 9 25 48 60 66 70
Campo	85	Oval, round	Well-netted	Salmon	Adapted to arid Southwest . . . resistant to downy mildew, Fusarium . . . thick flesh, yellow-green rind	16
Classic Hybrid	75-85	4-4½ lbs.	Netted with slight rib	Salmon	Resistant to powdery mildew and Fusarium	5 25 28 34 47 48 55 57 60 73
Cornell Delicious	83					48
Cum Laude			Well-netted	Bright-orange	Good flavor . . . small seed cavity . . . disease-resistant	73
Dessert Sun	80	6 x 7"	Almost ribless	Salmon	Resistant to downy and powdery mildew and to crown blight . . . recommended for South and West	16

CANTALOUPES—Mid-Season (Continued)

VARIETY	DAYS	SIZE	NETTING	INTERIOR	REMARKS	SOURCES
Edisto 47	88	Oval, 6½"	Heavy	Salmon	Resistant to downy and powdery mildew	11 41 47 51 70 73
Field's Daisy	76	Round, medium-size		Orange	Easy to grow . . . thick flesh	21
Gold Cup	84		Heavy	Deep-orange		48 73
Hale's Best	80-86	6½", heavy, oval	Heavy	Orange	Thick, sweet flesh . . . compact seed cavity	3 12 21 22 38 49 58 62 72
Hale's Best No. 936	82-87	5-5½"	Heavy	Salmon	Thick flesh . . . small seed cavity	73
Hale's Best No. 36	80-85	5½-6", round, oval	Medium	Salmon	Thick flesh . . . sweet	10 11 12 16 48 51 55 56 58 73
Harper Hybrid	74-85	Round, oval, 3½-4 lbs.	Fine	Deep-salmon	Tolerant to Fusarium wilt . . . AA winner	5 29 48 60 67 70
Hollybrook Luscious	85	6 lbs., 8 x 7"	Heavy, deep ribs	Salmon	Use for home or roadside stands	57
Imperial 45 (Hale's Best No. 45)	87	3½ lbs., oval, 6½ x 5½"	Solid, slight ribbing	Bright-orange	Resistant to powdery mildew . . . firm and sweet flesh . . . small seed cavity	12 14 51 73
Jenny Lynn	85	2 lbs.	Mottled-green	Orange	For home or local market	73
Kangold	88	Slightly oblong, 4-5 lbs., 6 x 7"	Heavy	Salmon	Resistant to alternaria and powdery mildew . . . high sugar content	38 48 70 73
King Henry	87	Oval, 5½-6"	Well-netted	Salmon	Small seed cavity	51 57
Market Pride	83		Well-netted	Deep-orange	Thick, firm flesh . . . delicious flavor	70
New Ideal	80	Oval, jumbo	Solid-net	Deep-salmon	Excellent flavor . . . small seed cavity	73
Perfected Perfecto		Large, uniform	Solid-net	Salmon	Fine-grained flesh . . . excellent flavor . . . strong vines are disease-resistant	73
Planters Jumbo	86	Round, oval, 4 lbs.	Well-netted		Very vigorous vines . . . resistant to downy and powdery mildew . . . good yielder . . . seed cavities are small	11 14 16 41 48 51 70
Powdery Mildew Resistant No. 45	88	Oval, 5¼ x 6"	Well-netted	Salmon	Firm, fine-textured flesh . . . most used in Rocky Ford District	11 16 48 73
Rio Gold		Large	Well-netted	Orange	Resistant to downy mildew . . . sweet, fine flavor	55 73
Roadside (hybrid)	85-90	7 x 6"	Well-netted	Orange	Sweet, thick flesh . . . resistant to powdery mildew and Fusarium wilt	5 48 52 55 57 70 73
Samson (hybrid)	85-90	Large	Well-netted	Orange	Keeps well	9 10 11 16 21 28 30 31 48 50 53 62 66 73
Sierra Gold	85	Nearly round, 6½-6"	Well-netted	Salmon	Resistant to powdery mildew	51
Sugar Rock	85	Almost round	Heavy	Deep-orange	Sweet, sugary, firm rind	14
Super Market Hybrid	82-84	4½ lbs., 7 x 6"	Well-netted	Deep-orange	Delicious flavor . . . high yielder . . . resistant to Fusarium wilt and downy mildew	9 11 21 22 28 32 47 52 67 70
Texas Resistant No. 1	85		Moderate	Salmon	Sweet, slightly mushy . . . resistant to aphids and downy mildew	73
Vedrantais	85	Small, round	Slight ribbing	Dark-orange	European type sometimes grown on trellis . . . earliest of French Charantais type . . . Fusarium-resistant	37

CANTALOUPES—Medium, Late

VARIETY	DAYS	SIZE	NETTING	INTERIOR	REMARKS	SOURCES
Edisto	90-95	Oval, 5 lbs., 5½-6"	Heavy	Rich-salmon	Resistant to alternaria powdery and downy mildew . . . tender but firm flesh . . . vigorous vines	11 14 16 31 51 53 67 73
Eureka	94	6 x 7"	Well-netted	Deep-salmon	Resistant to downy and powdery mildew and alternaria	51
Four-Fifty (Granite State)	90	Blocky, oval	Heavy net, moderate ribbing	Salmon	Tolerant to several strains of powdery mildew . . . large 45 type . . . firm, sweet flesh	3 11
Greeley Wonder	90	5-6 lbs., large	Heavy net, deep ribs	Salmon	Large melon for home gardens	57
Gulfstream	85-90	5-6" around	Well-netted	Orange	Very small seed cavity	51 56
Haogen	86-90	5-6" around, 3 lbs.	No net			10
Harvest Queen	90-92	Oval 6½ x 5½"	Coarse net, heavy with shallow ribs	Deep-orange	Resistant to Fusarium wilt . . . superior quality	11 12 16 21 32 45 47 48 51 52 70
Ohgon Melon	105	Oval		Crisp-white	High sugar content . . . nice melon for home garden	50
Perlita	94	Nearly round	Well-netted	Salmon	Mildew-resistant . . . adapted to Southwest	16 51 73
Pride of Wisconsin (Queen of Colorado)	88-92	Nearly round, 4-5 lbs., 6½-7"	Coarse net	Orange	Good-quality melon . . . thick flesh	10 14 16 21 22 25 47 48 49 52 62 67 70 73
Smith's Perfect	90-95	5½"	Sparse	Deep-orange	Well-suited to the South . . . small seed cavity . . . disease-resistant	31 32 41 51 55
Spartan Rock	93	5¼ x 5"	Coarse	Salmon		16 48 51 72
Spear Melon	95		Sparse		Matures early . . . suitable to northern gardens	50
Top Mark	90	6-7"	Well-netted	Salmon	Sweet, firm flesh . . . small seed cavity	16 51

CANTALOUPES—Midget

VARIETY	DAYS	SIZE	FLESH	REMARKS	SOURCES
Early Sugar Midget	60		Golden-yellow	Medium-size vines . . . sugar-sweet . . . small seed cavity . . . thick, juicy flesh	19
Ha-Ogen (Mini-Melon)				Each vine produces 10 melons plus . . . will grow well all over the U.S.	68
Midget Muskmelon	60		Salmon	3-foot vines produce many melons . . . high sugar content	62
Minnesota Midget	60-65	4"		3-foot vines produce small melons with high sugar content	21 28 53 57
Short 'N Sweet		Round		Bush growth . . . sugary, good flavor . . . resistant to heat, drought, powdery mildew	53

CANTALOUPES—Odd-Shaped

VARIETY	DAYS	SHAPE/SIZE	REMARKS	SOURCES
Aouri	67-72	12 x 4"	Thick flesh . . . dark-green . . . long and narrow	42
Banana	90-94	18 x 24" up to 7 lbs.	Resembles a giant banana . . . flesh is salmon-pink . . . sweet, spicy, delicious	9 12 16 19 22 31 38 47 50 51 55 56 58 62 67 73
Bitter Melon			Similar to a cucumber . . . heavily warted	42
Cavallion Red Flesh		4 x 6" egg-shaped	Flesh is shiny green	28
Gold Crown		1½ lbs., egg-shaped	Casaba type . . . early, very productive . . . cross between Oriental and European melon . . . smooth skin, golden-yellow when mature	50

CANTALOUPES—Odd-Shaped (Continued)

VARIETY	DAYS	SHAPE/SIZE	REMARKS	SOURCES
Golden Crispy		1 lb. each, looks like a gourd	Heat-resistant . . . sweet flavor . . . enticing odor	21 68
Honey Gold No. 9	90	10 oz., egg-shaped	Small Japanese cantaloupe . . . smooth, shiny, golden-yellow skin . . . white, crisp, sweet flesh . . . good keeper	50

CANTALOUPES—Honeydew

VARIETY	DAYS	SIZE	FLESH	REMARKS	SOURCES
Golden Honeymoon (Gold Rind Honeymoon)	92		Emerald green	Should be left on vine until fully ripe for best flavor . . . gold rind	11 16 73
Honeydew (Orange Flesh)	110	5-6 lbs., 7½ x 7" nearly round	Orange	Small seed cavity . . . smooth skin . . . creamy-white when ripe	51 57
Honeydew (Green Flesh)	110-112	6-8 lbs., globe 7-7½"	Emerald green	Prefers a warm, dry climate . . . smooth, ivory skin . . . thick, juicy flesh	9 10 11 16 31 32 34 36 41 48 50 51 53 56 57 58 62 67 73
Honey Drip Hybrid				Replaces honeydew . . . 14% sugar	68
Honey Mist	92		Greenish-white	Ripens in northern states . . . high sugar content . . . delicious	10
Honey Sweet	85	5 x 5½" oval		Extra-early . . . can grow in the North . . . superb quality	38
Kazakh	70	2-3 lbs.	Cream	Early, slightly netted . . . orange skin, distinctive flavor	28
Minnesota Honeymist			Greenish-white	Greenhouse strain . . . good in Minnesota . . . high sugar content	21
Tam Dew		6½ lbs., 8 x 6" oval	Green		16 53 73

CANTALOUPES—Casaba-Crenshaw-Persian

VARIETY	DAYS	SIZE	FLESH	REMARKS	SOURCES
Burpee Early Hybrid (Crenshaw)	90	Large, oval, pointed at stem, up to 14 lbs.	Salmon	No netting . . . turns yellowish when ripe . . . can be raised easily in gardens anywhere	10 45
Crenshaw	90-110	Over 5 lbs., 6 x 8"	Salmon	Rough, dark-green skin turns yellow at maturity . . . sweet flavor	16 19 22 28 51 57 58 73
Early Hybrid (Crenshaw)	88-90	Large, oval	Salmon		9 16 70
Golden Beauty (Casaba)	110-120	6-8"	Nearly white	Wrinkled, golden skin . . . keeps in good condition for months	10 11 16 36 48 51 55 57 73
Golden Crenshaw	110				48
Persian Medium	95	7-8 lbs., almost round, 7 x 7½"	Deep-orange	Heavily netted . . . small seed cavity . . . flesh is thick, sweet, with distinct flavor . . . does well in arid areas	16 36 50 51 55 57
Santa Claus (Casaba)	108	8-9 lbs., 12 x 6"	White to pale-green	Faint netting . . . wrinkled gold and dark-green mottling	51 57
Sungold Casaba	85	6-8 lbs.	Green-yellow	Persian type . . . will ripen in northern climates	21 28 52

CANTALOUPES—Preserving Melon

VARIETY	DAYS	SIZE	NETTING	INTERIOR	REMARKS	SOURCES
Colorado Preserving Melon	95	Globe-shaped	Pale-green stripe, and spotted deeper-green	White, firm, almost tasteless	Delicious in preserves	72

Watermelon (Citrulus vulgaris)

It used to be that you needed a long, hot growing season and lots of space to bring watermelon to maturity. That's still true for many varieties, but the icebox types have changed all that for many gardeners. The vines of these varieties take up very little space, and the watermelon range in weight from 3 to 10 pounds. *Burpee's Sugar Bush,* for instance, takes only six square feet of space, and the slightly oval melon weighs 6-8 pounds. *New Hampshire Midget,* a cantaloupe-sized watermelon, is good for short-season areas since it matures in 60 days. Every gardener short on space should try at least one of these, and northern gardeners especially should consider growing the smaller, earlier maturing varieties.

On the other hand, if you like to show off or to win blue ribbons, try the giant ones such as *State Fair,* which weighs 50-100 pounds or more, or *Week's Giant Watermelon,* the largest melon ever recorded at 197 pounds.

You can also choose from round, oval, and long types . . . solid-green or striped-skin melons . . . or melons with red, orange, or yellow flesh.

HOW TO PLANT: Start indoors in pots six or eight weeks before you intend to plant outside. When the weather warms up, set out transplants 12-18 inches apart in rows 4-6 feet apart. Or plant in hills, three plants to a hill, with 8 feet between hills (less for the smaller, icebox types).

Harvesting: For testing watermelons there is nothing like thumping them. The ripe ones have a dull rather than a sharp sound. This is a good test for early morning. Once the watermelons get hot late in the day, the bong sound gives way to a dull thud. You should also look at the discolored spots on the melons where they touch the ground. If the melons are ready, these spots have turned from white to a pale-yellow.

WATERMELON—Icebox Type

VARIETY	DAYS	SIZE/SHAPE/COLOR	REMARKS	SOURCES
Burpee Sugar Bush	80	6-8 lbs., medium-green	Bright-scarlet flesh . . . sweet, juicy . . . needs only about 6 sq. ft. of growing space per plant	10
Family Fun (hybrid) (formerly Early Midget)	88	Dark-green, round, slightly oblong	Crisp red flesh . . . black seeds	25 70
Golden Midget	65	8", green, turns golden-yellow when ripe	Red flesh . . . small, dark seeds with a thin, tough rind . . . can be grown in small places	14 19 21 28 53
Lollipop	70	3-5 lbs.	Yellow and red melons	53
Market Midget	69	3-5 lbs., slightly oval	Real sweet	28 48 66
New Hampshire Midget	68	4-6 lbs., 7 x 6", striped, dark-green	Black seeds . . . AA winner . . . very early . . . good for short-season areas . . . strawberry-red flesh . . . heavy yielding	3 10 12 14 21 25 30 45 47 51 52 53 70 72
Petite Sweet		8 lbs., round	Brown seeds . . . bright-pinkish-red flesh . . . extra-high sugar content	28 38 48 70 73
Sugar Baby	73-90	10 lbs., round, dark-green, 8"	Crisp, sweet, dark-red flesh . . . not too seedy . . . excellent home variety	9 10 11 12 14 16 19 22 28 29 30 32 36 38 40 41 44 47 48 51 52 53 56 57 60 62 66 67 70 72 73
Sugar Ball	65	12-15 lbs., grayish-green	Fiery-red flesh . . . crisp and sweet . . . very prolific, producing many melons on each vine	19 72
Sugar Doll (hybrid)	72	8-10 lbs.	Ideal for small gardens . . . more prolific and uniform than others . . . very sweet, red flesh	31 48 53 57 70
Sugar Lumps	75-80	8-9" diameter	Yellow, white, and red melons	22
Sunny Boy	80	12-15 lbs., light-green, nearly round, faint darker veining	Brown seeds . . . highly resistant to sunburn . . . deep-red flesh, unusually sweet . . . does well in South and Southwest	16
You Sweet Thing (hybrid)	70	Round, striped, 12-13 lbs.	Rose-colored flesh . . . high in sugar . . . recommended for roadside stands	32 34 50 53 60 62

WATERMELON—Giant

VARIETY	DAYS	SIZE/SHAPE/COLOR	REMARKS	SOURCES
Cobb Gem	100	130 lbs., grayish-black	Red flesh . . . heavy producer	73
Mountain Hoosier	85	75-80 lbs., oblong, dark-green	Very tasty and productive . . . deep-red flesh . . . white seeds, slightly black rim and tip	73
Mountain Sweet		100 lbs., striped	Crisp, deep-red flesh . . . very productive	73
State Fair	90	50-100 lbs.	Firm, sweet, deep-red flesh . . . finest quality	9 22
Texas Giant	95	40-50 lbs., round	Deep-red flesh . . . improved strain of Black Diamond	48 73
Weeks NC Giant Watermelon	90	197 lbs., oblong, striped	Largest melon recorded	27 43
White-Seeded Watson		100 lbs., blue-green, shiny rind	Red flesh . . . very vigorous	73

WATERMELON—Oblong, Green

VARIETY	DAYS	SIZE/SHAPE/COLOR	REMARKS	SOURCES
Candy Red		40 lbs., mottled, pale-green	From Australia . . . deep-red flesh . . . resists hollows	26
Congo	90	30-40 lbs., blocky	Bright-red flesh is sweet and crisp . . . highly resistant to anthracnose . . . AA selection . . . grayish-white seeds	10 11 14 16 28 31 32 40 41 47 51 52 56 70 73
Family Fun Hybrid	80	13-15 lbs., tough rind, medium-green	Early . . . crisp, red flesh . . . tolerant of Fusarium, anthracnose, and mildew	5 26 50 52
Faribo Hybrid 5-11		7-9 lbs.	Rich, red flesh, high in sugar . . . brown seeds	21
Faribo Black Giant Hybrid		25-40 lbs.	Sugary, red flesh . . . strong resistance to Fusarium wilt	21
Fourth of July	70	8-10 lbs.	Dark-red flesh . . . unusually sweet and rich	22
Kleckley Sweet (Monte Carlo)	87	25-40 lbs., dark-green, square ends	Bright-scarlet flesh with broad, solid heart . . . high quality . . . stringless	14 21 22 30 45 47 52 58 62 67 73
Kleckley Sweet Improved (Wonder Melon)	85	Thin rind	Earliest of the long green melons . . . sweet, bright-red flesh . . . recommended for home gardens	12 25 51
Klondike	78-90	20-25 lbs.	Extra-sweet, deep-red flesh . . . heavy yielder	9 14 36 51 52 57 58
Klondike Peacock Ebony	85-90		Resembles Peacock Improved . . . black seeds	16 57
Klondike Peacock Improved	85-90	20-22 lbs., oblong, rounded to blocky, thin, tough rind	Particularly adapted to Southwest . . . bright-orange-red flesh, sweet and crispy	16 55
Klondyke Sugar	90	25 lbs.	Scarlet flesh to the rind . . . high sugar content	21
Marketmaster (hybrid)		12-15 lbs., marbled, light-green	Crisp, bright-red flesh	21
New Wonder	88	45-70 lbs.	Bright-scarlet flesh . . . sweet, stringless . . . heavily productive under trying conditions	14
Northern Sweet	68	15 lbs.	Extra-early . . . crisp, sweet, deep-red flesh	9 28 62
Peacock Improved	85	20-25 lbs.	Appearance of Black-Seeded Klondike . . . most used in Arizona and California . . . not Fusarium-resistant	11 40 51
Peacock WR-60	88	20-25 lbs.	Bright-red flesh . . . seeds almost black	51
Peerless	80	20-25 lbs.	Well adapted for early planting . . . red, sweet flesh	66
Pride of Muscatine			Wilt-resistant	62
Royal Charleston (hybrid)	84	20-25 lbs., blocky, light-green, tough rind	Sweet, red flesh . . . few seeds . . . tolerant of Fusarium, anthracnose and mildew	5 22 28 55 70 73
Smokeylee	85	20-25 lbs., 7 x 16"	Bright-red flesh . . . large, cream-colored seeds	51 57 70 73
Stokes Sugar (hybrid)	70	15 lbs.	Firm, deep-rose flesh . . . heavy-yielding vines	66

WATERMELON—Oblong, Green (Continued)

VARIETY	DAYS	SIZE/SHAPE/COLOR	REMARKS	SOURCES
Summer Festival (hybrid)	88	15 lbs., 12 x 15"	Ripens as early as Sugar Baby . . . pink-red flesh is sweet . . . seeds are small, black	29 32 48
Summit		25-40 lbs.	Wilt-resistant . . . red flesh . . . grayish-black seeds	73
Sweet Meat Hybrid	73	Blocky, oblong, 10-12 lbs.	Small size . . . high sugar . . . very small brown seeds	19 55 57
Tom Watson	90	35-40 lbs., 22 x 12"	Bright, deep-red flesh . . . sweet and crisp . . . large brown seeds	16 47 51 57
Verona		30-40 lbs.	Black Diamond type . . . medium-rose flesh . . . black seeds . . . disease-resistant . . . good yields	73
Wondermelon	85	30-50 lbs., 22", glossy, bluish-green	Solid red heart . . . free from cores	56

WATERMELON—Oblong, Grayish Skin

VARIETY	DAYS	SIZE/SHAPE/COLOR	REMARKS	SOURCES
Calhoun Gray	85	20-25 lbs., 10 x 24"	Bright-red flesh . . . Fusarium-tolerant	51 67 70 73
Charleston Gray	85-90	20-40 lbs., gray-green	Deep, solid-red flesh . . . extra-sweet . . . high quality, very productive	9 10 11 14 16 22 28 31 32 38 40 41 44 47 48 51 53 55 56 58 62 67 70 73
Charleston Gray No. 5	90	30-40 lbs., long, gray	Resistant to anthracnose and Fusarium	52
Graybelle	80	15 lbs., globe shape, gray-green	Very firm red flesh . . . good keeper . . . not Fusarium-resistant	16
Irish Grey	85	30 lbs., 22 x 12"	Red, sweet flesh . . . high sugar content	57

WATERMELON—Oblong, Dark-Green Stripes

VARIETY	DAYS	SIZE/SHAPE/COLOR	REMARKS	SOURCES
Allsweet	90-104	25-40 lbs.	Bright-red flesh is high in sugar . . . tolerant to Fusarium wilt and races 1 and 3 of anthracnose	11 28 32 48 51 55 70 73
Chris Cross	85	Up to 50 lbs.	Tolerant to Fusarium and anthracnose . . . bright-red flesh, sweet and fine-textured	14 57 73
Early Canada	75	10-15 lbs., 10 x 12"	Red flesh . . . fine for northern growers . . . small, reddish-brown seeds	16 28 36 51 72
Early Kansas (Hutchinson Stripe) (Wichita Red Seeded) (Red Russian) (Kansas Sweet)	85	30-40 lbs., 13 x 15"	Rich, red flesh . . . sweet and delightful flavor . . . medium-thick rind	14 19 21 57
Fairfax	85	30-40 lbs., green	Resembles Garrison . . . red flesh . . . adapted to South and Southwest	16 51
Faribo Hybrid 57	60	8-10 lbs.	Rich, red flesh . . . ripens quickly in northern sections . . . brown seeds	21
Florida Favorite	90	Large, medium-green	Does well in moist climate . . . not Fusarium resistant . . . bright-red flesh, white seeds	16 47
Garrison	85-90	35-45 lbs., 12 x 24"	Anthracnose-resistant . . . deep-red flesh . . . tan seeds with dark tips	16 22 40 48 51 56 57 70 73
Jubilee	95	25-40 lbs., 13 x 24"	Heavy yielder . . . bright-red flesh . . . dark seeds . . . resistant to Fusarium wilt and race 1 anthracnose	11 14 16 31 38 40 41 48 49 51 52 55 56 57 58 67 70 73
Klondike Striped Blue Ribbon	85	25 lbs.	Does best under irrigation . . . useful for Pacific Coast growers	11 16 32 40 51 57 58
Northern Delight (hybrid)	75	12-15 lbs., medium-green	Excellent melon	66
Rattlesnake	90	22 x 10"	Bright-rose flesh is sweet	28 57
Redcrisp (hybrid)	80	15 lbs.	Deep red flesh . . . very prolific . . . Fusarium-resistant	16
Sweet Favorite (hybrid)	64	Prominent dark-green stripes	Vigorous, highly productive . . . high sugar content	72
Sweet Princess	85-90	Medium-green	Deep-pink-red flesh is very sweet . . . exceptionally small seeds	16 39 48 53 67

WATERMELON—Oblong, Dark-Green Stripes (Continued)

VARIETY	DAYS	SIZE/SHAPE/COLOR	REMARKS	SOURCES
Top Yield (hybrid)	82	20 lbs.	Bright-red, firm, juicy flesh . . . few small seeds . . . seldom has a hollow heart or misshapen fruits . . . resistant to anthracnose and Fusarium wilt	10 32 60 70

WATERMELON—Round, Dark-Green

VARIETY	DAYS	SIZE/SHAPE/COLOR	REMARKS	SOURCES
Black Diamond (Florida Giant) (Cannonball) (Shipper)	88-92	40-60 lbs., medium-thick, very tough rind, deep-bluish-green	Deep-red flesh . . . full-flavored . . . seed is large, mottled, dark-brown	11 14 16 22 28 30 32 38 40 41 51 52 53 56 58 62 67 70 73
Black Diamond Yellow Belly	90	30-40 lbs., 17 x 19", dark-blue-black rind, yellow belly	Bright-red flesh . . . black seeds	11 48 51 55 57 58 73
Blackstone	89	25-30 lbs.	Relatively free from hollow heart . . . seeds stippled black . . . heavy yielder	11 16 48 51 73
Burpee's Fordhook (hybrid)	74	12-14 lbs., glossy dark-green	Top-quality, early, productive hybrid . . . bright-red flesh, small seeds	10
Chilean Black Seed	85	10 lbs., 9 x 10"	Bright-red flesh . . . very sweet . . . large, almost black seeds	14 16
Cole's Early	80	Round	Deep-red, sweet flesh	3 30 62
King Winter Keeper	80	8 x 12"	Bright-red, sweet flesh . . . remarkable keeper	38
Louisiana Queen	70	20 lbs., 8 x 9", light-green, some dark-green	White seeds, red flesh	51 70
New Shipper	75	30 lbs.	Deep-red flesh . . . good in Midwest	28 73

WATERMELON—Round, Striped Green

VARIETY	DAYS	SIZE/SHAPE/COLOR	REMARKS	SOURCES
Crimson Sweet	80	25 lbs., round	Dark-red flesh . . . firm, sweet, fine-textured . . . vigorous vines resistant to Fusarium and anthracnose	10 11 14 16 19 22 28 29 32 38 40 41 47 48 51 52 57 67 70 73
Dixie Queen Hybrid	75-90	30-50 lbs., 12 x 15"	Deep-red flesh . . . fine sweet flavor . . . tolerant of Fusarium wilt	5 9 10 12 14 16 19 21 22 28 30 31 32 34 47 51 52 53 55 56 57 62 66 67 73
Early Northern Sweet	78	10-12 lbs.	Dark-red flesh has sugary taste . . . pick when ripe, or it becomes stringy	21 52 62 72
King and Queen Winter (Christmas)	85	10-14 lbs., 9½ x 9"	Of Russian origin . . . a sure cropper . . . stores well	14 16 51 52
Super Sweet	93	10-15 lbs., 8 x 8"	Red flesh . . . small, dark-brown seeds	51 70 73

WATERMELON—Round, Solid Color

VARIETY	DAYS	SIZE/SHAPE/COLOR	REMARKS	SOURCES
Ice Cream (Peerless)	75		A large crop of high quality . . . white seeds	36 62
Rio Gray	75-80	Gray-green, 10 x 12"	Bright-red flesh . . . crisp and sweet . . . dark-brown seeds . . . tough rind	16 57
Stone Mountain (Dixie Bell)	85	60-80 lbs., very large, smooth, light-green rind	Deep-red flesh . . . very sweet . . . almost solid heart . . . white seeds tipped with black	14 31 47 51 56 62 67 73
Winter Melon	78	10 lbs., pale-yellow when ripe	Bright-red flesh . . . crystalline . . . very sweet	21 28 62
Winter Queen Black Seeded	90	About 15 lbs., greenish-white	Largely grown for storing and use during late fall and early winter . . . deep-red, crisp flesh	11 48 50 51 57

WATERMELON—Yellow or Orange Flesh

VARIETY	DAYS	SIZE/SHAPE/COLOR	REMARKS	SOURCES
Black Diamond Yellow		60-70 lbs.	Just like the red-fleshed Black Diamond . . . mid-season melon	73
Desert King Yellow	85	Yellow rind	Yellow flesh . . . will not sunburn . . . grayish-black seeds	48 73
Golden Honey Long	85-90	20 lbs., oblong, dark-green stripes	Golden-yellow flesh is firm, crisp, and sweet . . . seeds are light tan	9 14 16 36 40 55 56 58 62
Golden Honey Sweet	80	Oblong, mottled-green stripes	Golden-yellow flesh . . . high-quality	38
Honey Cream (hybrid)	65	3-4 lbs., round, striped	Yellow-orange flesh . . . sweet flavor and aroma	50
Orangeglo	50	50 lbs., oblong, striped	Orange flesh . . . sweet and flavorful . . . cream-colored seeds	73
Tendersweet Orange	90	35-50 lbs., 18 x 12"	Very sweet, tender, orange flesh . . . white seeds	11 22 51 55 56 57 73
Tendersweet Yellow	80	30-40 lbs., dark-green rind	Golden-yellow flesh	28 31 51 58 73
Yellow Baby (hybrid)	70	10 lbs., 7" diameter	Yellow flesh . . . AA winner . . . fewer seeds, more edible flesh, than red melons	5 10 12 19 21 22 29 32 41 52 53 57 66 72
Yellow Doll (hybrid)	75	5-8 lbs., round	Crisp, yellow flesh . . . very productive vine	48 50

WATERMELON—Seedless

VARIETY	DAYS	SIZE/SHAPE/COLOR	REMARKS	SOURCES
Burpee Hybrid Seedless (Tri X-313 hybrid)	80	10-15 lbs., oval, striped	Solid-red flesh with a few soft white seed coats throughout . . . healthy, disease-resistant vines	10 55 70
Gurney's Seedless	85	24 lbs., oval, striped	Crisp, sweet, red flesh . . . a few undeveloped seeds	28
Hybrid Seedless	80	20-24 lbs., oval, striped	Crisp, extra-sweet, firm . . . long-producing melon	9 29
Seedless		10-15 lbs., 10-15"	Deep-red flesh	22
Super Seedless	90	20 lbs.	Absolutely no seeds . . . juicy red flesh	19
Supersweet Seedless Hybrid	85	15 lbs., striped, round	Red flesh up to the rind	48 53
Triple Sweet Hybrid	80	12-20 lbs., oval, striped	Early . . . produces melons even in short-season areas . . . extra-sweet	10 48

WATERMELON—Edible Seeds

VARIETY	DAYS	SIZE/SHAPE/COLOR	REMARKS	SOURCES
Edible Seeded	80	Globe-shaped	Grown for its large, very thick seeds . . . delicious eaten like squash seed, dried or roasted . . . very vigorous and disease-resistant	26

Citron

Citron is a round melon that is used primarily for preserving and for making candied peel. Cultivate and harvest like muskmelons.

CITRON

VARIETY	DAYS	SIZE	FLESH	REMARKS	SOURCES
Citron		10 lbs.		Skin is green-striped . . . excellent for pickles . . . should not be planted near other melons	31
Colorado Preserving		Large	White	Used for pickles and preserves	16 38
Green Seeded	98	Round	Light-green	Use exclusively for preserving	16 52 66
Red Seeded	90-95	10-12 lbs.	Green	Very productive	50 52 62 66

Mustard (Brassica juncea)

The South shall rise again—with mustard greens, that is. This old Southern favorite is rapidly gaining popularity everywhere. It is a fast-growing vegetable, coming up knee high in 35-45 days and developing large, wide leaves. Cool weather improves the flavor. In hot weather the peppery flavor becomes especially strong.

Choose between curled or smooth types. *Florida Broad Leaf* is one of the favorite smooth-leafed types; it has a greenish-white, flattened midril. *Southern Giant Curled,* a favorite curled variety, has fringed leaves and a very mild flavor.

HOW TO PLANT: As early in the spring as the soil can be worked, plant seeds a half-inch deep, 1-2 inches apart, in rows 18 inches apart. Thin plants to stand 4-6 inches apart. The plants thrive in cool weather and quickly go to seed in the heat of the summer. In mild-winter areas plant in the fall and winter.

Harvesting: Pick the leaves just before they mature. Be sure to keep the plants cut back to hold off flowering. After flowering, the leaves become tough and bitter.

MUSTARD—Curled

VARIETY	DAYS	LEAVES	REMARKS	SOURCES
Burpee's Fordhook Fancy	40	Deeply curled, fringed, dark-green	Mild flavor . . . slow to bolt	10 16 47 62
Green Wave	45-55	Edges finely cut, curly, ruffled, dark-green	Improved fringed type . . . much used for southern "greens" . . . AA selection	11 12 14 16 19 21 25 28 29 31 32 37 47 48 57
Kyona (Mizuna)	40	Deeply cut, fringed	Very popular mustard of Japanese origin . . . narrow white stalks	37 42
Osaka Purple Mustard		Purplish-red, fringed	Very mild in flavor	26
Ostrich Plume	35	As tender as lettuce	Will stand without bolting for 2 weeks longer than regular strain	14
Prizewinner	50		Exceptionally long-standing curled type	53
Southern Giant Curled	40-60	Bright-green, wide, crumpled edges	Large, moderately broad leaves . . . for spring or fall planting . . . 18-24" spread . . . slow to bolt	10 11 12 14 16 30 32 34 36 38 40 41 47 48 49 51 52 55 56 58 62 67 70

MUSTARD—Plain

VARIETY	DAYS	LEAVES	REMARKS	SOURCES
Florida Broad Leaf	43-50	Medium-green, broad, smooth, with flattened, greenish-white midrib	Desirable for greens because the leaves are easy to work with . . . 16-22" spread	10 11 12 14 16 30 31 32 40 41 44 48 51 56 57 67 70 72 73 76
Large Smooth Leaf	40		Fine-flavored . . . most popular . . . easy to clean	55 58
Tendergreen (Mustard Spinach)	34-40	Large, broad, thick, dark-green	Rapid-growing . . . has spinach flavor . . . 16-22" spread . . . especially suited to South	3 10 12 14 16 21 22 28 31 41 42 45 47 51 52 53 56 57 58 62 67 72 73

Okra (Hibiscus esculentus)

Okra, a member of the Hollyhock family, is another long-time Southern favorite. The long pod is cut and used as soup stock, with seafood, and in other types of cooking. Okra pods grow on large, erect, bushy plants with tropical-looking leaves. If your garden will grow sweet corn, it will grow okra.

You have a choice of tall varieties (which grow 5-10 feet) or dwarf varieties (which grow 3-4 feet tall); pod colors are green, white-green, and red. (The red is excellent in salads, or it can be dried for arrangements.) Varieties differ in pod shape—short to long, round to ridged—leaf shape, and flowers. Some types are quite ornamental. Favorite varieties are *Clemson Spineless, Emerald, Louisiana Green Velvet,* and *Gold Coast.*

HOW TO PLANT: Soak the seeds in water for 24 hours before planting. Plant a half-inch deep, in rows 36 inches apart, after the soil has warmed to at least 75 degrees. Thin plants to 15 inches apart.

Harvesting: Pick the pods four to six days after the flower opens. Harvest the ripened pods every two or three days. Pods left on the plant to overripen will become tough and stringy and will shorten the picking season.

OKRA—Green, Full-Sized

VARIETY	DAYS	SIZE/SHAPE/COLOR	REMARKS	SOURCES
Clemson Spineless	55-60	6-9" pods, rich-green	4-5-foot plants . . . very heavy yielder . . . AA selection	9 10 11 12 14 16 30 31 32 34 36 40 41 44 45 47 48 50 51 52 53 55 56 57 58 67 70 73
Emerald Green Velvet		7-9" pods, medium-green, smooth, with some ridging	6-9-foot plants . . . leaves are green with grayish cast, lobed with circular appearance	32 48 55 70
Evertender		Extra-long, green	From India . . . tender pods . . . disease-resistant	26
First Choice	50	Dark-green pods, fluted, slender	3½ feet tall . . . pods are fiber-free and tender	14
Green Louisiana Long		Pods up to a foot long	Stalks look like trees before season is over	6
Green Velvet Spineless	60	7" pods, slender, light-green	5-foot plants, very vigorous, heavy yielders . . . very tender pods	16 53 55
Louisiana Green Velvet	60	6-7" pods, velvety-green, spineless	Excellent variety . . . plants are 6 feet tall and branching	31 56
Perkins Mammoth	60	8-9" pods, brown-green, ribbed	6-12-foot plants . . . pods retain their tenderness and color longer than other types	12 47 56 62 66 67 73
Perkins Spineless	53	6-9" pods, ribbed	4½-6 feet tall . . . leaves are medium lobed . . . pods not as thick as Clemson	32 41
Vining Green			Edible in early growth . . . grows on trellis, fence, or ground	6

OKRA—Green, Dwarf

VARIETY	DAYS	SIZE/SHAPE/COLOR	REMARKS	SOURCES
Dwarf Green Long Pod	50	7" pods, dark-green, ribbed	2½-3-foot plant . . . early, prolific	3 9 10 12 14 16 21 30 31 32 47 49 51 55 56 58 67 72 73
Dwarf Stalked Long Green Prolific	55	7-8" pods, dark-green, fleshy	3-foot plant . . . sturdy, prolific . . . canning sort	11
Emerald	56	Dark-green, round, thick-walled, spineless	3-foot plant . . . vigorous . . . excellent for home or market	11 14 29 38 51 53 56 57 60 73
Gee Gwa (Chinese Okra)	90	6-8" pods, green	Summer crop . . . delicately sweet . . . tender flesh . . . eat fresh or cooked	27 69
Gold Coast	55-60	Short pods, free of fluting	Strong root system . . . very heat-resistant . . . excellent freezer	16 55 56
Perkins Dwarf Spineless	53	7" pods, dark-green, almost spineless	3½-foot plant . . . suitable for home or market	40 51 57

OKRA—Other Colors

VARIETY	DAYS	SIZE/SHAPE/COLOR	REMARKS	SOURCES
Red Okra	60		5-6 feet tall . . . bush and pods are rich, violet-red tones . . . unusual and delicious	6 53
Red River	60-69	Maroon	Tall stems have attractive yellow flowers . . . withstands hottest weather	41
Red Wonder		Long pods	Super quality . . . tender pods to maturity	26
White Velvet	60	6-7" pods, velvety white, smooth	5-foot plant . . . a very prolific variety	14 31 41 51 56 58 62

The onion family

Onion (Allium)

Onions are a large happy family and so easy to grow that every gardener should try a few. Onions, however, are not just onions, they come in all shapes and sizes: round, flat-thick, top-shaped, spindle-shaped and in colors of roughly red, yellow-brown and white.

Round: This category includes the red, white, and yellow globe types, the small round pear or pickling onions, and the large, round Spanish type.

Flat: These are flat, wide, and round. Many of them

resemble a cartwheel. Granex is flat on top and pointed on the bottom.

Half-flat: These are the Bermuda onions. They are mild flavored and come in red, yellow, and white.

Top-shaped: These are the Grano types.

Spindle-shaped: These are pointed on both ends, like the *Italian Torpedo Onions.*

Any variety of the standard onion can be grown as green bunching onions if they are harvested when the bulb is small. (You will find a number of these, such as *White Sweet Spanish* and *White Libson.*) There are also perennial bunching types that divide at the base to form new shoots. They do not produce bulbs. There are also Welsh Onions *(Allium fistulosum),* often listed as *Japanese bunching,* Winter Onions *(Allium perutile),* listed as *evergreen bunching,* and *everlasting bunching.*

Egyptian Onion (Allium cepa vivaparum), walking onion, top onion. This onion multiplies by forming a cluster of bulbs at the top of a long stem. Frequently a second cluster will form on top of the first. Though the underground bulb is edible, the flavor is extremely strong. The top bulbs are used in cooking.

Multiplier Onions (Allium cepa solanium), potato onions. These onions are propagated by a division of underground bulbs. Each bulb multiplies into a cluster of bulbs, which also multiply at maturity.

HOW TO PLANT: Onions can be grown from seeds, seedlings, or sets.

Sow seeds a quarter-inch deep in rows 12 inches apart. Thin the rows to 4 inches apart (eat the young onions as scallions), then let the mature bulbs develop.

Plant seedlings purchased from a nursery 1 inch apart; thin to 2-3 inches apart.

Sets, which are tiny bulbs, are the best way to grow onions. Plant sets 1-2 inches apart; harvest green onions until the plants are spaced 2-3 inches apart. Let the remaining bulbs develop to maturity.

Harvesting: When the tops of ordinary bulbs begin to dry and yellow, bend them over to a nearly horizontal position on the ground or break them off. This will divert all growing energy to the bulbs. When all the tops are dead, dig the bulbs up and let them dry on top of the ground for a few days; then store them in a dry, frost-free place indefinitely. Harvest green onions as needed.

ONIONS—Globe, White

VARIETY	DAYS	REMARKS	SOURCES
Peerless (hybrid)		Short day . . . globe-shaped, medium to large . . . firm, moderately pungent flesh . . . must be protected from strong sunlight . . . stores well . . . pink-root resistant	16
Southport White Globe	110	Long day . . . medium-large, high globe . . . clear, white skin . . . fairly mild . . . not as good a keeper as the colored Southport Globes	11 14 16 21 29 30 32 38 47 48 51 52 57 62 70
White Sweet Keeper		Sweet and mild . . . firm, solid . . . good keeper . . . smooth round . . . average ½ to ¾ lb. each . . . frostproof	16
White Sweet Slicer		Globe shape . . . fine-grained, sweet, mild flesh . . . often weight 1 lb. each . . . fine keeper	28

ONIONS—Globe, Yellow

VARIETY	DAYS	REMARKS	SOURCES
Abundance (hybrid)	104	Long day . . . good yields . . . bulbs are high-globe . . . medium-yellow scales . . . flesh is fairly firm and pungent	16 32 51
Ailsa Craig		A large, round bulb . . . golden-straw color . . . mild . . . good for spring or autumn	36 68
Aristrocrat (hybrid)	105	Long day . . . medium-high globe . . . yellow scales . . . firm, pungent flesh	32 66
Australian Brown		Does best in cool coastal climate of central California . . . late-maturing . . . flattened globe, medium size . . . chestnut-brown scales, lemon-yellow flesh . . . extremely pungent flavor	16 51 57

ONIONS—Globe, Yellow (Continued)

VARIETY	DAYS	REMARKS	SOURCES
Autumn Spice (hybrid)		Long day . . . grown in northern onion-growing districts . . . noted for its uniformity and long storage qualities . . . medium size, globe shape . . . dark-yellow scales . . . hard flesh is pungent	16 21 32 40 52 66 68 70
Autumn Splendor	104	Long day . . . storage onion . . . high-globe, medium size . . . creamy-white, pungent flesh . . . medium-to dark-yellow scales . . . proven storage and yielding ability	52
Brigham Yellow Globe		Long day variety for northern areas . . . mid-season to late in maturity . . . medium size, globe to high-globe bulbs . . . firm, pungent flesh	16 48
Brown Beauty (hybrid)		Large globe . . . modification of Brigham Yellow . . . white flesh . . . mild flavor	32
Buccaneer (hybrid)	99	Early storer . . . round bulbs . . . firm flesh . . . heavy yields	29
Burpee's Yellow Globe Hybrid	102	3-3½" across . . . outstanding for earliness . . . exceptional keeping quality . . . smooth, light, golden-yellow skin . . . fine-grained yellow flesh	10
Canada Maple (hybrid)	98	Extra-hard . . . long storer . . . excellent yields in deep muck	66
Copper Cache	98-100	Medium size, globe to high-globe shape . . . dark-yellow scales . . . long keeper	70
Cooper Gem (hybrid)	93	Round, brownish skin . . . medium size . . . firm flesh	51
Downing Yellow Globe	112	Long day . . . excellent, long storer . . . does best in north-central states . . . late-maturing . . . medium size, globe-shaped . . . dark-yellow scales . . . hard flesh, pungent flavor	16 22 23 28 32 40 51 52 60
Early Beauty	98	Extra-early . . . very large bulbs, almost globe . . . dark, rich-yellow skin . . . long keeping qualities	14
Early Gold (hybrid)		Intermediate day length . . . medium size, deep-globe shape . . . yellow skin . . . firm, white, mild flesh . . . not recommended for storage	40
Early Harvest (hybrid)		Long day . . . rapid growth in early stages . . . bulbs vary from globe- to slightly top-shaped . . . yellow, dry scales . . . soft flesh, mildly pungent . . . very productive when grown as a winter crop in South	16 25
Early Yellow Globe	95-100	Long day . . . deep-yellow skin with clear-white flesh . . . mild-flavored . . . early, uniform, large. . . heavy yields . . . good keeper	10 14 16 21 30 32 38 48 51 52 60 66 70
Early Yellow Globe H-36		Vigorous and highly productive storage onion . . . widely grown in northern states . . . medium size, semi-globe . . . golden-colored scales . . . medium-firm, mildly pungent flesh	40
Elite (hybrid)	110	Long day . . . widely adopted in the north . . . produces excellent crop in both peat and mineral soils . . . bulbs are globe to high-globe in shape . . . yellow scales . . . fairly firm, pungent flesh	16 32 51 66
Empire (hybrid)		Long day . . . very productive . . . globe to high-globe shape . . . yellow scales . . . long storer . . . one of the best hybrids for late-spring storage . . . firm; pungent, flesh	16 32
Encore (hybrid)	99	Long day . . . adapted to northern onion-growing districts . . . very productive . . . not extra-long storer . . . high-globe shape . . . dark-yellow scales . . . fairly firm, pungent flesh	16 66 70
Epoch		Long day . . . earliest maturing of the northern storage-type onions . . . high-globe shape . . . dark-yellow scales . . . hard flesh, pungent flavor	16 51 70
Faribo Yellow Globe (hybrid)		Matures earlier . . . keeps longer than ordinary strains . . . globe shape . . . large . . . light-brown skin	21
Gladiator (hybrid)		Spring-planted, long-day storage onion . . . full-globe shape . . . medium size . . . deep-yellow skin . . . ivory-white flesh has true pungent onion flavor	40

ONIONS—Globe, Yellow (Continued)

VARIETY	DAYS	REMARKS	SOURCES
Golden Beauty (hybrid)		Long day . . . bulbs are large, high-globe . . . golden-yellow scales . . . fairly firm flesh . . . moderately pungent . . . under good storage conditions, bulbs can be kept till January	16
Golden Globe	110	Long day . . . chiefly for production of dry onion sets . . . similar to Southport Yellow Globe . . . medium-firm flesh, fairly pungent	16 32 51
Golden Mosque	105	Almost round at maturity . . . the supreme variety for yellow sets	66
Henry's Special		Grown as winter crop in South . . . flattened globe, and slightly top-shaped . . . flesh is crisp, firm, mild . . . pink-root resistant . . . usable 4 to 5 months if stored properly	16
Hy Pak (Exp. 3347)	106	Long day . . . round to globe shape . . . straw-colored skin . . . medium-large, firm flesh . . . long storer	51
Improved Autumn Spice	98	A valuable variety where the muck is not too deep . . . matures about 20% larger than regular Spice	66
Indian Queen	113	Long day . . . high yields . . . uniform size . . . yellow-brown skin, clings tight	21 51 70
Mountain Danvers		Long day . . . adapted to western slope of Colorado . . . medium-large, flattened-globe to globe in shape . . . brownish-yellow scales . . . not an extra-long storer, but can be held till mid-winter . . . fairly firm flesh, pungent flavor	16
Mucker (hybrid)		Long day . . . widely adapted to northern areas . . . bulbs are high-globe in shape . . . flesh is hard and pungent . . . yellowish-brown scales . . . long storage	16 32
Northern Oak	108	Long day . . . large storage onion . . . rich-oak-colored, thin skins . . . shows tolerance to Fusarium and some strains of pink root	66
Nugget (hybrid)		Developed for Wisconsin mucklands . . . medium size, high globe shape . . . golden-bronze scales . . . long storer . . . hard flesh, distinctly pungent	16
Oregon Danvers		Long day . . . grown in western Oregon on muck soils . . . long storer . . . dark-yellow scales . . . hard, pungent flesh	16
Parks Early Harvest (hybrid)	80	Early maturing . . . straw-colored . . . globe-shaped . . . mild flavor . . . short top growth with a small neck . . . very productive	53
Paydirt	100	Long day, hard storage onion . . . round to globe . . . brown scales . . . medium-large . . . firm flesh	51
Premier (hybrid)		Long day . . . adapted to northern growing regions . . . good yields . . . high-globe shape . . . dry, dark-yellow scales . . . fairly firm, pungent flesh	16 32
Ringer		Chiefly for the production of onion rings . . . top-shaped bulbs . . . dry yellow scales are thin . . . storage life is short	16
San Joaquin		Adapted to the San Joaquin Valley of California . . . very refined . . . mostly globe-shaped, slight tendency towards top-shaped . . . highly nonbolting . . . light, dry, thin, yellow scales . . . soft, mild flesh . . . short storage life	16
Simcoe (hybrid)		Long day . . . developed for mucklands of the north . . . high-globe bulbs . . . flesh is hard and pungent . . . golden-bronze scales	16 70
Southport Yellow Globe	115	Long day . . . bright-golden-yellow skin . . . fine-grained, creamy-white flesh . . . fairly strong flavor . . . deeply globular, with broad shoulders . . . good keeper	10 14 16 21 38 62
Spano (hybrid)		Short day . . . early-harvest type . . . high-globed, almost top-shaped bulbs . . . pink-root resistance . . . thin, dry, yellow scales . . . short storage life . . . soft flesh, mild flavor	16

ONIONS—Globe, Yellow (Continued)

VARIETY	DAYS	REMARKS	SOURCES
Spartan Banner (hybrid)		Long day . . . same growing areas as Downing Yellow Globe, matures one week later . . . most productive storage onion . . . high-globe shape . . . bright-yellow outer scales	16 32 40 66
Spartan Bounty (hybrid)		Long day . . . same growing areas as Downing Yellow Globe . . . high-globe shape . . . very productive . . . hard flesh . . . stores well over a long period	16
Spartan Era (hybrid)		Long day . . . adapted to same areas as Early Yellow Globe . . . high-globe shape . . . yellow-brown scales . . . long storer	16 40 70
Spartan Gem (hybrid)		Long day . . . medium-size, deep-globe shape . . . tight, amber skin . . . flesh is very firm and pungent . . . noted for upright tops	40
Sunburst	98	Large, straw-colored, round globe . . . firm . . . good keeper	70
Super Spice	97	Long day . . . produces extra-hard, long-storage bulbs . . . good tolerance to Fusarium wilt	66
Yellow Globe Danvers	110	Long day . . . quite globular . . . entirely free from thick necks . . . heavily productive	3 14 16 21 25 30 45 47 49 50 52 62 67

ONIONS—Spanish, Yellow-Brown

VARIETY	DAYS	REMARKS	SOURCES
Amigo (hybrid)	100	Large, globe-shaped bulb . . . long day . . . heavy, dry scales . . . stored properly, it will last a while . . . mild, fairly firm flesh	16 27 48
Bullring (hybrid)		Long day . . . bulbs are large, high-globe, blocky . . . golden-bronze scales . . . hard, pungent flesh . . . long storage life	16
Burpee's Sweet Spanish Hybrid	110	Huge, globular, with light-yellow skin . . . crisp-white flesh . . . mild-flavored . . . transplant type	10
Burrell's Yellow Valencia	115	AA selection . . . full-globe shape . . . deep-bronze color . . . vigorous tops are slow to ripen . . . withstands thrips . . . keeps well	11
Chieftain	115	Long day . . . slightly earlier and larger than Fiesta . . . rich, copper-color skin . . . bulbs are 5½ to 6" in diameter . . . mild flesh . . . extremely hard, will store well until spring	66
Conqueror (hybrid)		Long day . . . high-yielding . . . bulbs are globe to high-globe shape . . . dark-yellow, dry scales . . . medium-firm flesh has mild flavor	16
Dessert Brown (hybrid)		Matures 2 to 3 weeks ahead of the late Spanish varieties . . . bulbs are globe-shaped . . . dark-yellowish-brown scales . . . firm, pungent flesh . . . can be stored if ventilated and kept dry	16
El Capitan (hybrid)		Long day . . . excellent storer . . . globe to flattened-globe in shape . . . yellow to reddish-tinged scales . . . fairly firm, pungent flesh	16 32
El Diablo (hybrid)		Long day . . . mostly high-globe shape . . . light-yellow, dry scales . . . a favorite transplant with home gardeners . . . if stored properly, will last a long time	16
Faribo Hybrid Sweet Spanish		Much earlier than any other yellow Spanish strain . . . long keeper . . . matures big, crisp, sweet, mild . . . slicer	21
Fiesta (hybrid)	110	Long day . . . early . . . medium to large, globe-shaped . . . stores well . . . small necks, firm, pungent flesh	5 16 22 32 40 66 70
Grandee (hybrid)		Long day . . . high-yielding . . . matures a few days before Fiesta and Treasure . . . globe-shaped bulbs . . . dark-yellow outer scales . . . medium-hard flesh . . . moderately pungent	16
Gringo (hybrid)	105	Long day . . . deep globe, thick skin . . . medium-large . . . copper color	66

ONIONS—Spanish, Yellow-Brown (Continued)

VARIETY	DAYS	REMARKS	SOURCES
Hancock (hybrid)		Adapted to same areas as Fiesta, but matures later . . . very productive . . . flesh is hard and pungent . . . yellow outer scales	16
Monarch (hybrid)		Long day . . . very productive . . . globe-shaped . . . firm flesh, mildly pungent	16
Patti King (hybrid)		Bun-size onion . . . high-globe shape . . . golden-brown skin . . . keeps well . . . sow seed direct into garden . . . best adapted to areas north of San Francisco and D.C.	53
Reliance (hybrid)		Long day . . . matures same time as Grandee . . . medium top growth, small necks . . . bulbs are globe-shaped . . . dry, yellow scales are thin and soft . . . fairly firm flesh, moderately pungent, can be stored	16
Riverside (op)	115	Used principally for starting in the greenhouse in February and March . . . large, thick skin . . . good keeping qualities	66
Spanish Main Hybrid	115	Heavy, dark-copper skin . . . globe-shaped . . . firm flesh has good storage capabilities	48
Summer Favorite (hybrid)		Very large, deep globe . . . dark-brown skin . . . firm flesh . . . excellent storage type . . . used in long day zones as a transplant	16
Sweet Spanish Las Animas	112	Deep globe . . . straw-yellow color . . . large, medium-firm flesh . . . good keeping qualities	51
Sweet Spanish Yellow Colorado No. 6	115	3½-4" diameter . . . best keeper of the Sweet Spanish types . . . very deep, almost bronze color . . . thrips-resistant	11 40 57
Sweet Spanish Yellow Utah Jumbo	110-130	4-6" across . . . large, globe-shaped, jumbo bulbs . . . mild and sweet, with excellent flavor . . . limited storage ability . . . white flesh	5 10 11 16 25 30 32 40 48 51 52 58 60 67 70
Talbot (hybrid)		Long day . . . adapted to the same districts as Fiesta, but matures later . . . high-globe shape . . . firm, rather pungent flesh . . . yellow scales	16
Treasure (hybrid)		Long day . . . can be grown where late-Spanish types do not do well . . . fairly firm flesh, moderately pungent . . . stores well under proper conditions	16
Victory (hybrid)		Long day . . . dark-yellow to copper scales . . . mostly globe-shaped . . . slightly pungent, firm flesh	16 48
Winner (hybrid)		Long day . . . very productive . . . globe-shaped . . . medium-yellow, dry scales . . . only slightly pungent . . . medium-firm flesh	16 32
Yellow Skin Hybrid		Large, round, globe shape . . . mild, sweet flavor	8 10 52 65
Yellow Sweet Spanish (Prizetaker)	110	Long day . . . round, globe shape . . . light-yellow skin . . . white flesh, mild, sweet flavor . . . good keeper . . . withstands unfavorable growing condtions . . . 12 or more inches in diameter	3 8 14 19 20 21 22 23 28 29 31 34 38 44 45 47 48 50 53 54 55 56 57 62 65 67 67A 73
Yellow Sweet Spanish Peckham		Long day . . . large bulbs . . . excellent for storage . . . very firm texture	16
Yellow Sweet Spanish Tucker		Long day . . . few days earlier than Utah Spanish . . . high-globe shape . . . light-yellow skin . . . high pink-root resistance . . . firm flesh . . . good keeper	16

ONIONS—Spanish, White, Red

VARIETY	DAYS	REMARKS	SOURCES
Cima (hybrid)		True globe shape . . . creamy-white, crisp flesh . . . better curability than other Spanish types . . . adapted to western areas where bolting is a problem	40
Ringmaster White Sweet Spanish	110	High percent of single growing centers . . . high yielder of large, uniform bulbs . . . pine-root-resistant	11 16 22 23 28 34 48 50 51 53 57
Snow White (hybrid)		Long day . . . matures a few days earlier than Utah Sweet White Spanish . . . bulbs are globe-shaped . . . flesh is fairly firm and crisp . . . mild flavor . . . store properly	16 53

ONIONS—Spanish, White, Red (Continued)

VARIETY	DAYS	REMARKS	SOURCES
Sunrise		Mature bulbs are dark-red and globe to high-globe shape . . . medium-firm, pungent flesh	16
Sweet Spanish Utah (Jumbo White)	110	3½-4" diameter . . . very large . . . paper-white scales . . . thrips-resistant . . . not a storage onion	11 48 49 50 51 53 54 57 58 62 65 67A 73
White Sweet Spanish	110	Bulbs are large and globular-shaped . . . mild flavor . . . firm flesh, but limited storage qualities . . . plant in the spring . . . grown in the north	5 8 10 14 20 22 25 28 32 39 40

ONIONS—Flat, Red

VARIETY	DAYS	REMARKS	SOURCES
Calred		Dark-red . . . latest-maturing of the short-day varieties . . . foliage is moderately resistant to downy mildew . . . pink-root-resistant . . . thick, flat-to-flattened, globe shape . . . soft flesh . . . short storage life	16
Red Creole	95	Short day . . . southern-type red onion . . . good keeper . . . flesh is firm and very pungent . . . bulbs are small, thick-flat in shape	14 16 32 40 51 56
Red Wetherfield	103	Long day . . . excellent keeper . . . large, flat, deep-red bulbs . . . crisp, juicy, white flesh . . . mild flavor . . . popular with home gardeners and for growing onion sets	3 14 16 30 32 39 51 52 70
Tropicana (hybrid)	175	Short day . . . good storage onion . . . thick, flat bulbs . . . firm, pungent flesh . . . pink-root-resistant	16 41

ONIONS—Flat, Yellow

VARIETY	DAYS	REMARKS	SOURCES
Dessex (hybrid)		Short day . . . matures 2 to 3 weeks earlier than Granex . . . thick, flat bulbs . . . bright-yellow skin . . . pink-root-resistant . . . firm, crisp flesh	16
Ebenezer	105	2½-3" across . . . keeps in good condition until spring . . . flattened globe, yellowish-brown skin, yellowish-white flesh . . . mild flavor . . . widely grown for sets	3 10 16 28 29 30 32 50 51 53 57 62 66 67
Golden (hybrid)		Excellent storage qualities . . . bright-golden-yellow scales . . . bulbs are medium-size and thick, flat in shape . . . hard, pungent flesh . . . pink-root-resistant	16
Osye		Stores exceptionally well . . . when mature, it produces large, slightly flat onions with yellowish skin and firm, mild flesh	31
Yellow Creole		Short day . . . matures 10 days ahead of Red Creole, and adapted to same conditions . . . golden-yellow scales are tough . . . pink-root-resistant . . . stores well through hot southern summers	16 32
Stuttgarter		Large, flattened shape . . . dark-yellow skin . . . excellent keeper . . . matures early . . . suitable for growing onion sets	32 60 66
Yellow Flat Dutch		Large, flat bulbs of golden-yellow color . . . mild and sweet	36 62A
Yellow Vertus		Large, flat, yellow bulbs . . . very popular variety known for its storage qualities	15

ONIONS—Flat, White

VARIETY	DAYS	REMARKS	SOURCES
Early Supreme (hybrid)		Short day . . . toward harvest, bulbs should be protected from strong sunlight . . . fairly firm flesh, slightly pungent . . . short storage life . . . pink-root-resistant	16
Majesty		Short day . . . for the Deep South winter crop . . . thick, flat bulbs . . . should be protected from strong sunlight . . . short storage life . . . moderately pungent	16

ONIONS—Flat, White (Continued)

VARIETY	DAYS	REMARKS	SOURCES
Robust	175	Short day ... vigorous grower, highly productive ... thick, flat bulbs ... fairly firm flesh, moderately pungent ... pink-root-resistant ... short storage life ... before and after harvest protect from strong sunlight	16
White Alamo (hybrid)		Short day ... thick, flat bulbs ... tops have distinctive upright-growth habit ... should be protected before and after harvest from sun-scald and greening ... firm, slightly pungent flesh ... short storage life	16
White Ebenezer	100	Long day ... used almost entirely for production of dry onion sets ... home gardeners use for growing of green onions	16 32 48 51 57 62 66
White Early Paris		Large, flat, white bulb ... cold-resistant ... heavy yields	15
White Mexican (El Toro)		Short day ... adapted to southernmost onion growing districts ... may bolt to seed if too large a plant is overwintered ... thick, flat shape ... protect from strong sunlight ... fairly firm flesh	16
White Portugal (Silverskin)	100	Short day ... bulbs are small to medium and flattened ... firm, fine-grained, pungent flesh ... fine for sets, pickling, bunching, and mature onions ... good keeper ... plant in spring ... normally grown in the North	5 10 11 14 16 21 25 29 30 32 38 45 47 48 51 66 67
White Queen		Short day ... matures about the same time as Crystal Wax ... mature bulbs are flat ... dry, soft scales ... soft flesh, mild flavor	16

ONIONS—Granex, Thick, Flat

VARIETY	DAYS	REMARKS	SOURCES
Granex Red (hybrid)	107	Short day ... red-tinged, white flesh, firm and mild ... high-yielding ... plant in spring or fall ... grown in South	5 16
Granex White (hybrid)	105-175	Short day ... mild flavor ... crisp, firm flesh ... distinctive, high-yielding type for southern latitudes ... plant in spring or fall ... grown in South	5 16 41 55
Granex 33 Yellow (hybrid)	80	Short day ... bulbs vary from thick-flat to almost-globe ... slightly sloping base ... thin, yellow skin ... medium-firm, mild-flavored flesh ... can be stored for up to 5 months	16 31 32 40 53 56

ONIONS—Bermuda, Flattened

VARIETY	DAYS	REMARKS	SOURCES
Burgundy (Hamburger Onion)	95	Bulbs are thick and somewhat flattened ... soft, mild flesh ... storage life is short ... normally grown in South ... plant in spring or fall	5 8 10 14 16 19 21 22 28 31 32 34 53 55 58 62 65 73
Crystal White Wax (Eclipse) (1-303)	95	Short day ... medium size, flat ... mild, white flesh ... very little bolting ... plant in spring or fall ... grown primarily in South	5 8 10 14 16 21 22 31 32 40 41 48 51 52 53 54 55 56 57 58 62 65 67A
Excel 986	180	Yellow ... short day ... fairly firm, crisp, mild flesh ... excellent pink-root resistance ... good keeper when kept dry and aerated	16 31 32 40 41 57
Miss Society (hybrid)		Medium large, semiglobe, flat top ... mild, sweet, white flesh ... dependable yielder, good keeper ... unexcelled for pulling green ... mature onions weight a half-pound each	19
Red Bermuda	93	Short day ... bulbs are early, large, and flat, with red skin ... fine-grained, solid, pinkish flesh ... sweet and mild	14 25 32
White Bermuda	92	White flesh, very mild ... not hurt by frost or freeze	14 19 21 22 23 25 28 34 47 53

ONIONS—Bermuda, Flattened (Continued)

VARIETY	DAYS	REMARKS	SOURCES
White Skin Hybrid		Round, semiflat shape . . . very mild taste . . . excellent in salads	8 10 38 57
Yellow Bermuda	92	Short day . . . bulb is medium size with a flattened shape . . . straw-colored, loose skin . . . mild, juicy, coarse flesh . . . planted in spring or fall . . . normally grown in southern states	5 10 14 25 51 55 56 62 65 67A

ONIONS—Grano, Pear-Shaped

VARIETY	DAYS	REMARKS	SOURCES
New Mexico Yellow		Latest-maturing Grano grown in South . . . light-yellow scales are thin . . . flesh is soft and mild in flavor . . . short storage life . . . light-green foliage is somewhat resistant to thrips	16 51 57 58 73
Red Grano		Dark-red . . . matures a few days after Burgundy . . . top-shaped bulbs with very few splits or doubles . . . red color extends to center . . . pink-root resistance . . . bulbs store for 2-3 months	16
Ring Gold (hybrid)		High percentage of bulbs have single centers . . . mild flavor . . . pink-root resistance . . . well-cured bulbs are usable 3-4 months after storage	16
Texas Early Yellow Grano 502	168	Adapted to southernmost onion-growing districts of U.S. . . . foliage has considerable thrips resistance . . . dry, yellow scales are thin . . . flesh is soft and mild-flavored . . . short storage life . . . pink-root resistance	16 20 31 32 40 41 51
White Grano	178	Very productive . . . pink root resistance . . . top-shaped . . . mild flavor, soft flesh . . . short storage life	16 56 57 58 67A
White Grano New Mexico Strain	185	Short day . . . large half-globe . . . thin, white skin . . . soft, mild flesh	51
Yellow Grano		Large, top-shaped . . . mild, white flesh . . . straw color	55 67A

ONIONS—Red, Spindle Shape

VARIETY	DAYS	REMARKS	SOURCES
Italian Red (Torpedo)		Grown chiefly in central California . . . highly nonbolting . . . large spindle-shaped bulbs are unexcelled in mildness and sweetness . . . dry scales are thin, purplish-red . . . short storage life	16 36

ONIONS—Bunching

VARIETY	DAYS	REMARKS	SOURCES
Beltsville Bunching	65	Spring or fall planting . . . slight swelling . . . winter-hardy	31 40 48 66
Beltsville Improved		Winter-hardy . . . heat-tolerant . . . white shoots are crisp and mild . . . later in season they become more pungent	16
Evergreen Long White Bunching	65-120	Long, silvery-white stems . . . used in northern and southern states . . . pungent stalks divide continously from base . . . will not bulb	5 10 14 25 34 36 41 49 50 53 56 62 70 73
Ha Ski Ko Evergreen (Long White Bunching)	80	Perennial, nonbulbing . . . continues to grow and divide at the base . . . winter-hardy . . . small leaves, upright growth . . . white, pungent flesh	16 21 28 32 51 60
Home Garden Bunching		Excellent vigor . . . winter-hardy and heat tolerant . . . flesh is crisp and mild, has pinkish tint	16

ONIONS—Bunching (Continued)

VARIETY	DAYS	REMARKS	SOURCES
Japanese Bunching (White Spanish) (Hardy White Bunching)	70	Hardy green scallion . . . does not form a bulb, but makes long, slim scallions of good quality . . . multiplies several stalks per plant . . . hardy	29 52 66 67 70
Long White Shank		Long, white shanks . . . dark-green leaves keep their fresh appearance a long time after pulling . . . flesh is crisp and mild	16 32
Long White Tokyo Bunching		Dark-green leaves, single-stalked . . . excellent for summer to winter crop . . . white stalks grow 16-18"	32 47
Perfecto Blanco		Selection of White Sweet Spanish used for green bunching . . . dark-bluish-green leaves . . . long, clear-white stalks are slow to bulb	16 51
Prolific White		Light-green leaves . . . matures early . . . resistant to hot weather . . . grows in clusters of 2-3 stalks . . . white stalks are 12-14" long	50
Rose Libson		Mild, crisp, quick-growing	68
Shamrock		Bulbs slowly and has silvery-white shanks . . . out of Southport White Globe for stripping	51
Silver Queen	80	An early, fast-maturing, white pickling onion . . . round bulbs have waxy appearance desired for pickling	66
Southport White Globe (Green Bunching Strain)	65	Most popular strain of Southport White Globe . . . used exclusively for production of green bunching . . . mild and sweet	57 66
Stoke's Early Mild Bunching	60	Long, white, single, upright . . . mild and sweet . . . highly suitable for harvesting during early summer	66
White Bunching	120	Produces an abundance of mild, tender, bulbless stalks . . . sow seed in spring or fall	3 19 22 38 44
White Knight Bunching	60	Makes a long stem, longer than ordinary bunching onions . . . pure-white, no bulbs . . . resistant to pink root, thrips, and smut	41
White Libson (Improved Green Bunching)	60	Widely grown for green bunching . . . dark-green foliage resistant to heat and cold . . . retains freshness long after being pulled . . . crisp flesh, moderately mild	16 21 40 48 51 57 58 66 68 70
White Pearl (Barletta)		Small, round bulbs used for pickling	32 36 66 70
White Bunching	40	White tender stalks, 14-18" high . . . stands heat well . . . stays in bunching condition a long time . . . if left standing to full maturity, bulbs grow 3" in diameter . . . not recommended for large onion	14
White Sweet Spanish Bunching		Used for bunching or stripping . . . slow to bulb . . . mild flavor . . . white onion with slender, blue-green tops	11 57 66
White Sweet Spanish Valencia	75	Most popular green bunching onion . . . long day . . . does not have tendency to bulb early . . . crisp, mild flesh	16 70
Wonder of Pompei		Best pickling onion . . . very early, small, round onions	32 50

ONIONS—Egyptian and Multiplying

VARIETY	REMARKS	SOURCES
Egyptian Tree Top (Pickle Onion) (Salad Onion) (Winter Onion)	Top sets ½" diameter, bottom onions about 1" diameter . . . multiplies at top, divides at bottom . . . very hardy, plant anytime . . . makes good green onions when small . . . strong flavor when mature	2 12 14 61
Old Fashioned (Potato Onion) (Hill Onion)	The largest multiplier . . . multiplies in soil only . . . does not go to seed . . . can be planted in spring or fall	2
White Nest Egg	1½" diameter . . . mild flavor . . . multiplies in soil only . . . spring planting preferred	2

Chives (Allium schoenoprassum)

Chives are a gourmet's delight, with hollow, grass-like leaves that will persist in the garden for many years. There are several varieties. Generally we think of chives as having rounded globes of soft, purple flowers, but *Molly* has yellow flowers, *Ostrowskianum* has dark-pink flowers, and *Neapolitanum* white.

Harvesting: Clip off leaves whenever you need them.

HOW TO PLANT: You can buy pots of chives from a nursery and separate. You can also sow seeds outside in the garden almost any time—except winter in the North. Chives prefer full sun but will tolerate some shade. Once the plants are established, cut them back regularly to encourage new growth. Lift and divide established clumps every few years in the spring or fall.

CHIVES

VARIETY	DAYS	HEIGHT	REMARKS	SOURCES
Ciboulette			Used in many dishes	15 72
Curled Chives		6"	Sun location	76
Garlic Chives			Onion-scented herb grown for leaves . . . multiplies rapidly	6 44 75 76 83 86 88 91
Chives Grass Onion	80	1 foot	A perennial that is quickly started from seed . . . leaves have mild onion flavor . . . use in soup, eggs, soft cheese, mashed potatoes . . . divide clump every 3 years	5 10 12 16 19 25 28 29 30 31 32 38 41 44 45 46 48 49 50 51 53 56 57 60 62 66 68 70 74 75 76 78 81 82 83 86 88 89 91
Lilacea			Plant in sunny or partial-shade location	37
Molly		10"	Yellow flowers in June	76
Neapolitanum		10"	Plant in sunny location . . . white flowers in June	76
Oriental Chives				76
Ostrowskianum		6"	Sunny location . . . dark-pink flowers in June	76
Roseum		14"	Sunny location . . . pale-pink flowers in June	76
Schnittlauch			Thick tufts . . . dark-green, hollow foliage . . . cut throughout the summer . . . can be used many ways	14 22 47 52 83

Garlic (Allium sativum)

Garlic is really strong medicine in any garden. Besides being an essential vegetable in the kitchen, many gardeners believe that it can be used to control a wide variety of insects. There are two basic types available—regular garlic bulbs, which contain a number of small cloves, and large garlic bulbs (elephant garlic), which have the flavor of regular garlic but none of its pungency.

HOW TO PLANT: In very early spring plant garlic cloves, or sets, 1-1½ inches deep, 2 inches apart, in rows 12-18 inches apart.

Harvesting: Dig up the roots when the tops fall over.

GARLIC

VARIETY	DAYS	REMARKS	SOURCES
California White Garlic	110	The best variety . . . stores like onions, or may be left in garden over winter	22 38
Extra Select		A pound of garlic sets plants about a 20-foot row	10
Garlic Sets		Most pungent flavor of the onion family . . . use in soups, salad, stews	12 19 21 23 28 29 44 52 62 66 74 76 82 86 89
Mexican Garlic sets		An easy and interesting plant to grow	31
Oriental Garlic		18" Perineal	89
Rocambole (Spanish Garlic)		Makes cloves in small bulbs	44 81
Garlic Powder/Granular			90

GARLIC—Large Bulbs

VARIETY	REMARKS	SOURCES
Bavarian Garlic	Bulbs are larger than those of common variety . . . keeps a very long time	14
Elephant Garlic	True garlic flavor, but more delicate . . . short growing season . . . often produces single, large, onionlike bulb . . . many bulbs weigh 1 lb., size 4-5"	21 27 28 43 46 50 61 62 89
Extra Large	Three bulbs will plant about a 10-15-foot row	41
Jumbo Garlic	6" cloves . . . can be harvested in 18 months	68
Italian Garlic	Superior to standard . . . hotter than Elephant garlic	61
Silverskin	Very hardy . . . strong flavor . . . large bulbs	46 50

Leek (Allium porrum)

Leeks look much like a fattened green onion. They do not bulb, as onions do—the stem simply thickens. The most popular variety is *Broad London* (Large American Flag).

Harvesting: Pull leeks in about 120-130 days, when they are about an inch in diameter. Harvest before frost. In mild climates you can leave them in the ground and dig as you need them.

HOW TO PLANT: In early spring sow seeds in a trench, and thin to 2-4 inches apart in rows 12-18 inches apart. The trench is gradually filled as the leeks develop. This blanches the leeks white as they grow.

LEEKS

VARIETY	DAYS	REMARKS	SOURCES
American Broad Flag	90-130	Tall, hardy, large-stalked . . . very strong-growing and productive	3 12
American Flag (Giant Musselburgh)	120-150	8½-9½" uniform size and shape . . . fine for fall and winter . . . quick-growing	14 16 20 32 36 47 48 50 56 57 67 68 72 73
Conqueror		Hardy strain for winter . . . medium length . . . blue-green tops will stand cold	29
Blue Solaize		The hardiest, very cold-resistant . . . truly blue	15
Broad London (Large American Flag) (London Flag) (Broad Scotch)	130-150	7½-9 x 1½" stems . . . leaves are medium-green . . . hardy, sweet-flavored . . . good in South	10 16 19 21 22 25 28 30 36 38 44 45 46 49 51 52 53 57 62 72 89
Chinese Leeks		Strong-flavored perennial	50
Elephant Leek	85-150	Large, vigorous	48 66 72
Giant Leek Caretan		Cold-resistant . . . one of the most popular varieties . . . 6-8" variety prized in cooking	15 31
Giant Elboeuf		Early type of vigorous growth . . . light-green leaves	15
Helvetia		Very early . . . long, pure-white shafts . . . slimmer than other varieties	72
Italian Winter Leek		The best of all leeks . . . extremely hardy and of enormous size, up to 15" . . . mild flavor, tender . . . fine for bunching	14
King Richard L.D.	75	Leaves are light-green . . . grows over a foot tall and upright . . . will not hold up through continously heavy frost	37
The Lyon		Very hardy . . . produces tender, solid-white stems	68
North Pole		Very heavy cropper . . . winter variety	68
Siegfried L.D.	105	A late winter leek, with strong, stiff, dark-blue-green leaves . . . stem is short and thick, 5 x 1½" . . . both stem and foliage show good frost resistance	37
Summer Broad Flag		The earliest for summer use . . . pull soil progressively as they grow to blanch them	15
Titan	70	Extra-long, early type of vigorous growth . . . 6" stalks	66
Tivi		Excellent Danish variety . . . autumn harvest . . . large, tender stalks . . . early and vigorous . . . dark-green tops	29
Unique	100	Excellent long-stemmed, hardy strain for winter storage . . . 7-8" stalks	66

Shallot (Allium ascalonicum)

The shallot is a multiplier onion that is highly prized by gourmet chefs. It divides into clumps of small bulbs. Shallots have a very mild flavor, although they can become bitter in some soils. Most seed catalogs list them under the simple term shallots, but there is a choice of varieties.

HOW TO PLANT: Plant from bulbs 2-3 inches apart in rows 12-14 inches apart.

Harvesting: The tops start to brown and yellow when the bulbs are mature. Gardeners generally lift and store at this stage, but since shallots are perennials, they can be left in the ground.

SHALLOTS

VARIETY	REMARKS	SOURCES
Dutch Yellow	Will often keep for nearly 12 months . . . mild flavor	68
French Shallots	Plant in spring or fall . . . multiplies in soil	2 74 81
Frog's Legs Shallots	One shallot multiplies into a cluster of over 15	44
Giant Red	Mildly spicy, yet sweet . . . stores through winter and spring	68
Grey Shallot	Considered true shallot in France	44
Shallots (Yellow Multiplier Sets)	Good keepers . . . hardy everywhere . . . delectable, mild, onionlike flavor . . . use in sauces, soup, gravies, stews, roasts	10 12 19 21 22 23 38 43 44 46 61 62A 76 86 89

Parsley (Petroselinum crispum)

Parsley is a favorite with gourmet cooks because it makes a delicious garnish for salads, soups, and similar dishes. Plants quickly replace branches cut off for the kitchen, and a plant or two grown in the garden, a flower bed, or in a 4-inch pot on a windowsill is enough to maintain a steady supply.

Parsley varieties grow either as *deeply curled and cut . . .* , *flat, cut, or plain . . .* , or as *Parsley for roots* (Hamburg). Parsley has a long, edible, white root.

Harvesting: Pick parsley in the morning before the oils have evaporated. Pinch off old outer stems, and leave the new center growth to replace the pulled leaves. Small bunches can be hung upside down in the shade to make parsley flakes.

HOW TO PLANT: Soak seeds overnight before planting. Then sow half an inch deep, 3-6 inches apart, in rows 12-18 inches apart. Parsley seeds take at least three weeks to sprout, and when they do, they grow slowly. Spring-planted parsley will produce until killed by heavy frosts. Parsley will live through the winter in mild-winter areas and shoot up seed stalks when the days grow long and warm.

PARSLEY—Curled

VARIETY	DAYS	LEAF/COLOR	REMARKS	SOURCES
Banquet	76	Tightly curled, deep-green	Developed in Denmark . . . weather-tolerant, one of the best varieties for home gardens . . . grows erect	29
Bravour	75	Finely curled, dark-green	Long, stiff stems . . . tolerant to cold weather	66
Clivi	65	Very curled, deep-green	Very dwarf, very neat, and prolific . . . base leaves do not turn yellow	68
Darki	77	Tight, heavy curled, very-dark-green	Excellent cold-weather tolerance	66

PARSLEY—Curled (Continued)

VARIETY	DAYS	LEAF/COLOR	REMARKS	SOURCES
Deep Green	70	Densely cut, dark-green	More erect than Moss Curled	51 66
Delikat Original L.D.	80	Large, finely curled, dark-green	Long, stiff stems, easy to cut . . . fine aroma . . . Danish origin	37
Dwarf Triple Curled		Finely curled, dark-green	Vigorous, pretty, and flavorsome	15 86
Emerald (Extra Curled Dwarf)	85	Finely cut and curled, dark-green	Compact plants	10 25 48 50
Evergreen (Double curled)	70	Deep, coarse, compounded, deep-green	AA selection . . . more frost-resistant than other varieties	3 11 15 32 47 53 56 57 62 76
Extra Triple Curled (Moss Curled) (Champion)	75	Fine, closely curled, very-dark-green	12" high . . . very compact and productive . . . excellent for flavoring	5 11 12 14 16 19 21 22 28 30 31 32 34 36 38 39 40 41 44 45 46 47 48 49 51 52 53 55 57 60 62 66 67 70 72
Forest Green	70	Densely curled, dark-green	Grows 15" tall . . . very uniform	48 57
French	70		Unsurpassed for flavor	68
Green Velvet	80	Fully curled, deep-green	Top-quality variety with strong stalks	68
Japanese Parsley (Mitsuba)	90		Grows 2 feet tall . . . unique flavor . . . tender leaves	50 91
Minncurl Parsley		Curled, fine cut, deep-green	High flavor for garnishing	21
Multi Curled		Dark-green	Finest Moss Curled . . . normally tall	32
Optima		Divided, finely curled	Vigorous growth . . . more stems per plant, giving larger yield	32
Paramount	85	Densely triple-curled, dark-green	Handsome, extra-fancy . . . grows to 12" tall . . . stout stems	14 16 36 53 57
Perfection	75	Densely curled, deep-green	Holds its color both summer and fall	32 48 70

PARSLEY—Plain

VARIETY	DAYS	LEAF/COLOR	REMARKS	SOURCES
Chinese Parsley (Cilantro) (Yuen Gai)			Delicious fragrance and flavor, with no hint of bitterness	69
Dark Green Italian	72	Heavy, glossy-green	Celery-leaf type . . . erect, vigorous . . . strong flavor	29 40 47 51 66
Giant Italian (Celery Parsley)	85	Plain leaf	Plants are 3 feet tall and bushy . . . exceptionally strong parsley flavor	14 50
Plain Leaf (Common) (Single) (Italian)	72-75	Large, plain, flat not curled, dark-green	Fine rich flavor	3 10 11 12 15 16 30 31 32 37 44 47 48 50 51 56 57 67 72 76 78 86 89 91

PARSLEY—Long-Rooted

VARIETY	DAYS	LEAF/COLOR	REMARKS	SOURCES
Hamburg Long Rooted (Turnip Rooted) (Parsley for Roots) (Parsnip-Rooted) (Thick-Rooted)	85-90	6 x 2"	Parsniplike roots of white flesh . . . used for flavoring soups, stews etc.	10 12 14 16 21 25 29 30 32 36 37 38 45 47 48 50 51 52 53 62 66 72 86 91
Rooted Parsley Record		10 x 2" smooth roots	Best parsley-rooted parsley there is	14

Parsnips (Pastinaca sativa)

Parsnips are a root crop (sometimes called white carrots) that can try your patience. They require no less than four months to grow from seed. And during that time parsnips take up a lot of valuable space you could be using for other vegetables. It is one of the hardiest of root vegetables and actually improves in flavor after exposure to frost. There are long varieties, half-long varieties, and short varieties. The current tendency is to grow the smaller roots. Popular varieties are *All American, Harris Early Model,* and *Hollow Crown.*

Harvesting: Dig the roots, don't pull them up. You can also leave them in the ground over-winter. In spring store what roots you haven't used in peat or sand.

HOW TO PLANT: Sow a half-inch deep in rows 3 feet apart. Thin to 5 inches apart. In cold areas plant seed in late spring, let it grow all summer, and harvest in the fall. Leave the excess in the ground to be dug as needed. In mild-winter climates sow in the fall and harvest in the spring. Parsnips must have a loose soil worked to a depth of 18 inches.

PARSNIPS

VARIETY	DAYS	SIZE/COLOR	REMARKS	SOURCES
All American (Harris Model)	95-145	12 x 3"—white	Very fine quality	12 14 16 22 28 29 32 34 47 51 58 62 67 72
Harris Early Model	100	10 x 3½"—white		16 29 32 37 48 51 52 60 66 70
Hollow Crown (Gurnsey Long Smooth)	95-130	12 x 2 ¾"—white	Long and smooth, broad at the shoulders ... well-tapered ... fine-grained flesh ... heavy yields	3 10 11 14 16 19 21 25 30 31 36 39 45 48 49 52 55 62
Ideal Hollow Crown	130	12-14 x 2½"	The creamy, sweet flesh is smooth-textured	40
Improved Hollow Crown	95	10 x 3"—white	Decidedly hollow-crowned	47 51 66 67 68 72
Improved Stump Rooted		6-8 x 3"—white	Short ... fine texture ... sweet	38
Jung's White Sugar		White	Half-long ... stocky form ... heavy at shoulders ... expecially fine flavor	38
Large Sugar	100	White	Lift roots in winter or spring	53
Premium	80		Roots are two-thirds as long as those of Hollow Crown ... heavy yields ... easily pulled	14
White Model		Medium length—white	Smooth skin	21

Peas (Pisum sativum)

Peas are always star performers in the garden. They come up right away, bloom fast, and produce quantities of food within 60-70 days. Peas are a cool-season crop that thrive in soil and air filled with cool moisture. Although they'll continue growing when the days become somewhat longer and warmer, they do not do well in hot, dry weather. Pea varieties can generally be classified early, mid-season, or late—this indicates the time from sowing to harvest. Thus you can plant early, mid-season, and late for a succession of crops. Peas also have long vines (the tall types whose vines grow 48-72 inches), standard-height vines (30-36 inches), and dwarf vines (12-22 inches).

Most varieties grown have wrinkled seed since these are generally sweeter. There are some types with smooth seed, however; they don't rot as easily. Many seedsmen now treat wrinkled seed with a fungicide.

Other differences among pea varieties are length of pods, number of peas per pod, and their resistance to disease.

Sugar Peas (edible podded peas). Sugar peas have tender, fleshy pods similar to snap beans, with the flavor and sweetness of fresh green peas. The pods at this stage are stringless, brittle, and succulent. They are especially delicious to use as "snow peas" in Chinese dishes. The dwarf varieties, such as *Dwarf Gray Sugar,* reach about 24 inches high and can be grown without staking. Tall varieties such as *Mammoth Melt-*

ing Sugar grow to about 4 feet. *Dwarf Gray Sugar* produces red flowers—all others have white flowers.

HOW TO PLANT: Peas grow well only from seed planted in the spot where they are going to remain. In the spring, as soon as the ground can be worked, plant the seeds 2 inches deep, 2 inches apart, in rows 18-30 inches apart. Make subsequent plantings five to ten days apart, for a continuous crop.

Harvesting: Pick off all the pods as they mature in order to keep the plants producing vigorously. It is best to harvest only in the morning—this seems to preserve the flavor. After picking, shell the peas as soon as possible, then store in the refrigerator.

PEAS

VARIETY	DAYS	VINES/PODS/PEAS	REMARKS	SOURCES
Alaska (Earliest of All)	56	24-29" vine; 2½" smooth pods; 6-8 light-green peas	Extra-early . . . heavy yields . . . main variety for split pea soup . . . vines resistant to Fusarium wilt . . . smooth-seeded	9 10 11 14 16 19 21 22 28 31 32 37 40 51 52 53 55 56 57 58 62 67 71 72
Extra Early Alaska	51	30" vines	Can also be used as dry cooking pea	37 47 49
Alomota	60-65	30-34" vine; 3" dark-green, blunt pods; 6-8 peas per pod	Most disease-resistant, hardy pea . . . use fresh, canned, or frozen . . . patented	71
Anoka	65	3" dark-green peas		51
Century (Yellow)	87	4-ft. vines	Buff-yellow, dry soup peas . . . very hardy	37
Chieftain Improved	67	2½ ft. vines; 3½" dark-green, blunt pods	Excellent for quick-freezing, canning, or table use	14
Chinook	66	28" wilt-resistant vine	A very large green pea . . . especially developed for table use and freezing	71
Code 1	66	28-30" vines; 3" dark-green, blunt pods; 7-8 peas per pod	Used for canning	51
Drought-Proof	70	Medium-height vine; 4½" gray-green pods; 6-8 ½" peas per pod	Does well under a wide range of weather and soil conditions	9
Duet	63	25-29" vines; 3¼" dark-green, blunt pods; 7-8 peas	Good freezer	51
Early Abundant	64		Similar to Little Marvel	21
Early All Sweet	55	2½-3-ft. vine	A large, sweet Alaska . . . large crops . . . use fresh or canned	28
Early Frosty	64	24-28" vine; 3-3¼', blunt, dark-green pods; 7-8 peas	Delicious fresh or frozen . . . fine home garden variety . . . early	10 19 21 28 29 37 47 57 59 62 70 71 72
Early Perfection	66	26-30" vine; 3¼" medium-green, blunt pods; 7-8 peas	Use for canning . . . similar to Perfection	51 62
Early Wonder	58	26" vine; 2½-3" light-green pods; 6-8 peas		47
Fordhook Wonder	79	28" vine; 5-5½" pods; 10 dark-green peas	Excellent fresh, canned, or frozen . . . recommended for any area where later peas do well	10 71
Giant Stride	73	28-32" semidwarf vine; 4½-5" dark-green pods; 8-10 peas	One of the very best for freezing and canning . . . extra-sweet and tender	9 11 51

PEAS (Continued)

VARIETY	DAYS	VINES/PODS/PEAS	REMARKS	SOURCES
Gradus (Prosperity)	60-66	3-ft. vines; 4" rounded, dark-green pods; 7-10 peas	Remain tender . . . early variety . . . long shelf life after picking	16 62 71
Green Arrow	70	24-28" vine; 4" pods; 9-11 peas	High yield . . . exceptional sweetness . . . mid-season	3 10 12 19 21 22 28 29 30 37 40 50 52 53 55 66 70
Gullivert	74	30" productive vine	True French petite pea . . . magnificent flavor	68
Hurst Green Shaft	100	28" vine; 4-4½" pod; 9-11 peas	Super-yielding, double-podded . . . main-crop variety	68
Hustler	57	28" vine; deep-green	Patented variety . . . always a heavy, reliable cropper	71
Improved Gradus	62	2½-ft. vine; large pods	Early	30
Lincoln	66	25-30" vine; 3½" pods; 7-9 peas	A favorite with many home gardeners . . . mid-season	3 11 14 21 29 39 51 60 66 72
Mammoth Early Canner	60	24" vine; oval, green pods	Grown for freezing or canning . . . good shelf life after picking . . . patented variety	71
Midseason Freezer	63	30" vines	Especially recommended for home freezing	53
Miragreen Sweet Pea	70	48" vine; medium pods; 8-10 peas	Very hardy . . . unusually high sugar content	71
Morse's No. 60	75	28" vine; 5" slender pods; 8-10 peas	Known as "best in the West" . . . all-time favorite . . . delicious fresh, canned, or frozen	34
Onward		30" vine; blunt pods	A delicious, reliable pea	68
Pacemaker	59	28-32" vines; 2½" light-green pods; 5-7 peas	Good canner	51
Perfection Dark-Seeded	67	30" vines; 3" dark-green pods, blunt; 5-7 peas	Good freezer	51
Perfected Freezer	60-69	3½" dark-green pods	A Dark Green Perfection . . . excellent freezer . . . stands warm weather well	60
Prospector	71	24" vine;	Late, canning pea . . . recommended for growth under adverse weather conditions . . . disease-resistant	71
Scout	65	26" vine	All-purpose pea . . . similar to Hustler, but later-maturing	71
Sweetpod	68	4-ft. vines; 4-4½" pods		66
Superfection	64	Medium-small peas; round, oval pods	Extra-easy sheller . . . good fresh, canned, or frozen	71
Thomas Laxton	65	2½-3-ft. vines; 3½" broad, straight, dark-green pods; 7-9 peas	Early . . . high-quality, all-purpose pea . . . grows well under wide variety of conditions	3 10 31 36 37 40 41 47 51 52 55 56 59 62 66 67 71 72 73
Tonka	64	32-34" vine; 3" dark-green pods; 6-8 peas per pod	Good canner	51
Trio		32" vine	Multipodded variety . . . extra-high sugar content	68
Victory Freezer	65	30" vine; 3½" straight, dark-green pods	Excellent-quality mid-season variety . . . use fresh, canned, or frozen . . . heavy yields . . . Fusarium-wilt-resistant	14 28 68
Wando (Main Crop)	68	2½ ft. vines, very prolific; 2½" dark-green pods, 7-8 peas	Mid-season . . . tolerant of dry, hot weather	3 9 10 12 14 19 21 22 28 29 31 32 34 37 38 39 40 45 47 51 52 57 58 59 60 66 67 70 71 73

PEAS (Continued)

VARIETY	DAYS	VINES/PODS/PEAS	REMARKS	SOURCES
Wyoming Wonder (Icer) (Asgrow 40)	74	24-38" vines; 4-5" pods; 8-10 peas	Medium-late variety	3 52
World's Record	58	Over 2 ft. high; 4" medium-green pods; 7-9 peas	Early . . . improved Gradus type . . . good freezer	3 30 62

PEAS—Tall

VARIETY	DAYS	VINES/PODS/PEAS	REMARKS	SOURCES
Alderman (Tall Telephone)	70-75	4½-6-ft. vines; 4½-5" oval, curved, green pods; 8-9 peas	Holds color well in cooking . . . high-quality pea	10 12 21 29 40 47 51 58 59 60 66 67 71 72
Freezonian	60	2½-ft. vine; 3½" dark-green pods; 7-8 large peas	Early . . . AA winner . . . finest for quick freezing or canning . . . vigorous, wilt-resistant vines	3 9 10 11 12 14 21 22 29 30 32 45 47 50 52 53 57 62 70 71
Improved Tall Telephone	72	4-4½-ft. vines; 4½-5" pods	Medium-late crop	3 30 31 56

PEAS—Dwarf

VARIETY	DAYS	VINE/PODS	REMARKS	SOURCES
Alaska M 163 WR	56	18-22" vine; 2" light-green, straight, blunt pods; 5-6 peas		51
American Wonder	61	12" plants; 6 peas	Early . . . very large, sweet peas . . . drought-resistant	16 21 22 55 62
Banquet	62	18-24" vine; 2½-3" blunt- ended pods	Recommended for freezing . . . small and tender peas	29 51
Beagle	51	20" plant; 4-6 peas	Wrinkled, seeded pea . . . very sweet	37 40 53 68 72
Burpeeana Early	63	18-24" plant bears profusely; 3" pods, slightly curved at tip; 8-10 peas	Sweet, tender peas . . . retain color and flavor when quick-frozen . . . all-purpose pea	10
Cameo (Petite Pois)	58	Smooth pods, 6-8 tiny peas	High percentage of double and triple pods . . . small-seeded Alaska type	66
Di Giorgi's Model Pea	61	18" plant; 4" pods, 8-9 peas	Extra early . . . from one planting you will harvest two crops	14
Dwarf Telephone (Daisy)	70-76	20" vines; 2" pods, 8-10 peas	Medium-late pea	3 16 30 57 58 62 67 71 72
Feltham First		18" plant; 3½"pointed, deep- green pods	Very early . . . produces heavy crop	68
Gloriosa		20" plant	Main-crop pea . . . reliable under a variety of weather conditions	68
Greater Progress	62	18" vines; 4-4½" slightly curved, deep- green, pointed pods; 7-9 large dark-green peas	Most dependable and productive variety . . . quite early . . . ideal for market and roadside stands	29 60 70

PEAS—Dwarf (Continued)

VARIETY	DAYS	VINES/PODS	REMARKS	SOURCES
Honey Sweet	73	18" plant; 8-10 peas	Heavy bearer . . . never fails to produce a crop of giant pods . . . "sweet as honey"	38
Hundredfold (Blue Bantam) (Laxonia)	63	18", very-dark-green vines; deep-green, broad pods; 8 large peas	Early . . . excellent for home gardens . . . good freezer	3 10 14 16 28 38 47 50 52 62 71
Kelvedon Wonder		18" plant; 3" rich-green pods	Early wrinkled pea	68
Large Podded Marvel	65	Well-filled pods; dwarf vines	Sweet, tender, juicy peas	22
Laxtonian	62	16-18" sturdy vine; large, dark pods; 8-10 peas	Hardy and very early . . . best main-crop Marrowfat variety	14
Laxton's Progress (Progress No. 9) (Early Giant)	60	15-20" heavy vine; 4½" pods; 7-9 peas	Early . . . high resistance to Fusarium wilt	3 10 11 12 14 16 19 21 22 25 28 30 32 39 40 47 49 51 52 53 57 59 62 67 71 72 73
Laxton's Progress Improved	55	16-18" plant; 3½" pods; 7-9 peas	One of the best main-crop varieties	66
Laxton's Superb (Early Bird)	60	24" plant; 3½" pointed, medium-green pods, 7-8 peas	Semiwrinkled pea . . . early	47 67
Little Gem	60	15-18" vines; 6-8 peas	Outstanding for earliness . . . high quality and yield	28 51
Little Marvel	62	18" dark-green vines; 3" pods with square ends; 7-8 large, dark- green peas	Early . . . and sweet, tender peas . . . good for freezing . . . heavy yields	3 9 10 11 12 14 16 19 21 22 25 28 29 30 32 36 38 40 45 47 49 51 52 53 55 56 57 58 59 60 62 66 68 70 71 72 73
Little Marvel Improved	63	Low, compact vines; sweet, dark-green peas	Superior garden variety	34 41
Little Sweetie	60	16" compact vines; 2½" bright-green pods	Nonfibrous peas . . . high sugar content . . . can be harvested over long period	66
Mighty Midget (Extra Early Laxton)		6" vines; 3½" pods	Extra-early . . . very easy to pick . . . tender, sugary peas	21
Morse's Progress No. 9	64	20" vines; 4½" pointed, dark-green pods; 8-19 peas	Popular early variety	41
Perfection	65	16-18" vines; 4½" pods; 6-10 peas	Drought and heat-resistant . . . fine sweet quality	28 52
Petit Provencal		16" vines	Early and very productive . . . plant early	15 44
Potlatch (Big Dinner)	75	20-24" vines; 4" broad pods; 9-11 peas	Pods usually borne in pairs . . . early . . . variety of great merit	14 21
Premium Gem	64	20" vines; 6-7 peas	Good quality	21
Recette		24" plant; 8-9 peas	Produces 3 pods on every stem . . . tender, sweet peas	68
Sparkle	60	15" vine; 2½-3" blunt pods; 7-8 peas	Good for freezing . . . very early	3 12 29 39 47 57 59 60
Tasty Giant	72	20" vines; 4½-5½" dark- green pods	One of the best for home gardeners . . . heavy producer	70
Tiny Tim		6-9" vines; 3" pods	Midget variety . . . tender, sugary pods	21

PEAS—Edible Podded Peas (Sugar Peas)

VARIETY	DAYS	VINE/PODS	REMARKS	SOURCES
China Pea, Small Pod		Dwarf vines; tasty, tender pods	Red flowers	42
Dwarf De Grace		30" vines	Early . . . tender, fleshy, sweet	68
Dwarf Gray Sugar	62-65	2-2½ ft. prolific vines; 2½-3" light-green, curved pods	Ideal for home gardens	9 10 12 14 16 19 21 22 28 30 31 36 40 47 49 50 51 52 53 55 57 59 62 67 71 73
Dwarf White Sugar	50	30" vines; 2-2½" pods	Pick pods when young . . . steam-cook or stir-fry . . . an Oriental delicacy . . . very early	28 70
Green Sugar Pods	60	20" sturdy vine; medium-size, dark-green pods	Bears well in all climates	71
Mammoth Melting Sugar	68-72	5 x ⅞" light-green pods	Vines are tall . . . pods can be prepared like snap beans	9 10 12 14 16 29 34 41 45 49 51 52 53 56 62 71 72
Oregon Sugar Pod	68	28" set; high percentage of two-pod clusters; 4-4½ x ¾" pods	Resistant to Pea Enation Virus . . . produces large crops . . . superb for freezing and Oriental cooking	10 16 37 38 50 51 57 60 68 71
Osaya Endo		Pole type; large, tender pods	White flowers	42
Snow Peas (Sugar Peas)		Large, fleshy pods	Early variety	14 69
Snowbiz	66	4 ft. vines; 5 x 1½" thick, crisp, sweet stringless pods	Superior, large-podded snow peas	37
Sweetgreen	60	15" vines; thick, succulent pods	Sweet and tender	19 21

Hot Chili Peppers (Capsicum Annuum)

Hot peppers have a wide range of hotness. Actually there is no sure way to predict the hotness of any individual pepper, although each variety has its own range. In general, the smallest varieties are the hottest. Climate also affects hotness. Peppers grown in cool, moist climates are milder than the same variety grown in a hot, dry area.

When full size (fully formed and uniformly green), the mature pepper will have reached maximum hotness. Most peppers are harvested at this stage. If left on the vine, most varieties will turn slowly red and become sweeter.

Hotness is concentrated in the interior veins, or ribs, near the seeds. Yellow or orange veins usually indicate that the pepper will be extra-hot for its variety. Here are some of the choices you have:

Cayenne Group. This is the chili group characterized by slim, pointed fruit, 2-12 inches long, which can be hot or mild. The largest varieties are the Anaheim or New Mexico Chili, whose pods are 6-12 inches long. These are used in the green stage for chili relleno. *Anaheim M* is a popular strain within this group. *Hungarian Yellow Wax* is also one of the very popular large-fruit, tapering varieties. The mature red pods are used to make chili pepper.

The *Cayenne* pepper is 4-12 inches long, pointed and deep red. The mature fruit is frequently used in making hot sauces. The small peppers, cylindrical in shape, include *Serrano,* the hottest of all, and *Jalapeno.*

The Cone-Shaped, or Celestial, Group. This plant produces 1-4-inch cone-shaped fruits that may vary in color. Included in this group are the hot, yellow, wax types such as *Santa Fe Grande, Goldspike,* and *Caloro* and the green or red *Fresno* types.

Cherry Group: These are cherry-shaped, three-celled fruits; as previously mentioned, these have sweet as well as hot varieties.

Tabasco Group. The fruits are 1-3 inches long, slim, tapered, and very hot.

HOW TO PLANT: See planting instructions under Sweet Peppers.

Harvesting: Clip off peppers as soon as they turn a mature color. When growing hot peppers for dry storage, let them turn red before picking. Don't rub your eyes. The juice is irritating.

CHILI PEPPERS—Long, Tapering

VARIETY	DAYS	SIZE/COLOR	REMARKS	SOURCES
Anaheim Chili (California Long Green) (California Chili)	80	6-8 x 1"; green changes to scarlet when ripe	2-ft. high plants . . . extensively used in the south and California . . . mildly pungent	11 12 16 31 48 53 55 56 57 58 62 73
Anaheim College 6-4	78	5½-6 x 2"; medium-green to scarlet when mature	26" plants, upright and spreading . . . use for canning, drying, or fresh	11 55
Anaheim M Strain	77-80	Long, tapered; deep-green	24-28" plants . . . medium-hot pods, good dried or fresh	10 49 51
Anaheim TMR	70-80	Tapers to point; dark-green, turns red at maturity	Used for canning, drying, or frying . . . mildly pungent	5 70
Cayenne Long Red Slim	70-75	6 x ¾" slim, pointed, wrinkled; dark-green, matures to red	20-24" plants, strong and spreading . . . can be used for processing, drying, or sauce	5 14 32 40 41 51 53 55 72 73
Cayenne Long Thick Red	70-74	6-7 x 1¼"; bright-red when ripe	24" tall plants	3 14 30 32 53 55 66 70
Crimson Hot	60	6-6½", red, waxy	Medium-hot, fairly thick flesh	66
Hot Portugal	64	6" long, pointed shape	Ripens early to brilliant-red . . . fiery-hot flesh	29
Hungarian Wax Short (Rainbow Waxed)	60	Blocky, yellow to red at maturity	Thick-meated . . . medium hot . . . early . . . heavy yields	17
Hungarian Yellow Wax (Cayenne Long Thick Yellow) (Bulgarian Banana) (Hot Banana)	60-65	5-6 x 1¼"; light yellow, matures to red	14-22" tall, moderately bushy . . . medium-hot . . . good for pickling . . . used for canning, or fresh market	5 9 10 11 12 14 16 17 19 20 23 25 28 29 31 32 34 36 40 41 44 45 47 48 49 50 51 52 53 54 55 56 57 60 62 66 70 72 73
Long Red Cayenne	70-75	5 x ½" pointed; waxy-yellow, turns bright-red at maturity	Very hot	9 10 12 15 17 20 25 28 31 34 36 38 44 47 48 49 50 52 62 66 67 72
Louisiana Red Cayenne	52-70	5 x ¾"; green to red at maturity	A favorite hot variety, used for canning, drying, pickles	56
Medium Hot F-1	75	8 x ¾"; green to red at maturity	Mildly pungent	32
Mexican Chili			Hot and spicy	68
New Mexico Chili	75			48 55
New Mexico Improved	75	4½-5 x 1" pointed end; turns red when ripe	Plants are about 27" tall . . . thick-walled . . . good for drying, canning, or freezing	57
New Mexico No. 6		6-8 x 2" bluntly pointed; uniform green, turns red at maturity	Dries to dark-red to maroon color . . . mildly pungent	55 57 58
New Mexico Rio Grande		6-7" pods, large, smooth	Adapted for home gardens . . . medium-pungent . . . suitable for green or dry red use	55
New Mexico Sandia		6-7" uniform, green	Pungent . . . high yields . . . sets fruits under hot growing conditions	55 57 58
Nu Mex Big Jim (New Mexico Big Jim)		8-12" pods, 4-6 oz. each	16-24" tall plants . . . high yields . . . fleshy fruit . . . ideal for chow-chow and canning	27 55 57 58
Red Hot F-1	70	6-7"; dark-green to red at maturity	Very hot . . . resembles cayenne . . . very heavy setter	32
Rio Grande 21	75	5½ x 1½" yellow to orange-red at maturity	27" tall plants . . . medium-hot . . . thick-walled . . . good for drying, canning, freezing	57

CHILI PEPPERS—Cylindrical

VARIETY	DAYS	LENGTH/COLOR	REMARKS	SOURCES
Jalapeno	72-80	3½ x 1½" tapered to blunt tip; deep green matures to red	Hot . . . thick walls . . . upright 26-36" plants . . . popular in Mexico and Southwest for pickling	5 11 16 19 22 25 26 28 31 40 41 48 50 55 56 57 58 73
Jalapeno M	75	3½ x ¼"; dark-green turns red when ripe	Best pepper to grow for dried hot-pepper seasoning	37 51 53 70 73
Serrano	75	Dark-green tinged with orange	Hottest of all	48 55 57

CHILI PEPPERS—Medium and Small, Tapering

VARIETY	DAYS	LENGTH/COLOR	REMARKS	SOURCES
Fresno Chili	78	1½-2½ x 1" tapering to point; green with trace of red	24" high plant . . . resistant to tobacco mosaic . . . very pungent	11 55 57
Red Chili	70-85	3 x ½" tapered to blunt tip; medium-green matures to bright-red	Upright, bushy 18-20" plants . . . for drying or sauce . . . very pungent	5 9 14 19 23 25 31 32 36 51 55 62
Santaka		2½-3"; deep-scarlet	From Japan . . . great dried as chili powder . . . very hot	27
Tabasco	90-120	Small, smooth tapering; greenish-yellow, turns scarlet when ripe	Hottest of all peppers	14 31 32 50 62

CHILI PEPPERS—Yellow Waxy, Small, Conical

VARIETY	DAYS	LENGTH/COLOR	REMARKS	SOURCES
Caloro TMR	75	2½ x 1¼" conical; yellow-orange yellow-waxy, when mature	24" tall plants . . . medium hot	57
Floral Gem Grande	75	1 x 2½", yellow turns scarlet when ripe	20-24" tall, upright plants . . . fresh, pickled or canned	16 48 51
Goldspike (hybrid)	75	2½ x 1½" conical, tapered	For pickling and freezing . . . vigorous plants, 32-36" tall	5 53 55
Roumania Block Type Mild Hot	65	4 x 2½"; stubby yellow maturing to red	Medium-hot . . . 22-24" tall plants . . . use for home gardens and canning	5 25 32 48 50
Santa Fe Grande	75	3½ x 1½"; turns yellow at market stage, orange-red at maturity	25" tall, upright . . . use fresh, canned, or pickled	11 48 51 57 73

CHILI PEPPERS—Round and Clawlike Types

VARIETY	DAYS	LENGTH/COLOR	REMARKS	SOURCES
Large Red Cherry	75	1¼"; green, red when mature	Medium-hot . . . primarily for canning and pickling	3 5 6 10 12 14 25 29 30 32 47 48 49 50 57 66
Small Red Cherry	80	1 x ¼"; deep-green, turns red at maturity	Upright, bushy, 18-20" plants . . . very pungent . . . used for pickling	48 51 55 57 72
Tokanotsume (hot)		Small, narrow	Claw-shaped fruit . . . late variety . . . very hot . . . takes a long time to mature	32

Sweet peppers (Capsicum frutescens)

Peppers originally came to the attention of the Western world when explorers tasted the native American chili and mistook it for the spice "pepper," one of the trading spices from the Orient. The various sweet and hot peppers native to the "New World" are related to the tomato and eggplant.

Among the sweet peppers there are many common or commercial names for the hundreds of types of fruit. In order to help understand the choices available to home gardeners, they can be roughly classified by the different shapes and sizes:

Bell Group: The fruits are large, block about 3 inches wide by 4 inches long, have three to four lobes, and are slightly tapered. Most are dark-green, then turn bright red at maturity. Some turn yellow, then red. There are a few that, though they have a green stage, are especially valued for their red fruits. The *California Wonder* types are the most popular garden peppers in this group.

Perfection or Pimiento Group—The Tomato Group: The fruits of the pimiento group are sweet, conical, and slightly pointed, 2-3 inches wide and 3-4 inches long, with thick red walls. The tomato group fruits are distinctly flattened and bear a striking resemblance to a tomato. They are often used for pickling, canning, or for fresh pepper rings. One of the favorite varieties in this group is *Sunnybrook*.

Cherry Group: These are cherry-shaped, three-celled fruits that include sweet varieties as well as hot.

Long, Slender: Some of the *long slender reds* and *long slender yellows* also have sweet varieties as well as hot. In addition there are novelty *white* and *chocolate* peppers that are sometimes fun to grow.

Harvesting: Pick the bell peppers when they are firm and crisp. Most gardeners believe that peppers have a better flavor when picked green, not red.

HOW TO PLANT: You can start peppers from seed or from plants purchased from a local nursery. If you are going to use seed, start them indoors in peat pots, two to four seeds planted a half-inch deep in each. Do this about 10 weeks before all danger of frost will be over, when you can plant outdoors. Plant pepper plants in the garden 18-24 inches apart in rows 24-36 inches apart. Peppers like temperatures above 60 degrees and below 80 degrees. When the temperatures are out of this range on both sides, fruits do not seem to set well.

SWEET PEPPERS—Blocky, Green

VARIETY	DAYS	SHAPE/SIZE/COLOR	REMARKS	SOURCES
Ace F-1		Deep-glossy-green, medium size	Very early . . . 3-4 lobes . . . no pungency at any state . . . very prolific	32 66
All American Bell Boy (hybrid)		Blocky; deep-glossy-green, turning red at maturity	4 lobes . . . husky 18" plants	21
All Big (Illinois 5F)	65-83	Heavy	Early . . . for home gardens or market . . . 3-4 lobes . . . medium-thick walls	25
Belaire	74	Blocky, 3½ x 4½"	4 lobes . . . thick walls	47
Bell Boy (hybrid)	70	3¼ x 3½" square; glossy-green to red at maturity	AA selection . . . early, all-purpose . . . 4 lobes . . . tolerant of tobacco mosaic virus	5 10 19 22 23 25 30 31 32 34 47 48 53 55 57 60 66 67 70 72
Bull Nose (Large Bell) (Sweet Mountain)	55	Deep-green to red at maturity; square	Early . . . ribs are pungent . . . medium-size	14 21 25 30 53 56
Burpee's Bellringer	75	3½ x 4½" big, blocky; glossy-green to red at maturity	4 lobes . . . heavy crops . . . extra-thick walls	10
Burpee's Fordhook	66	3 x 3½" blocky; dark-green to red at maturity	AA winner . . . tender, crisp, and sweet . . . 3-4 lobes	10
Burpee's Tasty Hybrid	70	Blocky; dark-green, turns scarlet when mature	3 lobes . . . medium-thick walls . . . sturdy, spreading plants	10
California Mammoth Green	75	Emerald-green, large	Tremendous yielder . . . thick fleshed . . . very mild, sweet stuffing pepper	50
California Wonder	75	4½ x 4" blocky, green	Big, good stuffing pepper . . . thick walls	3 9 10 11 14 17 19 20 21 22 23 25 30 31 32 36 44 45 47 48 51 52 54 55 56 58 62 66 67 70 73
California Wonder PS	72	4¾ x 4"; green to red	Tolerant of tobacco mosaic virus . . . 4 lobes . . . thick walls	5
California Wonder 300 T.M.R.	71	4" blocky, emerald-green	24-28" tall plants . . . one of the best stuffing peppers	34 40 51 52
Calwonder	63	3-4"; green to bright-crimson when mature	Early . . . dwarf plant, vigorous and heavily productive . . . 3-4 lobes . . . thick, sweet	3 14 29 32 40 41 51
Canape Hybrid	60	2½ x 3½"; green to red	Heavy yields . . . early . . . 3 lobes . . . 20-25" tall plants	3 5 9 10 25 29 32 48 50 66 68 72
Delaware Bell	70	Large, heavy fruit	Fruits set early and continue to set all season	48
Early Bountiful (hybrid)	58-65	2¾ x 3" blocky, dark-green to red when ripe	Upright plants . . . extremely vigorous . . . tolerant of mosaic	5 25 32 72
Early Canada Bell	67	4 x 4"	26-27" tall, bushy plants . . . extra-thick walls . . . tolerant to tobacco mosaic	66
Early Giant		5 x 3"; green to red	Dwarf, compact plants . . . thick, sweet flesh	38
Early Giant Neapolitan	60	4½" square, green to red at maturity	Short plants to 20" . . . sweet, meaty peppers	14
Early Niagara Giant	65	4½" square; green to red	3-4 lobes with thick flesh . . . 24" tall plants set well during cool summers	66

SWEET PEPPERS—Blocky, Green (Continued)

VARIETY	DAYS	SHAPE/SIZE/COLOR	REMARKS	SOURCES
Early Set	67	Heavy crown set; large, blocky fruit	4 lobes . . . thick walls . . . heavy yields . . . good northern adaptation—sets well in cool weather	5 25 48 57
Emerald Giant	74	4½ x 3¾"	Thick walls . . . 4 lobes . . . vigorous plants . . . mosaic-tolerant	5 11 14 32 47 48 51 54 56 57 70
Faribo Hybrid		Medium-size	Very early . . . ideal for stuffing and baking . . . matures with Harris Early	21
Florida Giant	75	Blocky, large	2½ feet tall . . . vigorous . . . suitable to the South	16 70
Florida Giant Resistant	90	4-4½" blocky		48
Giant Resistant No. 3	74	4½ x 3¾"; glossy green to red	4 lobes . . . heavy yields . . . 28-36" plants . . . a resistant type . . . Florida Giant	56
Goliath	66	3½ x 5"; green to red at maturity	Very productive . . . thick, sweet flesh . . . keeps in prime condition for a long time	14
Harris Early Giant	60	3½ x 6"; green to scarlet	Extra-early . . . mild and sweet	14
Italian Sweet	60	6 x 2½"; deep-green to bright-red when ripe	Dwarf, upright plants . . . very productive . . . sweetest of all peppers	9 32 55
Kansas Wonder	70	Medium-size, blocky, good shape	Big yields . . . ripens a week earlier than California Wonder	48
Keystone Resistant Giant	70-80	4½ x 3½"	Most 4-lobed . . . thick flesh . . . very popular . . . tolerant of tobacco mosaic virus	5 11 14 17 20 23 25 29 32 40 41 47 48 51 54 57 66 67 70 72
King of the North (Ruby King)	57-65	6 x 3½"; brilliant-red when ripe	Takes cold well . . . sweet, mild . . . 3 lobes	9 14 25 48 57
Lady Bell (hybrid)	70	3-4" blocky	3-4 lobes . . . better for stuffing . . . sweet flavor . . . compact, husky plants	29
Liberty Bell	70	Blocky, deep-green	4 lobes . . . thick walls . . . heavy yields	66
Lincoln Bell	68	3½-4"; very-dark-green	Sets good-quality fruit during the cooler early-summer season . . . 3-4 lobes . . . thick walls	66
Melrose (Sweet Melrose) (Italianelle)	60	3" tapers to 1"; dark-green to red; crinkled skin	Heavy yields . . . ideal for frying	25
Mercury T.M.R.	75	4-4½" blocky, dark-green	4 lobes . . . compact plants . . . sets well in hot, dry weather	37 48 57 72
Merrimac Wonder	60-68	3½ x 3½"; green to red when ripe	4 lobes . . . use where growing season is short . . . sets in cold weather	5 10 25 30
Midway	70	4½ x 4½"; green to red when ripe	3-4 lobes . . . mild, sweet flavor . . . thick walls . . . bell-shaped . . . 18-24" tall . . . mosaic-tolerant	5 10 17 25 28 52 54 57 60 66 70 73
New Ace (hybrid)	68	3½ x 4" blocky	Good for northern areas . . . short, sturdy bushes . . . 3-4 lobes . . . medium-thick walls . . . freezes well	10 72
Ozark Giant	68	Long, very large, smooth, shiny-dark-green	Early . . . thick flesh . . . 4 lobes	14
Park's Whopper Hybrid	65	Big, blocky, deep-green	Early . . . 4 lobes . . . thick walls . . . large crop . . . disease-resistant	53
Pennbell	72	Glossy, deep-green, blocky	Compact plant . . . fairly thick flesh	66
Permagreen		Deep-green	Very early . . . retains green color when mature . . . New Hampshire sweet pepper	21
Slim Pim	65	2½"	Produces immense crop of little peppers . . . can be fried, or use fresh, or freeze . . . mild, sweet flavor	68
Spartan Emerald		Blunt, 3"	Michigan's early green pepper . . . 3-4 lobes . . . 18" tall plants . . . mild flavor	21
Staddon's Select (Missile)	72	Rough, blocky	Dependable . . . early . . . 4 lobes . . . great setting ability . . . thick flesh	17 29 32 37 60 66 72
Titan	80	High-gloss sheen	4 lobes . . . Yolo type . . . thick flesh . . . mosaic-resistant	70
Wisconsin Lakes		5" ripens to brilliant-scarlet	Early . . . ripens in North	21
Wonder Giant (hybrid)	65-75	Blocky	4 lobes . . . early . . . highly productive . . . very dependable in both warm and cool climates	16 70

SWEET PEPPERS—Blocky, Green (Continued)

VARIETY	DAYS	SHAPE/SIZE/COLOR	REMARKS	SOURCES
World Beater	74	Large, green to red when ripe	Early . . . sweet, fine variety	14 30 56
Yolo Wonder	75-77	4 x 4 ¾"; dark-green to red	4 lobes . . . smooth, firm, thick walls . . . mosaic-tolerant . . . good processor	5 10 14 15 20 22 25
Yolo Wonder A	75	Green to red	Early . . . 3-4 lobes . . . thick flesh . . . mosaic-resistant	32
Yolo Wonder B	77	4 x 4"; dark-green	4 lobes . . . mosaic-resistant . . . resembles California Wonder . . . thick flesh	11 16 29 51 57 60 67 70
Yolo Wonder L	75	3-4 x 3 ¾"	Taller than Yolo Wonder B . . . resistant to mosaic	11 16 17 40 48 51 54 57 70 73
Yolo Wonder L Improved	75	Smooth, blocky, dark-green to red	Tends to crop extra-large fruit . . . 3-4 lobes	32
Yolo Y	75	Dark-green to red	Recommended for home gardens . . . 4 lobes . . . sweet, thick walls . . . plants under 2 feet tall	16

SWEET PEPPERS—Yellow

VARIETY	DAYS	SHAPE/SIZE/COLOR	REMARKS	SOURCES
Cal Wonder Golden	72-75	3½ x 3½" blocky	Upright, sturdy plants . . . medium-thick walls	5 10 25 45 49 52 57 62 66
Golden Bell (hybrid)	65	4 x 3½"; matures to golden	Compact, vigorous, high-yielding plants . . . early . . . 3-4 lobes	5 22 31 32 48 53 55 60 66
Hercules Yellow Golden	79	Blocky	Large, sweet, and mild	50
Morgold		Big 3" glossy-yellow	12" tall plants . . . early . . . ripens in northern areas . . . extremely sweet	21
Sweet Romanian Yellow	67-80	4 x 2½" blocky, waxy yellow	Upright plants 22-24" . . . tall and bushy	5 57 62 66
Szegedi	70	5 x 3" tapering	Slightly larger, but similar to Yellow Romanian	66
Wonder Gold	55	Blocky, slightly tapered, glossy-green that turns golden-yellow	3-5 lobes . . . 20" tall plants . . . perfect for northern gardeners	28
Yellow Belle	65	3½ x 3"; turns bright-red if left to mature	4 lobes . . . medium-thick walls . . . mild flesh	5 38 66
Yellow Castle	70	Medium-size, heart-shaped, fairly long	Apple-sweet . . . flesh is very thick and sweet	66
Yellow Sweet Petite	70	3 x 1¼" tapered to blunt point	18-22" plant, upright and bushy . . . heavy yields . . . medium-thick flesh	57

SWEET PEPPERS—Heart- or Tomato-Shaped

VARIETY	DAYS	SHAPE/SIZE/COLOR	REMARKS	SOURCES
Burpee's Early Pimento	68	2½ x 3½" heart-shaped	Blocky . . . AA winner . . . heavy walls	10
Early Sweet Pimento	73	2½ to 3" across, flat, tomato-shaped, brilliant-scarlet	Exceptionally mild and sweet	22
Pimento (Perfection)	65-78	3 x 2½"; dark-green to red when ripe	Smooth, heart-shaped . . . very thick walls . . . sweet and flavorful	5 9 14 19 25 39 50 51 52 53 55 58 62
Pimento Select	73-75	Heart-shaped, dark-green	33" plants . . . thick walls	32 60
Spartan Garnet	64	Heart-shaped	Mild-flavored pimento . . . thick, sweet flesh . . . ripe fruit holds quality well	28
Sunnybrook (Tomato Pepper) (Cheese) (Sweet Squash)	65-73	2½ x 3¼"; deep-green, red at maturity, tomato-shaped	23-28" upright plants . . . mild flavor . . . very early and productive	10 25 30 48 51 62 66
Tompa	70	Tomato-shaped, red	Much juicier and sweeter than other varieties	68
Truhart Pimento	78		Ideal for home or market . . . finest pimento developed . . . sweet flavor, thick flesh	31

SWEET PEPPERS—Other Types

VARIETY	DAYS	SHAPE/SIZE/COLOR	REMARKS	SOURCES
Aconcagua	75	Yellow-green to red at maturity	Frying type . . . fruits 2-3 times larger than Cubanelle	12 26 28 41 53 57 70
Cubanelle	62-68	2 x 2½" long, yellow-green, red at maturity	Italian type . . . excellent fryer . . . medium-thick walls	5 11 12 17 25 29 30 32 37 41 48 53 55 57 60 66 70 72 73
Choco		Pimento type, chocolate-colored	Sweet, good for stuffing	26
Sweet Chocolate		Roundish, glossy-green to rich-chocolate color	Extra early . . . fine for freezing whole	21
Albino Pepper		White, then red	Sweet, very early . . . bell-shaped . . . dwarfed bush	26
Sweet Cream (hybrid)		4" creamy-white	Very early . . . dwarf 8-10" plant	21
Nosegay Pepper		¾" red and yellow clusters	Sweet cocktail peppers	21
Red Cherry Sweet	74-78	1 x 1½" round	20" plants . . . can be picked green or red . . . perfect for pickling	5 6 9 10 11 14 25 26 32 38 48 50 51 52 53 57
Hercules Sweet Red	70	Large, blood-red	Biggest fruit of all . . . sweet and mild	50
Parkwonder Hybrid	65	Medium, glossy-scarlet	Early, prolific, extremely vigorous . . . disease-resistant for short-season areas	53
Stokes Early Hybrid	60	Blunt, red	3-4 lobes . . . standard red hybrid	66

SWEET PEPPERS—Early Red

VARIETY	DAYS	SHAPE/SIZE/COLOR	REMARKS	SOURCES
Early Red Sweet	55	3 x 4" fiery-red	3-4 lobes . . . plants are small	66 72
Peter Piper Hybrid	57	3-4" bright-red	11-12 fruits per plant	21 28 53 62
Pick-a-Peck Hybrid		Medium-small, bright-red	Early . . . delightful, mild flavor . . . ideal for slicing or salads	22 32
Pinocchio Pepper		Fingerlike, bright-red	Ripens first of all	21
Shepherd	68	7" pointed	Strong, bushy plants . . . thick walls . . . fairly early to mature	66
Vinedale (hybrid)	60-65	4 x 2" pointed	14" dwarf habit . . . 3-4 lobes	48 66
Vinette	65	7" blocky	Dwarf plants, 14" tall . . . 3-4 lobes . . . thick walls	66

SWEET PEPPERS—Long

VARIETY	DAYS	SHAPE/SIZE/COLOR	REMARKS	SOURCES
Hungarian Yellow Wax	65	6 x 1½" tapered, waxy-yellow	18-20" tall . . . thick and very productive	14 16 22 30
Long Sweet Banana (Sweet Hungarian)	58-70	6 x 1½" tapered yellow to red	18-22" tall . . . medium-thick walls . . . use fresh and for pickling	5 10 11 12 14 17 19 20 25 29 31 32 34 40 41 45 48 51 52 53 55 56 57 62 66 67 72 73
Long Yellow Sweet	63	6 x 1¾" tapered, waxy-yellow turns crimson when ripe	Sweet flavor . . . use for frying, salads, sandwiches, pickling . . . compact bush	5 53
Paprika Pepper	80	Flat, thin-fleshed, red at maturity	Excellent for drying . . . 2-celled	50
Pepperoncini	65-75	5" pencil-thin, fiery-red	From southern Italy . . . trim upright bushes . . . good pickling pepper . . . expensive when bought in speciality shops	50 66

Potatoes (Solanum tuberosum)

The potato, a member of the same family as the tomato and the eggplant, is one of the most popular dinner-plate vegetables grown today. Potatoes are basically tubers grown underground at the end of short stems. In deciding which varieties to grow you have a choice of *color* (red, white, and russet), *season* (early, mid, or late), and *shape* (round, oval, oblong). Some good varieties for the home garden are:

Red: *Norland* is a good, early, table-quality, oblong-smooth potato. *Red Pontiac,* an oblong, mid-season variety, has only so-so cooking qualities, but it stores well. *Red LaSoda,* another oblong, mid-season variety, grows well in the South.

White: *Anoka* is one of the newer early, round-to-oval, smooth, white potatoes. *Irish cobbler,* an early round-blocky potato, is delicious cooked. *Bake King,* an oval, oblong, mid-season white variety, is one of the finest baking potatoes for the home garden. *Kennebec,* a white, late, thin-skinned potato, has excellent cooking qualities.

Russet Norgold, is an early-maturing oblong to long russet. *Russet Burbank* is a netted, brown, oblong potato that bakes well.

HOW TO PLANT: Buy certified seed potatoes or seed pieces from garden stores or seed companies. Cut pieces about 1½ inches square with one good eye per piece. Sow seed pieces with the cut side down, 4 inches deep, 12 inches apart, in rows 24-36 inches apart. When the plants are 5-6 inches high, scrape the soil from between the rows and hill. Cover the stems with soil (potatoes exposed to light turn green). Potatoes prefer long, cool seasons with temperatures that seldom rise above 65 degrees.

Harvesting: Dig early varieties when flowers form on the plants. For later varieties yellowing and dying vines indicate that tubers have reached maturity. Store in a cool, dark place.

POTATOES—Red

VARIETY	DAYS	SKIN/SHAPE	REMARKS	SOURCES
Chieftain		Large, smooth	Resistant to scab and mosaic	23
Norland		Oblong, smooth	Extra-early . . . great yields . . . shallow eyes	19 21 22 23 28 30 38 52
Red Pontiac		Round, big, red	Mid-season . . . shallow eyes . . . heavy yields	19 21 22 23 28 47 52 62A 67
Red Bliss		Round	Very early . . . white fleshed	47
Red LaSoda		Oval, bright-red	Medium-late . . . heavy yields	52

POTATOES—White

VARIETY	DAYS	SKIN/SHAPE	REMARKS	SOURCES
Anoka		Round	Extra-early	28
Bake King		Oval to oblong	One of the finest baking potatoes . . . shallow eyes . . . mid-season	28
Chippewa	110	Oblong, smooth	Mid-season . . . outstanding for northern states . . . shallow eyes	30 47 52 67
Green Mountain				30
Irish Cobbler	100	Round	Eyes strong and deep-set . . . early . . . popular in South	19 30 47 52 67
Katahdin	110		Shallow-eyed . . . glossy-white skin	30 47 67
Kennebec	115	Smooth	Great yields . . . shallow eyes . . . vigorous vines . . . good flavor . . . mid-season	19 21 22 23 28 30 38 47 52 67
Norchip		Smooth	Early . . . good flavor . . . ideal for chips and potato dishes	23 28
Sebago	110	Oval	Blight-resistant . . . stores for long periods . . . very heavy yields	23 52 62
Superior		Smooth, oval	Medium-early . . . shallow eyes . . . does not "gray" or discolor after cooking	21 23 38 52
White Cobbler			Early . . . wonderful eating	22 23 62A

POTATOES—Russet

VARIETY	DAYS	SKIN/COLOR	REMARKS	SOURCES
Early Gem		Medium-long, rough skin	Early . . . shallow eyes . . . good yields	52
Mayfair		Medium-large, slightly russet, creamy-buff skin	High yields . . . clear-white skin . . . shallow eyes . . . excellent all-around table quality	19
Norgold Russet		Golden netting, long, smooth	Mid- to early . . . strongly scab-resistant	21 22 23 28
Russet Burbank		Oblong, netted brown	Late . . . good all-around potato	22 23 52
Russet Sebago		Oblong, thin skin	Main crop . . . should be planted quite early and in good, rich soil	38 52

POTATOES—Other Types

VARIETY	DAYS	SKIN/COLOR	REMARKS	SOURCES
All Blue Potato			Yields well . . . blue skin and flesh . . . novel	28
Blue Victor		Blue skin, slightly flattened, oblong	White flesh . . . home garden favorite	28
Fingerlings		1" diameter, fingerlike, yellow skin	Boil with jackets on . . . use in salads or fried . . . yellow flesh	52
German Purple		1½" round, purple skin	Yellow flesh . . . boil in jackets . . . for salads	52
Lady Finger		1" diameter fingerling type	Far superior to any other for potato salads . . . delicious fried too	28

Pumpkin (Cucurbita maxima)

Everybody young and old alike loves pumpkins. They're great for canning, for pies, or for Halloween jack-o'-lanterns. The majority of the pumpkins are the vining type, with vines that spread as much as 20-25 feet. Some of the newer varieties, however, such as *Cinderella* and *Funny Face,* have their plants confined to about 6 feet of growing space. Pumpkins vary greatly in size and shape. Here are the choices:

Medium-Large to Small: The medium-large pumpkins such as *Connecticut Field* grow to about 25 pounds. Some of the medium-large types reach 50 pounds. They are used for canning and for large jack-o'-lanterns.

The medium-small to small sizes, which include such pumpkins as *Jack-o'-lantern* (10 lbs.), *Spirit* (10 lbs.), and *Spookie* (6 lbs.), make excellent carrying-size jack-o'-lanterns for the kids. *Small Sugar Pie* (Boston Pie) has a sweet, meaty flavor that makes the best possible pies.

Giant: These are the huge state fair prize-winning pumpkins. Some of them reach 200 pounds. Their vines require a lot of space—in fact, sometimes they can take over an entire garden!

Cushaw, Cheese, Naked Seeded Types: The *Cushaw Pumpkin* doesn't look much like a pumpkin, resembling a bowling ball in shape. They are popular for baking, boiling, canning, and pies. Cushaws look and taste as if they belonged to the squash family. The edible part is the neck.

The cheese types are very flattened, boxy pumpkins that have good, meaty flesh and an excellent flavor. Naked seeded types such as *Lady Godiva* were developed by the Department of Agriculture and are grown for their edible, hull-less seed and not the pumpkin flesh.

HOW TO PLANT: Start from seeds as soon as the ground warms up in the spring. Transplanting sets pumpkins back. Plant seeds 1-1½ inch deep, 24-36 inches apart, in rows 72-120 inches apart. Or plant in hills, three seeds per hill, 5 feet between hills. When the plants are about 2 inches high, remove all but the one strongest plant from each hill.

Harvesting: When the pumpkin is ready to pick, the skin darkens and becomes tough, and the vines dry up. Cut pumpkins before a heavy frost, leaving 3-4 inches of stem on the pumpkin.

PUMPKINS—Extra-Large

VARIETY	DAYS	SIZE/SHAPE/COLOR	REMARKS	SOURCES
Big Max	120	100 lbs. or more, 70" around, pink-orange skin	Fruits are flattened, round . . . 3-4" . . . yellowish-orange flesh	9 10 11 12 22 27 28 30 32 34 41 45 51 55 56 57 60 66 70 72 73

PUMPKINS—Extra-Large (Continued)

VARIETY	DAYS	SIZE/SHAPE/COLOR	REMARKS	SOURCES
Hundredweight	115	Orange	Grows pumpkins of record weight . . . needs very little attention	68
Jumbo	110	75-100 lbs.	Flesh is sweet, fine-textured, and excellent quality for pies and canning	9
King of Giants	120	As large as 200 lbs.	Although big, it is of high quality	14
Mammoth King (Potiron)	120	100 lbs. plus, orange-salmon	Fine-flavored, orange flesh	28 30 31 32 40 45 47 49 50 57 62
Mammoth Orange Gold	110	20 x 20", 80 lbs., orange	Thick, orange meat . . . matures firm and smooth	47 67 73

PUMPKINS—Medium-Large

VARIETY	DAYS	SIZE/ SHAPE/COLOR	REMARKS	SOURCES
Connecticut Field (Southern Field) (Large Yellow) (Big Tom)	100-120	10 x 14", 20-25 lbs., flattened at ends, deep-orange	Hard rind, smooth, somewhat ribbed . . . orange-yellow flesh, coarse and sweet	3 9 10 11 12 14 19 21 25 28 30 31 32 38 40 41 47 49 51 55 56 57 60 62 66 67 70 72 73
Howden's Field	115	Deep, round, ridged	Extra-thick flesh . . . keeps in prime condition for a long time	29
Jackpot (hybrid)	100	10", 15 lbs., round, bright-orange-yellow	Heavy yields . . . compact vines . . . fine pie quality	29
Mammoth Gold	105	40-50 lbs., golden-orange, smooth surface	Orange flesh . . . mostly used as novelty	32 38
Red Etampes		Very large, flat, orange-red	Keeps very well . . . good eating quality	15
Winter Queen (Luxury)	110	Medium-size, closely netted yellow skin	Of very high quality . . . best keeper	14 16 28 38 62
Yellow Large Paris		Large yellow fruit	Makes good soup, pies	15

PUMPKINS—Small

VARIETY	DAYS	SIZE/SHAPE/COLOR	REMARKS	SOURCES
Alagold	100	6-8 lbs., club-shaped, rich-orange	Heavy yields . . . hardly any seed cavity	31
Early Sweet (Sugar Pie)	90-110	6 x 7", 6-8 lbs., dark-orange, thick rind	Fine-grained, orange flesh	14 21 28 31 40 44 47 49 51
Jack O' Lantern (Halloween)	100-115	9 x 8", 10 lbs., medium-orange, round to elongated	Smooth skin . . . firm, even-textured flesh	3 9 10 11 12 14 16 19 21 22 27 28 30 32 38 39 44 45 47 49 51 53 55 57 58 60 62 66 67 70 72 73
Small Sugar Pie (Boston Pie) (New England Pie)	100-110	8 x 10", rich-orange, round, slightly ribbed	Meaty, sweet, fine-grained . . . general-use pumpkin	3 10 11 12 16 19 25 30 32 36 37 41 45 50 53 55 57 58 60 62 66 67 72 73
Spirit (hybrid)	90-100	12" diameter, bright-orange, 10 lbs.	Semibush with 6-ft. spread . . . earlier than regular pumpkins . . . AA winner	5 10 12 25 31 34 41 48 53 66 67 72
Spookie	90-105	6 x 6", 6 lbs., dark-orange, round	Orange-yellow flesh . . . sweet, thick, fine-textured	14 29 32 47 51 57 66
Tennessee Sweet Potato Pumpkin	100	Pear-shaped, white, striped light-green	Early . . . sweet potato flavor . . . fine for pies, or bake like squash	62
Triple Treat	110	6-8 lbs., 8-10"	Deep-orange flesh is as tasty as Small Sugar Pumpkin . . . hull-less seeds are delicious raw or roasted	10 45 72
Young's Beauty	100-112	7½ x 8", 8-9 lbs., globe-shaped, deep-orange	Moderately ribbed skin . . . highly recommended for home gardens	21 29 32 47 51 57 60

PUMPKINS—Special Types

VARIETY	DAYS	SIZE/SHAPE/COLOR	REMARKS	SOURCES
Cheyenne		Small, brilliant-orange	Compact bushes . . . fine-grained, solid flesh . . . deep-golden-yellow	21
Cinderella	95	10", uniform globe shape, bright-orange	Grow on well-drained land	10 28 32 50 53 66

PUMPKINS—Special Types (Continued)

VARIETY	DAYS	SIZE/SHAPE/COLOR	REMARKS	SOURCES
Cushaw, Green Striped	110-115	Crook neck, 10-15 lbs., 18 x 10", whitish-green, with darker-green stripes	Thick flesh, medium coarse . . . cream color . . . fine for pies and baking	11 16 28 31 32 36 41 47 51 53 58 62 67 73
Funny Face (hybrid)	100	10-17 lbs.	Makes excellent pies . . . can be grown in northern states	22 34 48 55 57 60 67 70 73
Golden Cushaw	118	12-18 lbs., golden-yellow, curved neck	Popular for baking, boiling, canning, pies . . . good keeper if stored properly	14 16 32 47 62 73
Kentucky Field (Large Cheese)	110	Flat, buff color	Very meaty . . . sweet and fine flavor . . . keeps well	14 36 45 56 58
Lady Godiva (Streaker)	110	6 lbs., 8", green-and-yellow stripes	Seeds are delicious raw or roasted	10 27 29 32 53
Thomas Halloween	110	15-30 lbs., deep-orange	Hard shell . . . thick flesh . . . excellent for home garden or roadside stands	32
Tricky Jack			Edible-seeded bush type . . . 4-ft. plants	21
White Cushaw (Jonathan Pumpkin)	75	2 ft. long, light color	Popular . . . yellow flesh excellent for pies	62

Radishes (Raphanus sativus)

The radish is a rather spectacular, quick-maturing, here-today-gone-tomorrow plant. Some mature in as few as 22 days, which is fast for most vegetables.

Radishes are easy to grow. Give anyone (even a four-year-old) a package of radishes, and you'll have an instant gardener. There are two main kinds of radishes—the ordinary, small, quick-spring radishes most of us visualize when we think of radishes, and the larger, longer-maturing, fall-winter ones.

Spring radish varieties grow *round* (all-red, red with a white tip, and all-white), *oblong cylindrical,* and *long slender* (red or white).

Winter radishes grow primarily long or round in white, black, or a red-rose color. The Oriental Radishes *(Daikon)* are covered in the Oriental section.

HOW TO PLANT: For spring radishes sow seed half-inch deep in rows 1 foot apart; thin to 1-2 inches apart. Sow seed as early in the spring as the soil can be worked. Repeat at ten-day intervals until early summer. Sow again about a month before frost.

For winter varieties sow seed a half-inch deep in rows 1 foot apart; thin to 3 inches apart. Fall and winter varieties need cool weather at the end of their growing seasons. Sow seeds in early summer for fall . . . mid-summer for late fall.

Harvesting: Pick spring radishes when they are still fairly small and young. Later on they become somewhat pithy. When winter radishes have developed into crisp roots, they should be pulled and stored in moist sand at temperatures just above freezing.

RADISHES—Red, Round

VARIETY	DAYS	SHAPE/COLOR	REMARKS	SOURCES
Acacia Globe		Globe-shaped, deep-scarlet	Medium-size tops . . . crisp, white flesh . . . uniform variety	16
Bright Scarlet Globe Greenhouse Special	22	Bright-red	Most attractive of the Scarlet Globe type	48
Cavalier	21-24	Oval, bright-red	Uniform, crisp, and mild . . . forcing type	21 32 48 51 52 66 72
Cavalrondo	24	Oval, brick-red	Either greenhouse or early-spring forcing	48 66
Champion	25-28	King-size, round, bright-scarlet	Seldom pithy . . . does well in hot weather	9 10 12 14 16 19 21 22 28 29 30 31 32 34 37 38 39 40 47 48 51 53 56 60 66 67 72
Cherry Belle	22-24	¾" round	AA winner . . . resembles a cherry . . . crisp and delicious	3 5 9 10 11 12 14 16 19 21 22 25 28 29 30 31 32 34 38 39 40 44 49 50 51 52 53 55 57 62 66 67 68 70 72 73
Cherry Belle Short Top	21	Bright-red, round	Does well in nearly every type of soil	48
Comet	25	Globe-shaped, cherry-red, 1"	AA winner . . . white flesh . . . short tops . . . excellent eating . . . good variety for forcing	10 14 16 47 48 51 52 57 60 66 67 72

RADISHES—Red, Round (Continued)

VARIETY	DAYS	SHAPE/COLOR	REMARKS	SOURCES
Crimson Giant (Butter)	29	1½" perfect globe, crimson	Solid-white flesh . . . firm, crisp, and mild . . . grows large without getting pithy and hollow	3 10 14 16 21 22 25 32 44 46 51 52 55 56 57 58 62
Early Bird	20	Globe-shaped, bright-scarlet	White flesh . . . fine-grained, crisp, and tender	19
Early Scarlet Globe Medium Top (Vicks)	24	Bright-scarlet, olive shape	Popular for home gardens . . . crisp, white flesh	3 11 14 16 21 22 25 30 31 36 37 40 44 47 48 51 52 57 60 62 70 72 73
Early Scarlet Globe Short Top	23	Roots regular and uniformly bright	Attractive color	9 12 14 25 41 49 51 58 72
Eighteen Days	18		The quickest . . . 18 days from seed to table	15
Fireball	21	Red-scarlet, olive shape	Always mild flavor	62
Giant Butter Radish	21	Globular, solid	Early . . . high-quality	14
Radar	18	Scarlet, globe-shaped	Fast-growing . . . extra early . . . very fine quality	14
Red Boy	25	Round, globe, short tops, sparkling-red	Spicy, crisp, white flesh . . . excellent for bunching	11 16 21 29 48 51 53 66
Red Devil	24	Small, bright-red, dime-size	Mild, pungent . . . grows no bigger than a quarter	19 70
Rojo Grande	25	1½", bright-red, medium tops	White flesh, firm, tender	16
Scarlet Globe	24	Olive shape, 1", scarlet	Medium-size tops . . . crisp, tasty flesh . . . good for forcing and for outdoors	10 32 45 56 66 67
Scarlet Globe Special	23	Perfectly shaped, scarlet		66
Scarlet King	30	Big, round, red	Excellent variety for a late-spring crop	50
Scarlet Knight	22	Round to globe shape, bright-red	Medium-size tops . . . good for home gardens	14 21 32 48 51 70
Silver Dollar	30	Big as a silver dollar	White flesh, crisp	19 28
Stop Lite	23	Medium-size, red, globe	Remains crisp, firm, and snappy a long time . . . 3-4" tops	21 51 66
Toro (hybrid)	22	Globe-shaped, scarlet-red	Outstanding for growth . . . medium tops . . . white flesh of excellent quality	16
Tendersweet	24	All-red, round		22
Zwaan's Champion	24	Small, ball-shaped, bright-red	Medium tops . . . excellent quality	57

RADISHES—White Tip

VARIETY	DAYS	SHAPE/COLOR	REMARKS	SOURCES
Copper Sparkler (National)	25		Most popular white-tip . . . good keeper	72
Half Long	24	Rose-red, white tip	Not pithy . . . sweet	68
French Breakfast	23	1¾" oblong to olive in shape; rose-scarlet skin, white lower	Short-top . . . flesh is white . . . pull when young	3 10 12 14 21 22 28 30 34 38 47 50 51 52 53 55 57 58 60 62 66 68 72
Perfection Extra Early	25		For home garden or market	38
Perfection White Tip	26	Round and smooth, uniform in size	Mild, crisp, tender . . . never pithy	14
Rosey Gem	21	Deep-scarlet top, pure-white bottom; globe-shaped	A desirable variety for home gardens	31
Scarlet Globe White Tip	26	Round	Early . . . does not get hollow or pithy	22 47
Sparkler (Early Scarlet Turnip) (Brightest White Tip)	25	1 ¾" almost round; scarlet upper, white lower	White flesh has an agreeable, snappy flavor	3 10 11 12 14 16 28 30 32 40 41 44 51 52 55 56 57 58 60 62 67 73

RADISHES—All White

VARIETY	DAYS	SIZE/SHAPE	REMARKS	SOURCES
Burpee White	25	¾-1", nearly round	Mild, crisp . . . very popular	10 66
Faribo White Snoball	28	1", slightly flattened	Highest quality	21
Giant White Globe	28	20-30 lbs.	Early, sweet, tender . . . white flesh . . . will grow in any climate	14 51

RADISHES—All White (Continued)

VARIETY	DAYS	SIZE/SHAPE	REMARKS	SOURCES
Hailstone	30		Early globe . . . larger than most . . . crispy sweet	50 58
Radish White Ball (White Pearl)	25	Uniform in size, smooth skin	Never gets pithy	14
White Globe (Giant Hailstone)	26		Medium tops	52
White Prince	28	Round	Very short tops . . . outstanding holding ability	21 28 38 40 72
White Turnip Box	26-35	Slightly flattened	Medium top . . . particularly adapted as a summer radish	62

RADISHES—Red, Long

VARIETY	DAYS	SHAPE/COLOR	REMARKS	SOURCES
Akahime	30	8" cylindrical, reddish-purple	Slow to bolt . . . good all year round	36
Brightest Long Scarlet	26	4-6"	Short-topped variety for home garden or market	40 56
Firecracker	22	Vivid-scarlet, long, slender	Early . . . remains crisp and tender longer than early types	21 28
Flamboyant		Semilong, bright-red, white tip	Fast grower . . . very popular	15
Long Scarlet Amiens		Long, straight, red root, white tip	Unusual summer type of good quality	15
Long Scarlet (Short Top)	30	5-6" deep-scarlet	Firm white flesh	41 47 51 55 72
Mexican Bartender	30-35	8-10 x 1¼", long, tapered, scarlet-red roots	Medium to tall in height . . . vigorous . . . pink, smooth flesh	16

RADISHES—White, Long

VARIETY	DAYS	SHAPE	REMARKS	SOURCES
All Seasons	45	6 x 1", long, straight	Holds up well . . . mildly pungent . . . crisp texture	10 14 19
Early Icicle	28	5" icicle shape	Brittle and mild . . . attractive appearance	14
Summer Cross (hybrid)	45	6-14"	Heat-tolerant . . . Oriental type . . . white flesh stays crisp, mild, and sweet	10
White Icicle	28	5-5½ x 1" long, slender	Crisp and tender, mild and sweet	3 9 10 11 12 16 19 21 22 28 29 30 31 34 36 37 39 45 49 51 52 53 55 56 57 58 60 62 66 68 70 72 73
White Icicle (Short Top)	30	4½-5" smooth	The young flesh is fine, sweet, and tender	32 40 41 46 48 51
White Strassbury	35	Icicle shape, but longer	Both flesh and skin are snow-white	14 62

RADISHES—Winter

VARIETY	DAYS	SHAPE/COLOR	REMARKS	SOURCES
China Rose Winter (Scarlet China)	52	6-7 x 2½", deep-rose	Pungent, good keeper . . . white flesh . . . stores well	16 19 22 28 31 32 36 38 40 47 48 51 55 57 58 62 66 67
Long Black Spanish	55-60	Large globe, 3½-4", black	White, crisp, pungent flesh . . . good for winter storage . . . lasts well	10 12 14 15 21 28 29 30 36 47 50 62 72
Round Black Spanish		Large, round, black	Firm, white flesh	36 45 47 48 52 57 60 62 66 72
Winter Cherry Belle		¾" around	Resembles cherries	40
White Chinese (Celestial) (California Mammoth White)	58-60	6-8 x 3"	Fall, winter . . . least pungent winter radish . . . icy white flesh	10 14 16 19 21 45 47 49 50 52 56 57 62 66 67 73
White Mammoth	58	7-8"	Solid white flesh . . . sow in mid-summer	22

RADISHES—Winter, Japanese

VARIETY	DAYS	SHAPE/COLOR	REMARKS	SOURCES
Minowase		1½ ft. long, pure-white	Early type . . . tender, with little pungency	41 68
Mino Early No. 1	49		Fast-growing . . . mild, brittle roots	37
Miyashige	60	12-15 x 3"; white, stump-rooted	High-yielding . . . best quality for pickling and storage	37 41 50
Nerima Long Neck	60	2-2½ ft.	Slow-bolting . . . late . . . well-adapted to spring sowing	37 42 50
Sakurajima Giant	150	13", 40 lbs., pure-white	Vigorous plant . . . root is sweet and of good quality . . . excellent for boiling or pickling	36 42 50 62
Shogoin	65	Globe-shaped, pure-white, 5-6"	Winter type, tender and crisp	41 50
Tokinaski (All Seasons)	70	1½ ft., pure-white	Slow-bolting . . . late . . . well-adapted to spring sowing	37 42 50

RADISHES—Other Types

VARIETY	DAYS	SHAPE/COLOR	REMARKS	SOURCES
French Golden	60	Light-golden	Mid-season . . . distinctive, piquant flavor	50
National		Round, bright-pink, white tip		15
Pink Beauty	27	Large, not pithy	Short top . . . white flesh	19
Pinkie	27	Pink	Stays crisp . . . extra mild . . . short tops	28
Radish De Gournay	65	Long, violet	Sweet and good	50
Yellow Gold		Egg-shaped, golden skin	Medium flavor . . . white flesh	68

Rhubarb (Rheum rhaponticum)

What a handsome, bold, textured plant this is! Not only are the stalks delicious in pies, but the plant blends right into the shrubbery in any flowerbed. It has broad, pink-tinged, crumpled leaves on tall, smooth stalks. Rhubarb is a perennial that won't do very much until it has at least one growing season under its belt. After that it will produce edible stalks. Rhubarb varieties may be divided into two classes: those with green stalks and those with red stalks.

Harvesting: Don't harvest rhubarb stalks the first year. The second season you can begin to pull stalks for eating. Select the larger outside stalks; grasp them firmly near the base and snap them off. Use only the stalks for eating; discard the dark-green leaves, which are somewhat poisonous.

HOW TO PLANT: In early spring or fall plant crowns 4-6 feet apart. Feed rhubarb in the early spring and fall. Water every two or three weeks.

Rhubarb dies back each fall and shoots out new leaves every spring. This plant needs a dormant period each year, thus doesn't do well in mild-winter areas. You can achieve dormancy by cutting back on the water for a few weeks after the plant has stopped producing stalks.

RHUBARB—Greenish

VARIETY	STALKS	REMARKS	SOURCES
Flare	From green to red	Good producer . . . tender, juicy stalks . . . excellent combination of tartness and sweetness	28
Giant Victoria		Produces lots of big, juicy stems	19 52 64 67 72
Victoria	Broad, thick, green-shaded red	Pleasant, tart flavor . . . heavy yielder . . . strong upright growth	10 16 21 22 23 32 39 46 58 62A 73

RHUBARB—Red

VARIETY	STALKS	REMARKS	SOURCES
Cherry Red	Large, cherry-red outside and greener on inside	Fine quality . . . tender, juicy . . . very productive and vigorous	14
Chipman Canada Red	Extra-heavy, deep-red	Tremendous yields . . . very tender and juicy	14 19 22 23 28 38 39 46 52
Everbearing Red Rhubarb	2 ft. tall	Extremely winter-hardy . . . withstands drought well	43
Linnacus Rhubard	Red	Juicy, tender stalks	62A
McDonald's	Brilliant-red	Excellent flavor . . . tender skin, peeling unnecessary . . . sauces and pies become a rich pink	10 64
Oregon Red Giant	Red all the way through	Mild flavor . . . makes fine pink sauce	16 57
Prince Albert	Red	A popular English variety	36
Strawberry	Rosey-red	Mild, pleasing flavor . . . stalks cook up well	23 30 52
Valentine	18-22" long, 1-1½ x 1"; deep-red	Supreme quality . . . deliciously sweet in pies or stewed	10 19 23 28 35 39 60 62A 64

Rutabaga (Brassica napobrassica) (Swede turnip)

Rutabagas are closely related to turnips, but they are larger, have smooth, waxy leaves, and develop much more slowly than turnips. In addition rutabaga roots are chockful of vitamin A and can be stored for long periods of time. There is a variation in skin color among varieties—yellow-purple top to white-red top to all-red. The flesh can be yellow or white. Laurentian types are generally mild.

HOW TO PLANT: Sow seeds a half-inch deep in rows 15-18 inches apart. Thin in stages to about 8-12 inches apart. Rutabagas like cool temperatures. Sow seeds in June or July so the roots develop in cool weather.

Harvesting: Pull and top rutabagas before roots are injured by extreme cold. If well mulched, rutabagas can be stored in the ground and dug as needed.

RUTABAGA

VARIETY	DAYS	ROOTS	REMARKS	SOURCES
American Purple Top	88-90	Purple tops, buttery-yellow globes	Sweet, fine-grained, light-yellow flesh . . . excellent winter keeper . . . plant like turnips	3 19 22 28 30 32 36 40 41 47 49 50 52 53 55 56 57 58 67 70
Burpee's Purple Top Yellow	90	Roots are large, smooth-globe-shaped, deep-purplish above, light-yellow below	Fine-grained, yellow flesh . . . cooks to bright orange . . . good keeper for winter storage	10 45
Golden Neckless	95	Yellow-purple tops	Yellow flesh . . . roots are better keepers than most	62
Improved American Purple-Top Yellow	90	Short-neck strain, smooth, not too large	Yellow flesh . . . solid, sweet . . . fine keeper when full grown	12 21 25 31 38
Improved Long Island	90	Large, spherical, purplish-red above, light-yellow below	Yellow flesh . . . fine-grained, firm, crisp, and sweet	60
Laurentian Neckless (Laurentian)	90	Purple tops globe-shaped	Rich-yellow flesh . . . smooth . . . free from excess roots . . . splendid keeper	21 37 38 48 52 66 72
Macomber	80	5-6" ovate, red, white top	White flesh . . . smooth Shinnea variety . . . outstanding for storage	31 32
Red Chief		Red	Yellow flesh . . . very vigorous . . . does well under adverse conditions	21
True Globe Shaped	80	Globe-shaped roots, purple tops, yellow bottom	Yellow . . . solid, sweet flesh	67

Salsify (Tragopogon porrifolius)

This little-known, little-grown vegetable got its nick-name, "oyster plant," because that's what it tastes like. Gourmets love it. In appearance salsify resembles a long, skinny parsnip. It is a long-season vegetable that takes up to 150 days to grow. *Mammoth Sandwich Island* is the commonly grown variety, but there is also a black salsify *(Scorrozanra hispanica)* which is actually a relative. Scorrozanra has a black skin that can be removed by scraping (the root is actually brown).

HOW TO PLANT: As early as possible in the spring, work the soil to a depth of 18 inches. Sow the seeds in rows 12-15 inches apart. When the plants are 2 inches high, thin to 3 inches apart. Since it is a long-season crop, you can make better use of space by planting it with fast-maturing vegetables such as lettuce, radishes, spinach.

Harvesting: Dig, do not pull the roots. Damaged roots will bleed and lose their flavor. Roots can be mulched and left in the ground to be used during winter.

SALSIFY (Oyster Plant)

VARIETY	DAYS	ROOTS	REMARKS	SOURCES
Duplex		Slender, black	From Holland . . . excellent quality	36
Gigantia	120	Black	Well-selected Danish variety	37
Improved Mammoth Sandwich Island	120	Long, slender white	Delicious baked or creamed	28
Long Black (Black Giant Russian) (Scorzonera)	140	Black	Very hardy . . . considered by many to be better than white salsify	14 15 36 72
Mammoth Sandwich Island	120-140	6-8" long, 1½" thick, tapering, smooth, dull-white	Not difficult to grow	3 11 14 16 19 21 29 30 31 32 38 41 45 47 48 50 51 55 58 60 62 66 67 72 73
White Mammoth		Whiter, has largest root		15

Spinach (Spinacia oleracea)

Spinach is probably America's favorite green. Although spinach is fast-growing, it can't take long days or hot temperatures. A few warm days and it suddenly starts to go to seed. This is one crop that definitely prefers cooler weather. Spinach is thus somewhat difficult to grow—but worth it, spinach lovers say. You have a choice of crinkled leaves (savoyed), semi-crinkled, or smooth . . . and erect, semierect, or prostrate plants.

By far the most spinach varieties are savoyed, up-right types. Favorites are *America*—a slow-bolting, glossy-green heavy yielder — and *Bloomsdale Long Standing,* a thick-textured spinach that resists heat. *Melody,* a vigorous and popular spinach, has semi-crinkled leaves; *Nobel Giant* has thick, smooth leaves.

In hot-summer areas, where spinach does not grow well, try one of the spinach substitutes such as New Zealand or Malabar spinach. You can grow them under conditions where spinach would be otherwise impossible.

HOW TO PLANT: Sow seeds half an inch deep, 2 inches apart, in rows 18 inches apart. After seedlings have begun to grow, thin to 8 inches apart and feed with a high-nitrogen fertilizer. Plant seeds in early spring and in early fall. Make successive plantings 10 days apart.

Harvesting: You can pick the outer leaves individually. When the first flowers start to form, pick the entire plant.

SPINACH—Savoyed, Upright

VARIETY	DAYS	LEAVES	REMARKS	SOURCES
America	50	Glossy, dark-green, heavily savoyed and crumpled leaves	AA winner . . . heavy yields . . . slow-bolting . . . good home garden variety	10 11 12 16 19 28 30 31 32 47 53 60 66 70 72
Badger Savoy	40-45		Downy-mildew-resistant . . . slow to bolt . . . spring and summer harvest	16

SPINACH—Savoyed, Upright (Continued)

VARIETY	DAYS	LEAVES	REMARKS	SOURCES
Bloomsdale	39-48	Thick, twisted, crumpled leaves	Extra-early . . . heavy yields . . . excellent fresh or canned . . . slow to bolt	14 19 22 30 32 34 39 44 47 48 49 55 56 58 70
Bloomsdale Long Standing	39-48	Thick-textured, very crinkled, glossy-dark-green	Slow to bolt . . . heavy yields	3 10 11 14 21 25 30 32 37 40 45 50 51 57 60 66 73
Dixie Market	45	Shiny, dark-green, rounded, deeply savoyed and curled at edges	Fall and winter variety . . . fast-growing, high-yielding . . . compact . . . good for canning, using fresh, or freezing	16 32 47 51 57
Dixie Savoy	40	Dark-green, slightly oblong, thick, well-savoyed	Fall and winter harvest . . . well-adapted to eastern and southern states . . . good fresh, canned, or frozen	16
Early Hybrid 11	40	Deeply savoyed, dark-green	For fall and winter crop . . . easy-bolting, fast-growing . . . used for fresh or for canning	16
Hybrid 56 Savoy	40	Deep-green	Fairly compact plant . . . not for spring and summer harvest	16 38
Hybrid 178		Savoyed, dark-green	Large, erect . . . fall variety	47
Hybrid 612 Savoy	40	Deep-green, deeply savoyed	For fall harvest	16 32 47
King of Demark	46	Broad, rounded, slightly crumpled, dark-green	Great canning spinach . . . very hardy and of good quality . . . large, spreading plant	3 19 52 60
Savoy Supreme	45-50	Dark-green, well-savoyed, distinct luster	Adapted for fall or early spring in those areas where Bloomsdale has been standard variety	16 47 51
Virginia Savoy Yellows Resistant	39	Massive, thick, heavily crumpled	Very hardy . . . grows vigorously in late fall, but cannot be sown at other seasons without going to seed	12 14 48 49 70
Winter Bloomsdale	45	Dark-green, thick, savoyed	Blight-resistant . . . hardy enough to winter over from fall sowing . . . slow-bolting	10 29 38 47 48 60

SPINACH—Semisavoyed

VARIETY	DAYS	LEAVES	REMARKS	SOURCES
			ERECT	
Avon	44	Large, dark-green, semicrinkled	Quick-growing . . . vigorous . . . slow to bolt . . . delicious raw or cooked	10 72
Chesapeake Hybrid	40	Medium-large	Will overwinter where winters are mild	16 40 47 51 67
Early Hybrid no. 7	40-45	Large, dark-green	Upright habit . . . resistant to downy mildew . . . good for canning or freezing	10 12 14 16 21 32 41 48 50 51 52 55 56 60 70
Early Hybrid no. 8	40-45	Uniform, semisavoyed, green	Chiefly used as a fall and winter crop . . . all-purpose spinach	16 48 53
			SEMIERECT	
Meldoy (hybrid)	42	Large plants, dark-green, semicrinkled leaves	AA winner . . . resistant to mosaic and powdery mildew . . . vigorous and fast-growing . . . heavy yields	10 19 21 29 32 53 66 70 72
Old Dominion	40	Medium-savoyed, dark-green	Medium-size . . . fall and winter season	12 47 48 67
			SPREADING	
Aragon Spinach	45	Giant, smooth, large, broad, thick, dark-green	Hardiest of all . . . stands a long time before going to seed	3
Giant Fill Basket	40	Thick, succulent, dark-green, glossy, moderately crumpled	Plants often measure 25 inches across . . . cooks tender . . . excellent flavor	14
Giant Thick Leaf	43	Somewhat crumpled, thick, large, broad, arrow-shaped	Very heavy yields . . . large, spreading plants . . . use fresh, or can or freeze	22

SPINACH—Smooth, Erect

VARIETY	DAYS	LEAVES	REMARKS	SOURCES
Big Crop	40	Long, stout stalks; thick, very large, rounded edges, bright-green	Long-standing . . . disease-resistant . . . unbeatable for canning	14
Crisp 'N Tender	43	Dark-green	Hardy . . . grows a long time without seeding	22
Early Smooth		Large, dark-green	For fall or winter crop	73
Giant Viroflay		Very broad, smooth	Early . . . quick growing	15
Hybrid 424	40	Dark-green, large, thick	Early . . . highly resistant to blue mold	16 40 53
Hybrid 425	40-45	Smooth, thick, dark-green	Vigorous grower . . . recommended for fall and winter crops . . . resistant to downy mildew	16
Nobel Giant (Long Standing Quadray) (Giant Thick Leaved)	46	Huge, thick, smooth, pointed with round tip, dark-green	Enormous yields . . . large plants, vigorous and spreading . . . very tender leaves	11 14 16 21 30 40 52 56 58 60
Viking	46	Dark-green, grow very large if not cut	Popular home garden variety . . . long-standing . . . grows rapidly	29 60
Viroflay 99 (Resistoflay)	40-45		For fall harvest . . . adaptable in southern and West Coast areas . . . large, erect . . . good resistance to downy mildew	16 40 51

SPINACH—Prostrate and Semi-erect

VARIETY	DAYS	LEAVES	REMARKS	SOURCES
Nores	48	Large, dark-green, arrow-shaped	Similar to Northland, but slower to bolt	51
Northland	40-48	Dark-green, slightly crinkled	Canning and freezing spinach . . . bears longer before bolting to seed . . . makes a great salad, too	28 51 72
Spinoza	45	Very large, dark-green	Very high yields . . . fast-growing . . . resistant to blue mold	57
JAPANESE SPINACH				
Hojo	45		Highly prized for its flavor and texture . . . very vigorous grower . . . for summer or fall planting	50

SPINACH—Spinach Substitutes

VARIETY	DAYS	LEAVES	REMARKS	SOURCES
Climbing Spinach	70		Use fresh or boiled . . . unusual, quick-growing vines . . . grow on a trellis or fence . . . ready to harvest by mid-season	28
Malabar Spinach (Basella Alba)	70	Large, bright-green, glossy	Excellent substitute for spinach . . . quick-growing . . . takes little space if trained on fence	10 26
Mustard Spinach	35	Long, tender, glossy, dark-green	One of the earliest greens . . . mild taste of mustard	19 21
New Zealand Spinach	70	Fleshy, brittle, green	Strong heat-resistant plants . . . good spinach flavor	3 10 11 12 14 16 19 21 22 25 28 29 30 31 32 34 36 38 41 45 47 48 49 50 51 52 55 57 58 60 62 66 67 72
Spinach Beet	50	Similar to swiss chard		50
Tampala Spinach (Fordhook)			Young, tender leaves . . . cooks fast . . . good raw, too . . . tastes like artichoke	10 48 53 72

Squash (Cucurbita sp)

Squash will grow easily almost anywhere in the United States at the drop of a seed (year-round in some sections of the South) and will produce more food for the space than anything else you can plant. Actually there's probably no vegetable that gives a gardener a bigger thrill to grow than squash. Some kinds grow rapidly and produce a tremendous quantity of small fruits. Others take months to produce a fruit almost as big as a house. There are two basic types of squash—summer and winter-fall.

Summer squash is fast-growing (45 to 65 days to maturity), produces an abundance of thin-skinned fruits, and grows primarily on bushy, compact plants that take up less space than winter squash. Take your choice among three basic colors—green, yellow, and white—and two shapes—cylindrical-blimp and squashed-up-flat-round.

Green: This is zucchini, the Italian squash, one of the most prolific producers in the garden. In warm weather zucchini grows so fast it will startle you. After blooming, the fruit forms so rapidly that you have to inspect the vines every day to keep up with it. Three plants will not only keep your refrigerator full all season long but will produce enough to keep your neighbors supplied as well. You have a choice among black-green, grey-green, mottled, and a few yellows.

Yellow: Try the long, straight, yellow, cylindrical variety (straight-neck squash) or the long, yellow, cylindrical fruits with a crooked neck and warted skin (crook-neck squash). These two are America's best-loved summer squashes and have been the favorite of gardeners for many years.

White: This is the squashed-up, flat, round squash (white bush scallop or *Patty Pan*) that looks like a miniature flying saucer with scalloped edges. It's a funny-looking little squash that comes in white, cream, or light-green varieties.

Winter Squash: This variety comes in such a profusion of types and shapes that you'll want to try them all. Some resemble a giant banana, others are acorn-shaped, heart-shaped, and a number of other forms in between. All have more flavor than summer squash. Although most produce tremendous vines, some are bush types.

Winter-fall squash grows slowly (to 120 days) on large, runner-type vines (a few bush varieties), takes up a lot of space, has hard, thick shells, and should be left on the vine until fully ripened.

Banana-shaped: Every gardener at one time or another needs to grow a banana squash. This gigantic vegetable is a blue-grey or pink and grows to 3 feet long and 6-7 inches in diameter. It yields prolifically, and every single squash will make a half a dozen or more meals.

Oblong, olive-shaped: This is Hubbard squash, which generally looks like a big, elongated balloon with a knob on each end. Hubbards are the most popular of all winter squashes. Growing to 18 inches long and weighing 10-18 pounds, Hubbard squash will easily keep all winter long.

Acorn-shaped: As the name says, acorn squash looks like a large, dark-green acorn with a hard shell. These have been a garden favorite for many years. The bush varieties are particularly suited for small gardens with limited space.

Bottle-shaped: What a strange-looking squash this is! Butternut squash resembles a penguin or a bulbous-based bottle with a light-tan skin. It is absolutely delicious, however, and grows well in most areas.

Drum-shaped: Buttercup squash is more or less drum-shaped, resembling a Turkish turban with a prominent button on one end. This squash has a tremendous flavor and stores well throughout the winter.

Heart-shaped: The heart-shaped Delicious squash is one of the best squashes for freezing. The flesh is orange, thick, and sweet.

Pumpkin-shaped: The Gold Nugget squash resembles a small, flattened pumpkin and is just right for an individual serving.

HOW TO PLANT: Squash is easy to grow, but it is a heat-lover and should not be set outdoors until night-time temperatures regularly stay above 55°F. To get a jump on the season you can start squash inside on a window-sill or under lights six weeks before time to plant outside.

Plant bush varieties 2 feet apart in rows. If you plant in hills, allow three plants each. Maintain 4 feet from the center of one hill to the next.

Plant vine types in rows 5 feet apart. If planted in hills, plant three plants each and allow 8 feet between hills.

Harvesting: Summer squash should be picked when they are young and tender. The seeds should be undeveloped and the rind soft. Usually summer squash is too old for eating if your thumbnail doesn't pierce the skin readily with little pressure. Let winter squash mature fully on the vine until the skin is very hard.

SUMMER SQUASH—Bush Scallop

VARIETY	DAYS	SIZE/SHAPE/COLOR	REMARKS	SOURCES
Benning's Green Tint	54	Pale-green, disk-shaped, scalloped edges	More tender and better flavored than white . . . Patty Pan type	37 47 51 67 73
Early White Bush (White Patty Pan)	54	Pale-green to creamy-white at maturity; rather flat, 7-8 x 3", deep-scalloped edges	Flesh is milk-white and delicious	10 11 14 22 30 31 32 36 40 41 47 48 49 50 51 55 56 57 58 62 67 72 73
Golden Bush		Large, golden-yellow, scalloped	Distinctive flavor . . . vigorous, bush-type plants	55
Golden Custard	65	Rich-golden-yellow, scalloped	Size and shape similar to White Bush	62
Mammoth White Bush		Scalloped, thick, creamy-white	Bush type	32
Patty Green Tint (hybrid)	50	White tinted green	Plant is open and clean . . . great yields	53 70
Patty Pan (hybrid) (Early Bush Scallop)	50	Pale-green, scalloped edges, shallow, flattened	Flesh is pale-green, meaty, and tender	5 11 25 28 29 32 34 52 55 60 66 68 70
Scallopini (hybrid)	50	Bright-green, scalloped fruit	AA winner . . . can be eaten raw or in a salad . . . cross between scallop and zucchini squash . . . compact bush type	5 10 11 12 21 25 32 41 50 52 53 57 60 66 72
Silver Dollar	50-55	1½-2"	White flesh . . . vigorous bush type . . . fine flavor and texture	38
St. Pat Scallop (hybrid)	50	Bell-shaped, Patty Pan type; light-green	AA winner . . . early, vigorous . . . best eaten when about the diameter of a silver dollar	10 16 21 31 32

SUMMER SQUASH—Crookneck

VARIETY	DAYS	SIZE/SHAPE/COLOR	REMARKS	SOURCES
Baby Crookneck	50	Harvest at 5-6"; light-yellow, slightly curved		53 66
Crookneck	50-62	Harvest at 6"; yellow	Yields later than the hybrids . . . superior cooked quality	37
Daytona (hybrid)	41	Harvest at 5-6"; yellow	Creamy-yellow interior . . . vigorous, semiopen plant	51
Dwarf Summer Crookneck	50	Harvest at 3½ x 10", warted, curved neck; orange-yellow skin	Heavy yields . . . good for home garden or market	11 12
Early Golden Summer Crookneck	48-53	Harvest at 3-10 x 3", warted, 3 lbs.; bright-yellow, changes to deep-golden-orange	Very popular . . . meaty fruits . . . fine texture, delicious flavor . . . bush type	3 10 14 16 19 30 32 40 47 49 51 52 55 56 57 67 70 73
Giant Crookneck	55	Very large when permitted to ripen; golden-yellow, finely warted	Salmon-yellow flesh	62
Golden Crookneck	53	Harvest at 4-6"; bright-yellow skin	Very prolific . . . heavy yielding . . . fine flavor . . . orange-salmon flesh . . . bush-type	28
Golden Swan	50	Smooth, semicrooked neck	For home gardens	48 73
Goldneck (hybrid)	50	Harvest at 4½ x 6½"; yellow, very uniform	High production over a long season . . . bush-type plant	5 12 22 26 30 32 34 48 50 53 56 60 62 67 70 72
Ranger Crookneck	49	Harvest at 6-7"	Mosaic-resistant . . . plants are smaller bush . . . seed cavity is small . . . adapted to same areas as Yellow Crookneck	16 48 51 57 73
Saticoy (hybrid)	45	Harvest at 4-5"; yellow, curved necks	Compact bush habit . . . good production	30
Sundance (hybrid)	50	Bright-yellow, smooth skin	An early crookneck . . . flesh is creamy-white	41 48 70 73
Yellow Summer Crookneck Improved	55	Light-lemon-yellow	Popular in South	41 48

SUMMER SQUASH—Straightneck

VARIETY	DAYS	SIZE/SHAPE/COLOR	REMARKS	SOURCES
Baby Straightneck	51	Harvest at 6"; butter-yellow	High yields	66
Butterbar (hybrid)	49	Long, cylindrical, butter-yellow	Vigorous bush . . . firm, solid meat	53 70
Early Prolific Straightneck	50	Harvest at 4-14 x 3½"; creamy-yellow	AA winner . . . heavy yielding, bushlike plants	3 10 11 12 14 22 25 28 30 31 32 36 40 41 45 47 48 49 51 52 55 56 57 58 67 70
Giant Summer Straightneck	55	Large, warted, heavy, yellow		58 62
Goldbar (hybrid)	50	Harvest at 6"; smooth, cylindrical	Compact, open bush . . . uniform . . . heavy yields	5 12 19 30 32 38 41 47 48 55 56 57 60 67 70 73
Golden Eagle (hybrid)	45	Harvest at 7-8"; cream-yellow, nearly cylindrical	Pale-cream-yellow flesh . . . vigorous, open bush	51
Golden Girl (hybrid)	50	Slim, uniform, buttery-yellow	Prolific . . . bears heavily over long season	29
Goldzini Squash (Improved Yellow Straightneck)	52	Extra-long, yellow, 4-6 x 10-12"	Delicious . . . ideal for home use or market	28 48 66
Seneca Butterbar (hybrid)	51	Smooth-skinned, long, cylindrical	Solid flesh . . . open habit makes fruit easy to pick	10 32 57
Seneca Prolific		Tapered, smooth, creamy-yellow	Bears very early . . . continues heavy production throughout season	32
Slendergold	52	Harvest at 8-10 x 2½", slender, sparsely warted, lemon-yellow	Very prolific . . . excellent quality	57
Sunbeam (hybrid)	50	Lemon-yellow, very smooth, uniform, cylindrical	Dwarfish plants, slightly open . . . flavor at edible stage sweet and mild . . . recommended for home gardens	16
Squash Creamy	50	Harvest at 6-8"; smooth, creamy-yellow	Dwarf, yellow, straight neck . . . plants 18" across . . . very prolific	53

SUMMER SQUASH—Zucchini, Dark-Green

VARIETY	DAYS	SIZE/SHAPE/COLOR	REMARKS	SOURCES
Ambassador (hybrid)	50-55	7-8"	Extremely early . . . produces fantastic yields over long season	12 14 32 47 48 50 53 57 60 70
Aristocrat (hybrid)	48		Single-stemmed . . . continues bearing over long period . . . AA winner	5 10 12 15 25 30 34 38 50 53 57 70
Ball's Zucchini (hybrid)	53	7-8" smooth, waxy appearance	Open bush provides easy picking	5
Chefini	51	7-8" glossy, dark-green, cylindrical	Matures earlier than regular zucchini . . . AA winner	21 25 26 31 47 52 53 55 67 72
Dark Green Zucchini	50-60	6-7"	Flavor is stronger than Gray zucchini . . . bush-type plant	16 41 48 49 53 58 70
Diplomat (hybrid)	53	7-8" uniform size	High yields	32 47 48 66
Elite (hybrid)	48	6-8" dark-glossy-green, flecked light-green	Extra-early . . . abundant yields . . . prolific, vigorous vines	29
Hyzini	55	6-7" cylindrical	Bears under adverse conditions	41
Market King (hybrid)		Averages 8"	High production	40
Senator (hybrid)	47	Nearly straight	Prolific . . . early . . . heavy yields . . . for home garden or market	60
Seneca Gourmet (hybrid)	46	2 x 8"	Highest yields . . . superior quality . . . upright, bush-type plant . . . pick often	3 11 52
Verdue Hybrid	40-45	Cylindrical, shiny, dark-green, flecking of light-green	Early, summer bush . . . highly productive . . . fine-textured flesh . . . recommended for home gardens	16 73

SUMMER SQUASH—Zucchini, Green-Black

VARIETY	DAYS	SIZE/SHAPE/COLOR	REMARKS	SOURCES
Black Beauty	58	6-8", very uniform in size	High yields . . . greenish-white flesh . . . good flavor	32 51 52 55

SUMMER SQUASH—Zucchini, Green-Black (Continued)

VARIETY	DAYS	SIZE/SHAPE/COLOR	REMARKS	SOURCES
Black Eagle (hybrid)	50	7" cylindrical	Vigorous bush . . . white flesh	51
Blackee (hybrid)	50	Darkest-green, cylindrical, smooth	Vigorous, bushy, upright plants	16 73
Blackini (hybrid)	62	3½ x 8"	Very early . . . fine texture . . . rich flavor	28
Blackjack	55	Smooth, cylindrical	Open bush . . . good for home garden	48 57 66
Black Zucchini	52-62	6-8" straight, cylindrical	Bush-type plant . . . flesh is greenish-white with fine flavor	11 12 14 22 30 31 36 37 39 40 45 47 48 51 57 67 73
Burpee's Fordhook	57	8-12" straight to slightly curved	AA winner . . . creamy-white flesh . . . freezes well . . . vigorous, bushlike plant	10

SUMMER SQUASH—Zucchini, Dark-Green Stripes (Cocozelle Type)

VARIETY	DAYS	SIZE/SHAPE/COLOR	REMARKS	SOURCES
Casserta	50	Light-green, striped with dark-green	Bush-type Cocozelle . . . extra-early . . . abundant yields	14 52
Cocozelle Bush (Italian Vegetable Marrow) (Long Green Bush)	60-65	14 x 4-5", cylindrical	Best when 6-8" long . . . greenish-white, firm flesh	3 10 12 30 41 50 51 62 66 67 73
Cuccuzzi (Long Cocozelle) (Guinea Bean) (Climbing Squash)		Pick at 6-15", edible gourd	Grows quickly . . . fruit should be eaten in the immature stage	27 32 47 51 57
Cucuzzi Caravasi	65	Extra-long, to 4 ft.	An edible running gourd	12 30
Green Cocozella	60	16 x 4"	Popular Italian strain	14 36 37 45 47 66
Green Cocozella Striato	50	Glossy, light-green with dark stripes	Early . . . high yields	32

SUMMER SQUASH—Zucchini, Other Colors

VARIETY	DAYS	SIZE/SHAPE/COLOR	REMARKS	SOURCES
Beautine	45	Glossy, medium-green	Earliest of all squashes . . . handsome appearance . . . compact bushes	38
Burpee Golden	54	Glossy, bright-golden-yellow, medium-long, slender, cylindrical	Distinctive zucchini flavor	10
Burpee's Hybrid Zucchini	50	6-8" cylindrical, medium-green	Medium-size, bushlike plants . . . excellent flavor . . . heavy yields	10
Caserta	52	5-6" cylindrical, slightly tapered, gray	White-cream interior . . . semiopen bush	51 58
Clarita Hybrid	50	7", light-green	Unique nutlike flavor . . . highly female, which means more production	15 26 53
El Dorado (hybrid)	49	Rich, glossy-yellow-gold, smooth, slightly tapered	Extremely popular . . . open habit	29
Grey (slate)	50-61	Gray-green, mottled dark-green, smooth 6-7"	Medium to large plants, rather open	16 37 40 48 51 57 73
Greyzini (hybrid)	55	Gray or slate-green	Bush . . . excellent vigor . . . produces quality fruit over a long season . . . AA winner	12 19 21 22 25 31 32 34 52 57 62 66 72
Long White Vegetable Marrow	60	6-7" cream white, oblong	Pale-green interior, tinged white . . . closed habit . . . favorite English variety	51
Mexican Globe	45-50	Globe-shaped gray-green	Vigorous bushy-type summer squash . . . flesh is creamy-yellow with solid center . . . early and very productive	16
Storr's Green (hybrid)	50	6½-7", medium-green, flaked light-green	Highly productive	32 55

WINTER SQUASH—Acorn

VARIETY	DAYS	SIZE/SHAPE/COLOR	REMARKS	SOURCES
Bush Table Queen (Acorn Bush)	78-82	4 x 5", green, deeply ribbed	High quality, orange flesh . . . semibush . . . extremely productive in less space	10 11 14 37 38 48 49 55 62
Ebony (Improved Table Queen)	80-85	5 x 6", rounder shape than Table Queen and slightly larger	Stores well . . . heavy yields	11 12 28 32 48 51 52 57 70
Royal Acorn (Mammoth Table Queen)	82	7½ x 6", dull-dark-green	Turns dull orange after being stored . . . fine-flavored, 1½"-thick flesh	10 11 14 16 25 36 44 51 57 60 66 70 73
Royal Table Queen	80	Dark-green, deeply ribbed	Light-yellow flesh . . . used as a summer or winter squash	67
Table Ace (hybrid)	78	4½ x 5½" black-green shell	Bright-orange flesh . . . semibush	29 34 48 55 57
Table King	70-80	5 x 6", 1½ lbs., dark-glossy-green	6 to 8 fruits per plant . . . golden-yellow flesh . . . small seed cavity . . . compact plant (4' x 2½')	5 10 12 19 21 29 30 32 34 38 41 48 51 52 53 57 60 66 72
Table Queen (Acorn) (Des Moines)	80-85	4½ x 5" ribbed, smooth, thin-shelled	Desirable for baking . . . vines trailing . . . light-yellow flesh . . . bakes dry and sweet	3 11 12 14 16 19 21 25 28 29 30 31 32 37 38 39 40 41 45 47 48 49 50 51 52 57 58 60 62 66 72 73

WINTER SQUASH—Bottle-Shaped

VARIETY	DAYS	SIZE/SHAPE/COLOR	REMARKS	SOURCES
Baby Butternut		6-7"	Extra-early . . . egg-size seed cavity . . . deep-yellow, fine-textured, tasty flesh	21
Burpee Butternut	85	8-10 x 4-5", smooth, dark, buff-colored skin, hard shell	Orange, dry, fine-textured flesh . . . sweet, nutty flavor . . . good keeper	10
Butternut	90-100	5 x 12", creamy-brown	Very popular in New England . . . dry, sweet, bright-orange flesh	3 14 16 25 28 30 31 39 40 44 45 49 51 53 55 57 60 67 72
Butternut Eastern Strain	85	3-5 lbs., blocky, uniform in size	Matures early	32
Butternut Waltham	85-95	3½ x 9", creamy-tan skin	Small seed cavity . . . deep-orange flesh . . . excellent texture and flavor . . . good keeper . . . AA selection	5 10 11 12 19 22 29 30 31 32 34 37 38 41 48 51 52 53 60 62 66 70 73
Butternut Improved Waltham	110	10-12 x 5"		48
Hercules Butternut	82-110	7½ x 4½", large, thick, solid, straight neck, blocky, buff	Rich-orange flesh . . . fine texture and flavor . . . high yields of long-lasting fruits . . . AA selection	14 16 19 21 25 31 47 51 52 58 60 73
Patriot	110	5 x 12", cylindrical, bulbous blossom end; tough, greenish-black shell	Light-yellow flesh has nutty flavor	48 51
Ponca	85-110	5-8 x 12", creamy-tan, nearly cylindrical	Smaller, earlier Butternut . . . small seed cavity	29 37 48 51 57
Special Butternut	85	3-4 lbs., thicker, straighter neck		66

WINTER SQUASH—Turban Shape

VARIETY	DAYS	SIZE/SHAPE/COLOR	REMARKS	SOURCES
Bush Buttercup	88	Round	Thick, orange flesh	3 12 28 73
Buttercup	100-105	4½ x 6½", 4-5 lbs., dark-green skin, silvery-white stripes, gray spots	Thick, orange flesh . . . cooks dry and sweet . . . rich flavor . . . keeps well in storage	10 11 12 14 16 19 21 22 25 28 29 30 32 34 36 37 38 45 48 52 57 60 62 66 70 72
Emerald		Gray-green	Thick, orange flesh . . . excellent keeper . . . true bush squash . . . high-quality	21 29 38
Golden Turban (Improved Buttercup)		Bright-orange skin	Golden flesh . . . New Hampshire's Improved Buttercup	21

WINTER SQUASH—Turban Shape (Continued)

VARIETY	DAYS	SIZE/SHAPE/COLOR	REMARKS	SOURCES
Gold Nugget	85-95	1-2 lbs., bright-orange skin	Bush-type . . . good keeper . . . good quality and flavor baked in shell . . . AA winner	3 12 14 21 28 29 30 31 51 52 53 60 62 66 70
Kindred	80	Thin, bright-yellow shell	Full inch of deep-orange flesh . . . fine-grained . . . bush type	21 30 31 51 52 53 66 73
Mooregold		6-7 x 4-5" bright-orange shell	Long keeper . . . bright-orange flesh . . . vigorous vines	38 52
Perfection	85	3¼ lbs., orange shell	Golden flesh	66

WINTER SQUASH—Hubbard

VARIETY	DAYS	SIZE/SHAPE/COLOR	REMARKS	SOURCES
Baby Blue Hubbard		Small size, light-blue skin	Very early in maturing . . . high-quality . . . thick, orange flesh . . . good keeper	21
Baby Hubbard (Kitchenette)	100	5-6 lbs.	Good yielder . . . thick, yellow-orange flesh	28 37 62 72
Blue Hubbard	120	Bluish-gray, slightly ridged, average size 15 lbs.	Larger than True Hubbard . . . bright-yellow-orange flesh, fine-grained . . . good freezer . . . keeps well	3 10 12 14 21 28 29 30 32 37 44 48 53 57 60 66 73
Genuine Hubbard (True Hubbard)	110-115	10 x 12" dark-bronze-green skin, about 12 lbs.	All-purpose squash . . . deep-yellow-orange flesh . . . fine-grained, sweet, and dry	10 22 30 49 52 58
Golden Hubbard (Red Hubbard)	100	10 x 7-9", reddish-orange with grayish-red stripes, lightly warted	Deep-yellowish-orange flesh, fine grained . . . useful for canning and freezing	3 16 32 39 47 50 51 52 60 66 70 73
Green Hubbard	100	9 x 14", oval, pale-green		3 47
Green Hubbard Improved	95-100	9 x 14", bronzy-green, slightly warted, tough rind	Orange-yellow flesh, thick and dry . . . a good keeper	12 16 21 38 45 66 67
Improved Warted Hubbard	110	More warted, darker-green, globular shape, thick, hard shell	Orange-yellow flesh	32 72
Sweet Meated Hubbard	103	Medium-size, 10-15 lbs., round, quite flattened	An old-time favorite . . . golden-yellow flesh . . . good keeper	29 32 50
Warted Hubbard (Chicago)	110	Heavily warted, about 12 lbs., dark-slate-green, 10 x 15"	Flesh is orange-yellow, dry, and sweet . . . keeps exceptionally well	11 14 16 19 21 22 28 48 51 57 62 66

WINTER SQUASH—Other Types

VARIETY	DAYS	SIZE/SHAPE/COLOR	REMARKS	SOURCES
Big Red	100	Exceeds 100 lbs., 4 ft. long	Good eating quality	50
Blue Banana (Gray Banana) (Green Banana)	105-120	20-24 x 5-6", smooth, greenish-gray skin, thin rind	Produces heavy crop even when other squashes fail . . . sweet flesh . . . often used for pies	14 16 22 38
Futtsu Early Black		Flat-globe shape, warted	Used in northern Japan . . . early . . . very sweet, fine-grained flesh	36
Guatemalan Blue Squash	110	3 feet long, 8" across, smooth, hard shell	Sweet-flavored . . . good keeper . . . good baker . . . freezes well	50
Hungarian Mammoth	110-120	378 lbs. is record	Great for pies and competition	27 28 43 66
Hyuga Early Black Winter Squash	100	Dark, ribbed, warty	From China . . . very old variety . . . flesh is sweet, full-flavored	50
Kikusa Winter Squash	100	4-4½ lbs., ribbed	Originated in South China . . . firm, sweet, fine-textured flesh	50
Mexican Banana	120	Long, cylindrical, grayish-blue skin	Golden-yellow flesh . . . a good keeper	62
Pink Banana Jumbo	105	Up to 30" long and 6-7" around; cylindrical shape with hard rind	Thick, yellowish-orange flesh . . . for limited storage	11 16 27 28 48 51 52 55 57 58

WINTER SQUASH—Other Types (Continued)

VARIETY	DAYS	SIZE/SHAPE/COLOR	REMARKS	SOURCES
Turks Turban	100-110	8 x 10", bright-orange-red, striped and spotted scarlet-orange, cream, white, and green	Exceptionally varied, rich colors... wonderful for fall and winter decoration	10 11 14 32 48 57 70
Vegetable Spaghetti	100	Medium-size yellow, oblong	Late-summer or fall harvest... excellent low-calorie substitute for spaghetti	10 14 27 28 36 37 41 43 48 52 57 62 66 68 72 73
Warren Turban	115-120	Ornamental, flat, drum-shape top; 9 x 12-14" hard shelled, heavily warted, 15-20 lbs.	Very thick, orange-colored flesh... sweet and dry... good keeper... fine-quality flavor	12 16 73

WINTER SQUASH—Oblong-Olive Shape, Heart-Shape

VARIETY	DAYS	SIZE/SHAPE/COLOR	REMARKS	SOURCES
Boston Marrow	100	7-10", 20 lbs., bright-orange rind	Yellow flesh... heavy yields	34 47 51 67
Boston Marrow Necky	97-100	16-20", orange rind, hubbard shape	Orange-yellow flesh... thick, fine-grained	51
Golden Delicious	103	6-7 lbs., bright-orange	Golden flesh... fine for canning or freezing... good keeper	3 28 29 32 51 66 72 73
Green Delicious	100-103	8 x 10", medium-size, dark-green	Bright-orange flesh... well adapted in many areas	32 48 60 66

Sweet potatoes (Ipomoea batatas)

The sweet potato is a sprawling morning glory of tropical origin. It withstands hot summers well and needs a lot of space. Today you can plant vining-type sweet potato varieties and the bush type.

Harvesting: Dig the tubers when the foliage begins to yellow. Dry them in the sun for several hours, then cure them for about a week at 80-85°F. Store them at 55-60°F.

HOW TO PLANT: Start sweet potatoes from nursery plants. Plant in light, sandy, warm, not-too-fertile soil 9-12 inches apart in rows 3 feet apart. Dangers: too-fertile soil produces all top; heavy soil produces long and stringy tubers; too much water makes the roots elongated.

SWEET POTATOES

VARIETY	TYPE	COLOR	REMARKS	SOURCES
All Gold	Vining	Golden-yellow	Very early... favorite of midwestern gardeners... most popular variety for storing	21 22 24 28 53
Centennial	Vining	Bright-copper	Uniform, medium size... early... deep-orange flesh... fine texture... keeps well in storage	19 22 23 24 28 53 65
Georgia Reds	Vining	Red	Heavy yields... stores well	24 31 53 65
New Bunch Porto Rica (Vineless Puerto Rico)	Bush		Easy to grow... semiupright... deep-orange flesh... high sugar content	21 23 24 53 65
New Golden Jewell	Vining	Bright-copper	Highest-yielding variety... deep-orange flesh	24 52 62 65
Porto Rica (Yam)	Bush	Orange-yellow	Deep-orange flesh, fine grained... rich, sweet flavor... high sugar content	19 22 24 28 31
White Yams (Triumphs) (Southern Queen) (Poplar Root) (Choker)	Vining		White as cotton, inside and out... (sugar-sweet)	24 65

Swiss chard (Beta vulgaris cicla)

If you've tried spinach and failed, or if you are just tired of fighting the weather requirements of spinach, you'll want to grow Swiss chard. It can take summer temperatures that would make spinach bolt to seed. Chard is a member of the beet family without the bulbous root. The leaves are cooked and served like asparagus.

The choice you have is basically among red, dark-green (with either smooth or deeply crumpled leaves), or light-green (with either smooth or crumpled leaves). Some red varieties have both red leaves and red stems. The most popular red variety, *Rhubarb Chard,* has crimson stems, which look much like rhubarb stalks, and green, heavily crumpled leaves.

HOW TO PLANT: Sow seed a half-inch deep in rows 18-24 inches apart. Later, thin plants to 12 inches apart. Sow seed in early spring in cold-winter areas, about two weeks before the final frost. In areas where winter temperatures stay above 25°F. plant in the fall for harvesting the next year. In regions of very mild climate plant almost any time of the year.

Harvest: There are two ways to pick Swiss chard. For one, you can cut the outer leaves every few days while the plant continues growing. (Don't let the old, tough leaves remain on the plant, or the plant will stop producing fresh leaves.) Or you can also cut off the whole plant a couple of inches above the root crown, in which case the plant should produce new leaves.

SWISS CHARD—Dark-Green, Crumpled

VARIETY	DAYS	STALKS/LEAVES	REMARKS	SOURCES
Burpee's Fordhook Giant	60	White stalks 2½", dark-green leaves, crumpled and savoyed	Heavy yields . . . prepare like asparagus	10
Dark Green White Ribbed (Large White Ribbed) (Silver Ribbed)	55-60	Broad, white rib, crumpled, dark-green leaves	The chard or midrib can be used like asparagus	16 19 21 29 48 49 51 52 57 60 70
Fordhook		Dark-green, savoyed leaves, thick, white midrib	Standard variety	32 34
Fordhook Giant (Dark Green Lucullus)	50-55	Heavily crumpled leaves, 2 x 1', snow-white midrib midrib	Yields continuously from early summer until frost	14 16 37 48 51 58 60 66 67
White King	55	Large, thick, white ribs, extra-dark-green, heavily savoyed leaves	Recommended for the critical gardener	66

SWISS CHARD—Red, Red Stem, Others

VARIETY	DAYS	STALKS/LEAVES	REMARKS	SOURCES
Red Burgundy	60	Red stalks, deep-maroon leaves	Useful and ornamental . . . extra-rich, delicious flavor . . . plants yield until frost	21
Rhubarb Chard	55-60	Crimson stalks, heavily crumpled, green leaves	Delicious stalks . . . leaves are sweet and tasty	10 14 16 28 29 30 37 51 52 53 57 62 66 72
Ruby Red	60	Red to white stalks, crumpled red leaves	Plant grows 20-24" tall	32 48 50 58 60
Silver Sea Kale		Large stalks, cream-colored leaves	Heat-resistant . . . best for summer sowing	36
Swiss Chard of Geneva	60	Large, celerylike ribs	Suitable for year round culture	53

SWISS CHARD—Dark-Green, Smooth

VARIETY	DAYS	STALKS/LEAVES	REMARKS	SOURCES
French Swiss Chard	60	Thick, green leaves; large, white stalks	Heavy yields	50
Perpetual	50	Dark-green leaves, very little midrib	Harvest begins early summer, with new leaves until late fall . . . resistant to heat, drought, frost . . . very productive	10

SWISS CHARD—Dark-Green, Smooth (Continued)

VARIETY	DAYS	STALKS/LEAVES	REMARKS	SOURCES
Silver Giant	50	Dark-green leaves; broad, silvery-white stems	Tender . . . fine flavor	14
Vintage Green (hybrid)	55-60	Large, dark-green leaves; narrow, fleshy ribs; 6-12" taller than other chards	Vigorous growth and regrowth after cutting	16

SWISS CHARD—Light-Green

VARIETY	DAYS	STALKS/LEAVES	REMARKS	SOURCES
Giant Lucullus	50	Yellow-green, heavily crumpled	Upright, 24-28" tall plant	51 56 72
Light Green Curled		Dark-glossy-green leaves, deeply crumpled; clear-white rib		72
Lucullus	50-60	Large mid-rib; heavily crumpled, yellow-green leaves; broad, white stalks	Popular variety . . . fine flavor	10 14 21 25 28 30 31 32 38 45 52 53 55 57 62 73
Spanish Green Perpetual		Smooth, green leaves; narrow stems	For cooking like spinach	36
Spanish Yellow Perpetual		Smooth, yellowish leaves, narrow stems	For cooking like spinach	36

Tomato (Lycopersicon esculentum)

The tomato is without a doubt the king of the vegetable garden. Today practically every gardener grows at least one or two plants. Basically there are two vine types: *determinate* (commonly called bush tomatoes), where the terminal bud sets fruit and stops stem growth, and the plant is self-topping and does not need stalking: and *indeterminate,* where the terminal bud does *not* set fruit, and the vine can grow indefinitely until killed by frost; most of the indeterminate varieties must be trained on stakes. There are also semideterminate types.

Plant breeders in the United States today have literally gone wild testing several thousand tomato varieties every year. As a result there are hundreds of successful varieties available to the home gardener. They vary in color, shape, size, disease-resistance, and other qualities.

Color: The fruit may be red, pink, yellow-orange, white, green, and combinations thereof. Most people, of course, see red when they think of tomatoes, but many varieties such as *Early Pink* and *Gulf State* are a definite pink color. When pink tomatoes are purplish-pink, they are often called blue.

Orange-yellow and white tomatoes are mild in flavor and have long been considered low in acidity. Despite these claims by garden writers and seed catalogs, however, studies by the United States Department of Agriculture show that color has very little to do with acidity. *Sunray,* for instance, a yellow variety, had a pH of 4.21 when tested. *Earliana,* a standard red variety, has a pH of 4.37. The variety charts here will include the acidity claims of the various catalogs. Certainly, the yellow-orange varieties are delicious; however, the white are just so-so.

There are also green tomatoes such as *Evergreen* and striped ones such as *Mr. Stripey.*

Shape: Tomato varieties vary from deep-globe (high-round), globe (round), deep-oblate (flat-round), to oblate (flattened). Some varieties are also heart-shaped, accordion-shaped, bell-shaped, and square (a new paste tomato).

Size: Tomatoes vary from huge to small. There are a number of really big varieties such as *Abraham Lincoln* that grow to a pound or more. Under proper conditions these varieties weigh considerably more. For instance, the Beefsteak tomato is almost a legend in America today. They can be large, and they have thick flesh with few small seed cavities.

The small, miniature tomatoes vary from round, cherry-size to pear-shaped; colors are red or yellow. A number of varieties are especially suited to container planting. *Tiny Tim,* a 12-inch plant with cherry-sized fruits, can be grown in 4-inch pots. *Small Fry* is slightly larger with clusters of small fruit. It should be staked in a 6-8-inch pot or used in hanging baskets. *Burpee Pixie Hybrid* grows 18 inches tall with clusters of small fruit. Grow in 6-8-inch containers. *Presto Hybrid* reaches 24 inches high; *Patio Hybrid* grows to about 30 inches high and has 2-inch fruits.

Disease Resistance: Many varieties on the market today have some resistance to verticillium wilt, Fusarium wilt, and to nematodes. This is noted by the initials V–Verticillium, F–Fusarium, and N–Nematode after the variety name in the charts.

Special types: *Tree Tomatoes* are often advertised in the seed catalogs. They are really another member of the family called *Cyphomadra betacea*. Once established, they bear fruit up to seven months a year. The ripe fruit is red-orange, smooth-skinned, and egg-shaped. A few catalogs also list some of the long-vined tomatoes as a tree tomato.

The Potato Tomato, or pomato, is really two plants. You can start one by raising tomato seedlings in a flat. When they reach 1½-2 inches high, cut a 1-1½-inch hole in a whole seedling potato, and transfer the tomato seedling into the hole in the potato. Plant the potato and its tomato in a 6-8-inch pot filled with soil. The tomato roots will then grow through the potato into the soil. When the plant is 6-7 inches high, transfer to the garden.

The *husk tomato* (ground cherry, poha, strawberry tomato) *Physallis pruiosa,* is about the same size as a cherry tomato. The fruits are produced inside a paper-like husk. When ripe, the husks turn brown, and the sweet, yellow fruit drops from the plant. Similar to the husk tomato is the *Tomatilla (Physalis ixocarpa).* In this variety the fruit completely fills the husk. The fruits reach 2¼ to 2¾ inches in diameter. Horticular Enterprises (Box 34082, Dallas, Texas 75243) specializes in peppers and tomatillos.

HOW TO PLANT: To start from seeds, plant the seed a quarter-inch deep in compressed peat pots or other containers. After the weather has warmed up, plant the seedlings outdoors, 18 inches apart, in rows 30-36 inches apart. You can also purchase seedlings from nurseries.

With bushy plants, bury the plant so that half to three-quarters of the stem as well as the root ball is below the soil level. Roots will form along the stem. For long-stemmed plants, place the root ball on its side so the stem is almost horizontal, then bend the stem so only the bushy part appears above the ground.

Tomatoes like the sun, moderate moisture, and a well-balanced, fertile soil. Apply fertilizer at transplant time and again when plants bloom.

Harvesting: Tomatoes are best harvested when they reach their full color. They may also be picked when they show only a tinge of red. To continue the ripening process, store them in a warm, dark place.

TOMATOES—Large

VARIETY	DAYS	FRUIT	REMARKS	SOURCES
Abraham Lincoln	70	1¼-3 lbs., dark-red, solid, meaty, sweet	Very few seeds . . . sturdy, bronze-green foliage . . . continues to bear until frost	62
Beefeater (hybrid)	85	Up to 2 lbs. solid meat	Should be staked or grown on trellis . . . almost seedless . . . main crop	28 66
Beefmaster VFN (hybrid)	80	2 lbs., oblate-shaped, deep-red	Late . . . delicious meaty interior . . . beefsteak type, but tolerant of cracking and splitting . . . indeterminate	5 12 22 25 30 31 34 41 52 53 55 56 57 60 67 72 73
Beefsteak (Crimson Cushion)	80-96	Large, oblate, firm, meaty	Late . . . home garden standard . . . indeterminate	3 5 9 10 12 14 25 32 36 39 43 44 45 47 48 51 52 53 57 58 62 70 72
Better Boy VFN (hybrid)	70	1 lb. range	Disease-tolerant . . . produces all season . . . high yields . . . large leaves . . . indeterminate	5 10 11 12 17 19 25 28 31 32 41 48 51 52 53 54 56 57 66 67 70 73
Big Boy Hybrid	78-80	1½ lbs., 4 x 2¾", semiglobe, bright-red	Vines are tall and spreading . . . fairly dense foliage that gives good fruit production . . . indeterminate	3 9 14 19 23 28 68
Big Seven (hybrid)	77	Extra-large, globe, solid	Strong, vigorous, indeterminate vines	70
Bragger VF (hybrid)	75	2 lbs. or more, meaty, deep-red	Determinate . . . excellent flavor . . . resistant to cracking and splitting	25 48 53 57
Burgess Colossal Tomatoes (Choice of Crimson, Golden, Red and Yellow)	90	Up to 2½ lbs., 6" across, deep, flat, thick, meaty	Large, spreading plants, well branched, with heavy foliage . . . indeterminate	9
Burgess Stuffing	78	Lobe-shaped, firm, thick walls, 3¼ x 2¾"	Unique . . . small core, easily removed for stuffing . . . high yields	5 9 31
Burpee Big Boy Hybrid	78	2 lbs., firm, smooth, thick-walled	Vigorous grower . . . long-time favorite . . . mid-season . . . indeterminate heavy foliage	5 10 17 20 21 25 30 31 32 47 48 49 51 52 53 55 57 60 66 67 70
Burpee Big Early (hybrid)	62	Up to 1 lb., bright-scarlet, thick-walled	Mid-early . . . vine vigorous with heavy foliage . . . indeterminate . . . bears heavily all season	5 10 20 25 47 48 54 66 70

TOMATOES—Large (Continued)

VARIETY	DAYS	FRUIT	REMARKS	SOURCES
Burpee's Big Girl VF (hybrid)	78	1 lb. plus, bright-red	Crack-free . . . excellent flavor	10 67
Burpee Delicious	77	1-3 lbs., smooth	Delicious . . . indeterminate . . . mid-season . . . very little cracking	5 10 25 27 48
Climbing Tomato		5 x 3", solid, crimson-red	Vines grow rapidly to 10 or 18 feet . . . unexcelled for slicing and canning	20 21 28 43
Delicious	77	Up to 2 lbs., smooth, solid	Excellent flavor and quality . . . little cracking . . . small seed cavities	49
Early Giant (hybrid)	65	Smooth, thick-meated, large, bright-red	Bears early and continues until October	19 25 48 53 55 56 70
Giant Belgium		2-4 lbs., dark-pink, solid	Mid-season, nonacid . . . makes fine, sweet dessert wine	26
Giant King (hybrid)		Scarlet, firm, meaty, few seeds	Mid-season . . . plants grow vigorously even in adverse seasons	21
Giant Tree	88-90	1½ lbs., oblate, firm, crimson	Standard Italian potato, leaved variety . . . low in acid . . . 10-12-ft. vines . . . indeterminate	5 25 30 48 53 56 57
Jumbo Hybrid	80	Up to 2 lbs., 4½ x 3¼", extra-dark-red	Vines are medium-tall with good foliage cover	9
Jung's Giant Climbing	85	Very large, smooth, solid, deep-red	Vines grow 6-8 feet tall and bear tremendously	38
Oh Boy Hybrid	82	Large	Indeterminate plant with good cover . . . crack-resistant fruit, sweet-flavored . . . heavy yields	48
Park's Whopper VFN (hybrid)	75	4" across, large, round, red	Heavy yields over a long season	53
Ponderosa Red	88-90	Up to 2 lbs., deep-red	Similar to Pink Ponderosa	25 56 57
Red Heart (hybrid)	72	1 lb., rich-red, solid, few seeds	Vigorous, healthy vines produce big crop	19
Red Whoppa		3½ lbs., red	Good disease resistance	68
Super Colossal Red Hybrid	85	Up to 2½ lbs., deep-red, thick	Developed from Colossal variety . . . larger, more productive, and uniform in size	9 31 43
Trip-L-Crop		6" across, meaty, crimson	Grown on a trellis, it quickly reaches a height of 12-18, sometimes 25 feet . . . unequaled for canning or slicing . . . indeterminate	9 23 31 32 53 55 70
Ultra Boy VFN (hybrid)	72	Smooth, deep-globe, over 1 lb.	Strong, indeterminate plants can be staked or field-grown	66
Wonder Boy VFN (hybrid)	68-80	1 lb. plus	Mid-season . . . strong vine . . . excellent flavor and quality . . . indeterminate . . . there are two Wonder Boys, one with and one without verticillium and Fusarium resistance	5 11 12 14 22 25 28 30 34 47 48 52 55 56 57 62 66 67 70

TOMATOES—Early

VARIETY	DAYS	FRUIT	REMARKS	SOURCES
Ace (op)	75-80	Large, smooth, scarlet	Early-maturing . . . bears well . . . sets heavily in cool weather	16 40 48 55 57
Asgrow Scarlet Dawn	70	Average-size, globe-shaped, scarlet	Early . . . determinate . . . canning variety, also used fresh or for market	72
Ball Extra Early	55	Medium, smooth, globe-shaped	Record yields . . . indeterminate plant habit	5
Bonny Best Hybrid	60-70	Medium-size	An outstanding long-time favorite . . . indeterminate . . . replaces John Baer	5 14 21 25 30 37 48 50 51 52 66
Bounty WR	65	Globe-shaped, red	Heavy producer	25
Burgess Hybrid No. 1	55	7 ozs., 3 x 2¼", deep-red	Extra-early . . . very compact vines will be literally covered with fruits . . . plants should be set early and 2 feet apart	9 52
Burgess Hybrid No. 2	65	9½ ozs., 3½ x 2½", bright-red	Ripens with larger fruit than Hybrid No. 1 . . . vines are compact and give good foliage protection . . . plant 2½ feet apart	9 52

TOMATOES—Early (Continued)

VARIETY	DAYS	FRUIT	REMARKS	SOURCES
Burpee Globemaster (hybrid)	65	7 ozs., thick, meaty, scarlet	Delicious flavor, hard to beat . . . free of cracks . . . sturdy vines protect fruit . . . bears early and continues until frost . . . indeterminate habit	10
Bush Beefsteak	62	8 ozs., rich-red, solid	Firm slicer, few seeds . . . vigorous plants produce well under adverse conditions . . . compact, bushy plants	66
California Pole Early	70-80	Large, smooth, deep-red, solid, meaty, globular	Plant is tall-growing and open . . . suited to the California coast . . . indeterminate	16
Cannabec	60	Above-average, round, firm	Determinate . . . developed for the Quebec climate	72
Coldset	65	4 ozs., red	Bred for the North . . . will set in cool soil	28 37 66
Crimson Sprinter	71	5 ozs.	Indeterminate . . . can be staked or pruned . . . high-quality canning tomato	37
Earliana (hybrid)	58-66	5-6 ozs., deep, oblate shape, scarlet	Old-time favorite . . . fair foliage cover . . . indeterminate	3 5 10 21 25 28 30 37 51 52 55 57 58 62 73
Earlibelle	68	Thick, meaty, scarlet	Early . . . heavy producer . . . ample foliage to protect from sunburn	28
Earlirouge	63	Medium-size	Determinate	72
Early Bird	57	5½ ozs., red, globe-shaped	Compact, determinate plants	66
Early Boy (hybrid)	65	Globular, oblate, smooth, large, deep-scarlet, firm	Highly prolific . . . dark-green foliage . . . adapted to Southwest and northern short growing areas . . . large, determinate plants	16 39 57 73
Early Girl (hybrid)	54-62	4-5 ozs., firm, meaty, smooth	Bears early and late . . . high yields . . . resistant to cracking . . . sturdy vine with good foliage protection . . . indeterminate	3 5 10 67
Early Red	62	Intense-red	18" upright plant . . . yields well in poor soil . . . defies drought . . . resists cracking, sunburn, fruit spots	26
Early Red Chief	70	Large, globe-shaped, bright-red, firm, smooth	Midwest . . . suitable for canning	48 66
Early Stokesdale No. 4	64	Scarlet	Indeterminate . . . ripens from the inside first	66
Early Summer VF (hybrid)	55	Medium-large, deep-ovate shape	Scar- and crack-free fruit . . . determinate, bushy plants	3 5
Early Wonder	60-65	8-14 ozs., 3 ¾ x 3", smooth, deep-scarlet	Tremendous yields . . . medium-small plants . . . plant 2½ feet apart	9
Fantastic (hybrid)	65	8 ozs., red, smooth, deep-globe shape	Medium-early . . . excellent results when used for greenhouse forcing in North . . . indeterminate	5 11 12 25 30 47 48 51 53 55 56 57 60 66 67 70 72
Faribo Hybrid "E"	60	Medium-size, smooth	Large, vigorous vines bear profusely . . . fruits free of cracks . . . resistant to blight	21
Faribo Hybrid "EE"	55	Larger than Hybrid E		21
Fireball	60-64	4-5 ozs., firm, deep-oblate shape	Compact dwarf plant with sparse foliage . . . short, concentrated harvest season . . . east . . . extra-early, determinate plant	3 5 12 21 25 29 30 32 45 48 60 66
Gardener VF	63	6 ozs., firm, bright-red	Staking variety . . . disease-tolerant . . . fairly crack-free	66
Germania Early Hybrid	68	Bell-shaped, bright-red, ½ to ¾ lb.	Highly resistant to disease	25
Highlander VF	68	4-5 ozs., smooth, nearly globular, bright-scarlet	Early high yielder with excellent flavor . . . recommended for canning, market, and home gardens . . . determinate . . . small- to medium-size plant	11
Hybrid Tomato No. 68E		Large, smooth, globe-shaped, deep-red	Extremely early . . . originated in Japan . . . heavily productive . . . indeterminate	14
Hy-Top	64	Extra-large, globe-shaped, scarlet	Vines have good foliage . . . strong, vigorous growers . . . excellent yields	28
Imperial (hybrid)	65	Semiglobe, medium-large, firm, scarlet	Early . . . semidwarf plant . . . dense foliage . . . Fusarium-wilt-resistant . . . determinate	16
Jetfire VF	60	Larger, firmer than Springset	Determinate	66

TOMATOES—Early (Continued)

VARIETY	DAYS	FRUIT	REMARKS	SOURCES
John Baer	72	Medium-size, globe-shaped, scarlet	Extra-early . . . good producer	3 14 25 48 66
Jung's Improved Wayahead	63	Good size, almost round, bright-scarlet	Vines bear for a long time	38
Manitoba	60	6½ ozs.	Good yields . . . suitable for early basket trade or canning, where seasons are short	66
Marbon	68	Medium-size, globular, red	Adapted to wide range of growing conditions . . . recommended for canning, shipping, and home gardens	11
Marmande VF	65	Medium-size, oblate, slightly ribbed	From France . . . medium-size plants . . . indeterminate	15
Merit VF		Globe-shaped	Medium-early . . . vine is small, determinate . . . fruits detach from vine free of stems . . . suited for whole-pack processing without coring . . . grown in South	17
Mocross Surprise	65-70	Medium to large, flattened shape	Ripens uniformly . . . good resistance to cracking . . . tolerant to Fusarium wilt . . . indeterminate	5
Moira	76	5-6 ozs., smooth, round	Compact, determinate plants . . . dependable grower in adverse weather . . . northern adaptation	37 66
Moreton Hybrid	70	Large, slightly flattened, solid, brilliant-red	Early . . . big yields over a long season . . . good-quality fruit	29
New Yorker	60	3-5 ozs., bright-scarlet	Sets fruits under cool conditions . . . recommended for northern or short-season areas . . . heavy crops . . . determinate	10 17 20 25 29 32 51 54 60 66 70 72
Northern Delight (op)	63	5½ ozs., round, smooth	North . . . extra-early . . . determinate, vigorous plants	70
Ottawa 78	65	4-5 ozs., smooth	Tolerant to verticillium . . . compact plants with good foliage cover	66
Outdoor Girl		Medium-size	Very early . . . 4-foot plant	68
Park's Extra Early	65	Smooth, thick, dark-red	High yields . . . fine for forcing under glass . . . mild flavor	53
Paul Bunyan	59	10-14 ozs., solid, meaty, scarlet	North . . . premium-quality tomatoes . . . resistant to sun-scald	21
Peron	68		Known as a Sprayless Tomato . . . worldwide adapted . . . stake- or ground-supported . . . 2½ times more vitamin content than others . . . Disease- and crack-resistant	26
Plainsman	65	5 ozs., globe-shaped, vivid-red	Extra-early . . . heavy yields . . . excellent quality . . . does well in dry climates like the High Plains of Texas . . . small, indeterminate plants	11 55
Pritchard	72	Large, smooth, globe-shaped, bright-red	Largest early variety continues to bear over a long season . . . fine home garden variety . . . indeterminate	12 21 25 30 31 62
Quebec No. 13	63	5-6 ozs., deep-red	Recommended for canning or fresh market	66 72
Queen's FWR	60	Smooth, firm, 5-7", deep-scarlet	Vines are open in growth and early	62
Red Ensign (hybrid)		Red, firm	Comes into full production very early	68
Red Knight (hybrid)	60	Medium-size, firm, scarlet	Disease-resistant . . . crack-resistant . . . tremendous yields . . . mild flavor	22
Rideau	64	4-6 ozs., dark-red	Popular variety in Montreal area . . . good canner	66 72
Scotia	60	4 ozs., red	Determinate plant . . . sets in cool weather . . . standard variety for the Maritime provinces of Canada	66 72
Selandia	64	3-4 ozs., solid, red	Does not crack . . . produces heavy crop . . . staking variety	66

TOMATOES—Early (Continued)

VARIETY	DAYS	FRUIT	REMARKS	SOURCES
Sheyenne		Smooth, globe-shaped, scarlet	Early . . . determinate, bush type . . . disease-resistant . . . stands hot, dry weather	28 51
Sioux	70	Globe-shaped, smooth, solid, deep-red	Free of cracks . . . extremely small seed cells . . . high eating quality, devoid of acidity . . . strong plant, medium foliage . . . indeterminate	14 28 48 73
Spring Giant VFN (hybrid)	65-70	8-10 ozs., smooth, deep-globular, bright-red	High yields in a concentrated harvest season . . . AA selection . . . widely recommended . . . determinate	5 10 16 19 21 25 31 38 50 52 53 56 57 58 60 66 68 70 72 73
Springset VF (hybrid)	65	5-6 ozs., firm	Vigorous, open vine . . . high yields in concentrated harvest . . . good crack resistance . . . determinate	3 5 12 17 23 25 29 32 34 48 51 60 66 70 72
Starfire	56	½ lb. range, round, meaty, deep-red	Determinate . . . ripens with Earliana . . . not inclined to sun-scald	20 21 66 72
Stokes Early Hybrid	54	4 ozs., rich-red	Excellent for early staking	66
Summer Sunrise	60	6 ozs.	Indeterminate . . . vines may be staked or field-grown	66
Sunset	65	5-7 ozs.,	Exceptionally early . . . very high quality . . . high yields . . . crack-free and resistant to sun-scald	21
Sunup VF (hybrid)	57	Bright-red, smooth	Extra-early . . . borne in great clusters on small vines . . . enough foliage to give good protection	19 48
Superearly Wonder	64	Thick-walled, long, cylindrical, scarlet	High yields . . . small seed cavities, few seeds	31
Super Sioux	70	Medium-size, globe to deep oblate	Does well in hot, dry areas of Midwest . . . indeterminate	5 11 12 19 25 28 51 55 57
Super 88 (hybrid)		½-¾ lb. range, deep-globe, firm, smooth, meaty, bright-scarlet	Highly resistant to diseases . . . extremely early . . . highly productive . . . indeterminate	14
Surprise Hybrid VF	65	Large, solid, slightly flattened, globe-shaped	Early, prolific fruit set . . . crack-resistant . . . indeterminate	14 18 19 22 32 48
Tanana		3½-4 ozs.	Very early . . . will not sun-scald . . . plants are cold-resistant and hold foliage well . . . determinate	21
Terrific VFN (hybrid)	70	8-10 ozs., smooth, firm, meaty, oblate to globe in shape	Medium-early . . . strong vines . . . good foliage cover . . . produces vigorously over a long season . . . indeterminate	5 25 31 32 48 53 55 57
Thessaloniki Tomato	68	Solid, smooth, red	Developed in Greece . . . high disease-resistance . . . mild flavor	26
Tomato Easy Peel (hybrid)	65	Round, medium-size, red	Skin slips off without scalding . . . produces a large crop . . . just right for canning	53
Tomato 100%	76	Solid, deep-red	Wilt-resistant . . . suitable for outside planting or greenhouse forcing . . . vigorous vines without excessive foliage . . . bears heavy clusters . . . indeterminate	14
Trimsom	78	Firm, meaty, scarlet	Fruits slightly larger than Moira . . . plants are large . . . vigorous branching	37
Ultra Girl VFN	56	7-9 ozs.	Good tolerance to cracking . . . semideterminate	66
Valiant	65-70	7-8 ozs., firm, smooth, meaty, medium-globe	East . . . open vines with fair cover . . . indeterminate	3 5 10 12 14 25 45 47 48 50 55 66 67
Veebrite VF	69	5-7 ozs., deep-globe, round, firm, deep-red	Early . . . interiors are blood-red and without white cores . . . excellent for canning, whole pack or strained	66
Veeset	65	5 ozs., deep-red, firm	Crack-resistant . . . cold-setting ability	66
Victor	65	Scarlet		25
Vigor Boy VFN (hybrid)		6 ozs. plus, smooth, red	Produces bigger crops . . . fruit ripens evenly	28
Vision	66	5 ozs.	Shows tolerance to verticillium wilt . . . recommended for canning, processing, or fresh market	66

TOMATOES—Early (Continued)

VARIETY	DAYS	FRUIT	REMARKS	SOURCES
Vogue	58	Rich-red	Plants are vigorous and thick-stemmed . . . staking type	66
Young Tomato		Firm, medium to large size, dark-red	Semideterminate vines are wilt-resistant . . . prolific . . . moderately early ripening	55

TOMATOES—Mid-season

VARIETY	DAYS	FRUIT	REMARKS	SOURCES
Ace 55 VF	76-80	Medium-large, smooth, extra-thick walls, bright-red	Meaty and delicious . . . widely adapted . . . fairly compact, semideterminate plant . . . bears heavily all season	10 20 47 48 51 73
Atkinson FN	70-75	Large, deep-oblate, firm, meaty	Disease-resistant . . . vigorous-growing vine, but thick and stocky	20 31 56
Avalanche (hybrid)	77	Medium-size, uniform fruit	Well-adapted to Midwest . . . top-quality fruit . . . indeterminate . . . resistant to Fusarium wilt and cracks	5 14 19 25 32 48 73
Bigset VFN (hybrid)	75	8-9 ozs., smooth, firm, meaty, oblate-shaped	Sets well under low and high temperatures . . . compact, vigorous vines . . . resistant to cracking . . . determinate	5 10 25 28 48 55 56 70 72 73
Bonanza	75	8-10 ozs., round, meaty, bright-red	Heavy yields . . . determinate bush . . . ample foliage cover . . . main crop	28
Bonus VFN	75	Medium-large, deep-oblate, 8 ozs.	Strong vine . . . highly resistant . . . determinate	5 14 25 31 53 55 70
Break O' Day WR	73	Globe-shaped, medium to large	Cold-resistant . . . fine producer	25 55 56 62
Burpee Hybrid VF	72	8 ozs., meaty, rich red	Strong vine with heavy foliage cover . . . resistant to cracking and catfacing . . . indeterminate . . . there is also a Burpee Hybrid VFN	5 10 17 25 47 48 66
Burpee's Big Girl VF (hybrid)	78	Up to 1 lb., scarlet	Remarkably crack-free . . . perfect to slice or wedge . . . bears bumper crop until frost . . . indeterminate	10 67
Cal Ace VF	75-80	Smooth, deep	General . . . good setting abilities under adverse weather conditions . . . superior to other Ace varieties in quality and yields . . . strong determinate	5 11 47 48 51 70
Campbell 1327 VF	75	8-10 ozs., oblate, deep	This includes Campbell No. 17, 19, 28, and 146 . . . crack-resistant canning tomatoes . . . grown in East and Midwest . . . vines are determinate and provide good cover . . . all varieties are basically alike	5 11 17 20 25 28 32 47 48 53 54 66 70 72 73
Chalk'se Alby Jewel	78	Round, smooth, bright-scarlet		14
Clinton Hybrid	75	8 ozs., globe-shaped, smooth, scarlet	Heavy production . . . free of cracks . . . little acidity . . . indeterminate	14
Crack-Proof	78-80	Up to 9 ozs., 3½ x 3½"	Will not crack under average growing conditions, seldom under adverse conditions . . . vines are medium-tall and give good protection	9 52
Creole	72	Firm, medium to large	Resistant to Fusarium wilt and blossom end rot . . . high-yielding, high-quality southern plant	56
El Monte	80	Semiglobe, red	Vine is large and determinate, with dark-green, soft-wilted-appearing foliage . . . developed primarily for the Lower Rio Grande Valley	16
Everbearing	74	10 ozs., light-crimson	Continues to bear until frost . . . plant 4 feet apart, or closer if trellised . . . indeterminate	9
Faribo Hybrid M		8 ozs., smooth, deep-red	Mid-season . . . fruit has few seeds	21
Firesteel	67-70	12-15 ozs., globe-shaped, smooth, meaty, dark-crimson	Free from acidity . . . fine for juice, and unbeatable as a slicer . . . medium vines, vigorous, fairly open with medium foliage . . . will set heavy crop no matter how hot and dry . . . indeterminate	14 21

TOMATOES—Mid-season (Continued)

VARIETY	DAYS	FRUIT	REMARKS	SOURCES
Fla. MH 1	70	Medium-size, deep-globe	South . . . disease-resistant . . . determinate	41 50
Floradel	85	Large, slightly flattened globe, smooth, thick walls, medium-red	South . . . large, vigorous indeterminate vine . . . resistant to several diseases . . . good resistance to growth cracks and blossom end rot	16 25 32 40 41 51 55 56 70 73
Floralu	75	Smooth, uniform, red	South . . . disease-resistant . . . plants are large and should be staked or trellised to provide sufficient cover	40 56
Floramerica Hybrid	75-80	8-16 ozs., slightly flattened globe, deep-red	Tolerant to 16 tomato diseases or defects . . . can be grown as bush crop or trained 4-5 feet . . . vigorous, determinate vines	11 41 56 57 72
Garden State	70	Globe-shaped, bright-scarlet	Main crop . . . large vigorous vines are productive . . . free of wrinkles and cracks . . . excellent home garden variety	62
Glamour	74-77	Medium, deep-oblate	Vigorous plant developed for the Midwest and Northeast . . . solid, crack-resistant fruit . . . Indeterminate	5 12 14 17 20 25 29 32 45 48 52 60 66 70
Greater Baltimore Tomato	81	Large, meaty, red	Heavy yielder . . . outstanding flavor . . . main crop . . . good canner . . . blight-resistant	14
Harris Jet Star VF (hybrid)	72	10.4 ozs., globe-shaped, somewhat flattened	North . . . quite free of cracks . . . fairly compact, indeterminate vines with good foliage cover	17 20 29 54
Heinz 1350 VF	75	6 ozs., fairly deep to slightly flattened, bright-red, meaty, solid	Heinz 1359, 1370, 1409, 1419, 1439, are similar . . . excellent size and color . . . all high yielders, fruits free of cracks . . . strong, compact, determinate vines . . . good canners	5 10 11 14 16 17 20 23 29 32 34 48 52 54 60 66 67 70 73
He-Man (hybrid)	75	Large, smooth, deep-red	Few seeds . . . little or no cracking . . . vigorous vines can be staked, pruned, or left down	19 25 48 53 57
Homestead FWR		Medium-size, solid, firm, bright-red	Semideterminate vine . . . good producer of quality fruit	55 57
Homestead 24	76-83	Medium-large, firm, smooth, deep-globe	Fruits set under a wide range of conditions . . . small plants, but good cover . . . determinate	5 11 12 16 31 32 40 41 44 51 53 56 67 70 73
Homestead 61	80	Uniform size and shape, firm, smooth, scarlet	Vines are semideterminate, compact, large-leafed . . . well adapted to southeast	16
Homestead 500 F	77	Round to slightly flat, medium to large	Determinate . . . good foliage cover . . . generally larger than most Homestead types	48 51 70 73
Hybrid Ace VFN	75-80	Very large, rich-red, smooth, firm	Well adapted where Standard Ace varieties are grown . . . determinate bush	5
Hybrid No. 23	75		Determinate . . . resistant to cracking in fruit . . . late mid-season . . . resistant to 15 diseases	72
Hy X	67	Medium-size, bright-red	Determinate, short, bushy vine . . . resistant to disease . . . does well in semiarid regions . . . high-quality	22
Indian River	75-85	Medium-size, globe-shaped, firm, thick walls, scarlet	South . . . disease-resistant . . . plants are vigorous, indeterminate . . . high yields under warm, humid conditions	16 41 51
La Pinta	75-80	Large, semiglobe, red	Adapted to Lower Rio Grande Valley of Texas . . . high yields . . . small, determinate plant . . . outyields Homestead in that area . . . can be picked pink or vine-ripened	16
Longred	76	Smooth, solid, thick walls, deep globe, red	Used extensively as a main crop canning variety	66
Marglobe	75	6 ozs., smooth, firm, thick-walled	Long-time favorite . . . vigorous, uniform vine growth, with good heavy cover . . . determinate	3 9 10 11 12 14 21 25 28 30 31 32 36 37 40 44 45 47 48 49 51 52 53 55 56 57 62 67 70 73

TOMATOES—Mid-season (Continued)

VARIETY	DAYS	FRUIT	REMARKS	SOURCES
Marglobe Improved VF	75	Oblate, firm, smooth	An improvement over other Marglobes . . . shorter, determinate plant . . . good cover . . . crack-resistant	5 58
Marion FWR	78	Large, smooth, deep-red	A Rutgers type, but larger . . . high yields	31 32 51 53 56 70
Mid-Summer VFN (hybrid)	65	Large, deep-globe, meaty	Recommend staking and training to two stems without pruning too severely	5
Mocross Supreme	70-75	Medium to large, slightly flattened globe	Produces heavily throughout the season . . . tolerant of Fusarium wilt . . . indeterminate	5 25
Monte Carlo VFN (hybrid)	75	9 ozs., large, smooth, deep-globe	Grows well on poles or trellis . . . suited for market or home garden . . . indeterminate	11 21 25 48 55 57 60 72
Morning Star VF (hybrid)	72	8 ozs., deep-oblate, thick walls	Excellent quality . . . can be grown as ground or staked variety	48
Nepal	80	Large, deep-red	Mid-season variety . . . from Himalaya Mountains . . . intense flavor . . . high yields . . . disease-resistant	21
No. 670 WR		Solid, scarlet	Mid-season . . . rugged, indeterminate growth withstands extremes in weather conditions . . . resists cracks and sunburn	26
Pelican FN	70	Large, smooth, red	South . . . fine for home gardens . . . some of the fruit may be misshapen and catfaced	56
Perfecta (hybrid)	75	Large, smooth	Big yields . . . disease-resistant	22
Perfection Hybrid	75	11 ozs., 3½ x 2 ¾", extra-meaty	Relatively free from cracking . . . vines are tall, with heavy foliage that gives good protection . . . plant 4 feet apart	9
Pinkdeal	77	6 ozs., ripens to bright-red, globe-shaped	Especially developed for picking at pink stage . . . highly crack-resistant . . . sets fruit in hot weather . . . adapted to East Texas . . . indeterminate	11 55
Porter Tomato		Smooth, medium-size, firm, solid, red	Produces on any kind of soil . . . is not affected by hot, dry weather . . . does not crack or sunburn	55
Porter's Pride (Improved Porter)		Smooth, meaty, scarlet	Ideal for home gardens . . . an improved Porter . . . vigorous, very productive . . . indeterminate	55 73
Red Champion (hybrid)	70	Medium-size, red	Disease-resistant . . . hardy . . . very heavy bearer	22
Red Glow VFN	72	Perfect globe, red	Recommended east of the Rocky Mountains . . . strong, vigorous, determinate plant	70
Red King	73	6 ozs.	Disease-resistant . . . free from cracks . . . tops for home garden or market	70
Red Pak VF	71	Large, round, bright-red	Dwarf vines . . . ripens fairly early . . . can be kept longer after picking than most	29
Red Mountain Hybrid	75	8 ozs., solid, red	Subacid . . . top quality	57
Rushmore VF (hybrid)	66	Medium-size, slightly flattened	Highly productive . . . determinate	5 28 48 66
Russian Red	74	Medium-size, round	Determinate, semitall, upright bush . . . thick, heavy leaves and foliage . . . tolerant to lower temperatures than other tomatoes	26
Scarlet Climber (hybrid)	75-80	Large, smooth, firm, scarlet	Pole type . . . has large, vigorous, spreading, productive vine with good fruit coverage . . . medium-early . . . indeterminate	16
Stokesdale	72	Large-size, rich-red	Heavy yields . . . vines are vigorous and productive	66 73
Sunlight		Large, red, firm	Medium to early maturity . . . disease-resistant . . . good foliage cover	73
Sunripe VFN (hybrid)	75	8-10 ozs., firm, bright-red	Widely adapted . . . disease-tolerant . . . performs well in cages, unpruned, staked, or on the ground . . . compact, determinate plants . . . tolerant to cracking	5

TOMATOES—Mid-season (Continued)

VARIETY	DAYS	FRUIT	REMARKS	SOURCES
Super Fantastic VF (Hybrid)	70	Deep, oblate to round, solid, meaty, smooth	Produces heavy yields until frost . . . good eating all summer long . . . strong, indeterminate plants	5
Supermarket		Medium-size, globe-shape, smooth, firm	Heavy yields . . . widely adapted . . . medium-small plants . . . resistant to Fusarium and gray leaf spot	17
Supersonic VF	79	Large, smooth, flattened globe, firm, meaty	East, Midwest . . . big, leafy vines . . . indeterminate	17 20 29
Superstar (hybrid)		Round, up to 1 lb., glossy-red	Main crop . . . disease-resistant . . . good slicing variety	34
Tamiami VF	75	Similar to Walter, but larger	Disease-resistant . . . determinate bush or short-stake type	41
Tropic VF	75-80	Large, smooth, thick walls, deep-red	South . . . compact, determinate vines . . . less cracking	10 16 25 32 41 51 55 57 66 70
Urbana	78	Solid, scarlet	High yields . . . compact growth	25 32 38 55
Vineripe VFN (hybrid)	80	9 ozs., medium-firm, smooth, deep-oblate shape	Mid-season . . . vigorous, indeterminate vines provide excellent fruit cover	5 32 48 53 55 62
Walter	75	7 ozs., smooth, firm	South . . . Fusarium-tolerant . . . determinate vines	5 20 25 32 40 41 48 51 55 57 70 73
West Virginia	70	8 ozs., solid, meaty, globe-shaped, bright-red	Highly productive, vigorous vines provide good fruit cover . . . crack- and wilt-resistant	9
Wisconsin Chief (Wisconsin 55)	72	Medium-large, oblate shape	Semideterminate vine	25 38 52

TOMATOES—Late

VARIETY	DAYS	FRUIT	REMARKS	SOURCES
California Pole Late	80-85	6½-7 ozs., regular globe, smooth, deep-red	Used as fall variety in California . . . very productive . . . useful for market, canning, and juice . . . indeterminate	16
County Fair No. 23		Medium-large, round	Tolerant to Fusarium . . . good foliage cover . . . indeterminate vine	51
Double Rich	80	Globe-shaped, medium-size, solid, meaty, bright-red	High in vitamin C . . . vigorous plant . . . good for canning, juicing	49
Earlypak No. 7	75-81	2¾ x 2½", globular, smooth, bright-scarlet	A good canner . . . heavy yields . . . Determinate . . . abundant foliage provides ample protection	11 16 48 51
Henry Field Tomato (hybrid)	100	½-¾ lb., meaty, thick, scarlet	Compact, bushy, strong-growing plants . . . highly disease-resistant	22
Immokalee	80-85	Medium to large, slightly flattened globe, firm, thick walls	South . . . disease-resistant . . . plants are large-leaved, compact, medium-determinate, and vigorous . . . adapted to warm, humid climates	16
J. Moran	95	Large	Outstanding variety for green shipping or canning . . . closely resembles Pearson Improved	11
Late-Summer VFN (hybrid)	75	Extra-large, deep-globe, meaty	Produces till frost . . . excellent flavor . . . large-leaved plants . . . recommend staking and pruning to one or two stems	5
Manalucie	82-87	Medium-large, deep-globe	South . . . tolerant of blossom-end rot, leaf mold, early blight, and Fusarium wilt . . . indeterminate	5 10 16 25 31 32 40 41 51 53 70 73
Manapal	80-85	Medium-large, globe-shaped, firm, thick walls	Adapted to hot, humid climates . . . disease-resistant . . . vine is determinate, suited for pole training . . . vigorous . . . good foliage cover, may require pruning	16 25 32 40 48 51 70 73
Market King VFN	80	Globe to somewhat flattened	Strong, indeterminate vines	70
Pearson A-1 Improved	93	Deep-globe, large	High-quality . . . resistant to Fusarium wilt . . . vigorous vines give good cover . . . indeterminate	11 48 41 47 48 73

TOMATOES—Late (Continued)

VARIETY	DAYS	FRUIT	REMARKS	SOURCES
Pearson No. 9 VF (hybrid)	72	½ lb., scarlet	Beefsteak type . . . semideterminate type	66
Ramapo 9 VF (hybrid)	80-85	8-9 ozs., round, smooth, deep-crimson	Vigorous, strong-growing vine . . . excellent production throughout growing season . . . resistant to cracking and blossom end rot . . . indeterminate	5 10 17 25 29 32 47 48 73
Rockingham		6-8 ozs., rich-red	Late-blight-resistant . . . desirable for home garden or market	21
Rutgers VF (hybrid)	85-90	Large, 6 ozs., oblate, smooth	Produces uniform-size fruits . . . highly resistant to cracking . . . indeterminate . . . Regular Rutgers is not resistant to verticillium or Fusarium, is medium globe, and grows 82 days to maturity	3 5 9 10 12 14 17 19 20 21 25 29 30 31 32 36 39 40 44 45 47 48 49 51 52 53 54 55 56 57 58 62 67 70 73
September Dawn	85	Smooth, large, firm	Fall tomato . . . resistant to Fusarium and cracking . . . vines are fairly compact and very productive	17
Stakeless	80	5-8 ozs.	No need to stake . . . dense foliage prevents sun-scald, cracking, Fusarium wilt . . . thick and determinate . . . can also be grown in containers	5 11 66 70

TOMATOES—Pink

VARIETY	DAYS	FRUIT	REMARKS	SOURCES
Beauty	82	Medium-large, pink	Prolific . . . medium-large plants . . . vigorous	25
Bradley	75-80	Pink, smooth	Good vines and foliage cover . . . Fusarium-resistant	20 48
Brimmer	83	Purplish-pink, well-shaped, solid, meaty	Must be staked . . . has no core and very few seeds . . . a fine slicing tomato	31 67
Crackproof Pink	78	Large, firm, rounded	Shows tolerance to cracking	66
Dutchman		Large, oblate, purple-pink, solid	Mid-season . . . no acid	26
Dwarf Champion	73	Rose-pink, 5 ozs., mild, firm, meaty	Novel 24" potato leaf foliage . . . low acidity	66
Early Detroit	78	Large, globular, smooth, firm, purplish-pink	Early-maturing	66
Gulf State Market	80 —	Pink, globe, smooth	Recommended for the southern home garden . . . indeterminate vines	5 56
Holmes Mexican Tomato	75	3 lbs. plus, pink	Subacid . . . vigorous grower . . . very productive . . . mid-season	33
Hybrid Pink Gourmet	70	1 lb. plus, firm, meaty, dark-pink skin	Few seeds . . . deep-red flesh . . . resistant to blight and wilt . . . excellent for slicing, canning, and catsup . . . grows better staked or on trellis	19
Hybrid Pink No. 1	63	5-6 ozs., slightly flattened, globe-shaped	Excellent for early market	66 72
Hybrid Pink No. 5	70	Large, pink	Early . . . large crops	72
Hybrid Pink No. 6	65	7-8 ozs., pink	Mid-season . . . vigorous plants	66 72
Hybrid Pink No. 12	67	8-9 ozs., pink	Fruit sets in clusters . . . vigorous, high-yielding plants . . . excellent for staking	66 72
Hybrid Pink No. 13	66	Large, semiglobe-shaped	Early . . . vigorous	72
June Pink	66-69	Large, smooth, pinkish	Extra-early	14 31 55 72
Kurihara	85	8 ozs., large, pink	Japanese tomato . . . yields heavy crops	50
Laketa		Long, pointed, purple-pink, pear type	Red flesh, solid as a lemon . . . nonacid and sweet	26
Livingstone Globe	75	Pink, smooth, meaty, globe	Popular in Quebec . . . plants are indeterminate and may be staked	66
Mac Pink	62	Pink, firm	Determinate . . . excellent fruit	72
Marvelous Pink Globe	74	Large, almost globular, solid, meaty, bright-rosy-pink	Borne in clusters . . . vines are medium-heavy and very productive . . . high-quality . . . indeterminate	14
McMullen	74	Reddish-pink	Very early . . . potato leaf vine . . . good qualities	66

TOMATOES—Pink (Continued)

VARIETY	DAYS	FRUIT	REMARKS	SOURCES
Mission Dyke	70	Medium-pink, large, globe-shaped, smooth	Large, determinate vines . . . vigorous, healthy foliage . . . disease- and drought-resistant	26
New Truckers Favorite FWR (Spartan Pink 10)	75	Crimson-pink, large	Mid-season . . . excellent for home gardens, shipping, or as a greenhouse crop	38
Olympic	76	Pink	Early . . . pink staking variety . . . good cracking tolerance . . . tolerant to Fusarium wilt . . . popular in Montreal area	66
Pink Delight (hybrid)	70	4", round, firm, pink	Red flesh . . . few seeds . . . almost crack-free . . . vigorous vines can be trained and pruned . . . produces big crop	19 32 70
Pink Giant		Giant-size, thick, meaty 1 lb.	Subacid . . . few seeds	27
Pink Skinned Jumbo			Ponderosa type . . . high quality	53
Pink Supreme (hybrid)	75-80	Pink, large, globe-shaped, firm	Vines very vigorous and productive . . . produces well in greenhouses . . . resistant to Fusarium wilt . . . indeterminate	16
Ponderheart		Pink, semiglobe	From Japan . . . nonacid	26
Ponderosa (Beefsteak Pink)	83-95	Large, 2 lbs., oblate, purplish-pink, solid, rather rough	General . . . mild flavor . . . few seeds . . . indeterminate	5 10 12 14 19 21 25 28 29 30 31 32 36 45 48 50 51 53 55 57 62 66 67 70 73
Resistant FR	70	Deep-pinkish-red, semiglobe	Matures after Hybrid No. 12	72
Supreme Gulf State	77	Large, globular, bright-purplish-pink	Plants set well in lower clusters . . . noticeably less cracking around the stem end	14 48
Tomboy	66	1 lb., solid, pink	Red flesh, few seeds . . . no acid tang . . . excellent for slicing, canning, or catsup	19
Traveler	78	6 ozs., pink, deep-oblate	Crack-resistant . . . stake . . . Fusarium-tolerant . . . indeterminate	5 70
Vivid	60	Pink	Early . . . staking variety . . . closely resembles Earliest of All	66
Watermelon Beefsteak	75	Pink, up to 2 lbs., oblong	Purplish-red flesh . . . nonacid	26

TOMATOES—Orange-Yellow-Gold

VARIETY	DAYS	FRUIT	REMARKS	SOURCES
Burpee's Jubilee	72	3¼ x 2 ¾", golden-orange, deep-globular	AA winner . . . subacid . . . heavy yields . . . indeterminate	10 72
Caro Red	80	Carrot-colored	High in vitamin A . . . distinctive flavor	21 28 38 66 68
Dixie Golden Giant	84	2-2½ lbs., golden-yellow	Mild . . . low-acid . . . good slicer	31
Golden Boy (hybrid)	75-80	Large, globe-shaped, golden-yellow	Very mild and low in acid . . . excellent quality . . . indeterminate	5 12 25 28 30 48 53 57 62 70 72 73
Golden Delight	60-65	5 ozs., solid, meaty	Mild, sweet flavor . . . crack-resistant . . . low acidity	28 66
Golden Giant	90	1½ lbs., thick, meaty	Mild, yellow flesh . . . low acidity	28
Golden Queen	83	Large, yellow	Mild, nonacid . . . late-August yields	25 30 66
Golden Sunrise		Butter-yellow	For greenhouse or outdoors	68
Goldie		Huge, slightly flattened, golden, round	Nonacid . . . tremendous . . . vigorous vines	26
Hotset		8 ozs., orange-red, globe-shaped	Productive, . . . heat-resistant . . . good quality . . . large vines	55
Jubilee (Orange Jubilee) (Golden Jubilee	72-80	Globe to deep globe, orange to yellow	General . . . nonacid . . . indeterminate . . . Rutgers type	5 14 19 25 45 48 49 50 51 52 53 55 57 62 73
Mandarin	75	Orange, thick flesh, thick walls, extra-large, smooth	A proven big cropper . . . from Japan . . . does well staked . . . most acid-free	19
Mandarin Cross (hybrid)		9 ozs., orange-yellow, semiglobe, solid, smooth	Second early . . . stake or ground support . . . low acid	26
Moon Glow	72	Medium-size, globe, blunt-pointed, orange	No acid . . . keeps indefinitely	26
Morden	70	Yellow-orange	Outstanding early tomato . . . bred in Canada	21

TOMATOES—Orange-Yellow-Gold (Continued)

VARIETY	DAYS	FRUITS	REMARKS	SOURCES
Orange Queen	65	Bright-orange, 4-6 ozs., Yellow skin	Early . . . low acidity	66
Pink Grapefruit			Pink flesh . . . delicious, mild flavor	26
Platense	75	Orange-red, medium-size, flattened globe, firm	Red flesh . . . south . . . plants are determinate, large, sprawling . . . heavy yields	16
Ponderosa Yellow		Orange-yellow	Mild flavor, nonacid	25 62
Sunray	72-80	Orange-yellow, 3" across, globe-shaped	Has a third less provitamin A than most reds do . . . prolific standard plant	3 10 11 12 22 25 27 28 29 31 32 39 41 43 47 48 52 60 70
Super Gold (hybrid)			Equals Super Colossal Red in every way, except that the color is deep-orange-gold	9

TOMATOES—Container Varieties

VARIETY	DAYS	FRUIT	REMARKS	SOURCES
Burpee's Pixie (hybrid)	52	1¾"	Early . . . 14-18" plants . . . strong, upright, stocky . . . dark-green foliage . . . good variety for small gardens	3 5 10
Droplet	65	1-1½", solid, crack-free	Determinate, 3"-diameter vine, produces from 90-120 fruits . . . extremely sweet and flavorful . . . can be eaten like grapes	21
Early Salad Hybrid	45	1½-1¼", bright-red, firm	Compact 6-8" plants . . . continues to produce until frost . . . suitable for freezing	9 25 52 53
German Dwarf Bush	45	2", red	Ultraearly . . . small, rugged plants for indoor pot culture or outdoors . . . resists 28°F. temperatures	26
Patio VF (hybrid)	70	2" fruit, deep-oblate	Early . . . upright, determinate . . . grows 24-30" and should be staked . . . designed for tubs and small spaces	5 12 22 25 30 31 32 34 41 48 52 53 55 56 57 60 66 67 70 72 73
Pixie (hybrid)	50		15-24" vine . . . compact, suitable for containers or windowboxes	68
Pretty Patio	70	Medium-size, deep-red, smooth	Upright 30" plants bear abundantly in large pots or patio tubs . . . should be staked	19
Presto	60	Round, half-dollar size, bright-red	Early . . . for pots or garden . . . small leaves, open vine . . . bears over a long season	29
Red Cushion	65	Cherry type	Can be grown in container or garden . . . plants spread to about 18" and grow a foot tall	57
Salad Top	45-60	1-1½", bright-red	Grows only 18" high . . . fully branched, dark-green foliage . . . compact, strong determinate habit	5
Small Fry VFN (hybrid)	60-65	1" round, red, grow in clusters	Early . . . heavy cropper . . . superior large cherry type . . . AA winner . . . determinate	5 10 12 19 21 22 25 28 29 30 31 32 34 38 52 53 55 56 57 60 66 72
Stokesalaska	55	1¾ ozs.	18" very bushy plant . . . a northern garden variety for tubs or stakes	66
Tiny Tim	45-55	¾" scarlet	Early . . . 15" vine ideal for pot or hanging basket . . . determinate	3 5 10 12 19 21 22 25 30 31 38 39 41 45 49 50 52 53 57 62 66 72 73
Toy Boy VF (hybrid)	55-68	Ping-pong ball size	Early . . . only 2 feet high . . . fruit sets quickly . . . grows indoors or out with plenty of light . . . determinate	5 12 21 25 34 48 50 52 72
Tumblin' Tom (hybrid)	48-72	1½-2"	20-24" vines . . . practical and decorative . . . determinate	5 11 25 43 66

TOMATOES—Small

VARIETY	DAYS	FRUIT	REMARKS	SOURCES
Basket Pak	76	1½" across, rich-red	Plants bear heavily all season . . . delicious in salads . . . indeterminate	10 49

TOMATOES—Small (Continued)

VARIETY	DAYS	FRUIT	REMARKS	SOURCES
Fancy Mixed	75		Assortment of small-fruited varieties . . . red and yellow; pear, plum, and cherry . . . prolific yields	38
Faribo Springtime	59	2-2½", bright-red	Small, compact vines . . . large quantities	21
Gardener's Delight	50	Bite-size	Sweetest of all small-fruited varieties . . . fruit produced in great abundance . . . best if staked	5 10 25 68
Jung's Sugar Lump	65	1½-2", deep-red	Heavy yields . . . extra-early . . . bears from summer until frost in clusters of 6-12 a bunch . . . superb quality	38
Plum Delicious FWR		Deep-red	Dwarf plants . . . up to 80 fruits to a plant . . . crack-resistant	32
Red Cherry, Large		Half-dollar size	Sweet and mild . . . indeterminate	5 11 25 29 40 56 60
Red Cherry, Small	72	Nickel size, ⅞"	Mid-season . . . indeterminate . . . favorite in salads, for preserving or pickling . . . should be staked . . . disease-resistant	3 5 10 12 14 15 25 29 30 31 36 41 47 49 52 55 58 62 67 72 73
Red Pear	73	1", pear-shaped	Good preserving tomato . . . disease-resistant . . . clusters bear over a long season	28 29 30 31 47 48 50 53 62 67 72
Red Plum		Plum-shaped, bright-scarlet	Good preserving tomato	25 30 48 56 62 72 73
Rocket	50	2 ozs., 1¼" across, round, firm	Fruit grows larger in northern areas . . . can be grown in tubs, too	66
Starshot	55	2" round, smooth, firm, red	Bushy, verticillium-tolerant plants . . . needs no staking . . . low-acid taste	66
Saladette	70	2 ozs., round	12-14" tall, 16" spread . . . strong stems, upright growth . . . disease-resistant	70 73
Sleaford Abundance (hybrid)		Mouth-size, shiny-red	Early outdoor variety . . . 18" plant	68
Sub-Arctic	45	1¾" cherry type	Heavy yields . . . earliest tomato	28 68
Sub-Arctic Early	56	1 oz.	Spreading, determinate plant . . . ripens an entire crop extra-early . . . 3 times the size of cherry tomatoes	37
Sub-Arctic Maxi	64	2½-3 ozs., bright-red	Flavor is milder than other Sub-Arctics	37
Sub-Arctic Midi	59	Slightly larger than Sub-Arctic Early	Free from cracking	37
Sub-Arctic Plenty	62	2 ozs.	Slightly later than Midi . . . upright, determinate habit . . . space 12-18" apart	37 68
Sugar Lump		Bite-size	Healthy, deep-green vines	53 57 72
Sugar Red	70	1½", red	Sweet and juicy	28
Sugar Yellow	70	1½", yellow-cherry type	Mild and sweet yellow skin and flesh . . . ideal for salads and preserves	28
Super Cherry (hybrid)	58	Resembles cherry tomato	Disease-resistant . . . crack-resistant	32
Sweet 100 (hybrid)	65	Cherry-size, red	Grows in clusters . . . up to several hundred fruits per plant . . . extremely sweet, high in vitamin C . . . should be staked . . . will produce up until frost . . . indeterminate	5 25 29 48 53 57 66 68 70 72
Swift	54	2¾ ozs., 1¾", deep-globe, brick-red	Early . . . free from radical cracking . . . good quality . . . sets at low temperatures . . . a northern favorite	66
Tamu Saladette		2 ozs., plum-shaped, thick-walled, meaty, firm	All-season production variety . . . disease-resistant . . . 14-16" plant spread . . . does well under adverse weather conditions	55
Yellow		Same as Red Cherry		25
Yellow Peach		Light-yellow	Largely used in fancy salads and for preserving	62
Yellow Pear	70	Pear-shaped, 2 x 1", bright-yellow	Preserving tomato . . . mid-season . . . indeterminate . . . productive . . . mild	5 10 14 19 25 28 29 30 31 36 45 47 48 55 57 60 62 67 72

TOMATOES—Small (Continued)

VARIETY	DAYS	FRUIT	REMARKS	SOURCES
Yellow Plum	70	Plum-shaped, 2 x ½"	Mid-season . . . indeterminate . . . productive . . . favorite for canning whole	3 5 10 12 14 25 29 30 31 36 47 48 49 50 52 57 60 62 67 72

TOMATOES—Paste

VARIETY	DAYS	FRUIT	REMARKS	SOURCES
Bellarina	72-75	3½" long, pear-shaped	Low juice, high meat . . . ideal for catsups and purees, tomato paste, and sauces . . . crack-resistant	28
Chico	75	Pear-shaped, bulbous on blossom end	High in solids and acids . . . well received in the Southeast . . . plants are medium to small . . . determinate . . . heat-resistant . . . there is also Chico 111 and improved Chico	16 17 38 40 48 55 60 73
Dorchester		Oval, elongated, firm	Maturity is medium . . . small, determinate, and open . . . crack-resistant	17
Italian Canner	80	Oblong, smooth	Dry, mealy flesh . . . intense flavor	9 12
Napoli VF	76	2½ ozs., elongated, bright-red, very firm	Compact, determinate habit	37 51
Nova	70	2 ozs., elongated, orange-red	Growth is compact . . . susceptible to early blight	37 66
Red Top	80	Plum-shaped, 2-4 x 1¼-2", solid, thick walls	Paste type . . . fruits remain in good, firm condition over a long period . . . there is also an improved variety	14 16 66
Roma VF	72-76	Pear-shaped, 2½-3" long	Mid-season . . . widely recommended . . . strong-growing determinate, with heavy foliage cover . . . superior to most other paste types . . . there is also Regular Roma, which is not verticillium-resistant	3 5 9 10 11 15 16 17 19 20 25 29 31 32 36 40 41 44 47 48 51 52 53 54 66 70 72 73
Royal Chico VF	80	3½ ozs., bright-red	Compared to Roma, Royal Chico ripens earlier and has more controlled plant size and larger fruit	28 37 70
San Marzano	78-80	Larger, rectangular, straight-sided pear-shaped, smooth	Drier than others in the group . . . intense flavor . . . indeterminate vine	9 10 25 30 32 36 40 48 49 50 51 52 55 57 58 62 66
San Pablo		Roma type	Top yields	26
Santa Cruz 22 VF		3-4 ozs., elongated	Compact plant . . . large yields of high-quality fruit	15
Square Tomato		Solid, red, square	San Marzano class . . . jointless stems, no stems ever on picked fruit	26 43
Veepick VF	73	3¼ x 2", elongated, flat-sided, blunt-ended		66
Veeroma VF	72	Medium-red	An early Roma Type . . . crack-resistant	66

TOMATOES—Greenhouse, Forcing

VARIETY	DAYS	FRUIT	REMARKS	SOURCES
Floradel	82	Large, slightly flattened	South . . . overall superior to Manapal and Manalucie . . . multiple disease-tolerance . . . indeterminate	5
Michigan-Ohio (hybrid)		Large, globe, red, uniform	(Greenhouse grown) Indeterminate . . . vigorous, highly productive	5 11 28 29 32 57 66 70 72
Michigan-Ohio (hybrid)		Red, medium-large, globe	(Outdoor grown) High-quality . . . Fusarium-wilt-tolerant . . . more productive in North during the winter	5 66
Ohio-Indiana O (hybrid)	74	Large, pink	Greenhouse type . . . vigorous . . . resistant to leaf mold and Fusarium wilt	32 53 72
Ohio WR 7		7 ozs., deep-globe, pink	Excellent for fall and spring forcing	25 66
Ohio WR 13 TMV		Pink, large, smooth	Good crack-resistance	66
Ohio WR 25		5-6 ozs., pink, firm	Popular with growers in Leamington and Ohio areas	66

TOMATOES—Greenhouse, Forcing (Continued)

VARIETY	DAYS	FRUIT	REMARKS	SOURCES
Super M (hybrid)		7-10 ozs., deep-globe, red	Sturdy stock . . . medium foliage . . . produces long after others have stopped . . . tolerant of gray mold and leaf mold . . . indeterminate	5
Tropic VF	82	Deep-globe	South and Southwest . . . can be harvested while in the pink or turning stage . . . indeterminate	5
Truckcross 520 (hybrid)		6-8 ozs., slightly flattened, globe-shaped	Vigorous . . . tolerant of leaf mold . . . indeterminate vine type	5 32 53 55
Truckcross 533 (hybrid)		8 ozs., smooth, green-shouldered	Larger than Truckcross 520, and slightly sweeter . . . vigorous vines tolerant of leaf mold and Fusarium wilt . . . indeterminate	5 55 66
Truck Queen			Able to set fruit under unfavorable or low light-intensity conditions	66
Vantage		3-4 ozs.,	Has some tolerance to leaf mold	66
Vendor Greenhouse		6-8 ozs., deep-globe, bright-red, firm	Best fall staking or greenhouse . . . has proved successful in New England and New Jersey	66 72

TOMATOES—Oxheart

VARIETY	DAYS	FRUIT	REMARKS	SOURCES
Faribo Golden Heart		Golden-yellow, thick-walled	Extra-early . . . typical tomato flavor	21 62
Jung's Giant Oxheart	90	Deep-pink, true-heart-shape, giant-size	Almost all solid meat, with few seeds	38
Oxheart Pink	86-90	Pink, heart-shaped, up to 2 lbs., firm, meaty	General . . . thick-walled fruit . . . large, open vine . . . old-timer, widely used . . . indeterminate habit	5 9 10 14 21 25 31 32 40 44 45 48 50 51 52 55 72
Oxheart Red	90	Large, red, heart-shaped, 1 lb. plus	Few seeds	19 56 62

TOMATOES—White

VARIETY	DAYS	FRUIT	REMARKS	SOURCES
Snowball	78		Almost-pure-white flesh . . . has few seeds and mild flavor	22 62
White Beauty	84	Ivory-white skin, large	Flesh is paper-white . . . subacid . . . excellent for slicing, canning, or juicing	9 25 28 43 52 53
White Queen	78	Ivory-white	Delicate, mild, nonacid . . . fine for slicing	19
White Wonder	85	Firm	Creamy-white skin and flesh . . . unsurpassed for white slicer . . . low acidity	38

TOMATOES—Ground Cherry

VARIETY	DAYS	FRUIT	REMARKS	SOURCES
Faribo Ground Cherry		2¼-2¾", firm	Sweet flavor . . . fine for making pies and preserves . . . plants are vigorous and very productive . . . turn yellow when ripe	21
True Yellow			Low-spreading plants . . . has a strawberry flavor . . . delicious as preserves	38
Yellow Husk	85	Deep-golden-yellow, round, cherry-size	Very sweet . . . heat- and drought-resistant . . . extremely prolific . . . makes delicious preserves and jams . . . thin, papery husks	5 12 14 19 25 28 36 52 72

TOMATOES—Miscellaneous Varieties

VARIETY	DAYS	FRUIT	REMARKS	SOURCES
Egg Tomato		Chicken-egg size and shape	Nonacid, solid-red flesh . . . keeps indefinitely	26
Evergreen Tomato	70	Green when fully ripe	Mild, delicious flavor . . . low in acid	26
Liberty Bell		Thick walls, bell-shaped	Red stuffing tomato . . . nonacid . . . small seed core looks like a strawberry and is easily removed	26

TOMATOES—Miscellaneous Varieties (Continued)

VARIETY	DAYS	FRUIT	REMARKS	SOURCES
Mr. Stripey		Red and yellow stripes	Grows well outdoors in all states	68
Ruffled Tomato		Yellow, accordion-shaped	Excellent to trim out interior to make dessert containers when cut in half	26
Tom-Pato Kit			Combination of potato and tomato . . . tomatoes ripen above ground, potatoes below ground . . . yields a big crop in little space	43
Tree Tomato, Red Seeded Strain		Plum-shaped, purplish fruit	12-foot trees . . . in North, grown in greenhouses . . . in South, outdoors	26 43 62

Turnip (Brassica rapa)

Turnips are hardy vegetables with rough-textured, somewhat hairy foliage. The roots are fast-growing and become pithy in a fairly short time. Several varieties are ready for harvest in less than a month.

There is a wide choice in turnip varieties. The main differences are color (white, yellow, red, black, and combinations) and shape (flat-globe and globe types). In the flat-globe types the tops and bottoms of the roots are flat, while the remainder is globe-shaped.

Just Right Hybrid is a solid-white, flat-globe type; *Early Purple Top Milan* is a flat-globe type with a purple top and white bottom. *Golden Ball* (yellow) and *Tokyo Cross Hybrid* (white) are solid-color globe types; *Purple Top White Globe* is a combination-color globe type.

There are also turnip varieties grown primarily for greens.

HOW TO PLANT: Sow seeds a half-inch deep in rows 15-18 inches apart. Thin the seedlings to 3-5 inches apart. Turnips are a cool-weather plant. In the north sow as early in the spring as soon as the ground can be worked. Plant again in mid-summer for fall harvest. In mild-winter areas plant in fall for winter harvest. Generally fall-planted turnips have a better flavor than spring-planted.

Harvesting: Pull turnips when they are 2-2½ inches in diameter. They become pithy if left in the ground much beyond this size. Despite their liking for cool weather, turnips are not frost-hardy.

TURNIPS—White

VARIETY	DAYS	SHAPE/SIZE	REMARKS	SOURCES
All Seasons	28	Globe-shaped, white-skinned	White flesh . . . retains its shape after roots are fully formed . . . stays sweet even during hot and dry weather	14
Early Six Weeks	42	White, globe	Early . . . sweet, juicy flavor	68
Early White Milan	45	Flattened roots	Early sort, for spring planting	36
Extra Early White Ball	25-30	Pure-white, ball-shaped	Very fine turnip	14 26 36 62
Hybrid Petite White		Pure-white, smooth, globular	Very hardy to frost . . . also gives good results when grown as a spring crop	14
Jersey Lily (Snowball)	40	Perfect, snow-white globe	White flesh . . . delicious whether cooked or eaten raw	14
Just Right Hybrid	60	Globe-shaped, smooth, white, 5-6" across	Can be planted anytime for greens and will be ready in 28 days . . . fine-quality turnip	9 10 12 14 19 21 28 29 31 32 41 48 51 53 55 70
Pomeranian White Globe	75	Flat, white globe	White skin and flesh . . . good producer of turnip tops	47
Presto	30	Small, uniform	Pure-white	32 62
Shiro		Egg-size, flattened globe	Early variety used both for greens and roots	40
Shogoin (Foliage)	30 for foliage 70 for roots	3-4"	Tops are 18-20" tall, plentiful and mild . . . fine-grained flesh	10 12 14 22 31 32 40 41 44 50 51 52 55 56 58 67
Tokyo Cross Hybrid	35	Smooth, semi-globe, pure-white, 2-6" across	AA winner . . . good resistance to virus and other diseases . . . keeps its perfect shape	10 21 22 30 31 32 38 53 55 67 70 72
Tokyo Market	50	Flattened roots	An excellent early white turnip	29 31 37 48 50

TURNIPS—White (Continued)

VARIETY	DAYS	SHAPE/SIZE	REMARKS	SOURCES
Tokyo Top (hybrid)	50	2-3" across	Sweet, pure-white turnip . . . disease-resistant . . . not affected by late-autumn frost	34 41
Vertus		White	Grows fast . . . should be pulled young to be at its best	15
White Egg	55	Egg-shaped root	Pure-white flesh, sweet . . . quick growth . . . winter variety	12 30 31 32 41 51 56 67

TURNIPS—Purple-Top

VARIETY	DAYS	SHAPE/SIZE/COLOR	REMARKS	SOURCES
Amber Globe		5-6" white globe	Yellow-fleshed fall variety . . . later than Purple-Top White Globe	32 38 47 55 56 57 67
Early Purple-Top Milan	45	3-4" across, flattened roots, white skin, purple top	Flesh is white, tender when young . . . one of the earliest varieties used in the home garden	10 12 21 28 36 37 56 72
Golden Neckless			Yellow flesh	3
Purple-Top White Globe	55	2-5" across, bright-purple upper, creamy-white lower	Flesh is pure white, tender, and fine-grained . . . heavy yielder . . . keeps well throughout winter	3 9 10 11 12 14 15 19 21 22 25 29 30 31 32 34 36 38 39 40 41 44 45 47 48 49 51 52 53 55 57 58 60 62 67 70 72 73
Red-Top Globe (Reselected)	58	Uniform, smooth, bright-purplish tops extending well down on the roots	Popular turnip	30
Strap Leaf Purple-Top Flat		Flat-shaped, white, with purplish crown	White flesh . . . used by home and market gardeners	32 51 52 55 62

TURNIPS—Other Colors

VARIETY	DAYS	SHAPE/SIZE/COLOR	REMARKS	SOURCES
Golden Ball Turnip (Orange Jelly)	60	4" across, yellow	Sweet, yellow-fleshed, fine-grained, flavorful . . . nice to cook for mashing	50 62 70
Large Yellow Globe	70	Large, light-yellow with green tops	Popular for table use . . . grows to large size . . . reliable winter keeper	12 30 31
Ohno Scarlet	55	Root is flat, red globe	White flesh . . . red-veined greens	37
Scarlet Ball		Looks like red beet top and root	True turnip flavor . . . white flesh	26
Turnip Longue de Caluire	55	Elongated black outer skin	From France . . . make wonderful turnip greens . . . flesh is buttery smooth and sweet	30

TURNIPS—For Greens Only

VARIETY	DAYS	REMARKS	SOURCES
Seven Top (Winter Greens)	45	No roots . . . grown for quick greens	12 14 30 31 32 40 47 48 51 53 57 62 70
Southerner		Extra early, similar to Shiro	40
Spring	40		48

Herbs

Herbs are fun to grow and great to use in the kitchen. Many gardeners insist that they have beneficial effects in the garden.

For the kitchen, you can always use herbs fresh; just pick pieces as you need them. You can also dry them for storage but they should be dried quickly and in the dark, in order to retain their best flavor. Dry the herbs by placing them on a cookie sheet and putting them in the oven for 2-3 hours at the lowest possible heat setting. The oven door should be left ajar (but without the light on). Store the dried herbs in glass or metal containers with tight lids to preserve the flavor.

Herbs grow best if you treat them like any other vegetable, although they tend to loose their flavor in extremely fertile soil. Most herbs should also be planted in full sun.

Plant them in the garden along with other vegetables; in a pot, tub, window box or even in 4-inch pots. Most herbs can be started from seed although transplants are available from most garden centers. Many of the sources listed here sell seeds and/or plants.

HERBS

VARIETY	SIZE	REMARKS	SOURCE
Angelica	3 feet	Flavoring for cooking fish. Thrives in moist, rich soil, partial shade. Stems used for candying.	12 16 30 36 37 44 50 52 53 72 74 76 78 79 81 82 86 88 89 91
Anise	2 feet	Slow growing. Does not transplant well. Fresh leaves in salad and as garnish. Seed flavoring for bread, cookies, stews, etc. Requires sunny, fairly dry, sandy, medium rich soil.	3 5 10 15 16 28 30 31 37 38 41 44 45 46 47 49 50 51 53 56 57 62 66 72 75 76 78 79 82 83 88 89 91
Balm, Mint	18"	Has strong scent of winter savory.	89
Basil, Sweet		Annual. All basils have clove-like flavor and spicy odor, some more pungent than others. Plant in sun to partial shade in average but moist soil. Use leaves, fresh or dried in Italian tomato paste, all tomato dishes, salads, pea soup and omelets.	3 10 15 16 19 22 28 29 30 31 34 37 45 47 49 50 51 52 53 56 57 62 66 68 72 74 76 78 82 83 84 86 88 89 91
Basil, Green Bush		Compact little bushes with small leaves and white flowers. Some have lemon odor.	15 44 50 72 74 76 78 83 86
Basil, Holy (Tulsi)	10"	Worshiped by Hindu people for medicinal value.	26 76 83
Basil, Large Leaved Italian	2 feet	Large leaves. Popular variety.	16 41 50 60
Basil, Lebanon	10"	Small leaves. Mound shape.	74
Basil, Lemon	10"	Culinary use.	74 76
Basil, Lettuce Leaved		Very large crinkled leaf, sometimes 6" in length. Grows quite tall.	5 32 50 53 72 76 78 83 86 91
Basil, Ornamental Dark Opal	15"	The foliage is attractive dark purple bronze, for show or culinary purposes	16 26 28 29 31 38 41 44 49 50 52 53 57 60 62 74 76 78 82 83 86 88 89 91
Bayberry		Leaves are culinary. Wax from the seeds.	74
Bay Leaf		Excellent in meat dishes and sauces with tomato.	44 74 76 81 82 86 91
Borage	2 feet	Does not transplant. Attractive gray foliage, blue flowers. Leaves used as tea in iced drinks, salads, pickles. Requires dry, poor soil, sun. High in potassium.	5 10 15 16 28 29 30 31 32 34 37 41 44 47 49 50 51 52 53 56 62 66 72 74 76 78 82 83 84 86 88 89 91
Burdock		Used in oriental dishes.	82
Burnet (Pimpernel)	2 feet	Does not transplant. Cut back leaves when 4" high for constant supply in salads. Used in vinegar and iced drinks, dips. Has a cucumber flavor. Plant in dry, poor, sandy soil, in sun.	15 32 44 45 50 53 74 76 78 81 82 83 84 86 88 89 91
Caraway	2 feet	Resembles Queen Anne's Lace. Seed produced second year. Used as flavoring in breads, crackers, soups, salads, cakes, apple pie and sauerkraut. Leaves used in salads, soup, roast pork, cheese and vegetable dishes. Likes dry, light soil, sun.	10 15 16 19 22 28 30 31 32 34 37 38 41 44 45 46 47 49 50 51 52 53 56 62 66 72 74 76 78 79 82 83 86 88 89 91
Cardamon		Fragrant leaves. Used a great deal in cookies, pastries.	79 82
Catnip (Catmint)	2-3 feet	Sow seed in sun or partial shade in sandy, rich soil. Cats love the leaves. Pioneers used it as tea for colds, fevers, headaches and to promote sleep.	3 5 10 16 28 30 31 32 34 37 41 44 45 47 49 50 51 52 53 57 62 68 72 74 76 78 81 82 84 86 88 89 91
Chamomile (Camomile)		Companion plant for cabbages and onions.	15 16 37 44 45 50 53 68 72 74 76 81 83 84 88 89 91
Chamomile, German		Used in teas.	78 82 86 91
Chamomile, Roman	1 foot	Best for tea.	32 45 74 78 82 86 89 91
Chervil	1½ feet	Leaves have a delicate flavor similar to parsley. Used as a garnish, in soup, egg dishes, salad. Light moderately rich, well drained soil, partial shade. Does not transplant well. Old remedy for hiccoughs.	3 10 15 16 28 30 31 32 36 37 44 50 52 57 66 74 76 78 82 83 86 88 89
Chervil, Double Curled		60 days. Excellent taste. Shorter than plain chervil.	15 32 36 51 53 86 91
Comfrey	4 feet	Leaves used in tea or fruit juice drinks. Also cooked as a vegetable. Roots used like Salsify or parsnip. 34% protein. Also used as medicine.	21 23 28 31 46 68 76 78 81 86 87 88 89 91

HERBS (Continued)

VARIETY	SIZE	REMARKS	SOURCE
Coriander	3 feet	Leaves and fresh seed have a rather unpleasant odor. Seeds become fragrant as they dry. Ground seeds used to flavor gingerbread, cookies, pastries, puddings, baked apples, and pears, applesauce, salads and ground meats. Whole seeds used in pickling, confections and in grog. Leaves used in Oriental and Spanish dishes.	3 5 10 15 16 30 31 32 34 37 44 45 46 47 50 51 52 53 56 57 62 68 72 74 76 78 79 82 83 86 88 89 91
Costmary Bible Leaf	2 feet	Used in salads, teas, ale, meats, poultry, fish chowder and soups. Pioneers placed Costmary leaves in their books to deter silverfish.	44 76 81 86 88 89 91
Cumin		Small plant of the parsley family. Aromatic seed like fruits are used in cooking and medicine.	16 41 45 53 82 83 86
Curry Plant	1 foot	Gray foilage with yellow flowers, with very strong curry fragrance.	89
Dill, Bouquet	3 feet	Grows easily in sunny, well drained soil. Leaves are popular in tuna and chicken salad, steaks, chops. Seeds used in apple pie and breads, pickling, soups, salad dressings, cottage cheese, omelettes, meats, fish and poultry, as well as herb butter. About 68 days.	3 5 9 10 14 15 16 19 22 26 28 29 30 31 32 34 37 38 41 44 45 46 47 48 49 50 51 52 53 56 57 58 62 66 67 68 72 74 76 78 82 83 86 88 89 91
Dill, Mammoth	2-2½ feet	About 70 days, the same uses as above.	32 44 48 50 51 53 60 86 91
Dittany of Crete	6"	Can be used the same as Oregano or in tea.	44 89
Elecampane	4 feet	Brilliant daisy like flowers, violet scented, roots used for candy.	68 74 76 78 82 89
Foot	2 feet	Excellent in bean dishes.	89
Feungreek	2 feet	Maple flavored seeds are used in cookies, cakes, syrups, curry powders, tea or sprouted for salads.	16 32 37 44 45 46 57 68 74 79 82 86 89 91
Ginseng		The root with the human shape. Roots are dried and eaten and the leaves are brewed for tea. Grows in any soil type. Thrives best in moist soil in shade.	22 28 31 44 45 68 76 79 80 82
Horehound	2 feet	Plant in dry, poor, light soil. Flavors beefstew, braised beef, cakes and candies. Use as a tea also.	5 10 16 22 28 30 31 32 37 41 44 45 47 49 50 51 52 53 56 62 68 72 74 76 78 81 82 83 84 88 89 91
Hyssop	1½ feet	Germinates easily, almost evergreen sub-shrub. Aromatic foliage. Bitter persistent taste. Grows in light, well drained, warm soil. Cut back after flowering to keep shape. Grow in sun or partial shade. Makes a good tea.	15 16 31 32 37 44 45 49 50 51 53 62 72 74 81 83 84 86 88 91
Hyssop, Anise	24"		76 86 91
Hyssop, Blue	24"		76 78 82 89
Hyssop, Pink	24"		76
Hyssop, White	24"		76
Ibosa	1 foot	Leaves used between meats in shish kebab and barbecue meats. Likes shade.	89
Lemon Balm	1-2 feet	Lemon balm is hardy but slow to germinate. Very fragant. Plant in dry soil, in partial shade. Use in teas, iced beverages, fruit cup, salads, soups, and stews.	12 15 16 30 37 44 45 50 51 52 53 62 68 72 74 76 78 81 82 83 84 86 88 89 91
Lemon Grass	18"	Delicious as an iced tea. Strong taste and smell of lemon. Contains a great amount of citral, an essential oil, and vitamin A.	89
Lemon Verbena	4 feet	Good in tea, fruit salads, jam, jelly and fruit drinks.	89 91
Licorice	4 feet	Excellent tea to flavor other medicines. Pale blue flowers.	89
Lovage	6"-2 feet	Aromatic leaves. Rich, moist soil, dug deeply. Plant in sun or partial shade. Has a celery flavored leaf used in soups, sauces, stews, teas and salads.	16 32 37 44 50 53 74 76 78 81 82 86 88 89 91
Marjoram, Creeping Golden	8"	Use the same as Sweet Marjoram.	76 89
Marjoram, Sweet	18"	All meat and meat dishes can be flavored with this herb, including fish and poultry. Good in salads, salad dressings, brown gravy, egg dishes, soups, tomato and potato dishes, vegetables, especially eggplant, summer squash and zucchini. Said to be helpful for an upset stomach. 70 days.	3 5 10 15 16 19 28 29 30 31 32 34 37 38 41 44 45 47 49 50 51 52 53 56 57 60 62 66 68 72 74 76 78 82 83 84 86 88 89 91

HERBS (Continued)

VARIETY	SIZE	REMARKS	SOURCE
Mint	18"-2 feet	This herb is excellent in mint jelly, custards, ice cream, fruit juices, mint sauce, stewed pears, salads, and teas.	15 16 22 34 57 62
Apple Mint (Round Leaf Mint)	18"		28 44 45 50 76 81 86 88 89 91
Corsican Mint (Jewel Mint)	2"		44 50 89
Curly Mint	18"		3 5 31 32 45 53 76 81 82 86 89 91
Egyptian Mint	4"		89 91
English Mint	3 feet		89
Golden Mint	15"		76
Mint, The Best	3 feet		50 89
Mountain Mint			78 86
Orange Bergamont (Bee Balm)	3 feet	Oswego tea.	50 74 76 78 81 82 86 89 91
Orange Mint	30"		44 76 88 89 91
Pennyroyal Mint		A dense mat of glossy leaves. Not winter hardy in New England. Used for teas but is toxic in large amounts. Refreshing minty fragrance.	15 32 37 44 50 68 74 76 78 81 82 83 84 86 89 91
Peppermint	3 feet	Sow in good soil, slow to germinate; rank feeder. The oil is used in candy, liqueurs and medicines.	5 19 28 32 37 41 44 45 49 50 53 66 68 72 76 81 82 86 88 89 91
Pineapple Mint	2 feet		44 50 76 86 88 89 91
Silvermint			44
Spearmint	3 feet		5 10 28 30 31 32 37 41 44 45 49 50 52 53 66 72 76 81 82 86 88 89 91
Stone Mint			44
Watermint	2 feet		89
White Peppermint	2 feet		89
Mustard Seed		Yellow or black seed.	45 72
Nasturtum		Unripe seeds can be used in place of capers in homemade pickles. Spicy leaves added to salads. Seeds germinate easily, plant in full sun.	12 14 16 19 21 22 25 30 31 32 34 38 39 41 50 52 55 56 57 60 66 68 74 76 83 86 91
Nettle, Stinging	5 feet	Makes a nutritional beer. Can also be cooked as greens.	74 82 89
Nutmeg		Used in many pies, pastry dishes.	86
Oregano	30"-2 feet	Seed germinates easily. Plant in full sun spaced 12" apart. Excellent for flavoring meats, fish, game poultry, stews, vegetables, Italian and Spanish dishes, sauces, soups and vinegar.	3 5 10 16 22 29 30 31 32 34 37 41 44 45 47 50 52 57 62 66 72 74 76 78 82 83 88 89 91
Oregano, Greek	30"		86 89
Poke	6 feet	Young shoots used in salads. Stems used in biscuits.	89
Purslane		Pleasant salad herb. Thick stems of plants that have run to seed are pickled in salt and vinegar for winter salads. Very high in vitamin C.	16 50 72
Rocket Salad (Roquette) (Rucola)	8"	Low growing French salad plant. Make several plantings during the growing season. Peppery, pungent taste.	10 16 28 30 32 36 50 51 53 72 76 78 83 86 91
Rosemary	8"-5 feet	78 days. Slow to germinate. Pungent, pleasant odor and taste. Favorite in beef, chicken, pork, lamb and veal dishes, sauces, sandwich spreads, herb butter and stew. Used in iced drinks, chopped in biscuits, fried potatoes, stuffings, jellies or teas. Lime should be dug in several times a year.	3 5 15 16 22 28 29 30 31 32 34 41 44 45 47 50 51 52 56 57 62 66 72 74 76 78 81 82 83 86 88 89 91
Rosemary, Beneden Blue	4 feet		89
Rosemary, Pink	3 feet		89
Rosemary, Santa Barbara	18"		89
Rosemary, Trailing	8"		76 86 89
Rosemary, White	3 feet		89
Rosemary, Wood	3 feet		89
Rosemary, Tuscan Blue	5 feet		89

HERBS (Continued)

VARIETY	SIZE	REMARKS	SOURCE
Rue (Galega)	2½ feet	Plant in full sun to partial shade in average garden soil, perfectly dry, stony and alkaline, a hardy perennial. Use sparingly in sandwiches, cottage cheese, vegetables, eggplant, asparagus, potatoes, peas and sauces.	16 31 32 37 44 45 50 51 53 56 62 68 72 74 76 78 81 82 83 84 88 89 91
Safflower (False Saffron)	1½-3 feet	Grows easily in most soils. Bright orange-yellow thistle-like blossoms which are used for dyes, cosmetics and food coloring. Oil pressed from the seed used like olive oil, leaves for flavoring.	16 50 51 53 74 82 86
Saffron	24"	Used for flavoring and coloring.	62 76
Sage, Broad Leaved	12-15"	Plant in full sun, average soil, tall, hardy, spreading, silvery grey-green foliage. Has pleasant aromatic odor and mildly pungent flavor. Makes an excellent tea and is great for soups, stews, stuffings, sausage, brown gravy, roast meats, poultry, pork, cottage cheese, stewed tomatoes, lima beans and eggs.	3 5 10 15 16 19 22 28 29 30 31 32 34 37 38 41 44 45 47 48 49 50 51 52 53 56 57 60 62 66 67 72 74 78 81 82 83 84 86 88 91
Sage, Clary		Gives muscatel flavor to wine.	50 74 84 88 91
Sage, Dwarf	18"		44 76 86 89
Sage, Golden	18"		76 86 89
Sage, Gray	15"		76
Sage, Holts Mammoth	2 feet		50 89 91
Sage, Pineapple	4 feet		44 76 86 89 91
Sage, Purple,	2 feet		76 82 86 89
Sage, Variegated	2 feet		50 76 86 89 91
Savory		Used in stews, soups, meat, chicken, green beans, sausages, vegetables and certain liqueurs. Plant in sunny location in well drained soil.	
Savory, Summer	18"	Annual, 60-70 days.	3 5 15 16 22 28 29 30 31 32 34 37 38 41 44 47 49 50 51 52 53 56 57 60 62 66 72 74 76 78 82 83 84 86 88 89 91
Savory, Trailing Winter	6"		37 50 89
Savory, Winter	2 feet		32 44 45 50 53 74 76 81 82 83 86 88 89 91
Scented Geraniums	3-4 feet	Their fragrant scented leaves are used for vinegar, flavoring jellies, sandwiches, potato salad, cakes, fruit salad, stewed fruit, punch, tea, wine, sachets and potpourri.	53 76 86 89 91
Geranium, Apple			53 76 86 89 91
Geranium, Cinnamon			53 76 86 89 91
Geranium, Lemon			53 76 86 89 91
Geranium, Nutmeg			53 76 86 89 91
Geranium, Peppermint			53 76 86 89 91
Geranium, Rose			53 76 86 89 91
Sesame		Seeds in breads, confectionary, pastries. Leaves are used for teas.	16 50 53
Smallage		Wild species of celery, slender stalks, fine leaves. Very powerful taste and aroma.	26
Sorrel, Belleville		Hardy and productive herb. Fast grower. May last 3 to 4 years. Look for receipe of Cream of Sorrel, its delicious.	15 50
Sorrel, French (Narrow Leaf)	3 feet	Use in soups, salads, cooked as greens or added to other greens. Especially good with spinach.	36 44 50 68 72 74 78 81 82 89 91
Sorrel, Broad Leaved Blond Lyon	4"	65 days. Very broad leaves. Early and slow bolting. May be used as greens or for soup flavoring.	15 16 30 32 37 51 62 67 76 83
Tarragon, French	30"	Flavoring for soups, fish sauces, salads, dressings, beef, poultry, game, eggs, vegetables, cheese spreads, tartar sauce, herb butter and tarragon vinegar.	3 5 16 30 32 34 44 45 50 57 62 68 76 81 86 88 89 91
Tarragon, Russian		Annual. Pleasing flavor for salads and vinegar flavoring. Plants of this type may be obtained from herb plant growers as they do not set seeds.	50 53 66 82 91
Thyme, Broad Leaved.	1 foot	85 days. All varieties have fragrance. Strong aromatic aroma. Very useful as dried herb in vinegar, egg dishes, meat and fish sauces, cooked with vegetables. Plant in light, sandy soil.	3 5 10 15 16 19 22 28 29 30 31 34 38 41 45 47 49 50 52 60 62 66 72 74 76 81 83 84 88

HERBS (Continued)

VARIETY	SIZE	REMARKS	SOURCE
Thyme, Caraway	3"		44 50 51 53 57 76 86 89
Thyme, Cat	1 foot		89
Thyme, Coconut	3"		89
Thyme, Dwarf (Compact)			32 44 53
Thyme, English	18"		50 68 78 82 83 86 89 91
Thyme, French	1 foot		44 50 56 78 82 83 88 89 91
Thyme, Golden	18"		76 89
Thyme, Golden Creeping	3"		50 76 81 88 89
Thyme, Lemon Scented	18"		44 50 76 81 86 88 89 91
Thyme, Scarlet			76
Thyme, Silver	18"		76 86 89
Thyme, Summer			32
Thyme, Varigated English	18"		89
Thyme, White Moss	3"		44 50 76 89
Thyme, Winter			15 32 37 44 86 89
Thyme, Wild (Mother of Thyme)	4"		74 78 89 91
Thyme, Woolly	2"		44 50 76 88
Yerba Buena	6"	Excellent tea as itself or mixed with other herbs.	89

Seed Catalog Sources

The sources indicated with an asterisk are wholesalers. You cannot order seed from them. But your local dealer can. If you cannot find their varieties on seed racks or in local nurseries, you can write to these wholesalers, and they will help you locate a source.

1   A. L. Castle, Inc.*
190 Mast St.
Morgan Hill,
Cal. 95037

2   Allen Farm
Route 2, Box 243
Scottsville, Ky. 42164

3   Allen, Sterling &
Lothrop
191 U.S. Route #1
Falmouth, Me. 04105

4   Mr. Artichoke
11000 Blackie Rd.
Castroville, Cal. 95012

5   Ball Seed Company*
Box 335
West Chicago,
Ill. 60185
[or]
Box 9055
Sunnyvale, Cal. 94088

6   Bea's Bric-a-Brac
15105 Lakeview
Houston, Tex. 77040

7   Brittingham Plant
Farms
P.O. Box 2538
Salisbury, Md. 21801

8   Brown's Omaha
Box 787
Omaha, Tex. 75571

9   Burgess Seed and
Plant Co.
P.O. Box 3000
Galesburg,
Mich. 49053

10   W. Atlee Burpee Co.
Riverside,
Cal. 92502
[or]
Clinton, Ia. 52732
[or]
Warminster,
Pa. 18974

11   D. V. Burrell Seed
Growers Co.
Rocky Ford,
Col. 81067

12   Comstock, Ferre & Co.
263 Main St.
Wethersfield,
Conn. 06109

13   The Conner Company,
Inc.
P.O. Box 534
Augusta, Ark. 72006

14   De Giorgi Company,
Inc.
Council Bluffs,
Ia. 51501

15   J. A. Demonchaux
Co., Inc.
225 Jackson
Topeka, Kan. 66603

16   Dessert Seed
Company, Inc.
P.O. Box 181
El Centro,
Cal. 92243

17   Dixie Plant Farms
P.O. Box 327
Franklin, Va. 23851

18   Earl Ferris Nursery
& Garden Center
Hampton, Ia. 50441

19   Earl May Seed &
Nursery Co.
Shenandoah,
Ia. 51603

20   Evans Plant Company
Tifton, Ga. 31794

21   Farmer Seed &
Nursery
Faribault,
Minn. 55021

22   Henry Field Seed &
Nursery Co.
Shenandoah,
Ia. 51603

23   Dean Foster Nurseries
Hartford,
Mich. 49057

24   Fred's Plant Farm
P.O. Box 410, Route 1
Dresden,
Tenn. 38225

25   Germania Seed
Company*
5952 N. Milwaukee
Ave.
Chicago, Ill. 60646

26   Gleckers Seedmen
Metamora,
Oh. 43540

27   Grace's Gardens
Autumn Lane
Hackettstown,
N.J. 07840

28   Gurney Seed &
Nursery Co.
Yankton,
S.D. 57078

29   Joseph Harris Co.,
Inc.
Moreton Farm
Rochester,
N.Y. 14624

30   The Chas. C. Hart
Seed Co.
Wethersfield,
Conn. 06109

Seed Catalog Sources (Continued)

31 H. G. Hastings Co.
Box 4274
Atlanta Ga. 30302

32 Herbst Brothers
Seedsmen, Inc.
1000 N. Main St.
Brewster, N.Y. 10509

33 Holmes Quisenberry
4626 Glebe Farm
Sarasota,
Fla. 33580

34 Jackson & Perkins Co.
Medford,
Ore. 97501

35 J. E. Miller
Nurseries, Inc.
Canandaigua,
N.Y. 14424

36 J. L. Hudson,
Seedsman
P.O. Box 1058
Redwood City,
Cal. 94064

37 Johnny's Selected
Seeds
Organic Seed and
Crop Research
Albion, Me. 04910

38 J. W. Jung Seed Co.
Randolph,
Wisc. 53956

39 Kelly Bros.
Nurseries, Inc.
Dansville,
N.Y. 14437

40 Keystone Seed
Company
P.O. Box 1438
Hollister,
Cal. 95023

41 Kilgore Seed Co.
1400 W. First St.
Sanford, Fla. 32771

42 Kitazawa Seed Co.
356 W. Taylor St.
San Jose,
Cal. 95110

43 Lakeland Nurseries
Sales
Hanover, Pa. 17331

44 Le Jardin du Gourmet
West Danville,
Vt. 05873

45 Mellingers
2310 West South
Range Rd.
North Lima,
Oh. 44452

46 Metro Myster Farms
Route #1, Box 285
Northhampton,
Pa. 18067

47 The Meyer Seed Co.
600 S. Caroline St.
Baltimore, Md. 21231

48 Midwest Seed
Growers, Inc.
505 Walnut St.
Kansas City,
Mo. 64106

49 The Natural
Development Co.
Box 215
Bainbridge,
Pa. 17502

50 Nichols Garden
Nursery
1190 North Pacific
Hwy.
Albany, Ore. 97321

51 Northrup, King &
Co.*
P.O. Box 959
Minneapolis,
Minn. 55440

52 L. L. Olds Seed Co.
P.O. Box 7790
Madison,
Wisc. 53707

53 Geo. W. Park
Seed Co., Inc.
Greenwood,
S.C. 29647

54 Piedmont Plant Co.,
Inc.
P.O. Box 424
Albany, Ga. 31702

55 Porter and Son,
Seedmen
1510 E. Washington
Stephenville,
Tex. 76401

56 Reuter Seed
Company, Inc.
320 N. Carrollton
Ave.
New Orleans,
La. 70119

57 The Rocky Mountain
Seed Co.
1325 15th St.
Denver, Col. 80217

58 Roswell Seed
Company, Inc.
115-117 South Main
Roswell, N.M. 88201

59 Stanford Seed
Company
560 Fulton St.
Buffalo, N.Y. 14240

60 Seedway, Inc.
Hall, N.Y. 14463

61 S & H Organic Acres
Montgomery Creek,
Cal. 96065

62 R. H. Shumway
Rockford,
Ill. 61101

62A Springhill Nurseries
110 W. Elm St.
Tipp City, Oh. 45366

63 Spruce Brook Nursery
Route 118,
P.O. Box 925
Litchfield,
Conn. 06759

64 Stark Bro's Nurseries
Louisiana, Mo. 63353

65 Steele Plant Company
Gleason,
Tenn. 38229

66 Stokes Seeds, Inc.
Box 548
Buffalo, N.Y. 14240

67 Geo. Tait and Sons,
Inc.
900 Tidewater Dr.
Norfolk, Va. 23504

67A Texas Onion Plant Co.
Box 871
Farmersville,
Tex. 75031

68 Thompson and
Morgan, Inc.
P.O. Box 100
Farmingdale,
N.J. 07727

69 Tsang and Ma
International
1556 Laurel St.
San Carlos,
Cal. 94070

70 Otis S. Twilley
Seed Co.
Salisbury, Md. 21801

71 Vermont Seed Co.
Way's Lane
Manchester,
Vt. 05255

72 W. H. Perron and Co.,
Ltd.
C. P. 408
Ville de Laval
Que. H7S 2A6
Canada

73 Willhite Melon Seed
Farms
Weatherford,
Tex. 76086

74 Borchelt Herb
Gardens
474 Carriage Shop
Rd.
East Falmouth,
Mass. 02536

75 Capriland's Herb
Farm
Silver Street
Coventry,
Conn. 06238

76 Gilberties Herb
Nursery
Sylvan Ave.
Westport,
Conn. 06880

77 Golden Gate Herb
Research, Inc.
140 Market St.
San Rafael,
Cal. 94901

78 Greene Herb Gardens
Green, R.I. 02827

79 Haussmann's
Pharmacy
Herb & Import Dept.
534-36 W. Girard Ave.
Philadelphia,
Pa. 19123

80 Heise's Wausau Farms
Route 3
Wausau,
Wisc. 54401

81 Hemlock Hill Herb
Farm
Hemlock Hill Rd.
Litchfield,
Conn. 06759

Seed Catalog Sources (Continued)

82 Herb Shop
    P.O. Box 362
    Fairfield,
        Conn. 06430

83 Hilltop Herb Farm
    P.O. Box 1734
    Cleveland,
        Tex. 77327

84 Indiana Botanic
        Gardens
    P.O. Box 5
    Hammond,
        Ind. 46325

85 Old Fashioned Herb
        Company
    P.O. Box 1000
    Springville,
        Utah 84663

86 Rutland of Kentucky
    Herb Specialists
    3 Bon Haven
    Maysville,
        Ky. 41056

87 Charles R. Short
    Route 2
    Hartwell,
        Ga. 30643

88 Stillridge Herb Farm
    10370 Route 99
    Woodstock,
        Md. 21163

89 Taylor's Herb
        Garden, Inc.
    1535 Lone Oak Rd.
    Vista, Cal. 92083

90 The Whole Herb and
        Spice Shoppe
    38 Miller Ave.
    Mill Valley,
        Cal. 94941

91 Yankee Peddler
        Herb Farm
    Route 4, Box 76,
    Hwy. 36N
    Brenham, Tex. 77833

J. L. Hudson Seedsman
P.O. Box 1058
Redwood City, Cal. 94064

The Krider Nurseries, Inc.
M
Middlebury, Ind. 46540

Letherman Seed Co.   MR
501 McKinley NW
Canton, Oh. 44702

McArdles Seed Co.   R
380-388 Greenwich Ave.
Greenwich, Conn. 06830

McLaughlin's Seeds   M
P.O. Box 550
Marshall, Mo. 65340

Robert Nicholson Seed Co.
MR
2700 Logan
Dallas, Tex. 75215

Redwood City Seed Co.
M
P.O. Box 361
Redwood City, Cal. 94604

P. L. Rohrer & Bro., Inc.
Smoketown, Pa. 17576

Wyatt-Quarles Seed Co.
MR
Box 2131
Raleigh, N.C. 27602

Additional seed sources

(Many of these are regional)
M—Mail Order   R—Retail, Own Stores

Agway, Inc.   MR
Box 4933
Syracuse, N.Y. 13221

American Seed
    Company M
35 N. Prince St.
Lancaster, Pa. 17604

American Seed
    Corporation*
58233 N. Gratiot Ave.
New Haven, Mich. 48048

Applewood Seed Co.   M*
833 Parfet St.
Lakewood, Col. 80215

Archias' Seed Store   MR
P.O. Box 109
Sedalia, Mo. 65301

Burnett Bros., Inc.   MR
92 Chambers St.
New York, N.Y. 10007

Burnett-Seedsmen,
    Inc. MR
483 Ashford Ave.
Ardsley, N.Y. 10502

FCX, Inc.   MR
Box 2419
Raleigh, N.C. 27602

Ferd Staffel Co.   MR
P.O. Box 2380
San Antonio, Tex. 78298

Garden Gems   M
3902 State St.
Quincy, Ill. 62301
(rare and unusual seeds)

Golden West Seed Co. MR
Box 275
Farwell, Tex. 79325

Helix Herb Seeds
P.O. Box 1808
Boulder, Col. 80306

Illinois Foundation Seeds
    M
P.O. Box 272
Champaign, Ill. 61820

Interstate Nurseries   M
Hamburg, Ia. 51640

Additional Canadian garden seed marketers

M—Mail Order Catalog, Home Garden
R—Retail Store Open to Home Gardeners

Alberta Nurseries & Seeds,
    Ltd.   M
Bowren, Alb. T0M 0K0

Buckerfield's   M
P.O. Box 7000
Vancouver,
    B.C. V6B 4E1

Canadian Garden Products,
    Ltd.   M
St. Lawrence Seed Div.
132 James Ave. E.
Winnipeg,
    Man. R3B ON8
(Canadian agents for
    Thompson & Morgan,
    Ipswich, England)

C.A. Cruickshank, Ltd.
    M
1015 Mount Pleasant Rd.
Toronto, Ont. M4P 2M1

William Dam Seeds   M
West Flamboro
Ont. L0R 2K0

Dominion Seed House   M
Georgetown, Ont. L7G 4A2

Gaze Seed Co., Ltd.   MR
9 Buchanan St.
St. John's, Nfld. A1C 5K8

J. Labonte & Fils   M
560 Chemin Chambly
Longueil, Que. J4H 3L8

Lindenberg Seeds, Ltd.   M
803 Princess Ave.
Brandon, Man. R7A 0P5

McFayden Seed Co., Ltd.
    M
P.O. Box 1600
Brandon, Man. R7A 6E1

Ontario Seed Company
    M
Box 144
Waterloo, Ont. N2J 3Z9

Pike & Co., Ltd.   M
10552 114th St.
Edmonton, Alb. T5H 3J7

Semences Laval, Inc.   MR
3505 St. Martin Blvd.
Chomedey, Laval,
    Que. H7T 1A2

Superior Seeds   MR
2051 Victoria
St. Lambert,
    Que. J4S 1H1

Vesey's Seeds, Ltd.   MR
York, P.E.I. C0A 1P0

8

WATERING

Proper watering is extremely important to any garden. In fact, according to U.S. government studies, "water is the most frequent factor limiting plant growth." This is particularly true of vegetables, because most of them are constituted principally of water. Beyond this, water is essential to the manufacture of food and to its movement through a plant's circulatory system. Both oxygen and carbon dioxide enter and leave plants in water solution. In this chapter we will describe the best techniques and products available to help gardeners ensure that their vegetables get the proper amount of water.

How much water is needed

In most areas of North America a rule of thumb is that vegetables need about an inch of rainfall per week. If nature doesn't provide this ideal, then it's up to the home gardener to fill the gap. For a plot 15 by 25 feet you should make available about 225 gallons per week. For a plot double that size, double the gallons—and so on. And if it rains a bit, you can probably reduce your watering a bit. But be careful. Although it's better to water too much than too little, try to do neither. A deluge may result in insufficient oxygen for the plant and interfere with root growth and function.

When you soak the soil thoroughly, you add water until it reaches "field capacity"—that is, roughly all the water that the air spaces in the soil can hold. Ideally you should keep your garden soil between this condition and the point at which moisture is so scarce that plant roots can no longer take water from the soil.

It's also important how often you water. If you sprinkle for a brief period each day, you will only wet the upper few inches of the soil. Light watering like this should be avoided because it causes roots to grow too close to the surface, and thus a sudden hot spell could severely damage plants. The soil should be wet to a depth of 6-12 inches each time you water. Then it need not be watered again until the top few inches begin to dry out. You can take a trowel to dig in and check. If it rains, don't water until this trowel test shows that watering is needed. For many gardens a good soaking once a week is just right.

Methods of watering

In addition to rain, which is not easy to control, there are two basic ways of bringing water to your garden. Some gardeners insist that the best way of watering vegetables is right on the ground, using some kind of

---

Soil moisture testers

Soil moisture testers can help take the guesswork out of watering your vegetable garden. Basically they let you know how much moisture is available to the roots of your plants. There are two types, mechanical and electrical.

The mechanical type (a tensiometer), sometimes called a dummy root, has a sealed, water-filled tube equipped with a vacuum gauge and a porous tip that is installed in the ground at root zone depth. In dry soil water is drawn out of the tube. When the soil takes on moisture, water is drawn back into the instrument. The amount of moisture in the soil can be read directly on the gauge.

Since wet soil is a better conductor than dry soil, the electrical type works by measuring the amount of electricity passing through the soil.

---

irrigation system. Others believe that watering from above more closely approximates rain and is therefore better for vegetables. We'll discuss both methods.

Watering from above is generally the easiest method. However, a fair amount of water is lost through evaporation. Another disadvantage to this method is that it can damage some hot-weather crops—for instance tomatoes may crack. This can be prevented by watering overhead until the plants start to produce fruit, then watering on the ground thereafter. Overhead watering can also encourage mildew, especially if you live along the coast or in a region with lots of fog or in other areas where the humidity tends to be high in growing season. You can generally overcome this problem by watering in the morning, so that plants dry out by evening and do not sit overnight in ground that is continuously wet.

Watering from below takes less water, but it generally involves more work. It is not easy to set up and maintain this type of irrigation. However, in recent years a drip system has been developed that does an excellent job of providing plants with a good water supply, and in addition is not difficult or expensive to have. (More about this later in the chapter.)

Overhead watering

Generally today's overhead watering devices can be divided into six major groups: pulsating sprinklers, oscillating sprinklers, rotating sprinklers, nonmoving (stationary) sprinklers, hand-held sprays (nozzles), and sprinkler spray heads (irrigation systems).

Pulsating sprinklers. This is the well-known "rainbird" type, where water striking an arm moves the sprinkler

around in a circle. Each sprinkler will cover an area 50-75 feet in radius and can be adjusted to water a full circle or part circle. They are available in brass or less expensive plastic. They can be used with a stationary underground pipe system and screwed into a standing pipe or utilized with a portable spike or sled base. One alone operating in a full circle is enough for a small garden. *Rated excellent for vegetable gardens.*

Oscillating sprinklers. These sprinklers are operated by water, moving back and forth to cover an area of about 50-by-60-feet. They can also be set for varying coverage within that area. Oscillating sprinklers are available with timing devices that allow you to dial the total amount of water you want up to 1,200 gallons. These sprinklers spray in squares or rectangles—the shape of most gardens. *Rated good for vegetable gardens.*

Rotating sprinklers. There are many types of rotating sprinklers on the market. Generally they consist of rotating arms or small rotating blades propelled by a

1
Stake out your system, positioning stakes where a sprinkler head will be indicated on drawing.

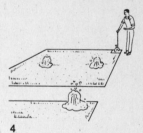

2
When coverage checks out, you are ready to bury the pipe. A "V" trench 6" to 8" deep is adequate.

3
Run pipe from valves to stakes — install pipe fittings — rigid risers — and RAIN JET heads — and tie heads to stakes.

4
Bury pipe so heads are flush with the turf — remove nozzle units from castings and flush lines.

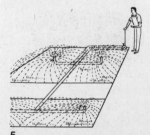

5
Turn on valves. Observe where water is covering. If coverage needs correcting, do it now.

INSTALLING A SPRINKLER SYSTEM

spray of water. They will water in a circle from 5 to 50 feet. Some types will also fertilize while they water. Traveling sprinklers are generally the rotating type and can be made to travel along a hose laid down the middle of the garden. These will water up to 15,000 square feet of space. Some water is wasted by these sprinklers because they water in a circle (although some are manufactured to water in a square). *Rated fair to good for vegetable gardens.*

Nonmovable sprinklers. Nonmovable (stationary) sprinklers have holes that sprinkle water in squares or rectangles (or circles) up to 100 square feet in area. This limited range makes them suitable for only very small gardens. *Rated poor to fair for vegetable gardens.*

Hand-held sprayers (nozzles, wands). Some gardeners insist that vegetable gardens must be hand watered. There is a wide variety of hose nozzles on the market today, including the aqua hand gun nozzles, straight nozzles, fan hand sprays, and bubbles for ground use. In addition there are many water wands available— ranging from 24 to 52 inches long—that allow you to put the water exactly where you want it. These are available with special seeding nozzles, which produce a very fine mist that won't disturb vegetable seeds, or soft rain irrigator nozzles, which keep water from splashing and cut down runoff. *Wands with special nozzles are excellent for hand watering vegetable gardens.*

Sprinkler spray heads (irrigation systems). Ground-level or pop-up sprinkler spray heads are used extensively for shrubbery and lawns. Sprayheads are utilized with PVC plastic pipe to form extensive underground irrigation systems. The heads can be made of plastic or brass and offer varying patterns: quarter-,

half-, three-quarter-, and full-circle. There are two general types—stationary (including the pop-up) and rotating (gear-driven). These systems can be automated with timers or moisture sensors.

An important disadvantage is that underground pipe makes cultivating vegetable gardens almost impossible. However, underground irrigation systems can be used in small gardens by keeping the pipe outside the garden, on the sides and corners. Unfortunately, the efficiency of these systems is cut as the garden reaches maturity. *Rated poor to fair for vegetable gardens.*

Automatic sprinkler controllers

It's important to control your watering to keep it at the optimum level. There are a number of automatic controllers on the market, and they incorporate many features. Basically every controller utilizes a clock that turns the water on and off for a specified period of time.

The simplest uses a mechanically timed hose bibb valve. Screw one end to the house outlet, the other end to a hose; then set the timer to shut off the water flow after a specified time.

Electric timers have become exceedingly complex. They consist of a clock (or clocks) that can be set to operate a valve and turn on the water for a given number of minutes a day. The more complex ones allow watering every day, every third day, every sixth day, and similar combinations. Some allow a different program to be set each day; others offer multiple watering several times a day. The more complex controllers also allow operation of 3, 6, 11, 14, and many, many more stations (or circuits) at one time. It is also possible to automate existing manual sprinkler systems.

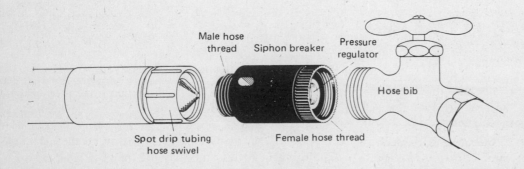

Male hose thread • Siphon breaker • Pressure regulator

Hose bib

Spot drip tubing hose swivel • Female hose thread

CONTROL VALVES

Every sprinkler system needs a control valve or valves. Each circuit needs its own valve. In a small garden one control valve is generally enough (see circuit explanation). Most plumbing codes require an antisiphon device to prevent foreign matter from back siphoning into the household water. These are built directly into the control valves.

MASTER PERFORMANCE CHART OF SPRINKLER HEADS THE 8 MOST POPULAR MODELS

SQUARE PATTERN HEADS	COVERAGE IN FEET	DISCHARGE IN G.P.M.	PRESSURE AT NOZZLE P. S. I.	SPACING MAXIMUM
Small Square. Adjustable from 6' x 6' up to 18' x 18' 836C or 36C	18' x 18'	2.5	25	18'
	17' x 17'	2.2	20	17'
	15' x 15'	1.8	15	15'
	11' x 11'	1.5	10	11'
	8' x 8'	1.2	7.5	8'
Medium Square. Adjustable from 18' x 18' up to 25' x 25' 866C or 66C	25' x 25'	5.8	25	25'
	24' x 24'	5.2	20	24'
	22' x 22'	4.5	15	22'
	20' x 20'	4.0	12	20'
	18' x 18'	3.5	10	18'
PARKWAY AND STRIP HEADS				
Parkway. Covers an area up to 5' x 40' 851C or 51C	5' x 40'	3.8	30	40'
	5' x 38'	3.5	25	38'
Strip. Covers an area up to 5' x 38' 852C or 52C	5' x 25'	2.8	30	25'
	5' x 23'	2.6	25	23'
FULL-CIRCLE PATTERN HEADS				
Small Circle. Adjustable from 10' up to 24' diameter 855C or 55C	24' Diam.	2.6	30	16'
	22' Diam.	2.3	25	15'
	19' Diam.	2.0	20	14'
	16' Diam.	1.8	15	12'
	14' Diam.	1.4	10	10'
Medium Circle. Adjustable from 24' up to 34' diameter 855C or 55C	34' Diam.	6.5	25	24'
	32' Diam.	5.9	20	21'
	28' Diam.	5.2	15	18'
	25' Diam.	4.5	10	16'
HALF- AND QUARTER-CIRCLE HEADS				
Half Circle. Adjustable from 5' up to 12' radius 832C only	12' Radius	1.7	25	16'
	11' Radius	1.5	20	15'
	10' Radius	1.3	15	14'
	9' Radius	1.1	10	12'
	8' Radius	1.0	8	10'
Quarter Circle. Adjustable from 5' up to 12' radius 831C only	12' Radius	1.2	25	Used in corners or odd shaped areas
	11' Radius	1.1	20	
	10' Radius	1.0	15	

Moisture sensor systems

Another way of regulating the amount of water for your garden is through use of one of the sensor systems that are on the market. A sensing device is buried in the root zone of the plants in order to determine the moisture content of the soil. When this content gets below a certain level that has been preset on a controller, the sensor activates another part of that same controller, which then "orders" an electric valve to turn on the water. After a predetermined time, the water is shut off.

Planning an underground sprinkler system

It is worthwhile to take all the time you need to shop around for different products and to plan the layout very carefully before you install a sprinkling system. There are a great many different products on the market, and one of them should be just right for your particular situation. Do some research, following the leads given in this chapter. Talk to your dealer, too, after you make sure that he knows what he is doing.

One point you'll want to determine is the number of circuits you'll need and the number of sprinkler heads per circuit. The first step here is to find out (1) how many gallons per minute are available through your water system, and (2) how many gallons per minute are used by the various sprinkler heads you're interested in. Sprinkler heads need a certain volume of water to maintain coverage. And the amount of water needed by the heads should never exceed the volume that is available.

For instance, if you have 17 gallons per minute available and if all your sprinkler heads use a total of 20 gallons per minute, you will need to eliminate some sprinkler heads from the system—or divide the system into two circuits. For information on the eight most popular models of sprinkler heads, see the chart on page 000.

An important sidelight here is that small- and medium-sized gardens can be watered by sprinklers located at the perimeter of the bed. This keeps the pipe from interfering with cultivation. For this layout heads at corners are ¼ pattern, while at the sides they are ½ pattern.

Bottom watering

Vegetables can be watered from the bottom by such simple methods as a ditch between the rows, an open-ended pipe, or a hose bubbler. Far better today, how-ever, are the drip-trickle irrigation systems. These work by providing small amounts of water to your vegetables along the root zone. Most cut water usage by up to 50 percent by putting water exactly where it is needed and by slowing evaporation.

There are two basic methods: The *drip method* emits water in small droplets along the entire hose; the *trickle method* emits a steady stream of water at a low volume from emitters spaced at intervals along the hose. Both provide small, even applications of water directly to the plant root zone. The volume of water used is controlled by varying the time of application.

Drip-trickle systems

There are four ways of getting water to your garden based on the drip-trickle methods.

The drip hose (soaker/oozer). This operates like the familiar lawn soaker hose. Perforated or porous tubing allows water to trickle from the entire length of the soaker hose at a uniform rate. Separate drip lines are attached to a pipe or hose laid across one end of the garden. One drip (soaker) line is run down each vegetable row. In some systems separate control valves are used for deep-rooted plants like tomatoes and shallow-rooted plants like lettuce. The lines that run down each row may be placed on top of the soil.

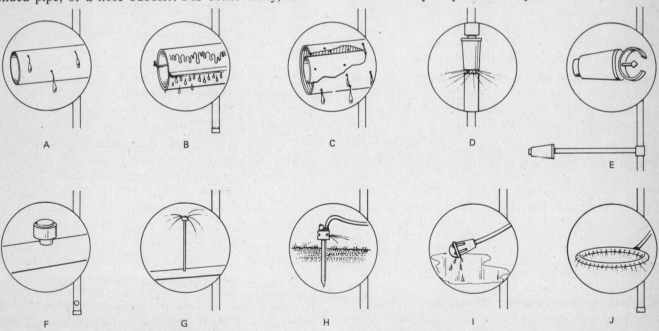

HOW THE DRIP-TRICKLE SYSTEMS WORK

Soaker-oozer: Perforated or porous tubing allows water to trickle from the entire length of the hose. (A) Single-wall drip hose has small holes spaced its entire length. (B) Viaflo porous plastic allows a slow trickle along entire length.

Twin-wall: (C) Double-wall drip hose provides constant water.

Drip Emitters: These are preassembled into plastic pipe at regular intervals; or the units snap in. (D) Emitters are avail-able in several preset flow rates. (E) Snap-on emitters can be attached anywhere; they are available with extensions of various lengths. (F) They can screw into polyethylene hoses.

Spaghetti Tubes and Nozzles: (G) Stand-up spray tube has various heads and is available in different spray arcs. (H) Stick-in sprayer has adjustable spray arc. (I) Drop-in bubbler has on/off feature. (J) Water loops come in various sizes, water all around each plant.

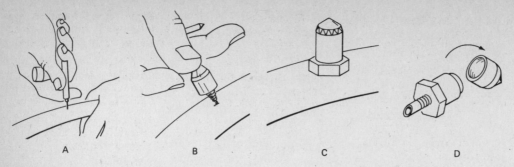

INSTALLING EMITTERS

(A) Punch access hole in feeder line (B) insert Microjet into feeder line. (C) Installation, with cap (D) that pops off for cleaning.

Twin wall (variation of the dip hose). Several manufacturers market a double tube. Some utilize an inner water-supply flow chamber with an outer ooze chamber. Others have side-by-side twin tubes. One tube receives the water and transfers it to the ooze/trickle chamber. Some double-drip hoses are prepunched for spacings of 4, 8, 12, 24, and 36 inches. This system is especially suited for long rows of vegetables.

Drip emitters (microdrippers). The system consists of polyethylene pipe laid alongside the plantings. Emitters have a preset flow rate and are installed exactly where needed along the row. Snap-on emitters can be attached anywhere along the line and are often available with various length extensions. A variation of this system utilizes *screw-in spray heads* (available in preset spray arcs), which screw into a polyethylene pipe. Spray heads vary from a coarse spray to a fine mist and fit into holes punched with an awl.

Spaghetti or microtube systems. Holes are punched into a polyethylene pipe along a row, and small spaghetti tubes, ⅛ inch or less in diameter, are then inserted into the pipe and run out to the individual plants. There are many variations. Spaghetti systems use a spaghetti tube, a rigid stand-up tube with a spray head, and tubes with stick-in sprayers, drop-in bubblers, and water loops of various sizes.

Spaghetti systems are especially good for watering the planter boxes, tubs, and hanging containers we discuss in Chapter 11. Tubes are run to each container and connected to stick-in sprayers, bubblers, or similar devices. Combinations of the drip emitter with spaghetti systems are also used, with the emitter being connected to a spaghetti tube, or a tube being connected to an emitter.

Water-supply regulators

Every drip setup utilizes one or more regulators or accessories to make the system work better. A *filter strainer* prevents small particles from clogging the system; an *antisyphon valve* prevents dirt and foreign matter from draining into the system (this may be required by local plumbing regulations); a *ball valve* regulates flow rate; a *pressure regulator and pressure gauge* precisely controls pressure; a *solenoid valve* is utilized with a time clock. All systems can be hooked to an automatic timer.

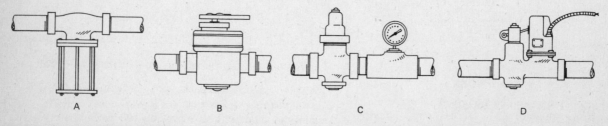

WATER SUPPLY REGULATORS

These installations are valuable in preventing dirt and other foreign matter from draining into the water system. (A) A filter-strainer prevents small particles from clogging tubes or pipes. (B) A bell valve precisely regulates flow rate and pressure. (C) A pressure regulator and gauge is the key to controlling the whole system. (D) A solenoid valve can be attached to a time clock and the source of electricity, thus functioning as the on/off mechanism.

Manufacturers of nozzles, sprinklers, and hose fittings

Armstrong LTG Systems
Los Angles, Cal. 90021

Ashflash (Ashton Div.)
151 Woodward Ave.
South Norwalk,
  Conn. 06856

Atlas/Hammer Co.
865 Lind Ave.
Renton, Wash. 98055

Bar Way Mfg. Co.
Box 6410
Stamford, Conn. 06904

Burgess Vibrocrafters, Inc.
Rte. 83
Grayslake, Ill. 60030

Champion Sprinkler Equip.
1460 Naud St.
Los Angeles, Cal. 90012

Continental Chemiste Corp.
2256 W. Ogden Ave.
Chicago, Ill. 60612

Deere & Co.
John Deere Rd.
Moline, Ill. 61265

Dexol Industries
1450 W. 228th St.
Torrance, Cal. 90501

The Dramm Co.
Box 528
Mantiowoc, Wisc. 54220

Ewing Irrigation Products
2462 Polvorosa
San Leandro, Cal. 94577

Gilmour Mfg. Corp.
Box 486
Somerset, Pa. 15501

Illinois B & G Corp.
1920 Waukegan Rd.
Glenview, Ill. 60025

F. D. Kees Mfg. Co.
700-800 Park Ave.
Beatrice, Neb. 68310

Lafayette Brass Co.
409 Lafayette St.
New York, N.Y. 10003

Melnor Industries
1 Carol Place
Moonachie, N.J. 07074

Moody Sprinkler Co., Inc.
3020 Pullman St.
Costa Mesa, Cal. 92626

National Greenhouse Co.
Box 100
Pena, Ill. 62557

L. R. Nelson Corp.
7719 N. Pioneer Lane
Peoria, Ill. 61614

Oetiker, Inc.
71-77 Okner Pkwy.
Livingston, N.J. 07039

Proen Products Co.
9th & Grayson St.
Berkeley, Cal. 94710

Rain Bird Corp.
7045 N. Grand Ave.
Glendora, Cal. 91740

H. B. Sherman
  Manufacturing Co.
207 W. Michigan Ave.
Battle Creek, Mich. 49016

Slip Seal Company
1325 Redondo Ave.
Long Beach, Cal. 90804

Spraying Systems Co.
North Ave. at Schmale Rd.
Wheaton, Ill. 60187

Supplex Div.
Box 509
Worthington, Oh. 43085

Traveltrain Power
  Sprinkler
239 N. Robertson Blvd.
Beverly Hills, Cal. 90211

Tri-Con, Inc.
27331 Tungsten Rd.
Cleveland, Oh. 44117

Winzeler Stamping Co.
129 Wabash Ave.
Montpelier, Oh. 43453

MANUFACTURERS OF SPRINKLER HEADS AND IRRIGATION SYSTEMS

COMPANY	PRODUCTS
Champion Brass 1460 Naud St. Los Angeles, Cal. 90012	Bubble, flush, flooding, pop-ups, sprinkler heads
Johns Manville Irrigation Systems Box 5108 Denver, Col. 80217	Sophisticated Irrigation systems and controls—rotary pop-up and other sprinkler heads
Moody Sprinkler Co. 3020 Pullman St. Costa Mesa, Cal. 92626	Complete line of sprinkler heads, impulse sprinklers, controls, and accessories
Rain Bird Corp. 7045 N. Grand Ave. Glendora, Cal. 91740	Complete systems, controls, accessories, sprinkler heads, impulse sprinklers
Rain Jet Corp. 301 South Flower St. Burbank, Cal. 91500	Underground sprinkler systems, heads, and accessories
Reed Irrigation Systems 585 Veron Way El Cajon, Cal. 92022	Sophisticated systems, browning sprinklers
Richdel, Inc. P.O. Drawer A Carson City, Nev. 89701	Automatic valves, controls, sprinkler heads
Skinner Irrigation Co. 5722 Este Ave. Cincinnati, Oh. 45232	Pop-up rotary sprinklers, controls, impulse sprinklers
Toro Irrigation Division 5825 Jasmine St. Riverside, Cal. 92504	Complete line of gear driven, large-area rotary sprinklers; controls and accessories
Vermeer Manufacturing Co. Box 200 Pella, la. 50219	Large-scale irrigation equipment

MANUFACTURERS OF DRIP IRRIGATION SYSTEMS

COMPANY	PRODUCTS
Allstate-Campbell, Inc. 5141 Lakeland Ave. No. Crystal, Minn. 55428	**Single-Wall Drip Hose:** Cotton soaker hose is attached to water supply by a brass hose coupling; the other end is sewn closed
J. C. Barrie Co. P.O. Box 2231 Wilmington, Del. 19899	**Single-Wall Drip Hose:** Header tubing with attachment to Viaflo tubing; comes in inexpensive Trickle Irrigation Kit form; can be installed with a pair of scissors; Viaflo tubing is cut to match the garden

Du Pont Viaflo porous plastic irrigation tubing

Viaflo is made from linear polyethylene. With the application of a few pounds per square inch water pressure from within, the tubing inflates and allows the passage of water through pores in the wall. Viaflo is utilized by many companies in the manufacture of their ooze-trickle drip hose home garden systems.

MANUFACTURERS OF
DRIP IRRIGATION SYSTEMS (Continued)

COMPANY	PRODUCTS

Care-Free Garden Supplies, Inc.
32141 E. Alipaz
P.O. Box 151
San Juan Capistrano, Cal. 92675

Twin-Wall System: Attached to main supply line with ¼" tubing; uses approximately 2 gallons per hour per 12-foot length of twin-wall hose; holes spaced every 4" in outer tubing, every 24" in inner tubing

Spaghetti System: ¼" spaghetti polyethylene tubing used from main and branch lines to make a system that waters planters, flower beds, pots, hanging planters, etc.; emitters deliver 1, 1½, 2, or 4 gallons per hour attached to ends of spaghetti tubes; mist sprayers also available for tropical plants

Conflow Irrigation Systems
P.O. Box 10
Pala, Cal. 92059

Screw-in Spray Heads: Uses an unusual water stretcher unit with a low flow rate; 6 spaghetti emitters are attached to each unit; electric timer available

Chapin Watermatics
368 N. Colorado Ave.
Watertown, N.Y. 13601

Single-Wall Drip Hose: 100 feet of dew hose connects direct to water supply; water oozes directly from dew hose. Can be tailored to fit your plantings with enclosed T connections and elbows

Drip Irrigation Sciences Division
Top Box 2121
Huntington Beach, Cal. 92648

Spaghetti System: Uses skinny drippers

Eastside Irrigation Service
645 W. Lamona
Fresno, Cal. 93728

Twin-Wall System: Small hose above large main chamber serves as water supply and will deliver 30 gallons per hour per 100"; ideal for close-spaced plantings of strawberries and vegetables; has optional fertilizer applicator or timer

Drip Emitters: Can be plugged directly into main hose or installed at the end of 3/16" distribution tubing; spaghetti tubes can be used from the emitters to individual plants; emitters can also be used as misters; has optional fertilizer applicator and timer; ideal for individual plants, potted plants, containers

Eaton Corporation
191 E. North Ave.
Carol Stream, Ill. 60187

Emitter: Incorporates a long, tortuous path of relatively large openings to achieve a low flow rate; installation is simple and quick; uses a flow control

General Irrigation Co.
South 12 A Road
P.O. Box 776
Carthage, Mo. 64836

Uses emitters

Gro Mor
3156 E. La Palma
Anaheim, Cal. 92806

Spaghetti system: Utilizes a hose and fitting filter with four distribution lines—these are run down the rows; the emitters are pieces of spaghetti tubing approximately 9" long, spaced along the distribution tubing at 18-20" intervals; can also be used for hanging baskets

Interior Techniques Thirst Quencher
2440 Ridge Park Lane
Orange, Cal. 92667

Spaghetti system: Uses an adjustable T tube; adjustable water deflector can be adjusted for each plant

Irrigro International Irrigation Systems
8956 Hennepin Ave.
Niagara Falls, N.Y. 14304

Single-Wall Drip Hose: T Kit contains four 25-foot Du Pont Viaflo tubes attached by T connections to a header tube; waters a 10x25-ft. garden

S Kit contains 100' Viaflo tubing. Utilizes an S-shape up and down the rows like a soaker hose; waters a 10x20-ft. garden

Leisure Time
2999 Monterey Salinas Hwy.
Monterey, Cal. 93940

Emitters: Utilizes poly tubing with emitters or foggers; for trees, roses, rectangular gardens using ½" perimeter tubing; ⅜" for lateral lines; also good for hanging plants and boxes

Micro Mist
P.O. Box 606
Winter Garden, Fla. 32787

Screw-in Spray Heads: 360-degree, 280-degree, 180-degree microjet misters that install on a hose or plastic feeder line

Rain Bird Corp.
7045 N. Grand Ave.
Glendora, Cal. 91740

Emitters: Uses a Rain Bird 30-mesh single-outlet emitter

Reed Irrigation Systems
585 Veron Way
El Cajon, Cal. 92022

Bi-wall system: Main chamber on bottom, secondary chamber on top; spacing 12", 18", 24", & 36"; good for vegetable gardens
Emitters: Side-mounted emitters can be easily installed or removed; good for a line of trees, grapes, etc.

MANUFACTURERS OF
DRIP IRRIGATION SYSTEMS (Continued)

COMPANY	PRODUCTS
Roberts Irrigation Products 700 Rancheros Dr. San Marcos, Cal. 92069	**Single-Wall Drip Hose:** Vegetable garden trickle system kit; drip hose attaches to feed hose by tubing; kit waters a 200-sq.-ft. garden **Spaghetti System:** Utilizes ⅛″ tubing with spot spitters; a Roberts-invented emitter with a mini spray; garden kit comes with 4-gallon containers with built-in spot spitters; other kits have individual spot spitters for trees, shrubs, etc.
Spot Systems 1559 Sunland Way Costa Mesa, Cal. 92626	**Emitters:** Vortex emitter can be used as a drip system for each plant or as a sprayer; may be put in a box, hanging basket, or planter with the use of a transfer tube, which comes in kit form
Submatic Irrigation Systems P.O. Box 246 Lubbock, Tex. 79408	**Emitters:** Drip line made of hard plastic with emitters spaced every 2 feet; emitters can also be purchased for garden hose; features a wide variety of kits
Vegeflo 5858 NE 87th Ave. Portland, Ore. 97220	**Single-Wall Drip Hose:** Comes in 300- and 600-foot kits; uses Du Pont Viaflo tubing
Waterguarde P.O. Box 1222 La Mesa, Cal. 92041	**Emitters:** Unit 1 foot in diameter is connected to ¼″ PVC pipe; especially useful for individual plants
Wilcox Tractor Irrigation Division P.O. Box 328 Rutherford, Cal. 94573	**Emitters:** ½″ to ¼″ poly tubing used with Rain Bird type emitters; for planter boxes, individual gardens, hanging plants

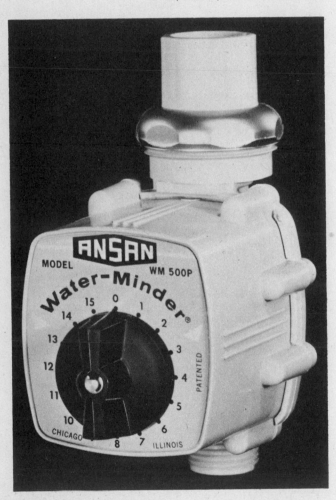

THREE-STATION GARDEN SPRINKLER CONTROLLER

The three stations control three sprinkler valves that can be individually adjusted to water from 5 to 60 minutes. A 14-day skip wheel permits watering schedule to correspond to the days of the week. Watering period can be set for any time of the day and repeated up to three times.

Richdel Model R-303

Richdel, Inc.
P.O. Drawer A
Carson City, Nev. 89701

ANSAN WATER MINDER

Hook one end to the faucet and screw a hose onto the other end. This simple timer keeps the water on for the number of minutes you set, then turns it off. Extremely useful since it turns the water off automatically. Just set it and leave. Prevents overwatering

Ansan Tools & Mfg. Co., Inc.
7400 W. Lawrence Ave.
Harwood Heights, Ill. 60656

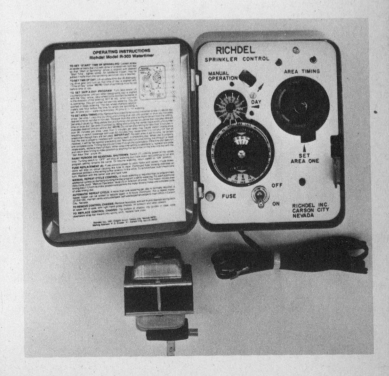

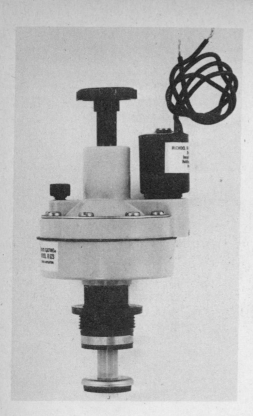

VALVE ACTUATOR

This product converts existing manual systems of watering to automatic control.

Richdel Model R-623

Richdel, Inc.
P.O. Drawer A
Carson City, Nev. 89701

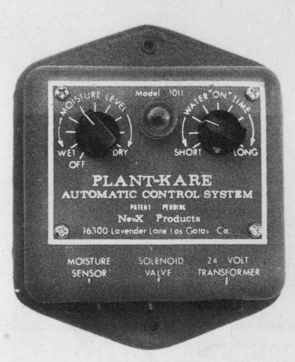

PLANT-KARE AUTOMATIC CONTROL SYSTEM

The controller on this system utilizes two knobs: one enables you to select the wetness for your garden, the other allows you to select the length of time you want the water to run.

New X Products
16300 Lavender Lane
Los Gatos, Cal. 95030

SHOWER STICKS, MODEL 200

Spike sprinklers deliver a gentle shower, good for sprinkling small areas. They come color-coded for different sprinkling patterns.

Burgess Vibrocrafters, Inc.
Rte. 83
Grayslake, Ill. 60030

ADJUSTABLE ROTARY SPRINKLER

By twisting the control you can adjust the arms to vary the water coverage from 5 to 50 feet. You can also vary the spray from a gentle mist to a drenching shower. This adjustability means even water coverage under any conditions. By varying the trajectory you can keep the water spray high for heavy sprinkling or low to the ground for effective sprinkling when the wind blows.

Burgess Vibocrafters, Inc.
Rte. 83
Grayslake, Ill. 60030

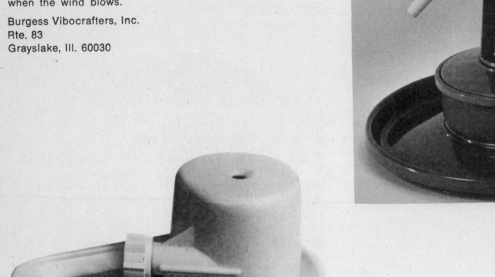

WATER WHIZ, MODEL F-71

Unusual nonmovable sprinkler waters up to 1,250 square feet.

Illinois B & G Corporation
1920 Waukegan Rd.
Glenview, Ill. 60025

OSCILLATING SPRINKLER

The adjustable setting permits watering of narrow gardens—covers up to 2,800 square feet.

Burgess Vibrocrafters, Inc.
Rte. 83
Grayslake, Ill. 60030

FLUIDIC OSCILLATING SPRINKLER

Operates with only two moving parts. There are no gears, no cams, no linkages. The lack of gears means instant whip return with no hesitation or puddling. Adjustments let you sprinkle up to 3,500 square feet.

Burgess Vibrocrafters, Inc.
Rte. 83
Grayslake, Ill. 60030

OSCILLATING SPRINKLER No. 885

Waters full, left, right, or partial. The Perma-Sealed motor operates the sprinkler at water pressures of from 5 to 100 pounds per square inch. Water flow is separated from the motor.

Melnor Industries
1 Carol Place
Moonachie, N.J. 07074

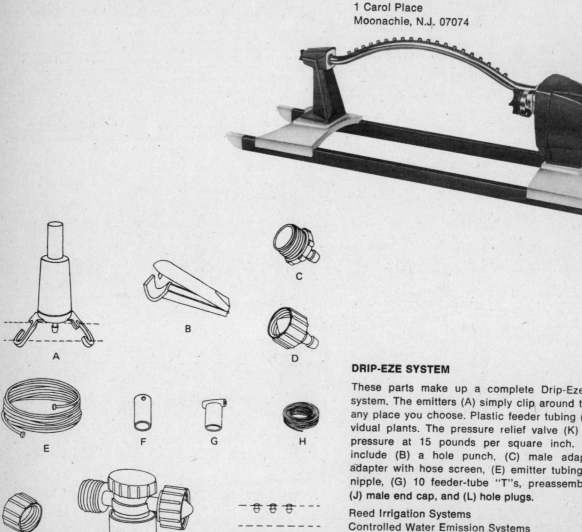

DRIP-EZE SYSTEM

These parts make up a complete Drip-Eze home watering system. The emitters (A) simply clip around the emitter tubing any place you choose. Plastic feeder tubing (H) is run to individual plants. The pressure relief valve (K) keeps the water pressure at 15 pounds per square inch. The other parts include (B) a hole punch, (C) male adapter, (D) female adapter with hose screen, (E) emitter tubing, (F) feeder-tube nipple, (G) 10 feeder-tube "T"s, preassembled on emitters, (J) male end cap, and (L) hole plugs.

Reed Irrigation Systems
Controlled Water Emission Systems
585 Veron Way
El Cajon, Cal. 92022

DEW HOSE

This ooze-trickler soaker has connections that fit any garden faucet and a controlled flow that provides deep moisture penetration without flooding.

Tailor the dew-hose to fit your plantings as follows:
1. Cut to desired length.
2. Put two turns of plastic tape on barbs of fittings, then slide dew-hose on fitting far enough to cover tape.
   Wrap two turns of plastic tape tightly over the end of the dew-hose and extend two more turns onto the fitting.
3. Close end by folding twice and wrapping with plastic tape.

Chapin Watermatics, Inc.
368 N. Colorado Ave.
Watertown, N.Y. 13601

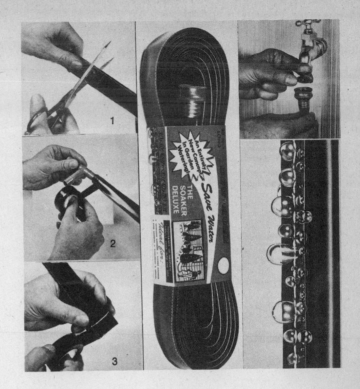

EMITTER SYSTEM

Systems with emitters can be utilized effectively for all types of plantings, planter boxes, trellis vines, hanging plants, and small gardens. Half-inch poly tubing is used for the main feeder line.

Wilcox Tractor
Irrigation Division
Box 328
Rutherford, Cal. 94537

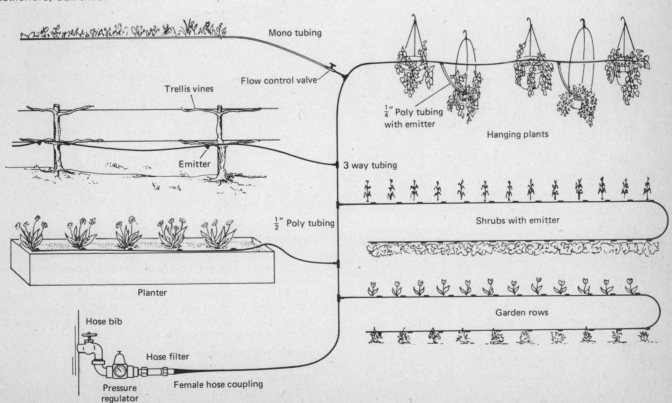

9

PEST MANAGE-MENT

This chapter will describe several different methods of managing bugs and other garden pests. There are essentially two approaches to this problem—organic and chemical. While a few people still follow only one or the other method, most gardeners try a little bit of both. They are aware of the dangers of manufactured chemicals as well as of their benefits in some situations. Besides sprays, there are also traps that can be used.

Different insects and different disease organisms affect different vegetables. The charts in this chapter will assist in the diagnosis of various problems as well as suggesting a cure.

Techniques

During the last two decades the attitude of most Americans toward bugs, diseases, and chemical controls has undergone quite a change. It used to be the common feeling that the only good bug was a dead bug—and that with modern super-strong chemicals it was just a matter of time before insects, germs, and other pests were eradicated from the face of the earth.

Of course, that didn't happen. In fact reports began coming in that some manufactured "miracle cures" were creating more problems than they were solving. Rachel Carson wrote her landmark study, *Silent Spring*, about the effects of DDT and other chemicals on the environment. People began paying more attention to the organic gardeners and farmers, some of whom turned the tables on the advocates of chemicals by demanding that manufactured pesticides, herbicides, and other unnatural substances be eradicated from the face of the earth.

The verbal battles between the users of chemicals and the boosters of the organic approach have had some useful results. Many discoveries have been made, and many new products have come on the market, that have made vegetable gardening much easier for the average person. Today there are still some gardeners—not many, to be sure—who run for the spray can everytime they see a bug. And there are some organic gardeners who believe that all chemicals are dangerous—hazardous to the lives of plants and animals alike. But most gardeners are somewhat in between these two groups. They recognize the dangers of chemicals but also know the advantages of using certain products at certain times. There are in fact wide gradations of toxicity and effectiveness among the chemicals. Some of them, like chlordane, are quite powerful and long-lasting. Others, like malathion, are relatively mild and last about a week. But all chemicals are dangerous in one degree or another, and so must be handled with care.

In this chapter we are going to present for the reader's consideration several different methods of pest management, involving both organic and chemical approaches. Actually, for the most part they're not different at all, because most gardeners find them compatible. First we'll deal with the organic way to manage pests, then go on to describe the many chemicals that can be of great help if the situation gets out of hand.

Organic insect management

Insect infestation in your garden can come and go. There are many factors that determine whether or not a particular pest will attack your plants. Insects move from one place to another and are often influenced by weather, day length, what your neighbors are doing, what crops you are raising (and what stage of life they are in), and many other factors. Almost any change can send insects out of your garden and off in another direction. In addition insects have their own life cycles. If you're aware of what these are likely to be in your area, you can schedule your planting accordingly. Thus, if a garden is started at a certain time of the year, it may be overwhelmed with pests. A few weeks later, you may be able to plant in almost complete safety.

There are two simple rules to follow if you intend to control insects in your garden organically:

1. Learn to live with some insects. After all, a few holes in a cabbage leaf aren't very important. (And you won't get rid of all bugs no matter what you do.)
2. Use only the controls you need to bring the insect population down to acceptable levels. If you think heavier measures such as sprays may be necessary, keep them in reserve and use only when all else has failed.

Controlling insects the easy way

Keep your eye on your garden. Inspect it daily, either in the morning or evening (most bugs stay under cover during the heat of the day). If an insect attack occurs, it may be an indication that you have other garden problems. Often pests attack only the unhealthy, less vigorous plants. Check to see that your garden is properly watered (the soil should not be dried out), that plants are not being crowded out by weeds, that they are getting proper nutrients, that the soil pH remains somewhere close to neutral, and that your vegetables are getting enough sun (at least six hours a day is the accepted standard).

Next, be sure that you keep the garden clean. Clutter is a breeding ground for both insects and disease organisms. Get rid of all dead weeds, clean up piles of trash, move lumber away from the edge of the garden, and don't allow any rotting material close to the garden bed. Haul away refuse and put organic materials into the compost pile.

As mentioned, one of the best ways to keep pests out of your garden is to keep your plants healthy. And one of the best ways to have healthy plants is to keep your soil in top condition. In Chapter 3, Organic Gardening, you read about two methods of soil maintenance that should be reviewed at this point—composting and mulching. By composting, you recycle your organic waste material into rich nutrients for your garden soil. By mulching, you lay a protective covering on your soil to conserve moisture, to maintain an even temperature, and to control weeds. If the mulch is organic, it will also supply the soil with nutrients as it decays.

But even if you have the best soil and the healthiest plants, some pests may find their way into your garden. If you see any large crawling insects such as the tomato hornworm feeding on your plants, simply pick them off into a wide-mouth jar. The same goes for caterpillars and other large bugs. Pick off pieces of leaf that contain insect colonies. Spray small bugs and flying insects with a hard, direct stream of water from the garden hose.

Many insects can be lured into home-made traps. Some beer or other fermenting carbohydrate in a glass jar, cooking pan, or similar receptacle will trap many moths and bores. Earwigs will crawl into rolled-up newspapers, from which they can be dumped each morning into a pail of hot water. Another method of trapping earwigs—and snails, slugs, grubs, and cutworms—is to place pieces of ripe fruits and vegetables around the garden. The bugs will gather for the feast, especially at night, and you can dispose of them in the morning.

If insects are especially bad, cover plants with a netting and enclose fruit in a plastic bag. Or you might consider using a spray of some kind.

Do-it-yourself organic sprays

There are many home-made concoctions that work well in eliminating or reducing insect populations. One idea is to mix about 20 tablespoons of soap flakes (like Ivory) in six gallons of water. The soap (not detergent) can be sprayed on the plants without danger of hurting them, and it will help to control aphids and some other insects.

Another spray can be made from plants with a disagreeable odor, such as garlic, marigolds, and chives. One method is to put the cloves, petals, leaves, or whatever into a pot, add enough water to cover, bring the mixture to the boiling point, remove from stove, and strain off the solid matter. Dilute the remaining liquid with four or five parts of water, stir for five to ten minutes, and spray. Another method is to liquefy the leaves, etc., with enough water to cover in a blender. Again, strain off solid particles, mix the remaining liquid in the proportion of two or three teaspoons to a quart of water, and spray.

Other simple formulas include the following:

Tomato stems and leaves boiled in water destroy aphids, etc.; lime mixed with wood ashes prevents maggot damage; ground hot pepper mixed with equal amounts of water and soap powder is effective on tomato worms.

Organic botanical sprays you can buy

There are many insecticides today that have natural origins—that is, they are not the product of the laboratory or factory, but are made from plants. Although they are poisonous, and therefore must be approached with caution, they are milder than most synthetic preparations and, perhaps most important, they break down in the soil after use and do not leave a poisonous residue. Among the most popular of these substances are pyrethrum, rotenone, ryania, and sabadilla. For purposes of comparison these have been included with nonorganic insecticides in the chart on page 264, Common Home Garden Insecticides and Their Use.

Also included in that chart are several bacterial organisms that can be used to kill some kinds of insects. Among these are Bacillus thuringiensis and Bacillus popilliae (milky spoor disease). These preparations have been in use for many years, and although their action is still not totally understood, they are considered safe to use by most authorities.

Insect predators

There are some common bugs that are harmless to your garden in themselves and have the further advantage that they eat large numbers of harmful insects. Other insect-eaters are birds. They're generally not difficult to attract, either: Set up a free lunch, with plenty of water on the side, and they'll come flocking. (And if they get out of hand and begin eating fruit off your trees and bushes, protect your produce with a net.)

The four most effective insect predators are lacewing flies, ladybugs, praying mantises, and trichogramma wasps. The larvae of lacewings go after aphids. Ladybugs have a greedy appetite for aphids, thrips, tree lice, and the eggs and larvae of other plant-destroying insects. Praying mantis young eat aphids, flies, and other small bugs. The larger adults consume large quantities of beetles, caterpillars, grasshoppers, and other pests. Trichogramma wasps are especially effective on the larvae of the cabbage worm.

There are other insect predators that you should know about: the assassin bug destroys several harmful

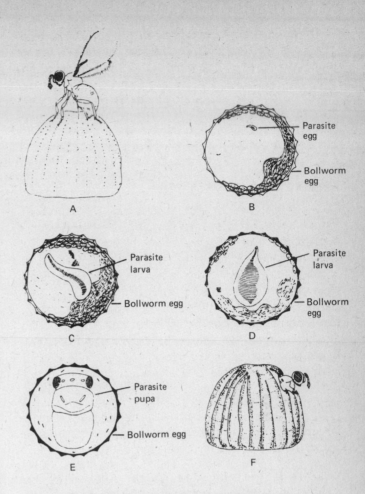

LIFE HISTORY OF A TRICHOGRAMMA PARASITE:

A Trichogramma female depositing her egg in a bollworm egg

B Trichogramma egg within a bollworm egg

C First stage of larval development

D Second stage of larval development

E Pupa of Trichogramma (dorsal view)

F Trichogramma adult emerging from a bollworm egg through hole chewed in the egg shell

insects, as do centipedes. Ground beetles prey on caterpillars.

Your area may be well supplied with predator insects. If it isn't, you can order them by mail (see list on page 262). Many people are skeptical about the effectiveness of this type of action. But plenty of gardeners who have brought in mail-order predators have found them to be quite sucessful.

Companion planting

Many gardeners have come to the conclusion that some plants attract insects, others repel them. And for this reason some types of plants do well in combination with certain other types. For instance, nasturtiums often attract aphids. If your melons, say, have been bothered by aphids in past years, nasturtiums planted right next to the melon plot might attract all the aphids away from the melons. On the other hand, garlic repels aphids; planted next to a melon patch it might just be able to keep all the aphids away. Results are not guaranteed in any of this companion planting, but enough people have done well with it to make it worthwhile trying. Here are some additional beneficial plants:

- Leeks repel carrot flies.
- Marigolds repel nematodes, bean beetles, Japanese beetles.
- Radishes repel striped cucumber beetles.
- Rosemary repels Mexican bean beetles.
- Sage repels cabbage worm butterflies.
- Tansy repels several different kinds of beetles.
- Thyme repels cabbage worm.

Summary

There is no doubt that the use of simple organic techniques can be effective in the management and control of all kinds of garden pests. This subject has been discussed first in this chapter because most gardeners prefer to give organic methods priority over attacks with chemicals. There are times and there are places, however, when pest problems get out of hand. At that point many people choose to use more powerful weapons, such as the laboratory-developed chemicals.

SUPPLIERS OF PREDATOR INSECTS

Allan's Aquarium & Exotic Birds
845 Lincoln Blvd.
Venice, Cal. 90291	Ladybugs
Bio-Control Co.
Route 2, Box 2397
Auburn, Cal. 95603	Ladybugs
Praying mantises
W. Atlee Burpee Co.
Philadelphia, Pa. 19132
Clinton, Ia. 52732
Riverside, Cal. 92502	Ladybugs
Praying mantises
California Green Lacewings, Inc.
P.O. Box 2495
Merced, Cal. 95340	Lacewing flies
Trichogramma wasps
Connecticut Valley Biological
Supply Co., Inc.
Valley Rd.
South Hampton, Mass. 01073	Damselfly nymphs
Dragonfly nymphs
Dahl Biological Supply, Inc.
P.O. Box 370
Canutillo, Tex. 79835	Tarantulas
Eastern Biological Control Co.
Route 5, Box 379
Jackson, N.J. 08527	Praying mantises
Fairfax Biological Laboratory, Inc.
Box 129
Clinton Corners, N.Y. 12514	Lacewing flies
Trichogramma wasps
Gothard, Inc.
P.O. Box 370
Canutillo, Tex. 79835	Praying mantises
Trichogramma wasps
King Labs
P.O. Box 69
Limerick, Pa. 19468	Praying mantises
Green lacewing
Lakeland Nursery Sales
340 Poplar
Hanover, Pa. 17331	Ladybugs
Praying mantises
Mongul-ED
P.O. Box 2482
Oshkosh, Wisc. 54901	Praying mantises
Organic Control, Inc.
P.O. Box 25382
West Los Angeles, Cal. 90025	Ladybugs
Praying mantises
Pyramid Nursery
P.O. Box 5274
Reno, Nev. 89503	Lacewing larvae
Ladybugs
Praying mantises
Trichogramma wasps
Rincon Vitova Insectaries, Inc.
P.O. Box 95
Oak View, Cal. 93022	Fly parasites
Lacewing flies
Ladybugs
Predatory mites
Scale parasites
Trichogramma wasps
Robert Robbins
424 N. Courtland St.
East Stroudsburg, Pa. 18301	Praying mantises
L. E. Schnoor
P.O. Box 148
Yuba City, Cal. 94991	Ladybugs
Turtox/Cambosco
MacMillan Science Co., Inc.
8200 S. Hoyne Ave.
Chicago, Ill. 60620	Praying mantises
West Coast Ladybug Sales
Rt. 1, Box 93A
Biggs, Cal. 95917	Ladybugs

SUPPLIERS OF BACTERIAL INSECTICIDES

DIPEL-THURICIDE (BACILLUS THURINGIENSIS)

Abbott Laboratories
Agricultural Veterinary Products
North Chicago, Ill. 60064	Burgess Vibrocrafters, Inc.
Rte. 83
Grayslake, Ill. 60030
Geo. J. Ball, Inc.
Box 335
West Chicago, Ill. 60185	Galt Research, Inc.
Trafalgar, Ind. 46181
Black Leaf Products Co.
667 N. State St.
Elgin, Ill. 60120	Organic Control, Inc.
P.O. Box 25382
West Los Angeles,
Cal. 90025

DOOM MILKY SPOOR BACTERIA

Fairfax Biological Laboratory, Inc.
Box 129
Clinton Corners, N.Y. 12514	Reuter Laboratories
7555 Gary Rd.
P.O. Box 1058
Manassas, Va. 22110

Chemicals in the garden

It is important for the gardener who wishes to use some of the chemical sprays and powders to find out as much as possible about them. Some of the dangers inherent in their use can be avoided through intelligent planning and careful application. In some cases overkill can be as damaging to the pocketbook, in these days of high prices, as it might be to the plants and animals (including man) in the area.

There are three major categories of chemicals for use in the garden: pesticides, to control insects; fungicides, to control fungus-caused plant diseases; and herbicides, to control weeds. There are also bacteriocides, to prevent or cure bacterial diseases; nematicides, to control nematodes; and rodenticides, to control rodents.

While all of these categories will be discussed in this section, emphasis will be on the first two.

Insecticides

Insecticides used in the garden come in either solid or liquid form. Dusts, baits, and granules are applied dry. Baits are mixed by the manufacturer with a pest attractant; dusts and granules are mixed with an inert carrier. Three types of insecticides are applied wet: emulsifiable concentrates (EC), soluble powders (SP), and wettable powders (WP). These last are mixed with water and transferred to spray apparatus.

When applying either dusts or sprays, it is important to make sure that they cover all surfaces of the infested plants. It's also important not to apply them to yourself or to anyone else. To protect yourself, cover your body with clothing. Wear a broad-brimmed hat and gloves, too. Try not to get any of the liquid or powder on your skin; if this happens, wash it off right away.

The most frequently used chemical insecticides in the garden are carbaryl, malathion, and diazinon.

Proper use of insecticides

1. Select an insecticide that can be used on a wide variety of crops.
2. Read the label instructions carefully and follow them exactly when preparing and applying insecticides.
3. Never use an insecticide on a crop that is not included on the label.
4. Never use more than the specified dosage.
5. Store insecticides out of reach of children.
6. Dispose of the container in a safe manner: break or puncture the pesticide container. Wrap in a newspaper and place in the trash or bury at least 18 inches deep in the ground.

(These are generic names; different manufacturers may call their own brands of these generics by different names. For instance, a popular make of carbaryl is Sevin.) Two other chemicals, trichlofon and methoxychlor, are also used at times, along with a host of minor preparations. Some manufacturers put out combinations of ingredients.

Slug and snail control

Most standard snail and slug control baits contain metaldehyde. Unfortunately, these are ineffective in wet weather. But slug baits based on methocarp will destroy slugs and snails even in the damp.

There are also two fairly new developments: mesurol (Slug-geta), a new molluscide from Ortho (Chevron Chemical Corporation, 200 Bush St., San Francisco Cal. 94120) does an extremely good job of ridding the garden of these pests. Another new one, Snail Snare (National Chelating Corporation, Box 352, West Covina, Cal. 91790), dehydrates the pests rather than poisoning them.

You can also exercise preventive control by utilizing chemical compounds based on zectran or mesurol.

Nematode control

Nematodes are tiny microscopic worms that live in the soil and on the insides of plant roots. Nematode root knot disease can be a serious problem in home gardens. Here's how to control it:

Nonchemical controls

1. Move the garden every two or three years.
2. Make sure purchased transplants do not show tiny root swellings or knots on the roots.
3. Place mulch material around the base of plants to keep the soil from drying out, and make sure the soil stays moist during dry weather.
4. Destroy the roots by pulling up and destroying after harvest.
5. Use resistant varieties where possible.

Chemical controls. Several chemicals (nematicides) can be used to kill nematodes in the soil:

NEMATICIDES	CROPS
D-D or Telone II	Any vegetable crop
Fumazone 86% liquid EC [or] Nemagon 86% liquid EC (Do not use granular formulation of Fumazone or Nemagon for snap beans, eggplant, peppers, onions, and sweet potatoes)	Beans, broccoli, cantaloupes, cabbage, carrots, okra, squash, tomatoes, melons

COMMON HOME GARDEN INSECTICIDES AND THEIR USE

INSECTICIDE	USE AND COMMENTS
Chlordane	Chlorinated hydrocarbon that kills by contact and stomach action; effective for control of ants and earwigs; do not use on any vegetables
Cygon-dimethoate	Kills aphids, spider mites, and serpentine leaf miner
Diazinon	Organic phosphate recommended primarily for use in the soil to control cutworms, grubs, wireworms, and other ground pests; toxic to fish and honey bees; has a brief residual action
Dipel-Thuricide (Bacillus thuringiensis)	Bacterial organism that paralyzes the digestive system of such leaf-chewing worms as caterpillars, cabbage loopers, and tomato hornworms without having any toxic effect on bees, pets, or humans
DOOM (Milky Disease Spoor Powder)	Odorless powder containing the living spores of the organism which produces the milky disease of the grubs of the Japanese beetle—effective for control of the Japanese beetle
Dormant oil	Highly refined petroleum oil mixed with water; some formulas contain fish or vegetable oils; effectively smothers scale and other sucking insects
Dylox (Trichlorfon)	Contact and stomach insecticide useful for controlling cutworms
Kelthane (Dicofol)	Effective miticide that kills red spider and clover mites; for control of mites on ornamentals, house plants, fruits, and vegetables
Lindane	Chlorinated hydrocarbon with action similar to DDT—effective on ants; do not use on any vegetables
Malathion	Contact phosphate compound that is useful on all sucking insects such as aphids; used extensively in home gardens
Methoxychlor (Marlate)	Contact and stomach insecticide that effectively controls a wide range of chewing insects; has a residual action—not recommended by many gardeners
Mirex	Kills ants; do not make more than one application every 2 months or three applications in 12 months
Nicotine sulfate	Organic insecticide made from the waste products of tobacco; especially useful on aphids; very poisonous
Pyrethrum	Organic insecticide made from the dried, powdered flowers of certain plants of the chrysanthemum genus; effective against aphids, leafhoppers, thrips, leaf miners
Rotenone	Insecticide derived from the roots and sometimes stems of certain New World tropical shrubs and vines of the genera Derris and Lonchocarpus; effective against beetles, caterpillars, leaf miners, thrips, aphids
Ryania	Insecticide derived from the ground stems of a tropical South American shrub, Patrisia pyrifera; used effectively against the corn borer
Sabadilla	Contact insecticide made from the seeds of a lilylike Mexican plant; sold as a wettable powder; useful for squash bugs, stink bugs, and harlequin bugs
Sevin (Carbaryl)	Contact phosphate that is useful to control over 170 chewing insects; widely used by home gardeners
Systemic insecticides	A systemic insecticide is absorbed by the plants' roots and circulated through the vascular system, killing chewing and sucking insects as they feed; not used on vegetables
Thiodan endosulfan	Used for the control of a wide range of insects

Insecticide manufacturers/suppliers

Aceto Agricultural
Chemicals Corp.
126-02 Northern Blvd.
Flushing, N.Y. 11368

American Cyanamid Co.
Agricultural Chemicals
Box 400
Princeton, N.J. 08540

BASF Wyandotte Corp.
Wyandotte, Mich. 48192

Geo. J. Ball, Inc.
Box 335
West Chicago, Ill. 60185

The Bishop Co.
Box 317
Lebanon, Pa. 17042

Black Leaf Products Co.
667 N. State St.
Elgin, Ill. 60120

Burgess Vibrocrafters, Inc.
Rte. 83
Grayslake, Ill. 60030

Carmel Chemical Corp.
Box 406
Westfield, Ind. 46074

Chacon Chemical Corp.
2600 Yates Ave.
City of Commerce,
Cal. 90040

Chemical Formulators, Inc.
Box 26
Nitro, W. Va. 25143

Chempar Chemical Co.,
260 Madison Ave.
New York, N.Y. 10016

Chevron Chemical Co.
Ortho Div.
200 Bush St.
San Francisco, Cal. 94104

Chipman Chemicals, Ltd.
Box 9100
Stoney Creek, Ont.
L8G 3Z1, Canada

Ciba-Geigy Corp.
Agricultural Div.
Box 11422
Greensboro, N.C. 27409

Clinton Nursery Products,
Inc.
Box 510
Clinton, Conn. 06413

Colonial Products, Inc.
1830 10th Ave. N.
Lake Worth, Fla. 33461

Continental Chemiste Corp.
2256 W. Ogden Ave.
Chicago, Ill. 60612

Ross Daniels, Inc.
1720 Fuller Rd.
Box 430
W. Des Moines, Ia. 50265

Dexol Industries
1450 W. 228th St.
Torrance, Cal. 90501

Dow Chemical Co.
Ag. Products Dept.
Box 1706
Midland, Mich. 48640

E. I. Du Pont de Nemours
& Co.
1007 Market St.
Wilmington, Del. 19898

Elanco Products Co.
Box 1968
Indianapolis, Ind. 46206

Faesy & Besthoff, Inc.
143 River Rd.
Edgewater, N.J. 07020

Fairfax Biological Lab, Inc.
Box 129
Clinton Corners,
N.Y. 12514

FMC Corp.
Agricultural Chemical Div.
100 Niagara St.
Middleport, N.Y. 14105

Germain's, Inc.
Box 3233
Los Angeles, Cal. 90058

Greenlight Company
Box 17985
San Antonio, Tex. 78217

Hercules, Inc.
910 Market St.
Wilmington, Del. 19899

Holland Bulb Co.
6441 Johnson Cr. Blvd.
Portland, Ore. 97206

Hooker Chemical Corp.
1050 Iroquois Ave.
Niagara Falls, N.Y. 14302

Hopkins Agricultural
Chemical Co.
537 Atlas Ave., Box 584
Madison, Wisc. 53701

Kaiser Agricultural
Chemicals
Box 246
Savannah, Ga. 31402

Lebanon Chemical Corp.
Box 180
Lebanon, Pa. 17042

Leeming/Pacquin
Division Pfizer, Inc.
235 E. 42nd St.
New York, N.Y. 10017

Leffingwell Chemical Co.
111 S. Berry St.
Brea, Cal. 92621

Leisur-Aid
I-29 & Hwy. 370
Council Bluffs, Ia. 51501

Lethelin Products, Inc.
15 MacQuesten Pkwy S.
Mount Vernon, N.Y. 10550

Chas. H. Lilly Co.
(Lilly/Miller)
7737 N.E. Killingsworth
Portland, Ore. 97218

Lite-Weight Products, Inc.
707 Funston Rd.
Kansas City, Kan. 66115

Miller Chemical Co.
Box 333
Hanover, Pa. 17331

Nott Mfg. Co.
Pleasant Valley,
N.Y. 12569

Patterson Green-Up
Chemical Co.
1400 Union Ave.
Kansas City, Mo. 64101

PBI Gordon Corp.
Acme Division
300 S. Third St.
Kansas City, Kan. 66118

S. B. Penick & Co.
1050 W. Wall St.
Lyndhurst, N.J. 07071

Plantabbs Corp.
Timonium, Md. 21093

Plant Marvel Labs
624 W. 119th St.
Chicago, Ill. 60628

Plantrac Corp.
38 W. Mall
Plainview, N.Y. 11803

B. G. Pratt Co.
204 21st St.
Paterson, N.J. 07509

Premier Brands, Inc.
350 Madison Ave.
New York, N.Y. 10017

E. Rabinowe & Co.
465 Saw Mill River Rd.
Yonkers, N.Y. 10701

Rhodia, Inc., Ag. Div.
Box 125
Monmouth Junction,
N.J. 08852

Robeco Chemicals, Inc.
99 Park Ave.
New York, N.Y. 10016

Rockland Chemical Co.,
Inc.
Box 809
W. Caldwell, N.J. 07006

Science Products Co., Inc.
5801 N. Tripp Ave.
Chicago, Ill. 60646

O. M. Scott & Sons Co.
Marysville, Oh. 43040

Smith-Douglass
Division Borden Chemicals
Box 419
Norfolk, Va. 23501

Sta-Green Plant Food Co.
Box 540
Sylacauga, Ala. 35150

Stauffer Chemical Co.
Ag. Chemical Div.
Westport, Conn. 06880

Swift Ag. Chemical Corp.
111 W. Jackson Blvd.
Chicago, Ill. 60604

Swift Farms, Inc.
3700 Prudential Tower
Boston, Mass. 02199

Techne Corp.
Box 10718
Gladstone, Mo. 64118

Tuco Products Co.
501 S. Line St.
Du Quoin, Ill. 62832

Union Carbide Corp.
Ag. Products Div.
Box 1906
Salinas, Cal. 93901

USS Agri Chemicals
Box 1685
Atlanta, Ga. 30301

Vaughan-Jacklin Corp.
5300 Katrine Ave.
Downers Grove, Ill. 60515

Velsicol Chemical Corp.
341 E. Ohio St.
Chicago, Ill. 60611

Virginia Chemicals, Inc.
Aerosol Dept.
3340 W. Norfolk Rd.
Portsmouth, Va. 23703

Walco-Linck Corp.
Box 769
Clifton, N.J. 07015

Wonderlawn
1072 West Side Ave.
Jersey City, N.J. 07306

Woolfolk Chemical Works,
Inc.
E. Main St., Box 938
Ft. Valley, Ga. 31030

Melvin E. Wyant
Rose Specialist, Inc.
Johnnycake Ridge Rd.
Mentor, Oh. 44060

VEGETABLE DISEASE CONTROL RECOMMENDATIONS

CROP	DISEASE	DESCRIPTION	REMEDY
Beans (snap, lima)	Anthracnose	Dark sunken, circular, or oval pod spots; brown borders and salmon-colored ooze in spots; leaves and stems also infected	Spray with Maneb or Zineb or dust with Maneb at first sign of disease and weekly thereafter; also, use Bordeaux mixture
	Bacterial blight	Brown or tan spots or blotches with a yellow border on leaves; pods may have brick-red or brown sunken blotches	Use disease-free seed
	Damping-off	Seeds fail to grow; young plants die	Treat seed with Captan dust, or apply Captan to soil at planting time
	Root and stem rot	Plant wilts and dies; plant is decayed on lower roots and stem	Apply Captan to soil at planting time
	Rust	Brown spots (pustules) on leaves	Use Maneb or Bravo. Sulfur dust can also be applied at weekly intervals
Broccoli, brussels sprouts, cabbage, cauliflower, and other "cole" crops	Club root fungus	Roots become enlarged; plants wilt and finally die	Grow only in well-drained soil
	Yellows	Leaves turn yellow; plants are often deformed	Choose resistant varieties
	Black rot	Infections make leaves yellow or tan; leaf veins and vascular ring in stem may be black; head may decay	Rotate cabbage with other crops; plant disease-free seed; use Bordeaux mixture
	Blackleg		Keep garden tools clean; remove debris; follow crop rotation
	Damping off Stem rot	Young plants die; seeds may rot	Treat seed with Captan dust; work Captan into soil in accordance with instructions
Corn	Bacterial wilt	Long pale-green or tan dead streaks on leaves; may cause stunting and death of plants	The disease bacteria is carried by flea beetles, so use insecticides to control; use resistant varieties
	Smut	Galls on leaves, stems, ears, or tassels continue to enlarge, turn black, and break open	Cut off the galls before they break open and destroy
Cantaloupe, cucumber, pumpkin, and watermelon	Anthracnose	Dark sunken, circular, or oval pod spots; brown borders and salmon-colored ooze in center, on fruits, stems, and borders	Spray with Maneb at first sign of disease and continue weekly as needed
	Bacterial wilt	Vines wilt and die	The bacteria is transmitted by cucumber beetle—use insecticide to control the beetles
	Fruit rot	Rotted fruit; gray, moldy growth; decay at blossom end of squash	Spray with Maneb at the first sign of disease and continue weekly
	Powdery mildew	White, powdery growth on surface of leaves and stems	Spray with Karathane or Benomyl . . . at weekly intervals sulphur dust
Peas	Damping off	Seeds fail to grow; young plants die	Buy treated seed; treat seed with Captan dust or apply to soil at planting time

VEGETABLE DISEASE CONTROL RECOMMENDATIONS (Continued)

CROP	DISEASE	DESCRIPTION	REMEDY
	Downy mildew	White mold on underside of leaves	Grow resistant varieties
	Fusarium wilt	Seedlings wilt and die; older plants growth is stunted	Grow resistant varieties
Pepper	Bacterial spot	Irregular tan or dark-brown spots on leaves	Spray with fixed copper at first sign of disease and then weekly as needed
Potato	Black leg	Stems decayed and blackened at or below ground line; tops grow poorly	Plants disease-free tubers. Do not plant cold potatoes into cold soil
	Late blight	Dead areas on leaves—brown or dark purple; white or gray moldy growth on leaf underside	Plant disease-free tubers; spray foliage at first sign of disease with zinc-ion, Maneb, Zineb, fixed copper, or Bravo
	Scab	Black, rough, scabby patches appear on the skin	Grow resistant varieties
Squash	Bacterial wilt	Leaves suddenly start to wilt; cucumber beetles in evidence, especially on young plants	Dust with Sevin or Diazinon; may be necessary to destroy all infected plants.
	Blossom end rot	Flowers become rotted, deformed	Spray blossoms with Maneb or Zineb
	Leaf Spot	Dried brown spots on leaves soon become holes	Spray with Zineb or Captan
	Fruit rot	Rot attacks squash resting on moist ground	Prevent by growing on black plastic
	Powdery mildew	Powdery white material appears on leaves	Dust with sulfur
	Scab	Brown holes in fruit	Spray with Maneb
Sweet Potato	Scurf	Irregular purple-brown discoloration	Use only disease-free potato roots
Tomato	Blossom end rot	Leathery black or dark-brown decay on the blossom end of fruit	Can be cut down or eliminated by maintaining a uniform soil moisture
	Early blight	Dark-brown spots with concentric rings on leaves, stems, and fruits	Spray foliage with zinc-ion Maneb, Maneb, Zineb, fixed copper, or Bravo at first signs of disease and at weekly intervals
	Fusarium and verticillium wilt	Leaves turn yellow and fall on one side of the plant before the other; vascular tissue may have dark discoloration; leaves wilt	Use resistant tomato varieties; rotate garden crops
	Late blight	Brown or dark-purple dead areas on leaves; white or gray moldy growth on leaf underside	Use partially resistant varieties apply zinc-ion Maneb, Maneb, Zineb, fixed copper, or Bravo at the first signs of disease and at weekly intervals
Vegetables in general	Southern stem blight	Decay of stem near ground line; often heavy white fungus growth	Rotate crops
	Virus	Mottling, mosaic yellowing of leaves or fruits; some malformation in shape of leaves or fruit	Use resistant varieties; clean up weeds and garden residue

Fungicides

Chemical fungicides are effective in preventing and controlling vegetable diseases. Because fungicides can be blown or washed off plants, they must be reapplied at regular intervals while the disease is active. The following chemicals are often used in vegetable gardens.

CHEMICAL	SOME TRADE NAMES
BENOMYL (1-butylcarbamoyl-2-benzimidazole carbamate)	Benlate, Tersan 1991
Bravo	Bravo 75%, Bravo 6F
Bordeaux: A mixture of copper sulfate and spray lime in water	Bordo-Mix
Captan (N-trichlormethylmercapto-4-cyclohexene-1,2 dicarboximide)	Orthocide 50 W, Orthocide Garden Fungicide
Ferbam (Ferric dimethyl dithiocarbamate)	Fermate, Ortho Ferbam, Stauffer Ferbam
Fixed copper (Copper oxychloride sulfate)	Basic Copper Fungicide, Corona 53, Ortho Copper 53 Fungicide, Triangle Brand Basic Copper Sulfate, Tribasic Copper Sulfate
(Copper hydroxide)	Kocide 101
(Copper ammonium carbonate)	Cal-Cop 10
(Copper salts of fatty and rosin acids)	Citcop 4E, Copoloid 6, TL-90
Folpet (Phaltan, N-trichloromethylthio-phthalimide)	Chevron Folpet 75W, Fungitrol 11, Ortho Rose and Garden Fungicide, Stauffer Folpet 75W
Karathane (Dinocap, Dinitro . . . 1-methyl heptyl-phenyl crotonate)	Karathane WD, Mildex
Lime sulfur 26-30% solution of calcium polysulfides	Orthorix spray, Security Lime Sulfur
Maneb	Chem Neb, Dithane M-22, Manzate Maneb Fungicide; with zinc added, Dithane M-22 Special, Manzate D, Vancide Maneb
Zinc-Ion Maneb	Dithane M-45, Manzate 200
Streptomycin	
Zineb (zinc ethylene bisdithiocarbamate)	Dithane Z-78, Ortho Zineb Wettable, Parzate C, Vancide Zineb, Stauffer Zineb, Orchard Brand Zineb

Herbicides

Weed killers (herbicides) are not all that useful for the home gardener. Most herbicides are practical only for large-scale agricultural and for single-crop fields. A chemical that is safe for one kind of vegetable may severely injure or destroy another. Weeds can be controlled more effectively in the home garden by a heavy mulch, by cultivating or by hand weeding.

Chemical weed killers can be classified as selective and nonselective—that is, they are selective and attack only one plant or group of plants, or they are nonselective and attack all vegetables.

Some nonselective herbicides are Aminotriazole, Diuron, Monouron, Silvex, 2,4 D, and Simazine. These are not for use within the garden. Silvex is found in most herbicides used to control chickweed, bent grass, clover, spurge, and similar weeds. It does not harm lawn grass. Octyly Ammonium Methyl Arsonate (AMA) is the universally recommended chemical to kill crabgrass in all stages. Amitrole is recommended for poison ivy, poison oak, clump grass, and similar vegetation.

Some selective herbicides are Betasan, Casoran, Chloro IPC, Dachthal, Trifluralin, Eptam, and Chloramben. Chloramben can be used around tomatoes and peppers as a pre-emergence weed killer to control weeds and grasses. Dachthal (DCPA) can be used among certain vegetables as a preemergence weed control.

A good reference on weed control is the booklet "Chemical Weed Control Bulletin 516," from the Kansas Agricultural Experiment Station, Manhattan, Kansas 66502.

Herbicide manufacturers and suppliers

Aceto Agricultural
Chemicals Corp.
126-02 Northern Blvd.
Flushing, N.Y. 11368

J. L. Adikes, Inc.
182-12 93rd Ave.
Jamaica, N.Y. 11423

American Cyanamid Co.
Agricultural Chemicals
Div.
Box 400
Princeton, N.J. 08540

The Ansul Co.
Chemical Group
Stanton St.
Marinette, Wisc. 54143

Aquashade, Inc.
Box 117
Dobbs Ferry, N.Y. 10522

BASF Wyandotte, Corp.
Wyandotte, Mich. 48192

Geo. J. Ball, Inc.
Box 335
West Chicago, Ill. 60185

The Bishop Co.
Box 317
Lebanon, Pa. 17042

Black Leaf Products Co.
667 N. State St.
Elgin, Ill. 60120

Bonide Chemical Co., Inc.
2 Wurz Ave.
Yorkville, N.Y. 13495

Chacon Chemical Corp.
2600 Yates Ave.
City of Commerce,
Cal. 90040

Chemical Formulators, Inc.
Box 26
Nitro, W. Va. 25143

Chempar Chemical Co.,
260 Madison Ave.
New York, N.Y. 10016

Chevron Chemical Co.
Ortho Div.
200 Bush St.
San Francisco, Cal. 94104

Chipman Chemicals Ltd.
Box 9100
Stoney Creek, Ont.
L8G 3Z1, Canada

Ciba-Geigy Corp.
Agricultural Div.
Box 11422
Greensboro, N.C. 27409

Herbicide manufacturers and suppliers (Continued)

Dexol Industries
1450 W. 228th St.
Torrance, Cal. 90501

Diamond Shamrock
Ag. Chem. Div.
1100 Superior Ave.
Cleveland, Oh. 44114

Dow Chemical Co.
Ag. Products Dept.
Box 1706
Midland, Mich. 48640

E. I. Du Pont de Nemours
& Co.
1007 Market St.
Wilmington, Del. 19898

Elanco Products Co.
Box 1968
Indianapolis, Ind. 46206

Encap Products Co.
Box 278
Mt. Prospect, Ill. 60056

Faesy & Besthoff, Inc.
143 River Rd.
Edgewater, N.J. 07020

Holland Bulb Co.
6441 Johnson Cr. Blvd.
Portland, Ore. 97206

Hooker Chemical Corp.
1050 Iroquois Ave.
Niagara Falls, N.Y. 14302

Hopkins Agricultural
Chemical Co.
537 Atlas Ave., Box 584
Madison, Wisc. 53701

Kaiser Agricultural
Chemicals
Box 246
Savannah, Ga. 31402

Lebanon Chemical Co.
Box 180
Lebanon, Pa. 17042

Leffingwell Chemical Co.
111 S. Berry St.
Brea, Cal. 92621

Leisur-Aid
I-29 & Hwy. 370
Council Bluffs, Ia. 51501

Lite-Weight Products, Inc.
707 Funston Rd.
Kansas City, Kan. 66115

Mallinckrodt, Inc.
Box 5439
St. Louis, Mo. 63147

Miller Chemical Co.
Box 333
Hanover, Pa. 17331

PBI Gordon Corp.
Acme Division
300 S. Third St.
Kansas City, Kan. 66118

Patterson Green-Up
Chemical Co.
1400 Union Ave.
Kansas City, Mo. 64101

The Pax Co.
Box 2310
Salt Lake City, Utah 84110

B. G. Pratt Co.
204 21st St.
Paterson, N. J. 07509

Rhodia Inc., Ag Div.
Box 125
Monmouth Junction,
N.J. 08852

Ringer Corp.
6860 Flying Cloud Dr.
Eden Prairie, Minn. 55343

Robeco Chemicals, Inc.
99 Park Ave.
New York, N.Y. 10016

Rockland Chemical Co.,
Box 809
W. Caldwell, N. J. 07006

Science Products Co., Inc.
5801 N. Tripp Ave.
Chicago, Ill. 60646

O. M. Scott & Sons Co.
Marysville, Oh. 43040

Smith-Douglass
Division Borden Chemicals
Box 419
Norfolk, Va. 23501

Sta-Green Plant Food Co.
Box 540
Sylacauga, Ala. 35150

State College Labs
800 Hiesters Lane
Reading, Pa. 19605

Stauffer Chemical Co.
Ag. Chemical Div.
Westport, Conn. 06880

Swift Ag. Chemicals Corp.
11 W. Jackson Blvd.
Chicago, Ill. 60640

Techne Corp.
Box 10718
Gladstone, Mo. 64118

3M Company
3M Center
St. Paul, Minn. 55101

Tuco Products Co.
501 S. Line St.
Du Quoin, Ill. 62832

Union Carbide Corp.
Ag. Products Div.
Box 1906
Salinas, Cal. 93901

Velsicol Chemical Corp.
341 E. Ohio St.
Chicago, Ill. 60611

Vineland Chemical Co.
Wheat Road
Vineland, N.J. 08360

Wonderlawn
1072 West Side Ave.
Jersey City, N.J. 07306

Woolfolk Chemicals Works,
Inc.
E. Main St., Box 938
Ft. Valley, Ga. 31030

Sprayers

Sprayers are essential for the application of pesticides and fungicides in the garden, for spraying liquid fertilizer, for administering weed killer, for applying dormant sprays to fruit trees, and for many other purposes. Today there are many improved designs on the market, giving you a choice of several kinds of sprayers.

Small hand sprayers or atomizers come in various types. There are some for small jobs that are quite like a Windex bottle—you simply pump the top with your fingers. These are especially useful if you want to spot-spray, keeping your application to a very limited area. Another type of hand sprayer is the old familiar standby, consisting of a hand pump (like a bicycle pump) mounted on top of a metal or glass container. There are single-action models, in which the spray stops at the end of each stroke, and continuous-action models, in which the spray is uninterrupted as long as you keep pumping. Many of these sprayers have a nozzle that adjusts for either a fog or a residual-type spray. It's best to choose a sprayer with an adjustable nozzle that is made of a noncorrosive material and that can be easily cleaned.

Hose end sprayers consist of a nozzle, a holding jar, and a female hose end that can be attached to your garden hose. The chemicals can be diluted or mixed in proper proportions right in the jar. Some of these sprayers come with an adjustable nozzle that allows you to mix chemicals and water in whatever proportion you desire during the spraying action. And some models are equipped with a pistol grip handle for easy operation. These sprayers are fine for applying chemicals to small gardens.

Slide sprayers. Sometimes called trombone sprayers, these sprayers utilize a small, round, brass slide pump. There is no tank; the hose end is placed in a bucket

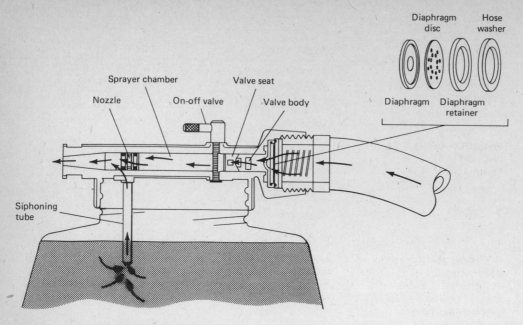

Diaphragm disc   Hose washer

Diaphragm   Diaphragm retainer

Sprayer chamber   Valve seat

Nozzle   On-off valve   Valve body

Siphoning tube

HOW A HOSE-END SPRAYER WORKS

Water enters through the hose. With the valve open, water enters the sprayer chamber, goes through the nozzle, and siphons the liquid from the jar in a set ratio.

or some other open source of water. These sprayers sometimes come with adjustable brass nozzles, and will reach to a distance of about 35 feet. Most are double-action and give a continuous spray.

Compressed-air tanks. These are usually made of galvanized steel or plastic and are pumped by hand to create air pressure that forces out the spray. They are highly adaptable and range in capacity from 1 to 15 gallons; the usual size is 2 gallons. The smaller tanks are generally carried by a shoulder strap. The larger ones use a golf-bag type of caddy. Compressed-air tanks can handle both oil-based sprays and wettables, and are excellent for use in large gardens.

Back pack sprayers. These fairly large metal or plastic containers can be strapped to the user's back. Most hold about four gallons of liquid and are pumped with a hand lever. Some are equipped with a small, gas-operated compressor.

Electric sprayers. These are quite similar to the other larger sprayers, but they utilize a rechargable battery for compressor power.

Power sprayers. There are a number of large-volume, all-purpose, power-drive sprayers on the market with tanks that hold 10 gallons of liquid and more. Some models are designed to be pulled by a garden tractor; others are self-propelled.

Dusters

Some gardeners prefer to apply insecticides in dry dust rather than liquid form. Dusters actually are an extremely convenient and effective method of applying chemicals to vegetables. There are two basic types available: The *Piston Duster,* for small- to medium-sized gardens, stores the dust in a dust chamber. The dust is forced out by hand action of the piston. These small dusters hold up to two quarts of dust. *Crank Dusters* are large enough for use on 8 to 10 acres. They are operated by a hand crank which forces the dust into a fan where it is blown out over the vegetables. Extension tubes put the dust exactly where it is needed. Some larger dusters utilize a power source.

Controlling larger pests

Some species of animals can be an extreme nuisance in the garden.

Gophers can be driven out using a gopher-mole windmill, which essentially sets up a vibration in the ground that gophers and moles can't tolerate. Mothballs or moth flakes can also be used to keep gophers out of the garden. Rabbits can be held off completely by surrounding your plot with a chicken wire fence.

Birds are a mixed blessing. They feed on damaging insects, and thus many gardeners build birdhouses to

CONTROLLING LARGER PESTS

CHEMICAL CONTROLS MOLES - GOPHERS	RABBITS-DEER	DOGS-CATS	MICE-RATS
Black Leaf Products Co. 667 No. State St. Elgin, Ill. 60120	Panogen Co. Ringwood, Ill. 60072 Improved Z.I.P.	Associated Laboratories 1771 Massachusetts Ave. Cambridge, Mass. 02138 Skat Stix, does not wash away	Chempar Chemical Co. 269 Madison Ave. New York, N.Y. 10016 Rozol—mouse killer
Carajon Chemical Co. Inc. Fremont, Mich. 49412 Force's Gopher Killer: whole grain, oats— strychnine alkaloid; Force's Mole Killer: peanuts, seed peas— strychnine sulfate	Pensalt Chemicals Corp. Box 1297 Tacoma, Wash. 98401	Chevron Chemical Co. 200 Bush St. San Francisco, Cal. 94104 Scram-Dog repellent, easy to use aerosol	Colonial Products Inc. 1830 10th Ave. N. Lake Worth, Fl. 33460 32, 42 rat and mice killer, dry pellets
Cooke Laboratory Products Pico Rivera, Cal. 90660 Gopher tabs with strychnine	State College Laboratories 800 Hiesters Lane Reading, Pa. 19605 Magic Circle rabbit and deer repellent	Johnson Nurseries Box 411 Dexter, N.Y. 13634 Scent Off	Cooke Laboratory Products Pico Rivera, Cal. 90660 poisoned barley—special formula attracts rats
Great Lakes Chemical Corp. El Dorado, Kan. 67042 Meth-O-Gas—100% Methyl Bromide	Sudbury Laboratory Inc. Sudbury, Mass. 01776 Chaperone rabbit & deer repellent	Samuel J. Milazzo Co. Pittston, Pa. 18640 Animal Chaser	Nott Manufacturing Pleasant Valley, N.Y. 12569 Rat Nots—kill rats overnight —a saline additive directs rats outside; Mouse Nots are tasty poison seeds; Sia Rat is an anticoagulant deadly to rats
Nott Manufacturing Co. Pleasant Valley, N.Y. 12569 Smoke'em generates sulfur smoke		Sudbury Laboratory Inc. Sudbury, Mass. 01776 Chaperone liquid dog and cat repellent	
Gopher-Mole Chaser 420 N. Bloomfield Rd. Nevada City, Cal. 95959 Windmill vibration frightens moles and gophers	Allcock Mfg. Co. North Water St. Ossining, N.Y. 10562 17 different Humane (Havahart) animal traps for garden predators, dogs, squirrels, skunks, rabbits, etc.		Allcock Manufacturing Co. North Water St. Ossining, N.Y. 10562 Katch-All Rat Trap, traps made of No. 2 galvanized hardware cloth, electrically welded

attract them. On the other hand, some birds will eat seedlings of such fruit as tomatoes. One defense: hang up metal foil strips on strings extended two or three feet over the garden. An extreme measure would be to enclose the garden completely with gauze or chicken wire held up by posts and a frame.

HOSE END SPRAYER

Vegetable gardeners will find the adjustable nozzle—2-, 6-, or 15-gallon mixing ratios—especially helpful.

Burgess Vibrocrafters, Inc.
Rte. 83
Grayslake, Ill. 60030

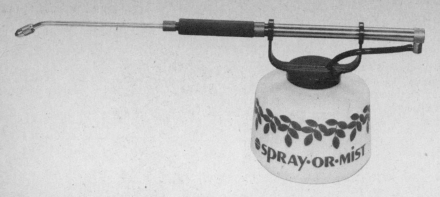

INDOOR/OUTDOOR SLIDE SPRAYER

Lightweight adjustable slide sprayer for misting house plants or spraying flowers, vegetables, shrubs, and trees. Double-action hand pump for continuous delivery from 2-qt. container.

Burgess Vibrocrafters, Inc.
Rte. 83
Grayslake, Ill. 60030

HOSE END SPRAYER

This all-purpose 10-gallon sprayer automatically mixes fertilizer, insecticides, and weed killers. Polyethylene container and twist-lock sprayhead.

Burgess Vibrocrafters, Inc.
Rte. 83
Grayslake, Ill. 60030

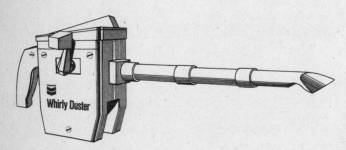

ORTHO WHIRLY DUSTER

This strong crank duster can be used with all types of dusts. Extension tubes put the dust exactly where you want it.

Chevron Chemical Company
Ortho Division
200 Bush St.
San Francisco, Cal. 94104

POWER DUSTER/MIST BLOWER

This multipurpose power duster/mist blower comes with straight dusting and mist spraying nozzles. Holds 2.2 gallons of liquid.

Kiorritz Corp. of America
Echo Chain Saw Division
350 Wainwright
Northbrook, Ill. 60062

BACKPACK SPRAYERS

Solo Jetpack 425 knapsack sprayer. Can be used for spraying in greenhouses, gardens, home orchards. Will handle any water- or oil-based chemical. All parts are made of high-grade plastic. Trouble-free piston pump builds to an 85-pound-per-square-inch pressure. Tank capacity 4 lbs.

Solo Motors, Inc.
P.O. Box 5030
Newport News, Va. 23605

BURGESS COMPRESSED-AIR TANK SPRAYER

This unusual looking sprayer has an impact-resistant polypropylene lightweight tank. It comes with a widemouth funnel top for easy filling and a fill indicator that lets you know when the liquid has reached the proper level.

Burgess Vibrocrafters, Inc.
Rte. 83
Grayslake, Ill. 60030

TANK SPRAYERS

This is a corrosion-resistant, stainless steel, compressed-air sprayer with corrosion-resistant, lightweight nylon-polyethylene-polypropylene pump, funnels, and shutoffs.

D. B. Smith and Co., Inc.
Main St.
Utica, N.Y. 13503

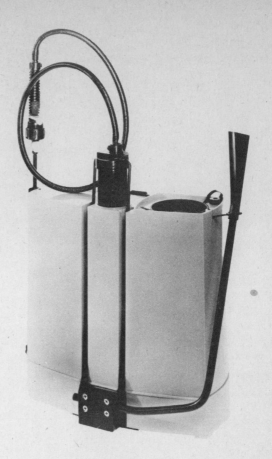

TANK SPRAYER

Q series: This unusual high-density, polyethylene, compressed-air sprayer has an easy-grip pump/carry handle. It is maintenance free.

D. B. Smith and Co., Inc.
Main St.
Utica, N.Y. 13503

BURGESS KNAPSACK SPRAYER

The low center of gravity makes this noncorrosive, polypropylene shell sprayer easy to carry. It also has a concave curvature and an adjustable padded shoulder harness that lets you work in comfort. Holds 4¼ gallons.

Burgess Vibrocrafters, Inc.
Rte. 83
Grayslake, Ill. 60030

POLYETHYLENE COMPRESSED-AIR TANKS

Tanks and pumps are formed from high-density polyethylene. They are easy to fill and nonspillable. They are extremely lightweight and durable. The trigger has a thumb release and lock. The dual swivel nozzle simplifies under-leaf spraying. Provides any spraying angle for complete coverage.

D. B. Smith and Co., Inc.
Main St.
Utica, N.Y. 13503

ANIMAL CONTROL TRAPS

Wire box-type trap opens at both ends. Both gates swing shut when the animal trips the trigger. Animals can be removed from the garden without harm.

Havahart
Allcock Manufacturing Co.
North Water St.
Ossining, N.Y. 10562

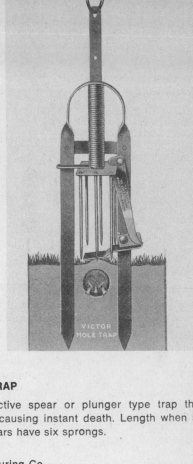

GOPHER TRAP

Improved type, spring trap of rugged construction.

Havahart
Allcock Manufacturing Co.
North Water St.
Ossining, N.Y. 10562

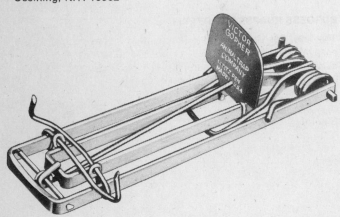

VICTOR MOLE TRAP

A sure and effective spear or plunger type trap that harpoons the mole, causing instant death. Length when sprung: 16¾ inches. Spears have six sprongs.

Havahart
Allcock Manufacturing Co.
North Water St.
Ossining, N.Y. 10562

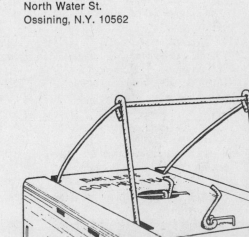

GOPHER TRAP

This traditional-style box trap needs no balt.

David W. Epstein & Co.
22711 Cass Ave.
Woodland Hills, Cal. 91364

VEGETABLES	SYMPTOMS	PESTS	DIAZINON	DYLOX	MALATHION	METHOXYCHLOR	PYRETHRUM	ROTENONE	RYANIA	SEVIN	CYGONDIMETHOATE	NICOTINE SULFATE	SABADILLA	THIODANENDOLSULFAN	THURICIDE	TOXAPHENE
Artichokes	Colonies of insects on leaves and buds	Aphids			X		X	X	X		X	X		X		
	Trails of silver slime	Slugs, snails														
Asparagus	Shoots channeled, leaves eaten by larvae of beetles	Asparagus beetle					X	X	X	X				X		
Beans	Colonies of black sucking insects on leaves	Aphids			X		X	X	X		X	X		X		
	Circular holes eaten in leaves	Bean leaf beetles	X		X			X	X	X				X		
	Hopping, running insects that suck sap from leaves	Leafhoppers			X	X				X						
	Lower surface of leaves eaten between veins; skeletionized	Mexican bean beetles			X			X	X	X				X		
	Scaly nymphs on underside of leaves; white adults flutter when disturbed	Whiteflies			X			X								
Beets	Leaves eaten leaving trail of slime	Snails, slugs														
Broccoli	Colonies of small green insects on leaves	Aphids			X		X	X	X	X	X	X		X		
	Plants sickly; maggots attack underground parts of plants	Cabbage maggots	X													
	Holes in leaves eaten by larvae	Cabbage worms, loopers			X			X						X	X	
	Small plants cut off at soil level at night	Cutworms	X	X						X				X		X
Brussels sprouts	Colonies of small insects on leaves	Aphids			X		X	X	X		X	X				
	Maggots attack underground parts of plants	Cabbage maggots	X													
	Holes eaten in leaves by larvae	Cabbage worms, loopers			X			X						X	X	
	Small plants cut off at soil level at night	Cutworms	X							X				X		X
Cabbage	Colonies of small insects on leaves	Aphids			X		X	X	X		X	X		X		
	Plants sickly; maggots attack under ground parts of plants	Cabbage maggots	X													
	Holes eaten in leaves by larvae	Cabbage worms, loopers			X			X		X				X	X	
	Small plants cut off at soil level at night	Cutworms	X							X				X		X
Cauliflower	Colonies of small green insects on leaves	Aphids			X		X	X	X		X	X				
	Plants sickly; maggots attack stems & underground parts of plant	Cabbage maggots	X													
	Holes in leaves eaten by larvae	Cabbage worms, loopers			X			X		X				X	X	
Corn	Silks cut off at ear; kernels destroyed by fairly large larvae	Corn earworms								X	X			X		
	Ears and stalks tunneled by larvae	Corn borers									X					
	Small plants cut off at soil level at night	Cutworms	X							X				X		X
Cucumber	Colonies of small insects on underside of leaves	Aphids			X		X	X	X		X	X		X		
	All parts eaten	Cucumber beetles	X		X			X		X				X		
	All parts of vines eaten	Pickleworm	X		X			X	X	X				X	X	
Eggplant	Plant defoliated (beetle—black striped, larvae—brick red	Colorado potato beetles	X					X	X	X				X		
	Colonies of small insects on underside of leaves	Aphids			X		X	X	X		X	X		X		
	Colonies on underside of leaves	Eggplant lacebug			X			X						X		

VEGETABLES	SYMPTOMS	PESTS	DIAZINON	DYLOX	MALATHION	METHOXYCHLOR	PYRETHRUM	ROTENONE	RYANIA	SEVIN	CYGONDIMETHOATE	NICOTINE SULFATE	SABADILLA	THIODANENDOLSULFAN	THURICIDE	TOXAPHENE
Lettuce	Colonies of small insects on leaves	Aphids			X		X	X	X		X	X		X		
	Leaves eaten by pincer bugs	Earwigs														
	Wedge-shaped insects found on leaves—tips of leaves turn brown	Leafhoppers			X		X	X	X	X						
	Leaves eaten, leaving trails of silver slime	Snails, slugs														
Kale	Colonies of small insects on leaves	Aphids			X		X	X	X					X		
	Small pin-size holes chewed in leaves	Flea beetles	X				X	X	X	X				X		
Melons	Colonies of insects on underside of leaves	Aphids			X		X	X	X		X	X		X		
	All parts eaten	Cucumber beetles	X				X	X	X	X				X		
Mustard greens	Colonies of small insects on leaves	Aphids			X		X	X	X					X		
	Leaves with holes eaten by larvae	Cabbage worms								X		X		X	X	
	Plants sickly; maggots attack root and stem underground	Root maggots	X													
Onions	Older leaves wither; small yellow insects feed at base of leaves	Onion thrips			X		X	X	X							
	Plants sickly, maggots attack parts below ground	Onion maggots	X													
Okra	Holes eaten in pods	Corn earworms								X	X					
Peas	Terminals deformed; colonies of small insects on leaves	Pea aphids			X		X	X	X		X	X		X		
	Beetles feed on blooms; larvae bore through pod and enter young peas	Pea weevils														
Peppers	Colonies of small insects on leaves	Aphids			X		X	X	X		X	X		X		
	Plants defoliated by orange and yellow-bodied beetles	Blister beetles					X	X	X					X		
	Small plants cut off at soil level at night	Cutworms	X							X						X
	Small pin-sized holes chewed in leaves	Flea beetles	X				X	X	X	X				X		
	Leaves and fruit eaten	Pepper weevils								X				X		
Radishes	Plants sickly; maggots attack plants below ground	Root maggots	X													
Spinach	Colonies of small insects on leaves	Aphids			X		X	X	X		X	X		X		
	Larvae tunnel through leaves	Leaf miners	X													
Squash	Colonies of small insects underneath the leaves	Aphids			X		X	X	X		X	X		X		
	All parts eaten	Cucumber beetles	X				X	X	X	X				X		
	Plants wilted (brownish flat bugs)	Squash bugs					X	X	X	X				X	X	
	Sudden wilting of runners; holes in stem near base	Squash vine borers								X						
Swiss chard	Colonies of small insects on leaves	Aphids			X		X	X	X		X	X		X		
Tomatoes	Colonies of small insects on leaves	Aphids			X		X	X	X		X	X		X		
	Small plants cut off at soil level	Cutworms	X							X						X
	Many shot-sized holes in leaves	Flea beetles	X				X	X	X	X				X		
	Leaves eaten (large green worm with horn)	Tomato hornworms					X	X		X				X	X	
	Scalelike nymphs attached to underside of leaves	Whiteflies			X		X	X								
Turnips & Rutabagas	Maggots attack plants below ground		X								X					
		Cabbage loopers			X					X	X					X

10

GREENHOUSES

In the 1960s you could count the number of greenhouse manufacturers on your fingers. Today you might need a computer to keep track of them. There's such a wide variety of structures and accessories available that most gardeners and hobbyists should be able to find a unit that is just about perfect for their individual situation.

This chapter describes over a dozen major styles of greenhouses.

In addition there are many accessories, from heaters to methods of cooling. Perhaps most significant of all is the ever-increasing number of practical, energy-conserving solar units now on the market.

Greenhouses are practical

More people than ever before are growing vegetables, and they want them the year round. Thus greenhouse manufacturers have increased their sales all over the country. This mass distribution and the use of plastics, fiberglass, and other inexpensive materials have brought greenhouse prices within the range of millions—some units sell for as little as $100. Even a nice-looking aluminum-and-glass greenhouse costs only around $500. And third, with experience and more highly developed technology, many companies are now able to offer greenhouse kits that can be built and installed in a single weekend. Obviously, this enables the consumer to save quite a bit in construction costs.

The multiplicity of choices available to the home gardener today is mind-boggling. Structural types include inflatable, lean-to, free-standing, quonset-hut, gothic, dome-shaped—and everything else in between. Structural materials range from steel to aluminum to wood, and coverings from soft plastic to rigid plastic to glass to other modern materials. Accessories include heaters, humidifiers, water systems, time controls, vents, and much more.

The best part of all this is that greenhouses are practical just about everywhere in the United States today. However, with recent and continuing increases in the price of energy, it is important to keep heat loss in a greenhouse to an absolute minimum. One of the most important developments of the 1970s has been the solar greenhouse, which we will describe in detail later in the chapter. Technology in this area is changing almost daily, and the 1980s should see the widespread use of solar greenhouses.

Temperature is of course a key factor in the operation of a greenhouse. As a general rule, for each square foot of surface of a greenhouse that faces the outside, you need 1.4 BTUs (British Thermal Units) per hour for every degree Fahrenheit of difference between the outdoor temperature and the level of heat you wish to maintain within. For example, if a greenhouse has 80 square feet of surface area and you want to keep the inside temperature at 50°F., you will have to produce over 3,360 BTUs per hour if the outside temperature drops to 20°F. Double glazing and other additional insulation will bring this figure down.

In general, then, the greater the surface area of your greenhouse, the greater will be the heat loss. (Other factors like materials and insulation will be discussed later in the chapter.) A quonsetlike structure uses less than the regular rectangular greenhouse of the same length because it is curved and therefore has less surface area. By the same token a round or dome-shaped greenhouse also has less surface area than a square structure whose sides are equal to the diameter of the round greenhouse.

Another factor in heat loss from a greenhouse is its placement on your property. You can keep heat loss to a minimum by placing it in a protected area—the downwind side of a row of trees, hedges, a fence, or any other barrier. If you're on more or less flat land and the wind is an important weather factor, it would be worth your while to construct or plant some kind of windbreak. It is important, however, not to restrict the greenhouse's access to light. Some people add a piece of clear plastic to the north side of their greenhouse, thus reducing heat loss without cutting down significantly on the light.

Greenhouse construction

There are many different types of greenhouses available, all with advantages and disadvantages in particular situations. Working with the following information, you should be able to determine what type is best for you.

Window models

The smallest permanent unit you would want to consider is a window greenhouse. Often you can leave the original window in place and use it to regulate the supply of air and heat in your window unit. Window greenhouse frames can be made of aluminum or wood. The basic structure is attached to the outside of the window, and sections of glass or plastic are then installed within this framework. Thus, sunlight enters on the two short sides and through the large front. You can build a window unit facing any direction as long as the window is not badly shaded by trees. One disadvantage of these greenhouses is that you can grow only limited quantities of vegetables. But they are in-

expensive. Prices range from $35 for a homemade fiberglass unit, to $185 for an aluminum-and-glass house 33 by 52 inches, to $200 for fiberglass, 48 by 57 inches, to $240 for 48 by 72 inches, aluminum and glass.

Conventional models

The typical even-span greenhouse looks like a tent with a high center ridge. (The Dutch variation has sloping sides.) *Advantages:* Good growing space (even under the benches); even circulation of air; fairly even, good light. Sections can be added easily if you want to expand. *Disadvantages:* Large heat loss due to large surface area. (The Dutch type is more efficient.) Sample prices include $80 for a 5-by-4-foot polyethylene-covered unit; $130 for a fiberglass model of the same size; $350 for 8-by-12-foot, wooden frame and acrylic; $1,025 for 11-by-11-foot, aluminum and glass; $2,250 for 10-by-30-foot, aluminum and acrylic.

INSTALLING A WINDOW GREENHOUSE ▶
STEP 1
Select an area of your home where the sunlight is most prevalent during the winter months—usually the south side. Try to avoid west sun exposure unless protected by trees or shrubs. Parts of your old existing window should be removed, such as the sash and upper fixed sash and screen; the jambs, head and sill (main frame) may be left intact.

STEP 2
For brick veneer, holes must be located around the perimeter of the window opening using a masonry drill. For wood siding your greenhouse window may be directly anchored with wood screws.

STEP 3
Insert rawl plugs (screw anchors) in brick as illustrated and attach wood furring strips with screws. The wood furring strips (pine or fir) should be at least 1" x 4" and given a coat of protective paint. Redwood may be used if desired, requiring no protection.

STEP 4
The wood furring strips must be installed around the entire perimeter including the brick sill (rollock) as illustrated. It may be desirable to rest greenhouse on top of rollock but this will depend upon the size of greenhouse window you have selected.

STEP 5
Drill small holes around greenhouse window in the outer flange. They should be at least 8" on center. A number "8" screw is recommended for anchoring.

STEP 6
Apply a good grade of caulking compound around perimeter of furring strips as illustrated. Vents should be slightly opened to allow easy installation of upper shelf.

Step 1

Step 2

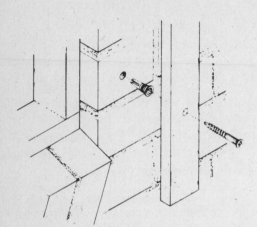

Step 3

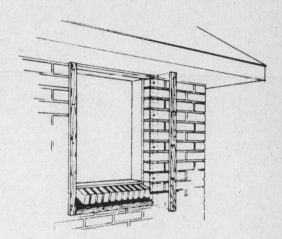

Step 4

Step 5

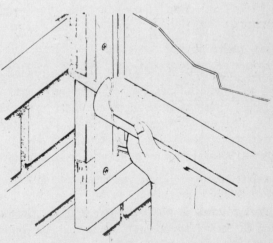

Step 6

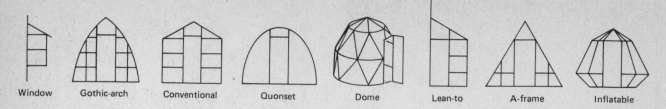

Window   Gothic-arch   Conventional   Quonset   Dome   Lean-to   A-frame   Inflatable

DIFFERENT TYPES OF GREENHOUSES

Lean-to

A greenhouse can be erected on the south or east side of a house, with three sides of glass or plastic and the fourth side supported by the house. *Advantages:* Accessible from house; can utilize heat from the house; less expensive than most types; may take up less space. *Disadvantages:* Difficult to seal the points where it joins the house. Sample prices include $215 for 8-by-7-foot, wood frame with fiberglass/acrylic; $900 for 5-by-20-foot, aluminum with acrylic; $915 for 9-by-9-foot, aluminum and glass.

A-frame

The ceiling and walls are one and the same. *Advantages:* Aesthetically pleasing; easy to build; good light transmission. *Disadvantages:* Heat gets trapped near the roof; floor space is hard to reach; provides less bench space than other types. Sample prices include $250 for a small wood and acrylic unit, $2,050 for a 10-by-10-foot wood and heavy-duty fiberglass model.

Gothic arch frame

This is a good-looking, popular model. *Advantages:* The curved shape utilizes interior space well; structurally strong; transmits more light and heat than many other types. *Disadvantages:* Difficult to ventilate. Sample prices include $200 for small plastic unit to $625 for a 10-by-11-foot wood and acrylic structure.

Quonset

Familiar half-oval shape. *Advantages:* Easy to erect; structurally strong; good light and heat absorption; plenty of growing space. *Disadvantages:* Must be well ventilated; not many models on the market. Sample prices include $550 for a 10-by-12-foot steel and polyethylene greenhouse.

Dome

Looks like a mushroom. *Advantages:* Relatively inexpensive; airy; strong; all surfaces transmit light; attractive; offers much usable space; everything is easy to reach from one spot. *Disadvantages:* Bench space hard to brace; hard to ventilate; benches must be round to fit against wall. Sample prices include $135 for a 10-foot-diameter unit with wood frame and acrylic walls.

Inflatable

A good model to start off with. *Advantages:* Easy to erect; relatively inexpensive; double walls give good insulation. *Disadvantages:* Relatively short life; not available in large walk-in size. Sample prices include $75 for a small economy unit.

Pentagon-hexagon

Five- or six-sided structure. *Advantages:* Good use of space; inexpensive. *Disadvantages:* Difficult to ventilate; benches must be built around walls to use available space. Sample prices range from $300 to $1,600.

Structural materials

Frames

There is a choice among galvanized steel, aluminum, or wood for your greenhouse frame. *Aluminum* is used by most greenhouse manufacturers because it is light and strong, and it will not warp. It transmits and thus loses heat, but only to a minor degree. *Galvanized steel* is very strong, but it sometimes flakes and rusts. *Wood* has been used for many years. Redwood and cypress are quite good, but construction-grade pine and fir should be looked at very carefully. Wood is strong, durable, and good-looking, but it's bulky and can sometimes crack.

Covering materials

Today's greenhouses are usually covered with either glass, hard plastic, or soft plastic. There are advantages and disadvantages to all of these products.

FOUNDATIONS AND FRAMES

Traditionally, greenhouses utilize a standard four-inch concrete foundation. You can also build a satisfactory base for your greenhouse this way: (1) Level a place for the greenhouse; (2) put the base in place; (3) fill the base with gravel, redwood chips, or some similar material. Then you can erect your frame on this solid foundation.

Glass. This has been the standard material for greenhouses for many years. It is durable and transmits light effectively. Glass is not cheap, but when you install double glazing of shatterproof glass, you've got a well-insulated structure that will last for a long time. Glass generally needs to be shaded in the summertime.

Hard plastic. Another material that is used extensively for greenhouses is acrylic plastic. Frequently it is reinforced with strands of glass or nylon. Fiberglass-reinforced plastic (FRP) is stronger, easier to cut and fit, and less subject to breakage than ordinary glass. FRP can also be made resistant to ultraviolet light. One disadvantage of plastic is that it turns very brittle in cold weather.

Greenhouses are constructed with flat or corrugated hard plastic sheets. The flat sheets need strong support to prevent sagging. Corrugated sheets remain firm, but they are harder to seal than the flat sheets. Double panels can be used to provide extra insulation.

Soft plastic. There are several types of soft plastic used in the construction of today's greenhouses, including polyethylene, mylar, lortex, and others. The soft plastics are inexpensive, have good light transmission, and are easy to work with. However, in cold weather they become rigid and inflexible. A good insulation can be achieved when two layers of polyethylene are used with spacers in between. Blowers can also be used to separate and to support the layers. How long soft plastic lasts depends on the quality of the material, its thickness, and the climatic conditions. You can replace it easily with soft plastic or rigid plastic sheets.

Sometimes soft plastic and hard plastic are used in combination. Greenhouses can have rigid plastic roofs and soft plastic or glass sides. Soft plastic can also be used to add to the insulation of a glass or rigid-plastic greenhouse.

Foundations

Styrene or styrofoam are sometimes used in the form of extruded foam boards as perimeter insulation for greenhouse foundations. There are also urethanes, which vary from very hard, rigid materials to elastomers or synthetic rubbers. All have tremendous insulation value. Urethane spray-in-place kits for insulation of foundation walls are now available in hardware and similar stores.

Solar greenhouse

Solar greenhouses work by gathering warmth and energy from the sun during the day through a south-facing wall and by storing that heat in the (opposite) north wall for use at night and during cloudy days.

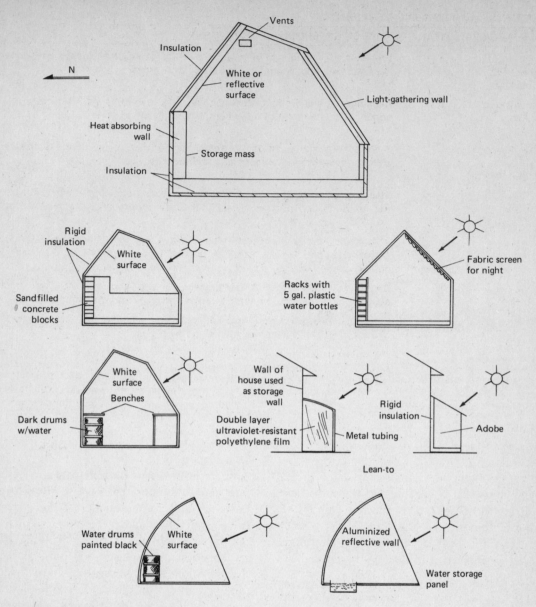

SOLAR GREENHOUSE: Eight Alternative Structures.

Light-gathering wall. The light-gathering wall should be two layers thick with an insulating air space between. You can utilize glass, ultraviolet-resistant fiberglass, or a combination of fiberglass panel outside, polyethylene film inside.

This wall should have a south or near south exposure and should be tilted at an angle equal to your latitude *plus* 20 to 50 degrees. This will catch the low winter sun but keep out the high summer sun. In summer, when there is too much heat, the greenhouse needs to be shaded and vented. In winter, especially on extremely cold nights, many solar greenhouse owners use some sort of screen inside the light-gathering wall to slow down the heat loss.

Heat-absorbing wall. Since the sun lies to the south the greenhouse must utilize a heat-absorbing storage mass at the north wall. This storage mass must be struck directly by sunlight and should be a foot thick or more. It can be constructed of the following materials: rock, masonry, concrete, adobe, or other heat-storing materials. You can also utilize water stored in 50-gallon drums painted black (black helps absorb heat).

GREENHOUSE MANUFACTURERS AND DISTRIBUTORS

MANUFACTURER—DISTRIBUTOR	TYPE OF GREENHOUSE—EQUIPMENT
Actus, Inc. 16778 Schoenborn St. Sepulveda, Cal. 91343	Free-standing aluminum and double-walled translucent plastic greenhouse in 2 sizes; accessories include coolers, fans, heaters, growing benches
Aluminum Greenhouses, Inc. 14605 Lorain Ave. Cleveland, Oh. 44111	Aluminum, glass models, free-standing and lean-to; price starts at about $300; accessories include benches, humidifiers, heaters, vent controls
American Solar Gardens 7861 Alabama Canoga Park, Cal. 91304	3 models—stand-up gardener, deluxe gardener, pro gardener; double-walled polyboard siding; accessories—exhaust fans, thermostats, etc.
Aquaponics 22135 Ventura Blvd. Woodland Hills, Cal. 91364	Many styles including gazebo; steel or wood; complete hydroponic system; growing bed of wood and plastic; from about $250; hydroponic nutrients also available
Birmid Qualcast Coleridge Street, Sunnyhill, Derby DE3 7JT, England	4 models: utilizes aluminum frames and glass, with neoprene elastic strips between glass and frame; 3 free-standing models, from 8 ft. wide by 5 ft. long; accessories—control panel, double glazing, heater, trickle-mist jet watering
W. Atlee Burpee Co. Warminster, Pa. 18974	Aluminum, shatterproof glass models, lean-to and free-standing, from about $600; accessories—electric heaters, exhaust fans, thermostat, vent controls
Clover Garden Products, Inc. Box 874 Smyrna, Tenn. 37167	7 models; many options, including aluminum locking rail, fans, heaters; fiberglass or Monsanto 602 with airspace maintained by blower
Comanche Steel Products Box 20128 San Antonio, Tex. 78220	Small wiki-up greenhouse; tribal greenhouse—8 ft. by 10 ft.; Monsanto 602 vinyl covering; some accessories
Early Garden Greenhouses, Inc. Mendenhall, Miss. 39114	Gothic arch style, free-standing, covered with Monsanto 602; about $200
Energy Absorption Systems 860 S. River Rd. Sacramento, Cal. 95691	Unusual dome-shaped, fiberglass greenhouse, 14-ft. dia.; about $850
English Greenhouses, Ltd. Turnpike Industrial Park Mt. Laurel, N.J. 08057	Eden aluminum greenhouse; free-standing, lean-to; aluminum and glass construction; roll shades, shelves available
Everlite Aluminum Greenhouses, Inc. 14605 Lorain Ave. Cleveland, Oh. 44111	4 free-standing models, 4 lean-to models; good quality glass; accessories—humidifiers, benches, vents, other
Fabricators, Inc. P.O. Box 1839 Seattle, Wash. 98118	Aluminum frame, high-impact D.R. acrylic plastic; free-standing, lean-to, window styles; accessories—bench tops, grow lights, heaters
Garden Way Research Charlotte, Vt. 05445	Kits and plans for free-standing and lean-to types
Gothic Arch Greenhouses Box 1564 Mobile, Ala. 36601	Lean-to and free-standing models; redwood frames; fiberglass; aluminum glass storm doors: from about $250; accessories—automatic mist system, evaporative cooler
Halls Europa, Church Rd., Paddock Wood, Kent, England distributed in U.S. by Sun/America Corp. Box 125 Houston, Tex. 77001	High-quality aluminum greenhouses; Europa 600 and 800 series; Europa Petite and Europa coldframe; some accessories available
Hansen Weather Port 313 Taylor Rd. Gunnison, Col. 81230	Free-standing model; steel & polyethylene from about $500; also sells coldframes
Janco Greenhouses 9390 Davis Ave. Laurel, Md. 20810	Free-standing, attached, lean-to, and window-box styles; aluminum and glass; about $500 to $4,500; accessories—single panel control, etc.; window gardens $135 to $185

GREENHOUSE MANUFACTURERS AND DISTRIBUTORS (Continued)

MANUFACTURER—DISTRIBUTOR	TYPE OF GREENHOUSE—EQUIPMENT
King Industries P.O. Box 21 Loma Linda, Cal. 92354	Suppliers of several lines of greenhouses; they also sell hydroponic systems
Lord & Burnham Irvington-on-Hudson, N.Y. 10533	Quality, free-standing, attached lean-to, and window models of aluminum and glass; start about $200 for window models, $750 for others; accessories include heaters, humidifiers, plant watering systems, shades
Maco P.O. Box 109 Scio, Ore. 97374	Gothic-style, free-standing, attached, or lean-to; aluminum and glass; from about $200 to $1200; accessories—fiberglass conversion kits, heaters, ventilator fans
McGregor Greenhouses 1195 Thompson Ave. Santa Cruz, Cal. 95063	Gothic-arch, free-standing, or attached; redwood and fiberglass; from about $170 to $400; accessories—exhaust fans, heaters, thermostats, etc.
Milan Greenhouses, Inc. 6306 Chef Menteur Hwy. New Orleans, La. 70126	Lean-to, free-standing models; redwood and Monsanto plastic polyethylene from $100; accessories available
Modular Greenhouse H & W Enterprises 208 Brand Rd. Santa Rosa, Cal. 95405	Molded fiberglass dome comes in ready-to-assemble sections; automated hydroponic equipment available; $500 to $1,000
Mother Nature's Greenhouses P.O. Box 390 Morristown, N.J. 08057	Aluminum & glass; lean-to, free-standing
National Greenhouse Co. P.O. Box 1000 Pana, Ill. 62557	Free-standing, lean-to styles; aluminum, glass, or fiberglass; large number of accessories; catalog available
Edward Owen Engineering Snow Shoe, Pa. 16874	Several free-standing models; aluminum and safety glass; from about $300; accessories—bench heaters, more
Pacific Coast Greenhouse 430 Burlingame Ave. Redwood City, Cal. 94063	Lean-to, free-standing, attached; redwood frame; glass, plastic, or a combination; from about $350
Paradise Garden Products, Ltd. P.O. Box 6 Cirencester, Gloucestershire GL72RJ, England Paradise Aluminum Int. Corp. Turnpike Industrial Park Roland Ave. and Church Rd. Mount Laurel, N. J. 08057	4 free-standing, 2 lean-to models; glass panels, aluminum frames with a special baked enamel; gutters, roof vents, extension units
The Plantworks Tiffany Industries, Inc. 145 Weldon Pkwy. Maryland Heights, Mo. 63043	Free-standing and lean-to; steel, fiberglass; traditional and modern; hydroponic systems available
Peter Reimuller 980 17th Ave. Santa Cruz, Cal. 95060	Lean-to and free-standing; gothic arch, dome; redwood frame, fiberglass Li'l Giant minigreenhouse; accessories—fans, heater, etc.; $99 to $500
Reliable Greenhouses 171 Washington St. Norwell, Me. 02061	Distributor for Baco greenhouses; free-standing, lean-to, window models; aluminum and glass
Santa Barbara Greenhouses 390 Dawson Dr. Camarillo, Cal. 93010	Free-standing, lean-to; redwood frame; quality fiberglass
Shelter Dynamics Round Rock, Tex. 78664	Solarsphere—a circular greenhouse with a fiberglass, bolt-together frame

GREENHOUSE MANUFACTURERS AND DISTRIBUTORS (Continued)

MANUFACTURER—DISTRIBUTOR	TYPE OF GREENHOUSE—EQUIPMENT
Southern Greenhouse Builders 2505 Bransford Ave. Nashville, Tenn. 37204	Kit models available; fiberglass panels attached to aluminum frames
Sturdi-Built Mfg. Co. 11304 S.W. Boones Ferry Rd. Portland, Ore. 97219	Free-standing, lean-to; redwood frame; glass or fiberglass; A-frame and other unusual designs
Sun America Corp. P.O. Box 125 Houston, Tex. 77001	Free-standing, lean-to, window units; aluminum frame; high-impact D.R. acrylic plastic
Sunglo Greenhouses 4441 26th Ave. W. Seattle, Wash. 98199	Acrylic, quonset type
Sunlan Greenhouses 412 Eighth Ave. P.O. Box 1874 Smyrna, Tenn. 37169	Lean-to, free-standing; extensions; aluminum frame; vinyl
Sunrise Dome Co. 393 Hilwood Dr. Akron, Oh. 44320	Geodesic dome; redwood frame, plastic panels; $600 to $1700
Texas Greenhouse Co. 2717 St. Louis Ave. Forth Worth, Tex. 76110	Redwood or aluminum frame; glass or fiberglass; accessories available; $580 to $5,400
Turner Greenhouses Hwy 117 S. Goldsboro, N.C. 27530	Free-standing or lean-to; aluminum frame; glass, polyethylene; $130 to $1,600
Trox Manufacturing Co. 18 Angell St. Battle Creek, Mich. 49016	Fiberglass or ultraviolet film
Vegetable Factory, Inc. 100 Court St. Coplague, N.Y. 11726	Free-standing, lean-to; aluminum frame; double fiberglass acts as a solar unit; $375 to $1,500
Verandel Co. P.O. Box 1568 Worcester, Me. 01600	Built around house wall or entrance; accessories available; $425
Victoria Greenhouses, Ltd. Box 947 Stump Bridge Rd. Southampton, Pa. 18966	Free-standing, lean-to; wood or steel frames; fiberglass or glass; high quality; from $600
Water Works Gardenhouses Box 2599 Castro Valley, Cal. 94546	Hydroponic and standard greenhouses; hydroponic supplies and starter kits
Weber Systems, Inc. New Hope, Ala. 35760	Precut, easily assembled; aluminum and glass
Wheeling Corrugating Co. Wheeling, W. Va. 26003	Fiberglass, 10 ft. by 10 ft.
Jack C. Williams Co. 21519 92nd Ave W. Edmonds, Wash. 98020	Free-standing, lean-to, attached models; aluminum frame; glass accessories available; $500 to $2,600
Working Water Gardens 300 Springdale St. Sebastopol, Cal. 95472	Standard and hydroponic; fiberglass; from $495

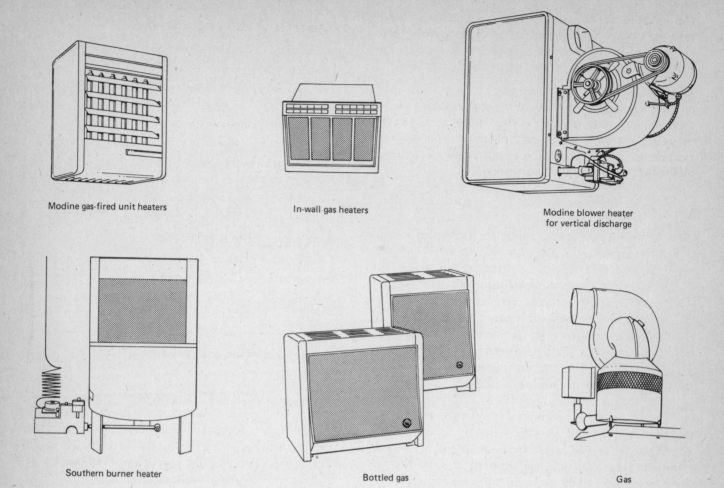

Modine gas-fired unit heaters

In-wall gas heaters

Modine blower heater
for vertical discharge

Southern burner heater

Bottled gas

Gas

GREENHOUSE HEATERS

The back of the north wall should be well insulated on the outside so the stored heat won't escape. The north wall can be curved to reflect added light onto the plants and keep them from bending toward the lighter south wall. (You can also store heat in a thick, well-insulated floor.)

Solar greenhouses can retard temperature loss for several days or longer, and the concept has been used successfully in the Pacific Northwest and Minnesota. In colder climates, especially where it may be cloudy for several weeks at a time, a solar greenhouse will need backup heat.

One New Mexico solar greenhouse, however, held 52°F. during a -2°F. night. A Pacific Northwest greenhouse held above 50°F. over a 10-day cloudy period.

Greenhouse accessories

Your greenhouse actually is a compact artificial ecosystem that needs warmth, humidity, water, and fresh air in order to grow vegetables. This means that you must provide some means of heating, cooling, ventilating and watering your greenhouse plus instrumentation and facilities such as benches and bins or shelves for storage.

Today you'll find a tremendous variety of accessories on the market designed to handle each of these needs. The question, of course, is what to use in your own particular greenhouse.

Heating

Greenhouses are heated with electricity, gas, oil, LP gas, or solar energy. Each has advantages and disadvantages.

Electrical heaters generally are least expensive to purchase. *Advantages:* small portable units are easy to install. *Disadvantages:* expensive to use, often create pockets of heat. Besides standard heaters, you can use soil heating cables or infrared bulbs directly above your plants. They supply an even, constant warmth to mature plants, cuttings, or seedlings.

Gas or oil heaters are useful for larger greenhouses, but such units take up quite a bit of room. In general these are less expensive to operate than electric heaters, but fans are needed to keep the warm air circulating.

Solar heaters take care of most greenhouse needs for growing vegetables at no operating cost as long as there is adequate sun. In most cases they would need a back-up heater for use on very cold nights and during long periods of overcast. However, advancing technology may change this situation very soon.

Ventilation

Every greenhouse needs some sort of mechanism, either automatic or hand operated, to allow you to regulate the fresh air in the structure. If air is not taken in periodically, the old inside air can become overheated and its moisture content lowered. Greenhouses can be ventilated with either vents or fans.

Most common vents are located at the peaks on either end or along the upper portion of the roof of a greenhouse. These vents vary from simple flaps to louvered windows to movable panels. They can be operated by hand or motor. Many automatic systems are hooked in tandem with an exhaust fan. When the temperature rises, the fan draws out the warm air and the vent opens to allow the fresh air to enter.

Small fans keep the air moving throughout the greenhouse and help maintain an even temperature. This prevents stagnation with accompanying mildew and other diseases.

What to look for in a greenhouse

Metal frames should be heavy-duty.

Aluminum frames should be painted.

Frames should be standardized throughout the greenhouse.

Bolts and screws should be rustproof, aluminum.

Wooden frames should be bolted, not nailed or stapled.

Greenhouses should have grooves in upper framing for hanging baskets.

Doors should be heavy-duty.

Ball-bearings on doors are desirable.

Sliding doors should be nonstick.

Glass panes should be shatterproof.

Fiberglass should be no. 1 grade.

Polyethylene should have some sort of nonrip connections to greenhouse.

Shade

Plants frequently receive too much intense light during the long summer days. An excess of light causes wilting and leaf burn. There are a number of ways to shade your greenhouse, ranging from aluminum, wood, or vinyl shades to a shading compound that can be applied directly to the glass surface.

Wooden shades resemble large window blinds. They can be extended or retracted by a system of ropes or

Greenhouse equipment

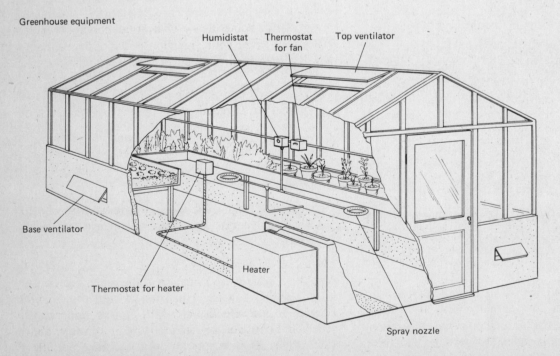

Humidistat · Thermostat for fan · Top ventilator · Base ventilator · Thermostat for heater · Heater · Spray nozzle

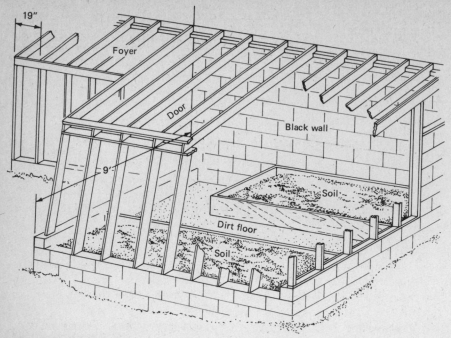

19"

Foyer

Door

Black wall

9'

Soil

Dirt floor

Soil

HOW TO BUILD A SUNPIT

pulleys. *Aluminum panels* are composed of slats fastened to a wooden or aluminum frame. There is also an aluminum roll-up type of cover that can be easily adjusted from the outside. Vinyl plastic shades are semitransparent and flexible; they can reduce light by as much as 65 percent. Shading paint or shading powder (which is mixed with water) can be sprayed on the glass wall.

Cooling system

You need some sort of cooling system for your greenhouse. This may range from a simple hose to an evaporator swamp cooler to a refrigerator unit. A hose can be used to sprinkle water on the plants, benches, and floors, thus cooling the area by evaporation. Humidity is not all that important to most vegetables. However, there are blowers that will put out a fine mist of water into the greenhouse from a unit that measures the humidity. This action helps to cool the area and to maintain the proper levels of humidity. For larger greenhouses an evaporator cooler that sucks air out through wet pads is quite useful.

Watering system

You can water by hand with a hose, as mentioned in the previous paragraph, or you can install some kind of a system. One automatic setup offers a flexible plastic hose with spray nozzles that can be attached along the bench. Another uses a length of plastic hose

---

Building your own greenhouse

Building your own greenhouse gives you more greenhouse for less money and allows you to have the size, shape, and design that you want.

A homemade greenhouse can be anything from a window greenhouse to a 70-foot structure. It can be built on a wood frame, a pipe frame, or a structural metal frame. It is even possible to make a greenhouse from recycled or salvaged materials.

Most experts recommend building a smaller unit before tackling a more ambitious project. Anyone, however, who can use a saw and hammer, has at least $5 and a little spare time, can build his or her own greenhouse.

Kits—precut greenhouses: Most greenhouses purchased today come either in kit form or as knocked down structures that must be assembled on the spot.

Most greenhouse owners report satisfaction with the way their units went together. Metal/wood, glass, or fiberglass kits are well designed and generally are assembled easily. The less expensive, soft plastic greenhouses (from $75) are sometimes more difficult to put together.

Sometimes, too, the larger units (over 20 feet in length) become a construction problem because they need a poured foundation and built-up sides. Often a local contractor with greenhouse experience can help with your construction problems. You can usually find one of these by asking your local nurseryman.

ACCESSORY SOURCES

SOURCE	HEAT	VENTILATION COOLING	WATER	INSTRUMENTATION	SHELVES STORAGE, ETC.
Birmid Qualcast Coleridge St. Sunnyhill, Derby DE 3 7JT, England	Electric	Shading panels	Mist, trickle, overhead systems		
Comanche Steel Products Inc. 343 N. White Rd. San Antonio, Tex. 78220	Fan-type wall heaters	Automatic exhaust fan	None	None	Shelf Units Shelf Brackets
D & M Enterprises P.O. Box 739 Wildomar, Cal. 92395	Arvin/Titan electric, hot-water, & gas heaters	Coolers, humidifiers, shutters, exhaust fans		Several kinds	Hardware
Environmental Dynamics 12615 S. La Cadena Dr. Colton, Cal. 92324	Electric heater systems, $20 to $80, soil cables	Fans, shutters, coolers, humidifer systems, $150 to $300	Several types	Thermometers, humidity meter, temperature alarms, others	Benches
Everlite Aluminum Greenhouses Inc. 14605 Lorain Ave. Cleveland, Oh. 44111	Electric, gas, hot-water heaters, heating systems, soil cables	Fans, vents, automatic humidifier	Automatic watering/ misting nozzles	Thermometer, others	Several kinds of shelves/benches
Gothic Arch Greenhouses P.O. Box 1564 Mobile, Ala. 36601	Electric 5 KW heaters $165, 24,000 to 84,000 BTU'S—$280 to $560	Exhaust fans			
Lord & Burnham Irvington-on-Hudson, N.Y. 10533	Several kinds of heaters—electric, gas, kerosene, oil, hot water	Shades, plastic films, shading powder, automatic venting	Misting/ watering systems	Several kinds	Shelves/tubs
Maco Products Box 109 Scio, Ore. 97374	Titan heaters, $40 to $80; ground cables	Ventilator fans	None	None	None
National Greenhouse Company Box 1000 Pana, Ill. 62557	126-p. catalog of all kinds of greenhouse parts and accessories; fiberglass accessories available	Several types	Several types	Several types	Several types
J.A. Nearing Co. 9390 Davis Ave. Laurel, Md. 20810	Janco - fan jet environmental-control system—heating, cooling, ventilating, dehumidifying	Manual and automatic	Bench misting and other types	Thermometers, humidity indicators	Benches
Edward Owen Engineering Snow Shoe, Pa. 16874	Titan 220 V heater $125	Vent opener $62	None	None	Aluminum benches $60 to $100
Pacific Coast Greenhouse Mfg. Co. 430 Burlingame Ave. Redwood City, Cal. 94063	Electric & gas heaters— 15,000 to 310,000 BTU's $125 to $574, heat cables, soil thermostat	Evaporative coolers, fog humidifiers, automatic vent openers, fans, shutters	Water valves	Maximum-minimum thermometer, other	Benches

ACCESSORY SOURCES (Continued)

SOURCE	HEAT	VENTILATION COOLING	WATER	INSTRUMENTATION	SHELVES STORAGE, ETC.
The Plantworks Tiffany Industries, Inc. 145 Weldon Pkwy. Maryland Heights, Mo. 63043	Four season system with hydro/environmental control, $900; individual components available	Automatic exhaust, evaporative cooler			
Peter Reimuller 980 17th Ave. Santa Cruz, Cal. 95060	Electric heaters, $29 to $70, 1200 cu. ft. kerosene heater, $65; has greenhouse accessories packages which include heater, fan, thermometer, shutters—$69 to $105	Exhaust fan inlet shutters, humidifier	Nozzles	Maximum-minimum thermometer, humidity meter	Benches
Santa Barbara Greenhouses 390 Dawson Dr. Camarillo, Cal. 93010	Electric, $30	Automatic airflow shutters, shutter-mounted exhaust fans	Waterfog nozzle	Several	Redwood benches
Shelter Dynamics P.O. Box 616 Round Rock, Tex. 78664	Electric	Exhaust fan, cooler/humidfier, shading, roof panels	None	None	Cedar benches
Sun America Corp. P.O. Box 125 Houston, Tex. 77001		Louver window autovent	Rain barrel		Shelves, benches
Sunglo Greenhouses 4441 26th Ave. West Seattle, Wash. 98199	Elec/gas, $26 to $165	Automatic wall shutters, blowers, shutter-mounted exhaust fans	Watermatic garden kit	Thermometers, light meters	Vinyl-coated ventilated shelving
Texas Greenhouse Co. 2717 St. Louis Ave. Fort Worth, Tex. 76110	Electric, gas, $21 to $800	Evaporative coolers, fans, shutters	Water kits, other	Complete line	Benches, fiberglass panels, hardware
Turner Greenhouses Hwy. 117 S. Goldsboro, N.C. 27530	Electric, gas, soil cables	Automatic fan ventilating systems	Watering and misting equipment, timers	Thermometers, etc.	Slat benches, asbestos-cement growing benches
Vegetable Factory 100 Court St. Copiague, N.Y. 11726	Electric, $35 to $95, soil cables	Cooling & venting system, square vent	None	Maximum-minimum thermometer, hygrometer	Benches

perforated with many tiny holes laid on the surface of the soil.

Instrumentation

Since most vegetables have an optimum growing temperature range from 60°F. to 80°F., it is important not only to keep track of the temperature in all areas of the greenhouse, but also to have the means to keep it generally within the safety range. (See page 90 for discussion of requirements for cool-season and warm-season vegetables.)

Thermometers placed in different corners will reveal surprisingly different ranges in temperature. A high-low thermometer is essential to let you know what is happening in the greenhouse both day and night even though you are not on the scene. This thermometer marks the high and the low temperatures reached during a specified period of time. Another valuable instrument is a temperature alarm, to let you know when it gets too hot or too cold in the greenhouse.

Thermostats help to keep the temperature fairly constant by regulating the source of heat. An important consideration in the installation of a thermostat is to keep it away from bright sun or from any other source of heat. Check your thermostat against the thermometers in the greenhouse from time to time, too.

Humidistats to indicate the relative humidity are useful, even though maintaining a constant or particular level of humidity is not as important with vegetables as it is with other types of plants. However, some greenhouse gardeners like to know what the humidity in their greenhouse is. When the temperature rises, the humidity should rise, too. This can be coupled with a mister or humidifier for automatic action.

Associated facilities

Besides the bare essentials, you will need benches to support pots, storage bins, and in some cases lights for use as supplements during stretches of cloudy weather. (See Chapter 12.)

Benches should be sturdy enough to support heavy pots and shaped so as to take advantage of the available space in the greenhouse. Bench tops should allow for air circulation, easy cleaning, and disinfecting. There are many commercially made benches that are worth consideration.

Storage bins or containers for soil amendments and fertilizers are a necessity for a neat greenhouse. You should also provide dry storage for seeds and fertilizers.

Hobby Greenhouse Association

The Hobby Greenhouse Association is a group of amateur gardeners who either own a greenhouse or who want to own one. The group puts out a newsletter (*The Planter*), a swap center where members may exchange seeds, plants, and cuttings; they have established a lending library, where members may borrow books by mail, and a film library, where members may obtain instructive slides and movies of how to assemble an aluminum frame greenhouse. They also make available seeds and samples and other services. Dues: $5.00 a year

Hobby Greenhouse Association
Box 695-F
Wallingford, Conn. 06492

Varishading

Varishading is a permanent variable greenhouse shading which transmits more light in winter than in summer. Applied to the interior of a glass or plastic house, it is transparent when kept wet by winter condensation. In summer, when no condensation occurs, it is dry and opaque. The amount of Varishade coating applied determines the degree of shading. When used on the outside of glass, rain will make it transparent.

Solar Sunstill, Inc.
Setauket, N.Y. 11733

GREENHOUSE MATERIALS AND PLANS

ABC Supply P.O. Box 26297 Sacramento, Cal. 95800	Materials for building your own greenhouse; Filon Greenhouse panels, steel frames, plans
Greenhouse Specialties Co. 9849 Kimker Lane St. Louis, Mo. 63127	Lascolite Acrylic fortified fiberglass panels; Lascolite accessories—screwshank nails, etc.; also, complete greenhouse, galvanized steel tube or redwood frame

A-Frame Home Green-house, Plan 210.
Agricultural Engineering
    Dept.
University of Connecticut
Storrs, Conn. 06268

10' x 16' A-Frame Greenhouse, Plan 48-6.
Louisiana State University
Baton Rouge, La. 70803

Building Plans with Filon.
Vistron Corporation
Dept. 152
12333 Van Ness Ave.
Hawthorne, Cal. 90250

Experimental Greenhouses: Dome, Plan 822-350; Gable, 822-352; Gothic Arch, 822-358; Multibarrel Vault, 822-356; Quonset, 822-360; Hyperbolic-Parab-olid, 822-354 & 822-362.
Pennsylvania State
    University
University Park, Pa. 16802
$1.00

A Gothic Greenhouse for Town and Country Homes, Circular 892.
Virginia Polytechnic
    Institute
Blacksburg, Va. 24060

Kentucky Rigid Frame Greenhouse, Plan 771-8.
Department of Agricultural
    Engineering
University of Kentucky
Lexington, Ky. 40506

Plastic-Covered-Greenhouse Plans.
Werth's
P.O. Box 1902
Cedar Rapids, Ia. 52406

A Simple Rigid Frame Greenhouse for Home Gardeners, Circular 880.112.
Mumford Hall
University of Illinois
Urbana, Ill. 61801

Slant-Leg Rigid Frame, Plastic Greenhouse, Plan 139.
Agricultural Eng. Dept.
Rutgers University
New Brunswick, N.J. 08903

SOME SOURCES FOR GREENHOUSE COVERINGS

Brighton By-Products Co., Inc.
P.O. Box 23
New Brighton, Pa. 15066

Monsanto 602 greenhouse film; Sol-Light fiberglass, regular or tedlar coated; Rapid-Glaze fiberglass panels

D & M Enterprises
P.O. Box 739
Wildomar, Cal. 92935

Filon greenhouse fiberglass panels, corrugated and flat

Eberspacher Glass
Esslingen, Germany

Glass and plastic that darken

Environmental Dynamics
Moreno Valley Enterprises
12615 S. La Cadena Dr.
Colton, Cal. 92324

Filon greenhouse fiberglass panels; Monsanto 601 greenhouse film; Rufco 1000 film

Life-Lite, Inc.
1025 Shary Circle
Concord, Cal. 94520

Colored plastics that control wavelengths

Reichold Reinforced
 Plastics
P.O. Box 81110
Cleveland, Oh. 44181

Alsynite/Structroglas panels

Texas Greenhouse Co.
2717 St. Louis Ave.
Fort Worth, Tex. 76110

Lascolite fiberglass greenhouse panels; crystal-clear acrylic

Redwood greenhouse frames

From an aesthetic standpoint, redwood is probably the best material for a home greenhouse. It blends well with residential architecture and landscaping, whereas metal frames generally distract from the appearance of a home.

There are many advantages to redwood. It is easy to insulate for winter use and transmits heat less readily than aluminum. Expansion and contraction are significant with redwood. It is extremely easy to work. Minor modifications and additions for shelves, hanging basket brackets and special vents are easy to make. Redwood does not have to be painted.

Co-Ray-Vac

This infrared vacuum-gas heating system consists of an overhead burner connected to an infrared heat-emitting pipe. The invisible infrared rays radiate in straight lines to all surfaces. Heated surfaces transfer to the air. Gas-operated.

Roberts-Gordon Corp.
44 Central Ave.
Buffalo, N.Y. 14206

WINDOW GREENHOUSE

You can easily convert a sunny window into a greenhouse with this window greenhouse. It has an all-aluminum frame, an insect screen, and adjustable air flow shelving.

Lord & Burnham
Irvington-on-Hudson, N.Y. 10533

LEAN-TO HOBBY GREENHOUSE

This model has an all-aluminum frame, commercial-quality glass, and a heavy-duty door. A complete set of erection plans is furnished with every greenhouse.

National Greenhouse Company
P.O. Box 1000
Pana, Ill. 62557

Filon fiberglass panels

Filon fiberglass is a top-quality brand product made with acrylic-enriched resins, fiberglass, and mineral pigment plus ultraviolet-absorbing agents for maximum color fastness and long life.

Filon Stripes: These multicolored panels are used for many building purposes.

Cool Rib Panels: These panels are manufactured in bright pastels. They block out much of the sun's rays.

Home Greenhouse Panels: These are special panels for the backyard gardener. They have a 95 percent light transmission.

Vistron Corporation
Dept. 152
12333 Van Ness Ave.
Hawthorne, Cal. 90250

A SIMPLE, WELL-DESIGNED GREENHOUSE: SOLARSPHERE

This easily erected greenhouse is an efficient producer of vegetables the year around. (A) Fiberglass panels can be interchanged to vary light intensity. (B) Height is 8½ feet at center, 7 feet at side, with a 14-foot diameter. (C) Plexiglass dome vent has adjustable flow control. (D) There are molded hanging-basket brackets. (E) Cedar-slat benches provide maximum growing area. (F) Fiberglass frame comes in brown, yellow, or green. (G) Molded fiberglass baseboards are around perimeter of unit. (H) Aluminum frame door has tempered glass and lower ventilating panel. (I) There are aluminum bench supports.

Shelter Dynamics
Round Rock, Tex. 78664

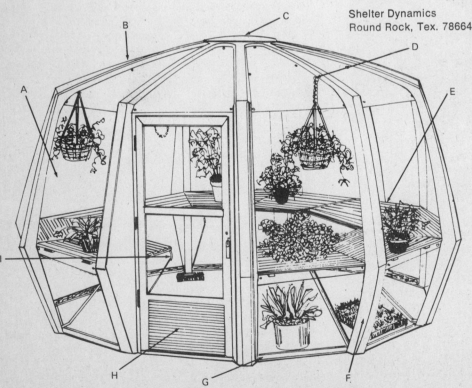

VICTORIA GREENHOUSES

This company makes kits and components for the home greenhouse. This is the basic 8-foot model, which may be expanded by adding new sections. Note the unusual peak vent which opens the entire length of the greenhouse.

Victoria Greenhouses, Ltd.
Box 947
Stump Bridge Rd.
Southampton, Pa. 18966

DOME GREENHOUSE

Right out of the space age, this modular-form, easily erected, 4-section fiberglass greenhouse offers a complete diffusion of light—no shadows. There's good ventilation through the dome shape. The high dome of 9 feet allows for full accessibility.

Energy Absorption Systems, Inc.
860 S. River Rd.
West Sacramento, Cal. 95691

QUONSET-TYPE GREENHOUSE

This greenhouse was engineered for two layers of plastic with a nylon rope used to fasten the outer layer. There are no slats, nails, or cleats to puncture, tear, or weaken the plastic. You can roll the sides up or down or take the covering clear off or put it back in a matter of minutes.

Maco
P.O. Box 109
Scio, Ore. 97374

PLANT CARE CENTER

The complete greenhouse furniture system. All components approximately 48 inches long by 24 inches wide and 36 inches high. The planting table is ideal for small vegetable growing and seed starting. The potting bench provides a work center and space for tools, pots, soil, or liquid. Includes four storage bins.

Christen, Inc.
59 Branch St.
St. Louis, Mo. 63147

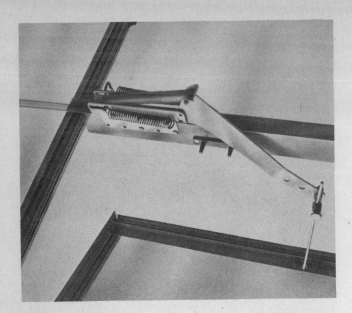

SOLARVENT

Solarvent operates using a heat-activated expanding chemical. It automatically begins to open the greenhouse window at 68° F. interior temperature. At 75° F. the window is wide open. When interior cools, the window closes automatically.

Dalen Products, Inc.
201 Sherlake Dr.
Knoxville, Tenn. 37922

SMALL FREE-STANDING GREENHOUSE

This greenhouse uses a bolt-together redwood frame and 4-ounce Filon fiberglass panels. It features straight sides, aluminum screened vents, and a dutch door. Bolt-on extensions allow the greenhouse to be easily enlarged.

McGregor Greenhouses
1195 Thompson Ave.
Santa Cruz, Cal. 95063

ALUMINUM LEAN-TO GREENHOUSES

Everlite Aluminum Greenhouses were the first prefabricated standardized aluminum greenhouses manufactured in the United States. Straight sides eliminate waste space created by slant-sided greenhouses. All Everlite greenhouses are permanently glazed with a specially formulated compound. Stainless steel clips maintain tension for weatherproof glazing. The Everlite greenhouse can be made nearly 100 percent automatic with accessory equipment.

Aluminum Greenhouses, Inc.
14605 Lorain Ave.
Cleveland, Oh. 44111

INTERIOR OF A SMALL FREE-STANDING GREENHOUSE

A variety of vegetables can be grown in raised beds and pots. This greenhouse covering is twin-walled acrylic and fiberglass, designed to cut down on heating costs. Every section has two panes of rigid acrylic reinforced by fiberglass, separated by a thermal air space that retains heat 2½ times longer than single-pane glass. These panels will not shatter.

Vegetable Factory, Inc.
100 Court St.
Copiague, N.Y. 11726

FREE-STANDING GREENHOUSE

This Burpee 8-by-12-foot greenhouse comes with a weatherproof sliding door with condensation channels to carry away the excess moisture. It also has a non-electric temperature-sensitive control that automatically opens and closes the roof ventilator and a side louver ventilator to assure uniform air circulation. The glass panels go all the way to the floor. This greenhouse can be expanded with easily attached extension panels.

W. Atlee Burpee Co.
Warminster, Pa. 18974

TRADITIONAL STYLE

This greenhouse has a center ridge, with one gable end eliminated and attached to the house for easy access. Janco also builds free-standing and lean-to models. These greenhouses are easy to erect. Each aluminum part is pre-cut to size marked and identified to correspond with a set of blueprints.

J. A. Nearing Co., Inc.
10788 Tucker St.
Beltsville, Md. 20705

SQUARE GREENHOUSE

This 10-by-10-foot greenhouse utilizes a hot-dipped galvanized steel frame and transparent fiberglass walls. The greenhouse includes an anodized aluminum door (a combination screen and fiberglass panel) and a 14-inch thermostatically controlled louvered fan.

Wheeling Corrugating Company
Wheeling, W. Va. 26003

SMALL FIBERGLASS GREENHOUSE

Here's a well-built fiberglass-and-galvanized-steel free-standing unit. Rocks or hailstones will not trouble you with this tough nylon-reinforced Filon. The greenhouse is available in lengths of 8, 10, 12, 16, and 20 feet. It can also be expanded in greenhouse lengths of 6, 8, 10, and 12 feet. The company has various accessories available including hydroponic conversion kits.

Environmental Dynamics
Sunnymead, Cal. 92388

11

GROWING VEGETABLES IN CONTAINERS

Before the 1960s very few gardeners, except for a small number of green-thumbed enthusiasts, grew anything indoors except for a few five-and-dime potted plants. Then came the "green revolution," and houseplants began to fill the great indoors everywhere. Then, in the 1970s, a second great plant revolution burst forth, with millions of people growing their own vegetables in containers not only indoors, but outdoors, too, on balconies, patios, and wherever there proved to be suitable space. Particularly if you have little or no tillable ground, container gardening is a real boon. Suburbanites as well as city dwellers can grow an amazing number of fresh vegetables.

Containers fit everywhere

In San Francisco a couple from the midwest grows corn, beans, squash, and other tasty crops on the roof of their ultramodern apartment house. In Chicago a 60-year-old widow grows a profusion of greens in one small, south-facing window. And in New York City a workingman grows a huge crop of lettuce, carrots, tomatoes, and more under lights in a four-by-seven-foot closet.

Vegetable gardening in containers is amazingly simple, and no matter where you live there is no reason you can't enjoy fresh vegetables the year round from your own container garden. All that's necessary are containers that will fit into your available space, a suitable growing medium (potting soil or other mixture), enough light and water, and maintenance. Of course, you'll need the right kind of seeds—many catalogs list varieties bred for container growing—and a healthy measure of intelligent planning.

The choice of containers is as wide as your imagination. From recycled coffee cans to large patio planters, from cut-down milk cartons to redwood boxes to wicker baskets to plastic garbage cans, there are containers to suit every space and pocketbook. Depending on the size of your containers and the material used to make them, you will buy ready-to-use soil or you will mix up your own blend. The amount and frequency of watering will also depend on the type of containers used. In this chapter we will consider each of these subjects separately and in relation to each other.

An infinite variety of containers

The first consideration in choosing containers is size. Where do you want to put them, and how much room do you have? Generally, the larger and deeper the container, the more prolific the yields . . . up to a point. If you've got eight inches of soil, that's enough for

301

just about any vegetable (see chart on page 302 for each plant's specific requirements). If you've got fairly small containers in mind, and you want to grow tomatoes, stay with the smaller patio-type plants; the larger varieties of this great favorite require up to 20 gallons (3 cubic feet) of soil to produce a decent crop.

With size comes weight. Will your plants be moved around at all? You can of course easily carry the lighter containers from place to place, but the larger pots are quite heavy when full of soil. So place them in permanent position, not where you'll have to move them to get them closer to water, to put them in better light, or whatever. Like all advice, this latter sentence is not true in all cases. You *can* increase the mobility of your heavy containers without taking a course in weightlifting simply by installing casters on their respective bases. Or you can use a moving man's dolly or a throw rug that will fit underneath a container and slide across the floor easily. Another alternative is to place several containers on a child's wagon, locking the wheels in place until you want to move it.

Containers are made of many different kinds of material, each with its own advantages. Wooden containers hold moisture well and need less watering than clay pots. The same is true for styrofoam pots. Then there are nonporous containers, such as those made of stone, glass, ceramics, and plastic, which do not need to be watered as much as wooden or clay containers.

Drainage

No matter what the container is made of, no matter how big or small it is, there must be an outlet for the

HOW MUCH CAN YOU GROW IN A CONTAINER?

	NO. OF PLANTS IN 4-INCH POTS	NO. OF PLANTS IN 8-INCH POTS
Beets	2-4	8-20
Carrots	2-4	12-24
Garlic	2-4	4-16
Green onions	4-8	16-30
Looseleaf lettuce	1	2
Mustard greens	1	3
Radishes	4-8	16-30
Spinach	1	2
Turnips	2-4	2-16

excess water that percolates through the soil. Otherwise, with no place to go, this water would sit and do more harm than good. So holes must be drilled or punched through the bottoms of strong containers, such as those made of wood, or through the sides (about ½ inch above the base) of plastic and many metal containers. These latter types of containers would be weakened at the base if holes were bored in the bottom, which must support the weight of the soil.

There should not be too many holes for drainage in a container, nor should the holes be larger than necessary. As a general rule, containers less than 10 inches in diameter need only one hole about ½ inch in diameter. The larger pots need anywhere from two to four holes just a bit bigger than ½ inch around.

Two final points on drainage: First, it's generally a good idea to cover the holes with a layer of gravel, pieces of clay, or other coarse material to prevent the soil from being washed away with the excess water. Second, it's obviously essential to place a dish or other receptacle under the container to catch the water that drains through the holes.

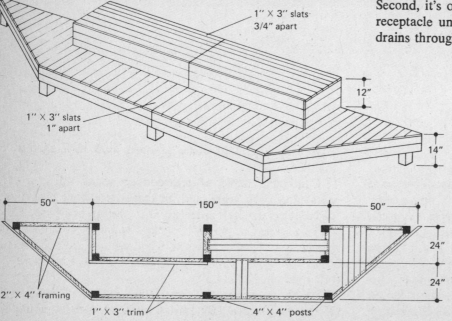

1" × 3" slats 3/4" apart

1" × 3" slats 1" apart

12"

14"

50"   150"   50"

24"

24"

2" × 4" framing

1" × 3" trim   4" × 4" posts

How to build a platform for a container garden.

OPTIONAL PLANTER STYLES

Top: Round, Vase, and Square
Bottom: Urn, Globe, and Triangle

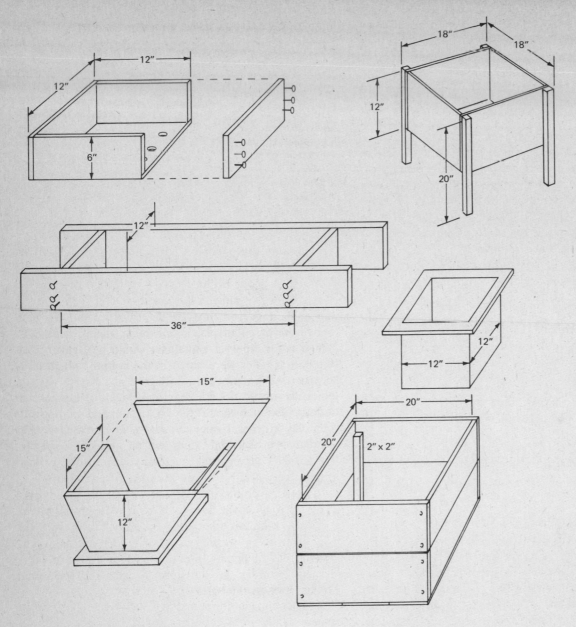

Illustrations of do-it-yourself planters.

Wooden containers

Since wood has a high insulating value, containers made of this material keep the soil from drying out quickly and so require less watering than other types. You can buy readymade wooden planters in a wide variety of shapes and sizes, or you can build them yourself. For instance, to build a planter that is one foot square, purchase five 12-by-12-by-1-inch pieces of lumber, two running feet of 2-by-1-inch stock, and a couple dozen penny nails. Nail the pieces together, four sides atop the base. Then cut the 2-by-1-inch piece into four equal sections and nail them to the four corners as

legs. You can build boxes of other sizes in a similar manner.

Containers made of redwood or cedar will resist decay for many years, and for that reason have proven to be popular with gardeners. For other types of wood, you can line the interior of the container with black plastic, or you can coat the wood with a preservative paint or asphalt compound available at hardware and other stores.

Another popular and interesting type of container is the barrel half. By law, barrels used for making whiskey must be discarded after just one batch. Many nurseries sell used whiskey barrel halves for use as

HOW FAR APART TO PLANT VEGETABLES IN A CONTAINER

VEGETABLE	SPACE BETWEEN EACH PLANT	VEGETABLE	SPACE BETWEEN EACH PLANT
Artichokes	Plant singly	Mustard greens	Thin to 4 inches apart
Beans	3-9 inches	Okra	20 inches (5-10 gal. soil per plant)
Beets	2-3 inches	Peas	2 inches
Broccoli	10 inches (5 gal. soil per plant)	Peppers	8 inches (2½ gal. soil per plant)
Brussels sprouts	10 inches (5 gal. soil per plant)	Potatoes	6 inches
Cabbage	10 inches (5 gal. soil per plant)	Radishes	1 inch
Carrots	1-2 inches	Rhubarb	12 inches (5 gal. soil per plant)
Cauliflower	12 inches (5 gal. soil per plant)	Spinach	Thin to 5 inches
Eggplant	15 inches (5 gal. soil per plant)	Squash	12-20 inches (5 gal. of soil per plant)
Kale	Thin to 16 inches apart	Tomatoes	½ inch (5 gal. soil per plant)
Lettuce	4-10 inches	Turnips	6 inches
Melon	15 inches (5 gal. soil per plant)		

planters. The size of these containers is one of their principal assets—being roughly 22 inches across, they hold enough soil to support good vegetable growth. A single barrel half can hold seven to eight corn plants, two to three zucchini plants, and two or three tomato plants. Some gardeners even intercrop their barrel halves—that is, they plant a low, quick-maturing crop right along with a larger, slow-maturing vegetable. Thus, corn can be planted with spinach, radishes, and green onions, tomatoes can be planted with radishes, green onions, and lettuce. There's no crowding out of one by the other because you pick the faster-growing vegetables before the slower-growing ones become very large.

Plastic pails

Most of them may not win any awards for outstanding design, but plastic pails are inexpensive and practical containers for use in vegetable gardening. You can buy the 2- or 3-gallon type at the local variety store, or you might be able to pick up larger, 5- or 10-gallon models that have been tossed away after use at home-building sites. There are many ways to dress up these plastic beauties, including covering them with metal foil or placing them inside larger wicker baskets.

Some companies, such as Rubbermaid, manufacture attractively designed plastic containers for gardeners. These ready-to-use pots come in many different sizes and shapes and have found a wide market among those who'd rather spend their time gardening than building containers.

Other types of containers

Paper pulp pots. An all-round good vegetable container, this type of pot can be carried from place to place without difficulty. The most popular sizes are 12 and 18 inches in inside diameter. In the latter you

can plant eggplant, tomatoes, and other large vegetables; the former are good for carrots and similar plants.

Wooden fruit boxes. You can still occasionally pick up an orange crate or similar wooden box outside the supermarket or vegetable store. Recycle it into a container by lining it with black plastic in which some drainage holes have been punched. Filled with good soil, one of these containers will hold several tomato, zucchini, or corn plants—or almost any other variety you'd like to grow.

Bushel baskets. Some people find these more attractive than the wooden fruit boxes. Aside from that, everything we said about the fruit boxes also holds true for bushel baskets. But act fast. The age of cardboard and plastic is with us, and the old wooden baskets and boxes are becoming scarce.

Wicker baskets. As wood becomes rare, wicker seems to be becoming more common. Well-designed containers are available in countless styles and sizes at many "import" and other variety stores. Use plastic liners, as noted above.

Windowsill containers

The supply of these smaller containers is virtually without limit. Here are some that are commonly available and that have been used by many gardeners with good success:

Coffee cans. These make fairly sturdy containers for plants. Just punch a few holes in the sides, close to the base, for drainage, fill with soil, and you're ready to grow.

Milk cartons. These plastic-coated, paperboard containers won't last as long as cans, but they'll do quite nicely for one crop. Cut them off six to eight inches

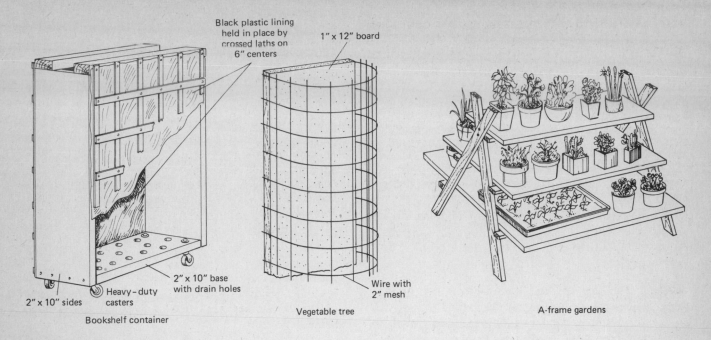

Black plastic lining held in place by crossed laths on 6" centers

1" x 12" board

2" x 10" base with drain holes

Heavy-duty casters

2" x 10" sides

Bookshelf container

Wire with 2" mesh

Vegetable tree

A-frame gardens

DO-IT-YOURSELF VERTICAL GARDENS

above the base, near which you have punched out with a pencil four holes for drainage.

Freezer containers. One-pint plastic freezer containers are excellent windowsill containers. Lightweight, durable, and inexpensive, they'll last through many plantings.

Flowerpots. The classic four-inch clay flowerpot is not as cheap as it used to be, but it fits very nicely onto most windowsills and is large enough to grow beets, carrots, radishes, and similar leafy and root vegetables.

A word of caution

When utilizing containers in which a crop has already been grown, scrub them with a vegetable brush dipped in clean, soapy water, then rinse them out in boiling water. This prevents any disease organisms from being transmitted from one crop to the next.

Vertical containers

One of the most innovative developments to come along in recent years is vertical vegetable gardening. This adds a new concept to balcony or patio gardening —height. Now you can plant gardens that go up the walls as high as you can plant and harvest. Following are some of the variations on this basic theme:

Vegetable trees. You can build one of these yourself without a great deal of hassle. For backing use a 2-by-12-inch board of any length (6 or 8 feet is most common). Cut standard chicken wire into two-foot widths

that are as long as the board you're using (see drawing above). Nail the wire lengthwise to each side of the board. Cut a semicircular board to fit at the base of the wire, and secure it in place. Line the wire and the boards with black plastic, fill with soil, and you're ready for planting. When using a vegetable tree, it's possible to garden in combination—that is, tomatoes at the base, topped by cucumbers, then lettuce, then carrots and radishes at the top. You can use a number of these containers, placed along a wall or at the edge of a patio or balcony.

Hanging basket trees. First, buy or make hanging baskets, half-round in shape, which can be attached to a flat backing. Set up a 1- or 2-by-12-inch board as above, probably about 6-8 feet long. Attach the baskets to the board, about two feet apart. Line them with sphagnum moss or black plastic, place a pie tin or other device at the base, and fill these pouches with soil.

Vegetable pot trees. This is another interesting and easy-to-make variation on the tree format. Anchor four 4-inch-by-7-foot posts to a base such as a Christmas tree stand. Keep the posts in place with sandbags. Mount 8-inch pots alternately up the posts on hooks strong enough to hold the weight. In a further variation you can eliminate the base and nail or mount the posts on a balcony railing.

Bookshelf containers. These are probably the most interesting and most useful of all vertical containers. You can put them in stationary positions or mount them on heavy-duty wheels so that you can move them around. To make a bookshelf container you mount 2-by-10-inch side boards on a base of the same size. A good length for the sides is 4-5 feet, but this can vary quite a bit according to individual requirements. Drainage holes are drilled in the base. The sides can be joined on both ends by construction wire or by crossed laths (see drawing 303). The container thus formed is lined with black plastic and filled with soil mix. Leave the top open because you are going to water from there, from halfway down, and from two-thirds of the way down.

It's important with this type of container to use hardy transplants. Insert them through the wire mesh. Keep them moist, and feed frequently with a liquid plant solution.

A-frame gardens. This type of setup is second in versatility only to the bookshelf. And you can build it yourself without a great deal of effort. First, make two A-frame sides using 2-by-4-inch standard boards and a metal sawhorse clamp (a workable design utilizes 5-foot-long 2-by-4 boards spread 5 feet apart). The A-frames should be joined by another 5-foot-long 2-by-4. This structure will become even sturdier when the A-frames are joined by three shelves, preferably of 2-by-8-inch board, mounted on large shelf brackets and braced by 2-by-4 boards. As shown in the drawing, the shelves are wide toward the base, narrow at the top. On these shelves you can place a number of 8-inch or similar-size pots and create a varied, attractive container garden.

Hanging Gardens

You can add significantly to your overall vegetable production by utilizing hanging containers on the patio, balcony, or almost anywhere. For instance, you can hang cherry tomatoes 2 feet apart under the eaves, or hang a whole garden of carrots, radishes, and similar

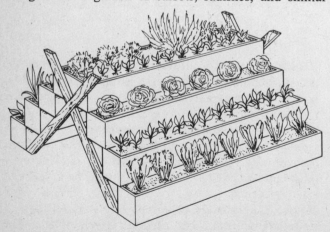

Stair-step, or A-frame, planter.

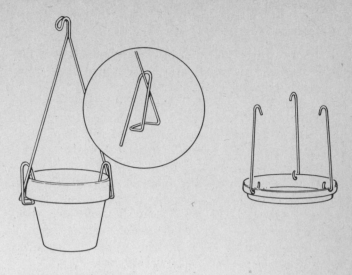

HANGING PLANTS

Left, a wire coat hanger can be twisted into a hanger for a pot. Right, lengths of wire attach a water-catching saucer to a hanging pot.

plants. In general, hanging containers will grow all medium-sized vegetables well, including the smaller tomatoes and cucumbers. In most cases you should not plant them with larger vegetables such as squash, cantaloupe, cabbage, and similar plants. There just isn't room.

Here are a few types of hanging containers:

Hanging wire baskets. Wire baskets make fine containers for lettuce, radishes, even small tomato plants. Place an aluminum pie plate in the bottom to keep soil from washing out. Stuff the open wire frame with moist sphagnum moss. You can add burlap if you like. Fill with soil, and pot as you would any other container. A hanging basket dries out quickly, so it should be watered daily. To water, immerse in a pail of water. You can buy these baskets from most nurseries.

Long, long baskets. To make these attractive containers cut standard-width chicken wire into 3- or 4-foot lengths and put the long edges together to form a 3-foot-long cylinder. Place a small plastic bucket at one end and tie in place with small pieces of wire. Line the entire container with black plastic. Fill with soil mix, punch holes in the plastic, and plant vegetables from top to bottom.

Vegetables in raised beds

Raised bed gardening, with the raised soil framed with stone walls, bricks, logs, adobe, railroad ties, redwood boards, and similar material, is becoming more and more popular today. The reason: raised beds solve a number of garden problems, especially those associated with backyard gardens.

Raised beds

- Allow you to mix a light rich soil on top of the ground that is perfect for root crops. This solves the problem of hard, infertile soil.
- Warm up the soil in the beds before the soil in the surrounding ground warms up. This allows you to plant earlier in the spring. Covered with clear plastic, a raised bed also becomes a coldframe to protect tender plants.
- Drain better than other types of gardens. The soil in raised beds never becomes too wet or too soggy.
- Allow the soil in the bed to be cultivated with kitchen utensils instead of standard garden tools.
- Eliminate the gopher problem when chicken wire is placed across the bottom of the bed.
- Make clear, workable gardens. The entire surface of a small raised bed can be reached from the garden paths.
- Make neat, uniform, attractive gardens that are aesthetically more interesting than other types of gardens.

Planting mixes

Some gardeners simply go out and dig up common garden soil to fill their containers for growing vegetables. In most cases this just won't do. An ideal soil for growing vegetables has 50 percent solid matter and 50 percent air space. Moisture should occupy about one-half the air space. Most garden soils are either too sandy or too clayey, giving a less than ideal balance. In addition, in a contained space even a good garden soil becomes compacted more easily than it does in the ground, thus closing the air spaces and causing water to run almost straight through. In addition it dries out faster and in some cases drains poorly, creating a root-rot problem. It is best, therefore, to use a special container soil for vegetable gardening.

Sorting out potting mixes

A good potting mix must be loose enough to let the roots develop freely. It must provide enough air space (despite container compacting) to allow good air and water movement, it must have the right pH balance, and it must retain nutrients and water yet still drain well.

To fulfill these requirements, most potting mixes are a combination of organic material and minerals. The organic component may be peat moss, compost, bark, redwood sawdust, shavings, or any combination of these. The mineral fraction may be vermiculite, perlite, pumice, builder's sand, or a combination of ingredients.

Garden stores everywhere sell "synthetic soil" or "soilless mixes" under a wide variety of trade names: Redi-Earth, Jiffy Mix, Metro Mix, Super Soil, Pro Mix, and many others. Most also contain a balance of nutrients. The exact formula may vary depending on what you intend to grow.

Jiffy Mix, for instance, is composed of equal parts of shredded sphagnum, peat moss, and fine grade vermiculite plus just enough nutrients to sustain initial plant growth.

A tomato formula contains a balance of fast- and slow-release nutrients formulated for tomatoes plus sphagnum moss, vermiculite, and solid soil materials.

Two of the most popular mixes were perfected at Cornell University and at the University of California. The California formula is available under the names First Step and Super Soil.

If you'd rather make your own potting mix here's the formula for the Cornell mix.

Vermiculite	8 quarts
Shredded peat moss	8 quarts
Superphosphate	2 level tablespoons
Limestone	2 tablespoons
Dried cow manure or steamed bone meal	8 tablespoons

Measure and place all ingredients in a garbage can liner. Shake vigorously. Since the Cornell mix has no smell, you can place it in plastic bags and store in the back of a closet.

Mixing your own vegetable potting soil

Although it is possible to grow vegetables in one of these potting mixes, they generally do better in a combination of soil, potting mix, and other ingredients. Vegetables in soil mixes require less frequent feeding than those in potting mixes. Also, a combination soil-potting mix holds water better.

All-Purpose Vegetable Soil Mix

One part of each of:
   Commercial potting mix
   Compost (homemade or purchased) or vermiculite
   Common garden soil

Purchased soil is already sterilized. Soil from the ground is not, and you might want to sterilize it to destroy weed seed and nematodes and to avoid passing on fungus diseases.

You can sterilize your soil by spreading it out in a shallow pan and baking it at 275° F. for an hour. To overcome the odor problem, soak the soil throughly before putting it in the oven. (It should be noted that some gardeners prefer to take their chances with disease. They will not bake soil because it destroys all the microorganisms, thus making the soil "dead." The compost, of course, brings it back to life.)

Watering techniques

There are a number of ways to water containers. In general, pots less than eight inches in diameter should be watered from above. The entire container can also be half submerged in a pail of water. When the bubbles stop coming up, take them out and let them drain.

Water larger containers from above with a watering can or a hose. There are a number of specialized types of watering cans on the market. To keep the stream of water from a hose from hurting your plants, use a gentle stream or one of the water-breaking nozzles.

(See Chapter 8 for complete information on watering.)

Water all vegetables until the soil is completely saturated. Don't water again until the soil is dry to a depth of 1 or 2 inches. To find out, poke in a finger, take some soil from this depth and rub between thumb and index finger. If soil is dry to your touch, it's time to water. If the soil is mud-coated or feels wet, don't water at least for another four hours.

You can also check to see if your container vegetables need watering with an electrical moisture tester. These testers operate on the principle that wet soil conducts electricity better than dry. There are many models on the market, some equipped with a light meter.

There are many gadgets and systems to help water your containers. Perhaps the simplest is a plastic jug and watering wand combination. There are also pots that water automatically from a built-in reservoir. In addition there are "plant pillows," which hold water like a sponge. When the soil becomes dry, water is drawn into the soil through a hole in the bottom of the pot.

To keep hanging plants from dripping on the carpet when watered you can purchase an easily removed drip pan. These will fit containers of any size.

Drip irrigation watering systems also make watering a number of containers fairly easy. Spaghetti tubes with drip spitters attach directly to the pots. To make watering "work-free" the system can be attached directly to an automatic timer.

The best way to set up containers for vacation or any other long period when you'll be away is with a drip system connected to a timer. Other methods: place a few containers in a flat foil pan partially filled with water, or place containers in a bathtub or sink in 2 to 3 inches of water.

For hanging containers you can place a pail of water underneath the container and run a piece of soft cotton rope between the water and pot. Water will work its way up the "wick" into the pot. You can also give each container a good soaking, slip it into a plastic bag, and seal the bottom with a tape. This forms a closed system in which the moisture given off by the plant leaves will return to the soil.

Feeding techniques

Container vegetables generally need supplemental feedings because the frequent watering leaches out many of the nutrients. Generally, plants need three major elements—nitrogen, phosphorus, and potassium—plus minor and trace elements. Each major nutrient affects vegetable growth different ways.

Nitrogen, for instance, is important for the leafy growth of lettuce, mustard, spinach, and other vegetables. Phosphorus is used in flowering and producing fruit such as tomatoes, cucumbers, eggplant. Potassium is necessary for strong root growth, thus essential for carrots, beets, radishes.

Use either time-release tomato and vegetable food or a liquid fertilizer.

If you use a time-release fertilizer, mix it with the "soil" when you originally fill the container at the rate of one tablespoon for each two gallons of soil. This will feed your vegetables throughout the growing season. Use liquid fertilizers every two weeks according to the instructions on the bottle.

Vegetables for containers

A number of midget or minivegetables are especially suited to container gardening. Some varieties extensively used are: Dwarf Morden cabbage, Little Finger carrot, Golden Midget corn, Little Minnie cucumber, Morden Midget eggplant, Tom Thumb lettuce, Golden Midget watermelon.

In addition, there are a number of tomato varieties that do well in containers: Tiny Tim, Small Fry, Burpee Pixie Hybrid, Presto Hybrid, Patio Hybrid, and others.

Many catalogs now have special sections devoted to these midget vegetables. See Chapter 7, where you will find descriptions of the special properties of thousands of different kinds of seeds.

Waterproofing baskets

Buy clear polyester resin and hardener (separately) and a brush from a craft store. Be sure to use the hardener according to the instructions. Tear some newspapers into long strips about five inches wide. Brush the polyester resin on the basket bottom and sides, then line with the newspaper strips until you have filled the entire basket. Continue the resin-paper process until you've lined the basket with six coats of paper. When finished, add an additional coat of resin.

Potting soil manufacturers and distributors

Geo. J. Ball, Inc.
Box 335
West Chicago, Ill. 60185

Black Leaf Products Co.
667 N. State St.
Elgin, Ill. 60120

Carefree Garden Products
Box 383
West Chicago, Ill. 60185

Clinton Nursery Products,
Inc.
Box 510
Clinton, Conn. 06413

DG Shelter Products
Vita Bark
Box 60158
Sacramento, Cal. 95860

J. T. Dimmick Forest Co.
Box 308
Garberville, Cal. 95440

Conrad Fafard, Inc.
Box 3033
Springfield, Mass. 01101

W. R. Grace & Co.
Terra-Lite Dept.
62 Whittemore Ave.
Cambridge, Mass. 02140

Green Thumb Products
Corp.
Drawer 760
Apopka, Fla. 32703

Greenlife Products Co., Inc.
Box 72
West Point, Va. 23181

H & M Fertilizer, Inc.
Box 1542
Fort Stockton, Tex. 79735

A. H. Hoffman, Inc.
Box 8
Landisville, Pa. 17538

Huber Peat Company
Box 3006
Houston, Tex. 77001

Hyde Park Products Corp.
10 Cottage Place, Box 320
New Rochelle, N.Y. 10802

IMS Corporation
3825 Edith N.E.
Albuquerque, N.M. 87110

Leisur-Aid
I-29 & Hwy. 370
Council Bluffs, Ia. 51501

Leoni's Power-o-Peat
Box 956
Gilbert, Minn. 55741

Lite-Weight Products, Inc.
707 Funston Rd.
Kansas City, Kan. 66115

Michigan Peat Co.
Box 66388
Houston, Tex. 77006

Joe Murphy Co.
Box 261
N. Little Rock, Ark. 72115

Oil-Dri Corp. of America
520 N. Michigan Ave.
Chicago, Ill. 60611

Organic Compost Corp.
Box 217
Germantown, Wisc. 53022

Organic Nutrients, Inc.
8909 Elder Creek Rd.
Sacramento, Cal. 95828

The Page Seed Co.
Box 158
Greene, N.Y. 13778

Premier Brands, Inc.
350 Madison Ave.
New York, N.Y. 10017

Ralston Purina Co.
Early Bird Nursery
Products
14 T Checkerboard Sq.
St. Louis, Mo. 63188

Sgt. Pepper Pottery, Inc.
2800 E. Miraloma Ave.
Anaheim, Cal. 92806

Stim-U-Plant, Inc.
2077 Parkwood Ave.
Columbus, Oh. 43219

Swiss Farms, Inc.
3700 Prudential Tower
Boston, Mass. 02199

Manufacturers and distributors of planter hangers, plant stands

Geo. J. Ball, Inc.
Box 335
West Chicago, Ill. 60185

Beagle Mfg. Co., Inc.
4377 N. Baldwin Ave.
El Monte, Cal. 91731

Bernard Industries
5252 S. Kolmar
Chicago, Ill. 60632

Bright Industries
4123 Station St.
Philadelphia, Pa. 19127

R. R. Brooks Co., Inc.
7326 Jefferson St.
Paramount, Cal. 90723

Burnett Mfg. Corp.
Box 420
Huntingdon Valley,
Pa. 19006

Carefree Garden Products
Box 383
West Chicago, Ill. 60185

Charleston Enterprises,
Inc.
4291 Leventis St.
Stark Ind. Park
Charleston Heights,
S.C. 29405

Christen, Inc.
59 Branch St.
St. Louis, Mo. 63147

Comanche Steel
Products, Inc.
Box 20128
San Antonio, Tex. 78220

Cordcrafts
Box 3332
Wallington, N.J. 07057

Fanon Designs, Inc.
Box 13162
Atlanta, Ga. 30324

Fleco Industries
3347 Halifax St.
Dallas, Tex. 75247

Germain's, Inc.
Box 3233
Los Angeles, Cal. 90058

Hall Industries, Inc.
2323 Commonwealth Ave.
North Chicago, Ill. 60064

Heath Manufacturing Co.
Wolfcrest Products Div.
140 Mill St.
Coopersville, Mich. 49404

Himark Enterprises, Inc.
270 Oser Ave.
Hauppauge, N.Y. 11787

King Cotton Cordage
617 Oradell Ave.
Oradell, N.J. 07649

Leoni's Power-o-Peat
Box 956
Gilbert, Minn. 55741

Lloyd Mfg. Co.
3010 Tenth St.
Menominee, Mich. 49858

Lockwood Products, Inc.
Box 160
Gering, Neb. 69341

Marathon-Carey-McFall
Co.
2156 E. Dauphin St.
Philadelphia, Pa. 19125

Meico Lamp Parts Co.
309 N. Ridgewood
Wichita, Kans. 67208

Mercury Products Corp.
236 Chapman St.
Providence, R.I. 02905

Mr. Chain
1805 Larchwood St.
Troy, Mich. 48084

Molded Fiberglass Tray
Co.
Linesville, Pa. 16424

Joe Murphy Co.
Box 261
N. Little Rock, Ark. 72115

Ohio Wire Products Co.
1025 E. Fifth Ave.
Columbus, Oh. 43201

Opus, Inc.
Foliage Div.
437 Boylston St.
Boston, Mass. 02116

Patio Products, Inc.
2522 State Rd.
Cornwells Heights,
Pa. 19020

Patrician Products, Inc.
483 E. 99th St.
Brooklyn, N.Y. 11236

Manufacturers and distributors of planter hangers, plant stands (Continued)

Phillips Products Co., Inc.
Box 466
Bartlett, Ill. 60103

Plantrac Corp.
38 W. Mall
Plainview, N.Y. 11803

PTC Patio Products
Box 6725
Jacksonville, Fla. 32205

Rubbermaid, Inc.
1147 Akron Rd.
Wooster, Oh. 44691

Seasonal Industries, Inc.
923 Fee Fee Rd.
Hazelwood, Mo. 63043

Sgt. Pepper Pottery, Inc.
2800 E. Miraloma Ave.
Anaheim, Cal. 92806

Stim-U-Plant, Inc.
2077 Parkwood Ave.
Columbus, Oh. 43219

Strand Corp.
Box 40417
Garland, Tex. 75040

Tube Craft, Inc.
1311 S.W. 80th St.
Cleveland, Oh. 44102

Union Products, Inc.
511 Lancaster St.
Leominster, Mass. 01453

Unitron
12824 S. Cerise Ave.
Hawthorne, Cal. 90250

Vandy-Craft, Inc.
1727 Merchandise Mart
Chicago, Ill. 60654

Weller Nurseries Co., Inc.
Box 1111
Holland, Mich. 49423

Whitehall Metal Studios
Inc.
8786 Water St.
Montague, Mich. 49437

Manufacturers and distributors of planters, pots, saucers

Abbott Industries, Inc.
940 N. Beltline Rd.
Irving, Tex. 75061

Atlas Asbestos Co.
5600 Hochelaga St.
Montreal, Que.
   H1N 1W1, Canada

Geo. J. Ball, Inc.
Box 335
West Chicago, Ill. 60185

Bernard Industries
5252 S. Kolmar
Chicago, Ill. 60632

Bright Industries
4123 Station St.
Philadelphia, Pa. 19127

Brighton By-Products Co.,
Inc.
Box 23
New Brighton, Pa. 15066

Carefree Garden Products
Box 383
West Chicago, Ill. 60185

Carefree Shrubbery Div.
5500 W. Touhy
Skokie, Ill. 60076

CCD, Inc.
RFD 2, Box 203A
Dodge City, Kan. 67801

CDP Corp.
Box 587
Richardson, Tex. 75080

Charleston Enterprises,
Inc.
4291 Leventis St.
Stark Ind. Park
Charleston Heights,
   S.C. 29405

Christen, Inc.
59 Branch St.
St. Louis, Mo. 63147

Concord Woodworking Co.,
Inc.
50 Beharrell St.
West Concord, Mass. 01742

Coneco Plastics
Box 3429
Fullerton, Cal. 92634

Contemporary
   Merchandisers, Inc.
2210 W. 75th St.
Shawnee Mission,
   Kan. 66208

County Plastic Corp.
361 Neptune Ave.
North Babylon, N.Y. 11704

Craftsmen, Inc.
Box 26
Orangeburg, S.C. 29115

Cross Newform Plastics Co.
124 Boston Turnpike
Shrewsbury, Mass. 01545

Encap Products Co.
Box 278
Mount Prospect, Ill. 60056

Esmay Products, Inc.
P.O. Box 547
Bristol, Ind. 46507

Red Ewald, Inc.
Box 519
Karnes City, Tex. 78118

Featherrock, Inc.
Box 6190
Burbank, Cal. 91510

Fiberglass Specialties, Inc.
5214 Fairlawn Ave.
Baltimore, Md. 21215

H. B. Fisher
Box 546
Longport, N.J. 08403

Germain's, Inc.
Box 3233
Los Angeles, Cal. 90058

Gilbert Plastics, Inc.
Box 68
Yorktown Heights,
   N.Y. 10598

Glendale Tool & Die Co.
1911 B Riverside Dr.
Glendale, Cal. 91201

Good-Prod Sales, Inc.
825 Fairfield Ave.
Kenilworth, N.J. 07033

Green Thumb Products
   Corp.
Drawer 760
Apopka, Fla. 32703

Hall Industries, Inc.
2323 Commonwealth Ave.
North Chicago, Ill. 60064

Heath Manufacturing Co.
Wolfcrest Products Div.
140 Mill St.
Coopersville, Mich. 49404

Henri Studio, Inc.
2260 Rand Rd.
Palatine, Ill. 60067

Herbst Bros. Seedmen, Inc.
Garden Supply Div.
1000 N. Main St.
Brewster, N.Y. 10509

Holland Bulb Co.
6441 Johnson Cr. Blvd.
Portland, Ore. 97206

Hyde Bird Feeder Corp.
10 Cottage Place, Box 320
New Rochelle, N.Y. 10802

IMS Corp.
3825 Edith N.E.
Albuquerque, N.M. 87110

Iterra Clay Products
5866 S.W. 68th St.
South Miami, Fla. 33143

Max Klein Co.
715 Lynn Ave.
Baraboo, Wisc. 53913

Leoni's Power-o-Peat
Box 956
Gilbert, Minn. 55741

Lockwood Products, Inc.
80 Sherman St.
Cambridge, Mass. 02140

McHutchison & Co., Inc.
695 Grand Ave.
Ridgefield, N.J. 07657

Meta Industries, Inc.
170 A Rte. 206
Somerville, N.J. 08876

Mr. Chain
1805 Larchwood St.
Troy, Mich. 48084

Joe Murphy Co.
Box 261
N. Little Rock,
   Ark. 72115

Ohio Wire Products Co.
1025 E. Fifth Ave.
Columbus, Oh. 43201

Opus, Inc.
Foliage Div.
437 Boylston St.
Boston, Mass. 02116

Original Equipment
   Mfg., Ltd.
584 Clinton Ave.
Sudbury, Ont.
   P3P 2T2, Canada

Patio Products, Inc.
2522 State Rd.
Cornwells Heights,
   Pa. 19020

Manufacturers and distributors of planter hangers, plant stands (Continued)

Patrician Products, Inc.
483 E. 99th St.
Brooklyn, N.Y. 11236

Perky Pet Products, Inc.
2201 S. Wabash St.
Denver, Col. 80231

Phillips Products Co., Inc.
Box 466
Bartlett, Ill. 60103

Plexite Industries, Inc.
1110 Nasa Rd. #1
Houston, Tex. 77058

Pots by Paul, Inc.
Box 3584
Sarasota, Fla. 33578

PTC Patio Products
Box 6725
Jacksonville, Fla. 32205

E. Rabinowe & Co., Inc.
465 Saw Mill River Rd.
Yonkers, N.Y. 10701

Reuter Laboratory, Inc.
2045 James Madison Hwy.
Haymarket, Va. 22069

Roberts Products
700 Rancheros Dr.
San Marco, Cal. 92069

Rubbermaid, Inc.
1147 Akron Rd.
Wooster, Oh. 44691

M. L. Sandy
Box 1535
Corinth, Miss. 38834

Seasonal Industries, Inc.
923 Fee Fee Rd.
Hazelwood, Mo. 63043

Sgt. Pepper Pottery, Inc.
2800 E. Miraloma Ave.
Anaheim, Cal. 92086

H. B. Sherman Mfg. Co.
207 W. Michigan Ave.
Battle Creek,
   Mich. 49014

The Sunny Green Garden
204 Andover St.
Andover, Mass. 01810

Swiss Farms, Inc.
3700 Prudential Tower
Boston, Mass. 02199

Tube Craft, Inc.
1311 S.W. 80th
Cleveland, Oh. 44102

Union Products, Inc.
511 Lancaster St.
Leominster, Mass. 01453

Unitron
12824 S. Cerise Ave.
Hawthorne, Cal. 90250

Valley View Specialities
   Co.
13831 S. Kostner
Crestwood, Ill. 60445

Vandy-Craft, Inc.
1727 Merchandise Mart
Chicago, Ill. 60654

The Vaughan-Jacklin
   Corp.
5300 Katrine Ave.
Downers Grove, Ill. 60515

Vining Broom Co.
2530 Columbus Ave.
Springfield, Oh. 45501

Weller Nurseries Co., Inc.
Box 1111
Holland, Mich. 49423

Woodstream Corp.
Lititz, Pa. 17543

World Garden Products
2 First St. E.
Norwalk, Conn. 06855

Zanesville Stoneware
309 Pershing Rd.
Zanesville, Oh. 43701

CERAMIC

Phillips Products Co., Inc.   High-quality ceramic
Box 466   handcrafted planters
Bartlett, Ill. 60103

Rain Bird Corp.   Unusual Italian ceramic
7045 N. Grand Ave.   tile planters
Glendora, Cal. 91740

FIBERGLASS-PLASTIC

Atlas Asbestos   Quality patio pots
5600 Hochelaga St.   and planters
Montreal, Que.
   HiNiWi, Canada

Carefree Garden Products   Deco pots, available in
Box 383   four colors, 4-inch and
West Chicago, Ill. 60185   6½-inch pot and saucer

Coneco   Plastic planters with
P.O. Box 3429   lock-on saucers
Fullerton, Cal. 92634

Fiberglass Specialties, Inc.   Fiberglass planters in many
5214 Fairlawn Ave.   shapes and sizes
Baltimore, Md. 21215

Gilbert Plastics, Inc.   Unusual plastic planters,
Box 68   architectural planters,
Yorktown Heights,   wood grains, metal effects,
   N.Y. 10598   rock group

Max Klein Co.   Many different kinds of
715 Lynn Ave.   containers
Baraboo, Wisc. 53913

Lockwood Products, Inc.   Fiesta planters, fiberglass
80 Sherman St.   plant tubs
Cambridge, Mass. 02140

Molded Fiberglass Tray Co.   Fiberglass boxes
Linesville, Pa. 16424

Patrician Products, Inc.   Plastic pots, hangers,
483 E. 99th St.   and trays
Brooklyn, N.Y. 11236

Phillips Products Co., Inc.   All sizes and colors of
P.O. Box 466   planters in durable non-
Bartlett, Ill. 60103   porous impact plastic

Rubbermaid, Inc.   Plastic planters of many
1147 Akron Rd.   shapes and sizes; weathered
Wooster, Oh. 44691   wood design, windowsill
                                     planters, and more

Valley View Specialties Co.   Tough reinforced
P.O. Box 277   fiberglass; stone
Oak Lawn, Ill. 60454   glaze finish

STONEWARE

Himark Enterprises, Inc.   Stoneware and
270 Oser Ave.   ceramic planters
Hauppauge, N.Y. 11787

Zanesville Stoneware   Stoneware planters
309 Pershing Rd.
Zanesville, Oh. 43701

HANGING PLANTERS

Carefree Garden Products
Box 383
West Chicago, Ill. 60185
— Several types of
hanging planters

Coneco
P.O. Box 3429
Fullerton, Cal. 92634
— Simulated redwood,
plastic planters

Cross Newform Plastic Co.
124 Boston Tnpk.
Shrewsbury, Mass. 01545
— Kangaroo pouch planters

Heath Manufacturing Co.
Wolfcrest Products Div.
140 Mill St.
Coopersville, Mich. 49404
— Hanging redwood planters,
wire baskets, paper pulp
liners

Lockwood Products, Inc.
80 Sherman St.
Cambridge, Mass. 02140
— Plastic hanging planters

Molded Fiberglass Tray Co.
Linesville, Pa. 16424
— Molded fiberglass planters

Patrician Products, Inc.
483 E. 99th St.
Brooklyn, N.Y. 11236
— Wire baskets

Phillips Products Co.
P.O. Box 466
Bartlett, Ill. 60103
— Garden scene hanging
plastic planters

Rain Bird Corp.
7045 N. Grand Ave.
Glendora, Cal. 91740
— Wood, tile, ceramic
hanging planters

Rubbermaid, Inc.
1147 Akron Rd.
Wooster, Oh. 44691
— Hanging plastic planters

WOOD PLANTERS

Heath Manufacturing Co.
Wolfcrest Products Div.
140 Mill St.
Coopersville, Mich. 49404
— Redwood planters,
novelties, wheelbarrows,
picnic table planters, etc.

Himark Enterprises, Inc.
270 Oser Ave.
Hauppauge N.Y. 11787
— Hardwood planters

Hyde's, Inc.
56 Felton St.
Waltham, Mass. 02154
— Redwood planters,
octagonal, square,
twelve-side, etc.

Stim-U-Plant, Inc.
2077 Parkwood Ave.
Columbus, Oh. 43219
— Redwood planters

Vandy-Craft, Inc.
1727 Merchandise Mart
Chicago, Ill. 60654
— Redwood planters

BRACKETS, SHELVES, MISCELLANEOUS

Beagle Manufacturing Co.
4377 N. Baldwin Ave.
El Monte, Cal. 91731
— Iron planter holders,
hanger brackets, stands

Edward A. Designs, Inc.
42-81 Hunter St.
Long Island City,
N.Y. 11101
— Plastic planters, brackets,
lucite decorator shelf
with drip rail

Fanon Designs, Inc.
P.O. Box 13162
Atlanta, Ga. 30324
— Plant perch wall, plastic
support for pots and
saucers

Heath Manufacturing Co.
Wolfcrest Products Div.
140 Mill St.
Coopersville, Mich. 49404
— Redwood planters,
metal plant stands

Himark Enterprises, Inc.
270 Oser Ave.
Hauppauge, N.Y. 11787
— Stoneware and
ceramic planters

Opus, Inc.
Foliage Div.
437 Boylston St.
Boston, Mass. 02116
— Sill-saver plant pedestals,
upper brackets

Patio Products, Inc.
2522 State Rd.
Cornwells Heights,
Pa. 19020
— Window greenhouse,
two-tier hanging shelf

Plantrac
38 West Mall
Plainview, N.Y. 11803
— Wire hangers, plant track
systems, accessories

Moisture meters

AMI Medical
Electronics Div.
116 E. 27th St.
New York, N.Y. 10016

Cleveland Cotton Products
Box 6895
Cleveland, Oh. 44101

Environmeter, Inc.
401 N. Velasco
Houston, Tex. 77003

Green Thumb Products
Corp.
Drawer 760
Apopka, Fla. 32703

Korex Industries
51 El Pueblo Dr.
Scotts Valley, Cal. 95066

RCF Developments, Inc.
2509 Browncroft Blvd.
Rochester, N.Y. 14625

Moisture/light meters

AMI Medical
Electronics Div.
116 E. 27th St.
New York, N.Y. 10016

Environmeter, Inc.
401 N. Velasco
Houston, Tex. 77003

Korex Industries
51 El Pueblo Dr.
Scotts Valley, Cal. 95066

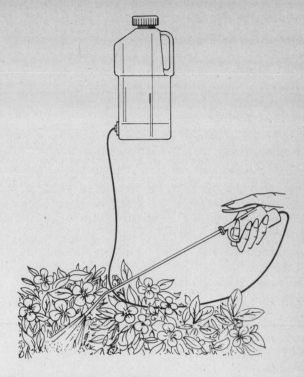

MIST'R SUN PLANT PROBE

One instrument measures both moisture and light, and a special sensor is built in for instant light reading. The probe measures moisture at the vital root level and has an extension for use with overhead plants.

Korex Industries
51 El Pueblo Dr.
Scotts Valley, Cal. 95066

PORTABLE WATERING SYSTEM

Here's an inexpensive, simple way to water your pots and containers, indoors or outdoors. You can quickly apply a gentle stream of water wherever you want it. The kit comes with a 21-inch aluminum wand, 8 feet of pliable plastic hose, and a 1-gallon plastic jug. Water flows by gravity, so the system is not good for high-hanging baskets.

Tube Craft, Inc.
1311 S.W. 80th St.
Cleveland, Oh. 44102

PLASTIC POTS DO THE JOB

The Decopot line of plastic growing containers offers several unique features, many different sizes, and a selection of attractive colors. (A) Rib-reinforced lip with molded-in holes at top makes it easy to hang these pots with plastic hanger, swivel-top Decohanger, or plain hooked wire. (B) Latticework exterior provides a good-looking and durable surface. (C) Permanent flexibility and smooth exterior ensure easy plant removal. (D) Lock-on saucers snap off base for cleaning and are easily reattached to keep water supply available, yet away from roots. (E) The ½-inch raised-center, recessed, outer-reservoir saucer design prevents rot by keeping excess water away from plant.

Coneco
Box 3429
Fullerton, Cal. 92634

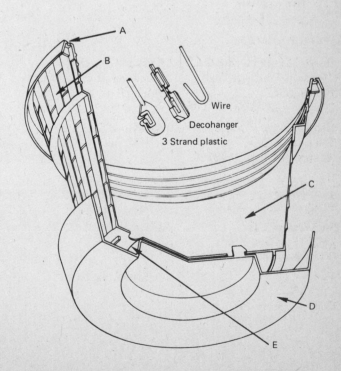

Wire

Decohanger

3 Strand plastic

◄ MINI REEL

Here's an excellent way to water indoor plants. The hose on a reel attaches directly to your sink faucet. The unit has a spray tip for misting and a cartridge fertilizer applicator, so that you can fertilize while watering.

Thirst Quencher Systems
2440 Ridge Park Lane
Orange, Cal. 92667

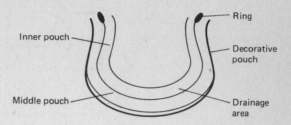

KANGAROO POUCH PLANTER

Lightweight, leakproof, and unbreakable, this unique planter is designed to provide a good growing environment for herbs and vegetables. Its built-in drainage system keeps plants moist and healthy. The diagram shows how it works. Excess water drains through the bottom of the inner pouch to a plastic middle pouch, which holds the water until it evaporates through the holes at the top. It can be filled with water to within one inch of the top.

Cross Newform Plastics Co.
124 Boston Tnpk.
Shrewsbury, Mass. 01545

TUBE DRIP IRRIGATION-DRIBBLE RINGS

All dribble rings feature individual shut-off. They supply from 8 - 30 oz. of water per minute. Useful for 4-, 6-, and 7-inch pots. Dribble rings can be used with cans and large pots.

The Dramm Company
P.O. Box 258
Manitowoc, Wisc. 54220

WINTER SALAD GARDEN

Grow vegetables in the winter on a windowsill with this sunny green winter salad garden kit. Contains two biodegradable 8-inch pots, two packages of seeds, fertilizer, pollination brush, and instruction manual. This is a useful novelty and will produce a fine crop if you follow the instructions carefully.

The Sunny Green Garden
204 Andover St.
Andover, Mass. 01810

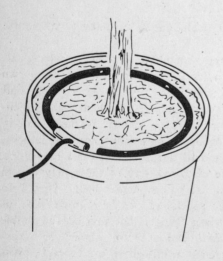

12

GROWING VEGETABLES UNDER LIGHTS

Since its introduction in the 1930s, fluorescent light gardening has made great progress. Used at first only in particular places and for certain plants, this method of gardening has now matured to the point where good equipment is available at the local hardware store. Prices are quite reasonable, and the whole operation is easier to manage than most people think.

Although vegetables have not been the most popular light-garden crop up to now, there have been some notable successes. The field is now beginning to experience significant growth. This chapter and Chapter 11 have all the information necessary for home gardeners to get started in this fascinating new way to raise vegetables.

Introduction to light gardening

Lights have several uses in growing vegetables. For one thing they can be installed in a cupboard, closet, planter, or part of a room to create a permanent garden where certain vegetables can thrive all the year round. Lights can also extend your outdoor growing season. By planting seeds indoors and exposing them to the proper amount of light, you can have healthy seedlings all ready to transplant into your garden when the temperature has risen to the proper levels (see Chapter 6 for further information about methods of transplanting, etc.).

Some vegetables do better under lights than others. Many root and leafy plants are quite easy to grow to maturity indoors, including beets, carrots, celery, Chinese cabbage, endive, lettuce, onions, radishes, spinach, and watercress. Some herbs do quite well in this environment, too, including basil, parsley, rosemary, and savory.

There are other vegetables and herbs which, although not recommended for beginners, can be grown under lights with a little more effort. After you've had some experience, you'll be able to extend your gardening range to include such plants as bush cucumbers and small tomatoes (especially cherry tomatoes), such herbs as sage and tarragon, and other fine crops.

Of course, you can grow any of these plants from seed to transplant size indoors under lights. They'll do beautifully. Other vegetables are best grown *only* as transplants. The large plants that produce an edible fruit, such as beans and zucchini, should be transplanted. Also included in this group are broccoli, brussels sprouts, cabbage, cantaloupe, cauliflower, and eggplant. Most of these vegetables take a great deal of light intensity to bring to maturity or are difficult to handle indoors because of their size.

Light requirements

Vegetables need both visible and invisible light rays for healthy, vigorous growth. Outdoor gardeners do not have to pay all that much attention to light. They simply place their garden where the sun shines in and hope that the growing season will not be excessively cloudy. Indoor gardeners have to be more knowledgeable. The following brief explanation should be sufficient for most needs, but additional information may be acquired from the many recent books on the subject of light gardening.

Natural light rays have a spectrum, rather like a rainbow, and different kinds of artificial light are made up of these colors in varying strengths. Blue light provides energy for both photosynthesis and chlorophyll synthesis; it also inhibits the elongation of cells and organs such as stems (so your plants won't get "leggy"). Red light also provides energy for photo- and chlorophyll synthesis; in addition it promotes many other plant responses such as seed germination, seedling and vegetative growth, cell and organ elongation, flowering, and pigment formation. While the red light thus causes plant growth, the far-red light causes it to stop. Thus a balance between these two types of light is desirable. There is some question about the value of green and yellow-orange light. Though they appear to be neutral, it is thought that they must have some effect on plant growth.

A plant's requirement for red light is generally greater than its requirement for blue light. In supplying artificial light it is of great importance to maintain the proper balance between the different light colors. Fluorescent tubes and the common incandescent light bulb each produce some of the needed rays. Fluorescent lights, for instance, produce blue and red rays; incandescent bulbs produce the red and far-red rays.

Lighting vegetables

Before buying lights for an indoor garden, it is necessary to find out the different light requirements of each vegetable. Leafy and root plants such as lettuce and radishes need about 1,000 footcandles (the equivalent of bright shade) for good growth. Vegetables from which we harvest the fruit—such as tomatoes, eggplant, and squash—need a minimum of 2,500 footcandles to reach maturity.

Few gardeners own a light meter to check on their indoor gardens. Generally this is not necessary because the plants themselves will become long and spindly or manifest some other abnormality if they are not getting enough light. (However, at that point it may be too late to take corrective measures.) One way to measure light without a special meter is to use a camera with

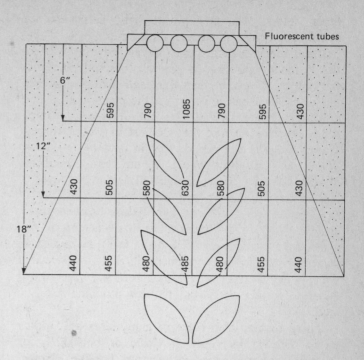

RELATIONSHIP OF FOOTCANDLE TO PLANT HEIGHT

Approximate footcandle values of plants 6-18 inches from four 40-watt fluorescent tubes. (At usual height of foliage the average footcandles delivered are 560-700.)

a built-in light meter that gives you an exposure setting. Set the film speed at ASA 100 and aim the meter at a white piece of paper placed so as to approximate the position of the plant's surface. The shutter speed reading that appears at F4 will correspond to the approximate footcandles of illumination. For example, if the indicated exposure is 1/250th of a second at F4, this means 250 footcandles.

There is a light gardening rule of thumb that utilizes watts per square foot. For example, a two-lamp fixture holding two 20-watt fluorescent tubes gives off a total of 40 watts. If the fixture and its bulbs cover a two-square-foot area when mounted one foot from the surface, then that surface is receiving 20 watts per square foot:

$$\frac{40 \text{ watts}}{2 \text{ sq. ft.}} = 20 \text{ watts per sq. ft.}$$

Most leafy and root vegetables need 20 watts per square foot or more, and most fruit-bearing vegetables need at least 40 watts per square foot.

What kind of lights to buy

There are many kinds of incandescent and fluorescent lights on the market. While the incandescent bulb is a good source of far-red light, it is deficient in the other colors. Therefore, most light gardeners use fluorescent lights. There are some "plant growth" fluorescent tubes that have been developed especially for use in indoor gardens. In general, these lamps reduce the output of yellow-green light and increase the output of red and blue rays, which the plants need. Some gardeners swear by these special fluorescent lamps, while others state that they do just as well with vegetables using two standard tubes in tandem, one warm white and one cool white. In any case, gardeners should not buy lamps designated *white* or *daylight*. These are not adapted for plant growth.

The standard fluorescent light fixture has two, three, or four 4-foot-long 40-watt tubes in a reflector—it will light a growing area of 2-by-4 feet. Two fixtures mounted parallel to each other will illuminate an area 3 by 4. For a larger area, 3 by 8 feet, you can use two 8-foot, two-tube industrial fixtures mounted side by side.

These fixtures also come in many sizes and widths to fit different locations. A closet or bookshelf, for instance, can be lighted by narrow, boxlike, channel fixtures (without reflectors). These come in many different lengths and can be mounted according to individual requirements.

There are also many, many manufactured units that you can buy at any garden center or from many seed catalogs. These units vary from simple two-bulb outfits to elaborate setups with a dozen or so trays. Some of them are quite well designed and resemble room dividers and other pieces of furniture. In addition, the plants themselves are attractive, so you have quite a handsome addition to your room decor.

Getting set up

A quick and easy way to start an indoor garden is to arrange your plants in a corner on a table about 3 by 4 feet in size. Mount two 4-foot reflector fixtures about 12 inches above the table's surface (go down as low as 6 inches if you've just planted seeds, as high as 18 inches if the plants are growing tall). To turn out large quantities of vegetables you can put together a basic A-frame, 5 feet long, 3 feet wide, with three shelves.

Special instructions for seedlings

As noted, many avid vegetable gardeners get a jump on the season by planting seeds indoors, under lights. The healthy seedlings can be transplanted to the garden bed

An A-frame light garden you can build yourself

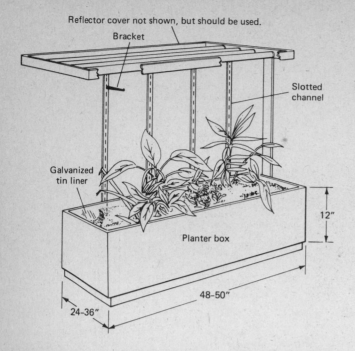

Reflector cover not shown, but should be used.
Bracket
Slotted channel
Galvanized tin liner
Planter box
12"
48-50"
24-36"

INDOOR GARDEN DESIGNING ADDS A DECORATOR TOUCH

You can bring the outdoors in by growing live plants under lights. The growing of plants indoors can change the whole visual concept of a living, working, or play area. Living plants can be displayed anywhere with the use of a portable lighted cart. Or you can use plants in a room divider, bookcase, or similar piece.

A simple piece of furniture is a room divider. This can be used in apartments as well as homes and if constructed in modular sections can easily be disassembled for moving to a new location. The units can be fashioned out of board lumber and painted or stained so the finish will blend with the existing furniture. Naturally the size will vary according to the area in which the divider will be used. The units may be built in checker-board fashion and storage cabinet bases be made to support the units.

when the weather warms up. Generally, fluorescent lights as described work out quite well for seedlings, but some experienced indoor-light people use in addition two 25-watt incandescent light bulbs to provide the far-red light energy that is necessary for the germination of light-sensitive seeds.

You can also sprout seeds with fluorescent lights. Simply place the seed trays (or peat pots, etc.) 3 or 4 inches below the tubes. Keep the lights on until the seedlings emerge. Then move the tubes so that they are 6-9 inches away from the plants. Give them 12-16 hours of light a day, adequate water, and nutrients, and you'll soon have a topnotch collection of seedlings.

How much light?

There are two elements in the equation that yields enough light for plant growth. The first involves the distance of the fixtures from the plants. As discussed, this depends to some extent on the size of the plants. The second element in providing adequate light is time, the number of hours the bulbs should be on. The sun doesn't shine 24 hours a day (except, in summer, above the Arctic Circle, an area not noted for its lush vegetation), and your plant lights should not be in continuous use, either.

The interesting point is that plants need not only light for proper growth, they also need darkness. This is called the photoperiod, and it varies from variety to variety. In general, vegetables require 14-18 hours of artificial light and 6-10 hours of darkness. Among these long-day plants are beets and spinach. There are also intermediate-day plants (12-18 hours of light), such as celery, and short-day plants (10-13 hours of light), such as some types of onions. It's important to pay attention to photoperiods. If you leave your lights on too long over, say, tomatoes, you'll find that your plants will produce lots of nice green foliage, but no tomatoes! If you don't have the kind of schedule that will enable you to control these lights manually, use one of the many good automatic timers that are on the market.

Temperature

Another environmental factor you've got to watch when growing vegetables under lights is temperature. Fluorescent lights don't produce much heat, but there is some (incandescent bulbs, of course, throw off quite a bit of heat for their size). Cool-season vegetables

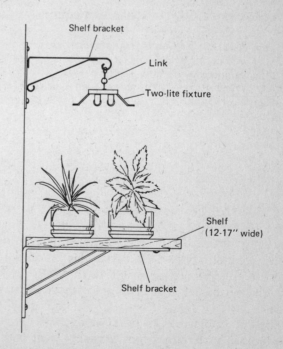

Shelf bracket
Link
Two-lite fixture
Shelf (12-17" wide)
Shelf bracket

SIMPLE LIGHT GARDEN ON A SHELF

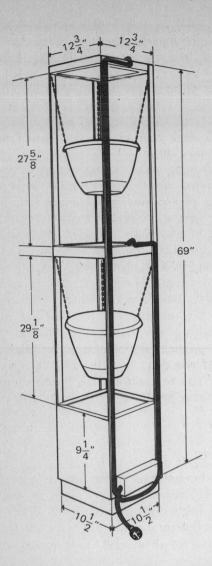

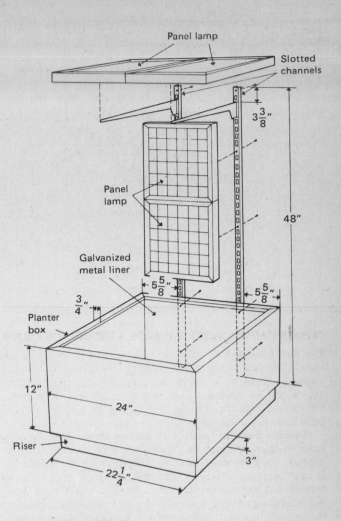

VERTICAL GARDEN WITH FLUORESCENT LIGHTS

You can build this good-looking, practical vertical indoor garden in a short time with readily available materials. This model is designed for hanging plants in waterproof baskets. Fluorescent lights are placed above each basket, as illustrated, in this drawing of a design from the U.S. Department of Agriculture.

BUILD IT YOURSELF

Here is another indoor garden that you can build yourself. Panel lamps are placed directly above, and at right angles to, the large planter box, as illustrated in this design from the U.S. Department of Agriculture.

such as lettuce like temperatures that don't get much above 65°F. Warm-season vegetables such as tomatoes grow and mature best when the temperature is above 65°F. but not above 90°F. And this is during the "day." Night temperature should be 50-60°F. for leafy and root vegetables, a bit higher for the warm-season varieties.

Thus, it is difficult to raise lettuce and tomatoes side by side, even though you probably want both for salads. What you can do is place cool-season vegetables

at one end of the garden, warm-season vegetables at the other end. You can vary the temperature by such devices as putting a heat-producing incandescent bulb at the warm-season end to supplement the fluorescent bulbs.

If your temperature is unsatisfactory and the air is stagnant around your indoor light garden, investigate the possibility of installing a small fan or other device to improve the ventilation.

SELECTED LIGHT FIXTURE MANUFACTURERS AND SUPPLIERS

MANUFACTURER/SUPPLIER	FIXTURE
Aladdin Industries, Inc. P.O. Box 10666 Nashville, Tenn. 37210	Indoor gardening equipment, growth chambers
Environment/One 2773 Balltown Rd. Schenectady, N.Y. 12309	Phytarium growth chamber
Esmay Products, Inc. P.O. Box 547 Bristol, Ind. 46507	Fine-quality indoor garden centers
Famco, Inc. 300 Lake Rd. Medina, Oh. 44256	Portable lighting unit
Fleco Industries 3347 Halifax Dallas, Tex. 75247	Butcher block and parquet decorative light units: adjustable plant lights trays
Floralite Co. 4124 E. Oakwood Rd. South Milwaukee, Wisc. 53172	Standard and special fixtures
Garcy Corp. 2501 N. Elston Ave. Chicago, Ill. 60647	Lighted units
Garden Way Research Charlotte, Vt. 05445	Plans for indoor light systems $2.50
House Plant Corner P.O. Box 121 Oxford, Md. 21654	Fixtures, tubes, timers; catalog 25¢
The Green House 9515 Flower St. Bellflower, Cal. 90706	Gro-cart garden center on wheels, fluorescent fixtures and tubes
Grower's Supply Co. P.O. Box 1132 Ann Arbor, Mich. 48106	2-8-unit trays; plant display stands
Lighting, Inc. P.O. Box 2228 Raleigh, N.C. 27602	Indoor garden supplies
Lord & Burnham Irvington-on-Hudson, N.Y. 10533	Solar planetarium—lighted case
Marko 94 Porete Ave. North Arlington, N.J. 07032	Fixtures, trays
Nature Island, Inc. 5360 Snapfinger Woods Dr. Suite 106 Decatur, Ga. 30032	Manufactures a number of sturdy aluminum tubing light units
Neas Growers Supply Co. Greensville, S.C. 29604	Tubes, fixtures
Plymouth Lighting 11485 Aspen Plymouth, Mich. 48170	Units, fixtures

Tinari Greenhouses 2325 Valley Rd. Huntington Valley, Pa. 19006	Fixtures, supplies; catalog 25¢
Tube Craft, Inc. 1311 S.W. 80th St. Cleveland, Oh. 44102	Indoor garden units

---

LIGHT GARDENS STARTER KIT

Some seed companies offer starter kits for gardeners who want to try indoor light gardening. Here are three:

Burpee's 4 Season Growing Kit. Here's a good starting unit. Contains two 40-watt Natur-escent growth light bulbs and a 48-inch metal fixture. Also has 6 qts. Burpee Planting Formula, 6 qts. Burpee Tomato Formula, 6 qts. Burpee Special Potting Mixture, 2 plastic work trays, 6-ft., 21-watt electric heating cable, 10 Kys-Pak containers, 10 Deep Root 6 packs, 25 plastic labels, garden marking pens, fifty 2¼-in. round peat pots. $54.95

W. Atlee Burpee Co.
Warminster, Pa. 18974
Clinton, Ia. 52732
Riverside, Ca 92502

Park's Expert Combination Kit. 48-inch tabletop plant light with two 40-watt fluorescent tubes. Kit includes Jiffy flats, sphagnum moss and plant food, a quantity of Jiffy pots, and other items. $64.95

Park's Improved Hobby House. These large frame units have from 2 to 4 shelves with 4 built-in 40-watt fixtures. The plants are placed on top of each shelf which holds a bed of vermiculite, sand, or peat moss. The Hobby House provides from 8 to 24 square feet of growing space and holds thousands of seedlings. The unit can be placed almost anywhere. $295 to $550

George W. Park Seed Co.
Greenwood, S.C. 29646

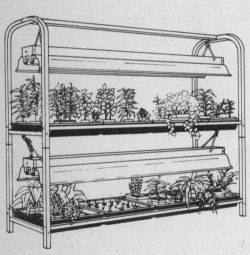

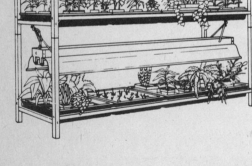

◄ **FLORA CART-INDOOR GREENHOUSE**

Obtains maximum results by combining fluorescent lights with incandescent lights in proper proportion and with proper specing.

Uses two regular 25-watt bulbs carefully spaced between two 40-watt fluorescent tubes. A specially designed reflector finished in white baked enamel spreads the light evenly. Rolls anywhere you wish.

Tube Craft, Inc.
1311 S. W. 80th St.
Cleveland, Oh. 44102

WONDER GARDEN

These apartment-sized units are designed to give the indoor gardener the flexibility of starting seedlings, growing indoor plants or vegetables. Constructed of heavy-duty one-inch-square aluminum tubing these Grow Light Stands will last for years.

Nature Island, Inc.
5360 Snapfinger Woods Dr.
Suite 106
Decatur, Ga. 30035

LITE GRO INDOOR GARDEN CENTER

This good-looking indoor plant center has all you need to grow vegetables. It comes complete with six 20-watt Naturescent grow lights and an automatic timer. Looks like a piece of fine furniture.

Esmay Products, Inc.
P.O. Box 547
Bristol, Ind. 46507

BRIGHT STIK

A new one-piece plant light from General Electric comes ready to plug in and brighten the lives of household greenery. Called Bright Stik Gro and Sho, the 25-inch unit puts light where's it's needed . . . in bookcases, cabinets, and shelves.

General Electric Company
Nela Park
Cleveland, Oh. 44112

INDOOR LIGHT NURSERY

The Agro-Lite indoor nursery permits the user to easily adjust the distance between plants and the fluorescent light source. This unit, will fit easily in a corner, a closet, or any other out-of-the-way-place.

Westinghouse Electric Corp
Fluorescent and Vapor Lamp
    Div.
Bloomfield, N.J. 07003

APPROXIMATE DISTRIBUTION OF COLORS IN FLUORESCENT LAMPS USED FOR PLANT GROWTH

MANUFACTURER	TYPE OF LAMP	RED	YELLOW -GREEN	BLUE	REMARKS
Duro-lite Lamps Inc. Lighting Div. Duro-Test Corp. 17-10 Willow St. Fair Lawn, N.J. 07410	Vita Lite				Provides full-spectrum light good for vegetative growth; useful for starting all vegetables—excellent for cacti, succulents, orchids; available in power-twist type which gives somewhat more light than straight tubes
	Natur-Escent	37%	34%	29%	Full spectrum bulb will grow all vegetables including tomatoes; takes the plant from seed to maturity
General Electric Lamp Marketing Div. Nela Park Cleveland, Oh. 44112	Gro and Sho Plant light				Produces a balance of red and blue light; useful for starting seeds, vegetative growth
	Bright Stik—Gro and Sho				Provides a balance of red and blue light; available in a 25-inch unit that can be plugged in for light in bookcases, cabinets, and shelves; no additional fixture needed
	Power Groove Fluorescent lamps				Comes in cool white daylight, warm white, deluxe cool white; puts out very high light output
Sylvania Lighting Center Danvers, Mass. 01293	Gro Lux Regular	43%	18%	38%	Developed solely for growing plants and flowers indoors; the output is almost entirely in the red and blue ends of the spectrum; designed for the propagation of low energy plants
	Gro Lux Wide Spectrum	38%	32%	30%	Supplies more light in the red than in the blue spectrum; excellent for starting seeds; promotes rapid growth; can be used for vegetables
Westinghouse Electric Corp Fluorescent and Vapor Lamp Div. Bloomfield, N.J. 07003	Agro-lite				A special phosphor which provides light rich in red while still providing considerable blue light; makes plants grow faster; has done well in tests with various types of vegetables
several	Daylight	12%	48%	40%	Deficient in the red end of the spectrum; not good for growing vegetables alone but can be used with Gro-lux, Gro Lux Wide Spectrum, Agro-Lite
several	Warm White	25%	55%	20%	This bulb provides more light in the red end of the spectrum; it is used in combination with cool white
several	Cool White	18%	52%	30%	The most common fluorescent, deficient in the red end of the spectrum; use with warm white
several	Natural white	26%	40%	34%	A more balanced bulb; it can also be mixed with cool white

13

HYDRO-PONICS

Hydroponics is simply a method of growing plants without the use of soil. Instead, seeds (or seedlings) are planted in a growing medium such as sand or cinders that is periodically flooded or otherwise supplied with the nutrients necessary for plant growth. Hydroponic installations can be indoors or outdoors, in a greenhouse or on a patio. Light, air, and water must be in sufficient supply, just as in the standard dirt garden.

Because of the way that they are fed, hydroponic vegetables grow bigger and faster than those in an ordinary garden. Water and fertilizer can be used over and over again. Problems of insects and disease can be kept to a minimum.

What plants need for growth

As noted in Chapter 2, plants need 15 nutrients for growth. The three most important elements, nitrogen, phosphorus, and potassium, all come from the soil (or growing medium). These three are used by vegetables in relatively large amounts and have a significant effect on the growth of stems, leaves, and fruit. Other necessary nutrients that come from the soil are magnesium, manganese, and copper—the three secondary nutrients—and zinc, iron, sulfur, calcium, molybdenum, and boron—the micronutrients. (The other three needed elements—oxygen, carbon, and hydrogen—come from the air and water.)

Of the three secondary nutrients, magnesium is an important component of chlorophyl, manganese is used by the plant enzyme system, and copper is utilized as an enzyme activator. The six microelements are essential for proper plant development, but each is required only in small quantities.

A good nutrient solution, of course, is the key to hydroponics, and regular, careful feeding produces optimum growth. It is important in using commercial mixes to follow the package directions carefully and not to burn the plants by overfertilizing.

Most solutions use one teaspoon of nutrient dissolved in one gallon of water. For starting seedlings dilute your solution to half strength and gradually increase the dosage as the plants become bigger.

Your choice of hydroponic methods

In all hydroponic methods, as mentioned, the plants absorb the nutrients directly from the mineral mixture dissolved in water and fed directly to the roots. You can grow your plants in sand, gravel, perlite, vermiculite, coarse sponge rock and similar material, or they can be grown directly in solution. Here are the favorite methods:

The flooding method

The growing medium is flooded one to three times a day for a period of one half to two hours at a time. The rest of the time the roots have oxygen available through the growing medium. After flooding, the nutrient is allowed to drain back into the solution reservoir. The flooding process can be handled automatically with a pump and timer.

You can make your own flooding system (see drawing) using a plastic dishpan, a bucket, and several feet of plastic tubing. Use epoxy glue to connect the system.

Once a day fill the bucket with solution and lift the bucket so the solution goes down the hose to the growing tray. Leave the bucket on a shelf or table until the entire solution has run into the tray. After about two hours lower the bucket so the solution can drain back into the tray.

To utilize a pump instead of gravity flow, replace the nutrient bucket with some type of plastic air-tight nutrient container (an inexpensive plastic air-tight jug will do). You will also need to purchase a simple aquarium pump (buy this at a pet store). Connect the pump to the container as shown in the drawing. When you turn on the pump, the air pressure forces the solution from the tank into the growing tray. When you turn off the pump, the nutrient drains back into the reservoir. To automate the system, hook the pump to an inexpensive timer and set it to run the pump about two hours a day.

The wick method

A synthetic fiber wick draws the water-solution into the growing medium, allowing both moisture and air to feed the plant continuously.

To make your own system place two plastic growing trays (such as a plastic dishpan) one on top of the other. Place the nutrient solution in the top tray and the growing medium (perlite, sand, or other material) in the bottom tray.

Drill small holes about three inches apart in the bottom of the top plant tray and thread pieces of fabric through the holes down into the solution. Make your wicks from synthetic fabric such as nylon, polyester, or rayon. Be sure the fabric you use will draw the moisture the entire length of the wick.

After you have completed your system, fill the bottom tray with nutrient material, and then wet the wick to start the action. After that you will need to replace the solution every two weeks.

Drip method

The plants, grown in a perlite/peat moss medium, are watered slowly with the nutrient solution through drip irrigation tubes—allow just enough solution to run so that all the moisture is absorbed by the growing medium.

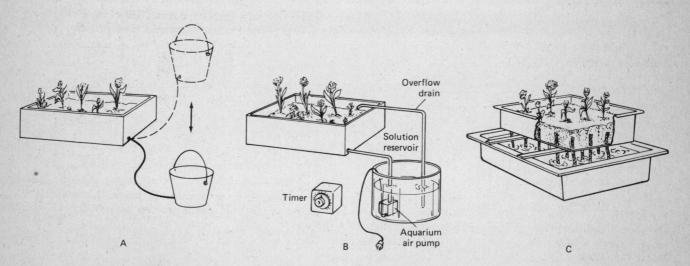

A   B   C

THREE WAYS OF FLOODING

Basic system: Using a bucket with a growing tray, the bucket is raised above the tray once or twice a day and the solution flows into the tray. Then the bucket is placed below the tray, and the solution flows back.

Automatic system: Using a submersible pump and a timer, the solution is automatically pumped into the growing tray as desired; then it flows back through the overflow drain into the reservoir. Using an aquarium pump and a nutrient solution in an airtight container, the pump can be turned on and off by hand.

Wick system: In this two-tray system the nutrient solution is placed in the bottom tray, the growing medium and plants in the top tray. Wicks made of synthetic fabric are placed in the solution, passed through holes drilled in the top tray, and then embedded in the growing medium. The solution is drawn up into the top tray continuously.

The standing solution method

Plants are grown directly in the nutrient solution. Root aeration is provided by bubbling air into the solution (this method is used infrequently).

Ready-made hydroponic systems

Hydroponics currently is one of the fastest growing commercial fields in home gardening. Over the past few years dozens of new firms have entered the hydro-ponics market and manufacture a tremendous variety of ready-made systems. All are variations of the general hydroponic methods outlined above and include (1) subirrigation gravel beds or flood system with recycled nutrients; (2) trickle irrigation on sand beds or sand culture; (3) top-feed gravel bed systems with recycled nutrients; (4) container systems using a rigid black polyethylene container with an inert, sterile growing medium; (5) nutrient film systems with no growing medium; and (6) tube systems with and without growing medium.

HYDROPONIC SUPPLIES

SUPPLIER	ITEM
Allenergy Box 695 Ben Lomond, Cal. 95005	K-Ran E-Z Gardens—a flood system that utilizes a 2-piece molded fiberglass tube; two sizes—3 x 3 feet, 2 x 6 feet
Aquaponics 22135 Ventura Blvd. Woodland Hills, Cal. 91364	Complete hydroponic greenhouse kit around $1,000; automatic growing beds; wick and dishpan hydroponic kits from $14.95; hydroponic books, accessories such as pumps, test kits
Howard Chandler Hydroponic Systems & Supplies 5645 Paradise Dr. Corte Madera, Cal. 94925	Water Farm—wick fed, gravity fed, from $14.95; fiberglass tank flood system, 3 x 3 foot, 3 x 8 foot, 3 x 12 foot; Raymond Birdwell Laboratories nutrient, 4-oz. to 5-lb. sizes; greenhouse covers—books, plant mix, other items
Conical Spirals Scientific 3435 Tennyson St. Denver, Col. 90212	Manakit 77, flood system—unusual twin tanks, kit form, preassembled $234.95; Green Gold, Blend B nutrient—from ½ to 25 lbs.; pH paper; hydroponic books
Continental Nutri-Culture Box 6751 Lubbock, Texas 79413	Several types of nutrient solutions, various formulas, dissolved-solids meter, plant-tissue test kits
D & M Enterprises Box 739 Wilomar, Cal. 92395 **Distributor for King Industries** **Box 21** Loma Linda, Cal. 92354	King Industries hydroponic systems—gravity systems; outdoor, indoor tanks; Raymond Birdwell Laboratory; Hydroking nutrient books, timers, controls, greenhouses
Dr. Chatlier's Plant Food Co. Box 20375 St. Petersburg, Fla. 33742	Nutrients
Earth Products P.O. Box 996 Pasadena, Cal. 91106	Semiautomatic growing units
Environmental Dynamics Box 996 Sunnymead, Cal. 92388 or 12615 S. La Cadena Dr. Collon, Cal. 92324	Hydroponic starter kits; gravity hydroponic systems; patio and balcony hydro wick kits; fiberglass conversion kits; hydroponic nutrients, perlite growing medium, books, hydroponic greenhouses, test kits
Family Farms 1108 Wilson Rd. Humble, Tex. 77338	Hydrohouse hydroponic systems, vinyl growing flow system three sizes; redwood and fiberglass greenhouses and accessories
Great Northern Distributing Co. 325 W. Pierpont Ave. Salt Lake City, Utah 84117	Hydroponic Garden Kit-Hydropak
Home Hydroponic Systems 90 Earlton Rd. Agincourt, Ont. MIT 2R6, Canada	Kits, supplies, consultation; nutrient 9-6-22; pails, fittings, pumps (gravity feed and automatic units)

HYDROPONIC SUPPLIES (Continued)

SUPPLIER	ITEM
Homeland Industries, Inc. 95 Evergreen Ave. Brooklyn, N.Y. 11206	Moduleponic double-unit upper growing tube, lower nutrient tube; commercial units; hydroponic nutrient solution, timers, books, light-assembly units
Hydroculture, Inc. 99 Ave. at W. Glendale Glendale, Ariz. 85311	Magic Garden home hydroponic units; commercial units for vegetables and grains; H-100 nutrient
Hydro Fresh Farm Box 511 San Martin, Cal. 95046	Nutrient, 8-oz. to 50-lb. size
Hydro Gardens of Denver 3900 Magnolia St. Denver, Col. 80207	Hydroponic kits, greenhouses, nutrients, accessories
Hydro Gardens, Inc. Box 9707 Colorado Springs, Col. 80932	Greenhouses, hyroponic growing systems, Chem Gro hydroponic nutrient
Hydro Greenhouse Systems 2 Binnacle Lane Mt. Harmony, Md. 20836	Hydroponic growing system (12 x 3 feet); Green Machine hydroponic greenhouse; nutrients including Mittleider elements, accessories
Hydroponic Greenhouses Box 336 Trona, Cal. 93562	Do-it-yourself plans
Liquid Gardens 723 Ocean Front Walk Venice, Cal. 90291	Kit for indoor/outdoor use
Monarch Hydroponics 22143 Cantlay St. Canoga Park, Cal. 91303	Monarch hydroponics—one-piece polyethylene-tank flow type, wick type; plant nutrient.
Natural Island, Inc. 5360 Snapfinger Woods Dr. Decatur, Ga. 30032	Semiautomatic growing units
Pacific Agriculture 3A Gate Five Rd. Sausalito, Cal. 94965	Flow-type units; also do-it-yourself kits; several types of nutrients, books, vinyl liners
The Plantworks Tiffany Industries, Inc. 145 Weldon Pkwy. Maryland Heights, Mo. 63043	Growing units, greenhouse and accessories, plantworks control center
Sunglo Greenhouses 4441 26th Ave. W. Seattle, Wash. 98199	Hydroponic kits, greenhouse accessories
Sunlan Greenhouses 412 Eighth Ave. Smyrna, Tenn. 33169	Gro-Tree units (4 models)
Tube Craft, Inc. 1311 S.W. 80th St. Cleveland, Oh. 44102	Home Grow Products, Flora Cart instruction booklet for setting up your own hydroponic unit
Water Works Gardenhouses Box 2599 Castro Valley, Cal. 94546	Greenhouses, planters, nutrient books
H. Wolff Manufacturing Co. 955 Celia Way Palo Alto, Cal. 94303	Foxy Farmer hydroponic kits (gravity flow); 148-sq.-in. container, window box units
Working Water Gardens 300 Springdale St. Sebastopol, Cal. 95472	Greenhouses, nutrient

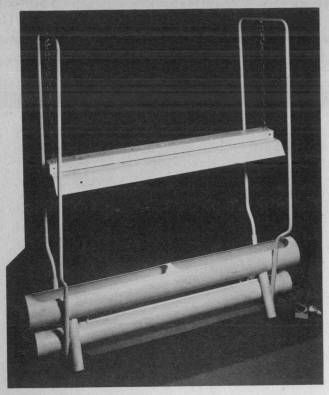

MODULEPONIC SYSTEM

This small unit is complete with its own light holder. It is completely automatic and can be used inside almost anywhere.

Homeland Industries, Inc.
95 Evergreen Ave.
Brooklyn, N.Y. 11206

SITES FOR MODULEPONIC SYSTEMS

Two of many suggested uses of the Moduleponic systems. Either indoor or outdoor use is possible.

Homeland Industries, Inc.
95 Evergreen Ave.
Brooklyn, N.Y. 11206

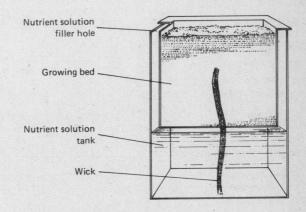

Nutrient solution filler hole

Growing bed

Nutrient solution tank

Wick

MONARCH'S HYDROPLANTER

This indoor/outdoor hydroplanter contains both the growing bed and the water-storage compartment in the same unit. It automatically delivers water and plant nutrients to the plant roots by capillary action.

Monarch Hydroponics
22143 Cantlay St.
Canoga Park, Cal. 91303

◄ **HYDROPONIC NUTRIENT**

Hydro Fresh Farm
P.O. Box 511
San Martin, Cal. 95046

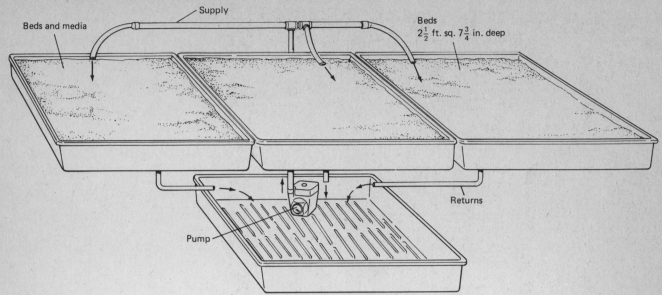

HYDROPONIC KIT

For around $150 you can buy a kit that includes just about everything needed to get started in hydroponic vegetable growing. The kit includes three beds and a collector tank, each 39" square and 7¾" deep; one timer; one pump; a feed-pipe system; a drain-pipe system; necessary wiring to hook it all up; a supply of nutrient; and an instructional book.

Sunglo Greenhouses
441 26th Ave. W.
Seattle, Wash. 98199

THE GREEN MACHINE

This self-contained hydroponic greenhouse has many interesting features. (A) A vent next to the door aids in ventilation. (B) A translucent skin of shatterproof Filon coated with Filoplate allows 92% of available light to pass through to the interior while retaining most of the heat in the greenhouse. (C) Redwood utility shelf provides necessary storage space. (D) Automatic timer turns pump on and off. (E) Electric fan changes the air in the greenhouse every minute. (F) Extra outlets are needed to plug in extra lights, etc. (G) Heater helps keep interior warm during cold snaps. (H) Fiberglass tank holds nutrient solution, which is circulated by electric pump submerged in the solution. (I) Ten steel anchors keep the unit in place even during high winds. (J) Redwood footings resist rot. (K) Fiberglass growing beds hold perlite, the growing medium. (L) Aluminum storm door won't rust or corrode.

Hydro Greenhouse Systems
2 Binnacle Lane
Mt. Harmony, Md. 20836

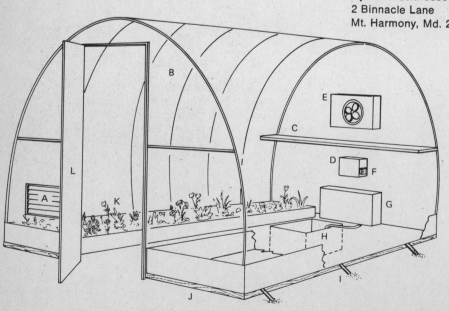

HOME HYDROPONIC SYSTEMS

Vegetables growing in a gravel medium with subirrigation. The nutrient tank sits directly below a 2-by-4-foot growing unit. This one is fully automatic and is ideal for growing under lights in a rec room or basement.

Specialty Gardens, Ltd.
90 Earlton Rd.
Agincourt, Ont. MIT 2R6, Canada

FOXY FARMER HYDROPONIC KITS

This small tabletop unit (6 x 29") will grow two tomato plants and some greens. The nutrient is fed into the plant tray by raising the nutrient container above the tray.

H. Wolff Manufacturing Co.
955 Celia Way
Palo Alto, Cal. 94303

INDEX